Mechanisms and Control

Mécanismes et contrôle du v

Colloques INSERM
ISSN 0768-3154

Other *Colloques* published as co-editions by John Libbey Eurotext and INSERM

133 Cardiovascular and Respiratory Physiology in the Fetus and Neonate. *Physiologie Cardiovasculaire et Respiratoire du Fœtus et du Nouveau-né.*
Scientific Committee : P. Karlberg, A. Minkowski, W. Oh and L. Stern;
Managing Editor : M. Monset-Couchard.
ISBN : John Libbey Eurotext 0 86196 086 6
INSERM 2 85598 282 0

134 Porphyrins and Porphyrias. *Porphyrines et Porphyries.*
Edited by Y. Nordmann.
ISBN : John Libbey Eurotext 0 86196 087 4
INSERM 2 85598 281 2

137 Neo-Adjuvant Chemotherapy. *Chimiothérapie Néo-Adjuvante.*
Edited by C. Jacquillat, M. Weil and D. Khayat.
ISBN : John Libbey Eurotext 0 86196 077 7
INSERM 2 85598 283 7

139 Hormones and Cell Regulation (10th European Symposium). *Hormones et Régulation Cellulaire (10e Symposium Européen).*
Edited by J. Nunez, J.E. Dumont and R.J.B. King.
ISBN : John Libbey Eurotext 0 86196 084 X
INSERM 2 85598 284 7

147 Modern Trends in Aging Research. *Nouvelles Perspectives de la Recherche sur le Vieillissement.*
Edited by Y. Courtois, B. Faucheux, B. Forette, D.L. Knook and J.A. Tréton.
ISBN : John Libbey Eurotext 0 86196 103 X
INSERM 2 85598 309 6

149 Binding Proteins of Steroid Hormones. *Protéines de liaison des Hormones Stéroïdes.*
Edited by M.G. Forest and M. Pugeat.
ISBN : John Libbey Eurotext 0 86196 125 0
INSERM 2 85598 310 X

151 Control and Management of Parturition. *La Maîtrise de la Parturition.*
Edited by C. Sureau, P. Blot, D. Cabrol, F. Cavaillé and G. Germain.
ISBN : John Libbey Eurotext 0 86196 096 3
INSERM 2 85598 311 8

Suite page 367
(Continued p. 367)

Mechanisms and Control of Emesis

Mécanismes et contrôle du vomissement

A satellite Symposium of the European Neuroscience Association

Proceedings of an International Meeting held in Marseille (France), 4-7 September 1992: "New Vistas on Mechanisms and Control of Emesis"

Comptes rendus d'un Colloque International qui s'est tenu à Marseille (France) du 4 au 7 septembre 1992: «Nouvelles données sur les mécanismes et le contrôle du vomissement»

Subventionné par l'Institut National de la Santé et de la Recherche Médicale, le Service de Santé Publique des USA ("National Institute of Neurological Disorders and Stroke" et "National Institute on Deafness and other Communication Disorders"), la Direction des Recherches, Etudes et Techniques, le Conseil Général des Bouches-du-Rhône, l'Université Aix-Marseille III.

Edited by

Armand L. Bianchi
Laurent Grélot
Alan D. Miller
Gregory L. King

British Library Cataloguing in Publication Data

A catalogue record for this book
is available from the British Library

ISBN 0 86196 366 0
ISSN 0768-3154

First published in 1992 by

Editions John Libbey Eurotext
6 rue Blanche, 92120 Montrouge, France. (33) (1) 47 35 85 52
ISBN 0 86196 366 0

John Libbey and Company Ltd
13 Smiths Yard, Summerley Street, London SW18 4HR, England.
(44) (81) 947 27 77

Institut National de la Santé et de la Recherche Médicale
101 rue de Tolbiac, 75654 Paris Cedex 13, France.
(33) (1) 44 23 60 00
ISBN 2 85 598 511 0

ISSN 0768-3154

Foreword

Nausea and vomiting (emesis) are complex and in general still poorly understood phenomena which occur under a variety of conditions. Our goal for this Symposium was to bring together a broad range of basic scientists and clinicians to address the basic mechanisms underlying these phenomena, their control under various conditions, and new directions for future treatments and research.

The first section of these Proceedings presents changing concepts regarding the organization of the neural control of vomiting and deals with the involvement and localization of different neurotransmitter receptor subtypes in the production of emesis. Also included are discussions of the gastrointestinal and somatomotor events that produce vomiting and of the blood-brain barrier which controls the access of toxins and therapeutic drugs to the brain.

The next sections of this book deal with the mechanisms and treatment of nausea and vomiting associated with cancer chemotherapy, radiation sickness, and motion and space sickness. An important part of these sections focuses on new anti-emetic drugs, especially those that act at serotonin type 3 and 1A receptors.

The final section of the book is devoted to new issues and directions. The involvement of neuroinhibition and the potential for plasticity in the regulation of emesis are discussed as are new concepts related to pregnancy sickness, the use of acupuncture to control vomiting, and psychological aspects of nausea and vomiting. Finally, a description of an algorithm for predicting radiation-induced emesis and possible animal models for studies of nausea and vomiting are presented.

Thus, this book contains a great variety of papers with a common interest, that is to provide a better understanding of how nausea and vomiting are induced and how to treat or to prevent them.

The Organizing Committee

A.L. Bianchi (Marseille)
L. Grélot (Marseille)
G.L. King (Bethesda)
A.D. Miller (New York)

Avant-propos

La nausée et le vomissement sont des phénomènes complexes en général encore mal compris, et qui se produisent dans des conditions variées. Notre but en organisant ce Symposium a été de réunir une large audience de scientifiques et de médecins pour discuter des mécanismes de base qui sous-tendent ces phénomènes, de leur contrôle dans diverses conditions, et des nouvelles directions des recherches et des traitements à venir.

La première partie de ces Comptes Rendus présente les concepts actuels sur l'organisation du contrôle nerveux du vomissement, et est consacrée au rôle de divers neurotransmetteurs et à la localisation de leurs différents récepteurs. Des résultats concernant les événements moteurs somatiques et végétatifs (gastro-intestinaux) sont présentés, ainsi que le rôle de la barrière hémato-encéphalique qui contrôle l'accès au cerveau des substances toxiques et thérapeutiques.

Les chapitres suivants de ce livre sont consacrés aux mécanismes et aux traitements de la nausée et du vomissement induits par la chimiothérapie anticancéreuse, l'irradiation, le mal des transports et le mal de l'espace. Un des chapitres importants de cet ouvrage est celui consacré aux nouvelles substances anti-émétiques, et plus spécialement à celles qui agissent par l'intermédiaire des récepteurs sérotoninergiques de types 3 et 1A.

La dernière section de ce livre est consacrée aux nouvelles données et orientations de recherche. Le rôle de la neuro-inhibition et la possibilité d'une plasticité dans la régulation de la réponse émétique sont discutés ainsi que les nouveaux concepts expliquant les malaises de la grossesse, l'emploi de l'acupuncture dans le contrôle du vomissement, et les aspects psychologiques de la nausée et du vomissement. Enfin, la description d'un algorithme pour la prédiction du vomissement radio-induit est présentée ainsi que des modèles animaux susceptibles de faciliter l'étude de la nausée et du vomissement.

Ainsi, cet ouvrage contient une grande variété d'articles dont l'intérêt commun est de fournir une meilleure compréhension des mécanismes de déclenchement de la nausée et du vomissement, et de la façon de les traiter et de les prévenir.

Le Comité d'Organisation

A.L. Bianchi (Marseille)
L. Grélot (Marseille)
G.L. King (Bethesda)
A.D. Miller (New York)

Acknowledgements

We wish to thank our colleagues from many different countries who contributed to the success of this meeting by their participation through lectures, poster presentations, and discussions.

We direct our thanks to Mrs Anne Marie Lajard, Jocelyne Roman, and Marinette Sellem who contributed to the organization of the meeting, and served as secretaries and hostesses. We must also mention the efficient collaboration of Daniel Catalin who managed the sound and video systems, and that of Gérard Ivaldi who constructed the poster boards.

We also thank the following public organizations and private companies whose support made this Symposium possible:

- the U.S. Public Health Service under grant # 1 R13 NS29952 from the National Institute of Neurological Disorders and Stroke and the National Institute on Deafness and other Communication Disorders,

- the "Institut National de la Santé et de la Recherche Médicale" (INSERM), which is also sponsoring the publication of this book,

- the research organization of the French Army, the "Direction des Recherches, Etudes et Techniques" (DRET), a division of the "Délégation Générale à l'Armement" (DGA), under grant # 91-1515,

- the "Conseil Général des Bouches-du-Rhône",

- the "Université Aix-Marseille III",

- the "Office du Tourisme" of the City of Marseille,

and:

- Marion Merrell Dow Product Development,

- Beecham Sévigné,

- Glaxo,

- Rhône-Poulenc Rorer,

- Boehringer Ingelheim,

- Yamanouchi Pharmaceutical,

- Anaquest.

Remerciements

Nous voulons ici remercier nos collègues de différents pays qui ont contribué au succès de ce Colloque par leur participation au travers de conférences, de présentations affichées et de discussions.

Nous tenons à remercier Mesdames Anne-Marie Lajard, Jocelyne Roman, et Marinette Sellem qui ont participé à l'organisation générale du Colloque, et ont servi de secrétaires et d'hôtesses. Nous devons aussi signaler la collaboration efficace de Daniel Catalin qui a pris en main le système audio-visuel, ainsi que de Gérard Ivaldi qui a fabriqué les panneaux d'affichage.

Nous remercions aussi les organisations publiques et les compagnies privées qui ont subventionné et rendu possible ce Colloque sur les mécanismes et le contrôle du vomissement :

- le «U.S. Public Health Service» (Service de Santé Publique des USA) sous le contrat n° 1 R13 NS29952 du «National Institute of Neurological Disorders and Stroke» et du «National Institute on Deafness and other Communication Disorders»,
- l'Institut National de la Santé et de la Recherche Médicale (INSERM), qui finance aussi la publication de ce livre,
- la Direction des Recherches, Etudes et Techniques (DRET) de la Délégation Générale à l'Armement (DGA), sous le contrat n° 91-1515,
- le Conseil Général des Bouches-du-Rhône,
- l'Université Aix-Marseille III,
- l'Office du Tourisme de la Ville de Marseille,

and:

- Marion Merrell Dow Product Development,
- Beecham Sévigné,
- Glaxo,
- Rhône-Poulenc Rorer,
- Boehringer Ingelheim,
- Yamanouchi Pharmaceutical,
- Anaquest.

List and address of contributors

Liste et adresse des intervenants

Aapro, M.S., Division d'Onco-Hématologie, Hôpital Cantonal, CH 1211 Genève, Switzerland

Andrews P.L.R., Department of Physiology, St George's Hospital Medical School, Cranmer Terrace, London, SW17 ORE, UK

Andrykowski M.A., Department of Behavioral Science, University of Kentucky, College of Medicine, Lexington, KY 40536-0086, USA

Anno G.H., Pacific-Sierra Research Corporation, 12340 Santa Monica Boulevard, Los Angeles, CA 90025, USA

Beleslin D.B., Department of Pharmacology, Medical Faculty, P.O. Box 662, 11000 Belgrade, Yugoslavia

Bensi G., Boehringer Ingelheim, Medical Division, Via Serio 15, 20139 Milano, Italy

Bhandari P., Department of Physiology, St George's Hospital Medical School, Cranmer Terrace, London, SW17 ORE, UK

Bianchi A.L., Département de Physiologie et Neurophysiologie, URA CNRS 205, Faculté des Sciences Saint-Jérôme, 13397 Marseille Cedex 13, France

Bingham S., SmithKline Beecham Pharmaceuticals, Medical Research Center, Coldharbour Road, The Pinnacles, Harlow, Essex CM19 5AD, UK

Brightman M.W., Neurobiology, National Institutes of Health, NINDS, Bld 36, Room 2A-29, 9000 Rockville Pike, Bethesda, MD 20892, USA

Del Río J., Department of Pharmacology, School of Medicine, University of Navarra, Room 273, 31080 Pamplona, Spain

Dick T.E., Division of Pulmonary and Critical Medicine, Department of Medicine, Case Western R.U., 2074, Abington Road, Cleveland, Ohio, 44106, USA

Ducreux Ch., Laboratoire de Neurobiologie, CNRS-LNB1, 31 chemin Joseph Aiguier, 13009 Marseille, France

Fatome M., Service de Santé des Armées, 24 avenue des Maquis du Grésivaudan, B.P. 87, 38702 La Tronche Cedex, France

Fitzpatrick K.T.J., Department of Clinical Anesthesia, Ground Floor Tower Block, City Hospital, 97 Lisburn Road, Belfast BT9 5PR, Northern Ireland

Fox R.A., School of Social Sciences, Department of Psychology, San José State University, San José, CA 95192-0120, USA

Fozard J.R., Preclinical Research, Sandoz Pharma Ltd, CH-4002 Basel, Switzerland

Gisanrin O., SmithKline Beecham Pharmaceuticals, Medical Research Center, Coldharbour Road, The Pinnacles, Harlow, Essex, CM19 5AD, UK

Golding J.F., Royal Air Force, Institute of Aviation Medicine, Farnborough, Hants, GU14 6SZ, UK

Grélot L., Département de Physiologie et Neurophysiologie, URA CNRS 205, Faculté des Sciences Saint-Jérôme, 13397 Marseille Cedex 13, France

Hartmann F., Centre de Recherche et de Traitement de l'Appareil Manducateur, Faculté d'Odontologie, 27 Boulevard Jean Moulin, 13385 Marseille Cedex 5, France

Hesketh P.J., Section of Medical Oncology, University Hospital, 88 East Newton Street, Boston, MA 02118, USA

Japundžić N., Department of Pharmacology, Medical Faculty, P.O. Box 662, 11000 Belgrade, Serbia, Yugoslavia

Jean A., Département de Physiologie et Neurophysiologie, Faculté des Sciences Saint-Jérôme, 13397 Marseille Cedex 13, France

Jovanović-Mićić D., Department of Pharmacology, Medical Faculty, P.O. Box 662, 11000 Belgrade, Serbia, Yugoslavia

Kamato T., Yamanouchi Pharmaceutical Co. Ltd., Medicinal Research Laboratory I, Central Research Laboratory, 21 Miyukigaoka, Tsukuba, Ibaraki 305, Japan

King G.L., Department of Physiology, Armed Forces Radiobiology Research Institute, Bethesda, MD 20814-5145, USA

Kris M.G., Memorial Sloan-Kettering Cancer Center, 1275 York Avenue, New York, NY 10021, USA

Lang I.M., Medical College of Wisconsin, P.O. Box 232, Surgical Research 151, Milwaukee, WI 53295, USA

Leslie R.A., Oxford University-SmithKline Beecham Center, Radcliffe Infirmary,Woodstock Road, Oxford 0X2 6HE, UK

Lucchini S., Laboratoire de Neurobiologie, CNRS, 31 chemin Joseph Aiguier, 13009 Marseille, France

Lucot J.B., Department of Pharmacology, Wright State University, 3640 Colonel Glenn Highway, Dayton, OH 45435, USA

Marini M.G., Boehringer Ingelheim, Medical Division, Via Serio 15, 20139 Milano, Italy

Martini F., Laboratoire de Neurobiologie, LBN1-CNRS, 31 chemin Joseph Aiguier, 13009 Marseille, France

Matsuki N., Department of Chemical Pharmacology, Faculty of Pharmaceutical Sciences, The University of Tokyo, Bunkyo-Ku, Tokyo 113, Japan

McClellan G.E., Pacific-Sierra Research Corporation, 1401 Wilson Boulevard, Suite 1100, Arlington, Va 22209, USA

Milano S., Département de Physiologie et Neurophysiologie, URA CNRS 205, Faculté des Sciences Saint-Jérôme, 13397 Marseille Cedex 13, France

Miller A.D., Laboratory of Neurophysiology, The Rockefeller University, 1230 York Avenue, New York, NY, 10021-6399, USA

Miolan J.P., Département de Physiologie et Neurophysiologie, URA CNRS 205, Faculté des Sciences Saint-Jérôme, 13397 Marseille Cedex 13, France

Money K.E., Defence and Civil Institute of Environmental Medicine, P.O. Box 2000, North York, Ontario M3M 3B9, Canada

Morrow G.R., University of Rochester Cancer Center, Medical Center, 601 Elmwood Avenue, Box 704, Rochester, NY 14642, USA

Naylor R.J., University of Bradford, The School of Pharmacy, Bradford, West Yorkshire, BD7 1DP, UK

Oman C.M., Massachusetts Institute of Technology, Man Vehicle Laboratory, Department of Aeronautics and Astronautics, Room 37-219, Cambridge, MA 02139, USA

Portillo F., University of Cadiz, School of Medicine, Department of Physiology, Plaza Fragela S/N, Cadiz, Spain

Priestman T.J., The Radiotherapy Department, The Royal Hospital, Cleveland Road, Wolverhampton, WV2 1BT, UK

Puizillout J.J., Laboratoire de Neurobiologie, LBN1-CNRS, 31 chemin Joseph Aiguier, 13009 Marseille, France

Rabin B.M., Psychology Department, University of Maryland, 5401 Wilkens Avenue, Baltimcre, MD 21228, USA

Reynolds D.J.M., Department of Clinical Pharmacology, Radcliffe Infirmary, Woodstock Road, Oxford OX2 6HE, UK

Roman C., Département de Physiologie et Neurophysiologie, URA CNRS 205, Faculté des Sciences Saint-Jérôme, 13397 Marseille Cedex 13, France

Rudd J.A., University of Bradford, The School of Pharmacy, Bradford, West Yorkshire, BD7 1DP, UK

Samardžić R., Department of Pharmacology, Medical Faculty, P.O. Box 662, 11000 Belgrade, Serbia, Yugoslavia

Schiantarelli P., Boehringer Ingelheim Research, Research and Development Division, Via Serio 15, 20130 Milano, Italy

Schilling C.J., Boehringer Ingelheim Deutschland GmbH, Humanpharmakologisches Zentrum, Postfach 200, 6507 Ingelheim, Rh, Germany

Stott J.R.R., Royal Air Force, Institute of Aviation Medicine, Farnborough, Hampshire GU14 6SZ, UK

Torii Y., Department of Chemical Pharmacology, Faculty of Pharmaceutical Sciences, The University of Tokyo, Bunkyo-Ku, Tokyo 113, Japan

Whitehead S.A., Department of Physiology, St George's Hospital Medical School, Cranmer Terrace, London, SW17 ORE, UK

Zabara J., Department of Physiology, Temple University, School of Medicine Philadelphia, Pa 19140, USA

Contents
Sommaire

237 **C.A. Rizzi, H. Ladinsky, A. Sagrada, P. Schiantarelli, A. Schiavone, A. Donetti**
Prokinetic and antiemetic properties of BIMU 1, a 5-HT_4 receptor agonist and 5-HT_3 receptor antagonist
Propriétés cinétiques et anti-émétiques du BIMU 1, agoniste des récepteurs 5-HT_4 et antagoniste des récepteurs 5-HT_3

239 **P. Bhandari, P.L.R. Andrews**
Resinferatoxin: a broad spectrum antiemetic in the ferret
La résinferatoxine: un anti-émétique à large spectre chez le furet

Poster presentations
Communications affichées

241 **D. Jovanović-Mićić, R. Samardžić, N. Japundžić, D.B. Beleslin**
Phenylephrine-induced emesis: alpha-1 adrenoceptors or alpha-2 adrenoceptor subtypes
Vomissement induit par la phényléphrine: adréno-récepteur alpha-1 ou sous-types d'adréno-récepteurs alpha-2

243 **D.B. Beleslin, S. Bošnjak, D. Jovanović-Mićić, R. Samardžić, S.B. Nikolić**
Suppression of clonidine-induced emesis by cyclophosphamide
Suppression des vomissements induits par la clonidine au moyen de la cyclophosphamide

245 **J. Del Río, B. Lasheras, A. Berjón, G. Romero, J.C. Del Castillo, J. Roca, A. Monge**
Novel 5-HT_3 receptor antagonists. Quinoxaline derivatives with antiemetic activity in ferrets
Les nouveaux antagonistes des récepteurs 5-HT_3. Dérivés de la quinoxaline à activité anti-émétique chez les furets

247 **T. Kamato, H. Ito, Y. Nagakura, A. Nishida, H. Yuki, M. Yamano, K. Miyata**
Mechanisms of cisplatin-and serotonin $(5\text{-HT})_3$ receptor agonist-induced emesis in ferrets: effects of YMO60 and section of vagus and greater splanchnic nerves
Mécanismes des vomissements induits par le cisplatine et les agonistes des récepteurs sérotoninergiques $(5\text{-HT})_3$ chez les furets: effets du YMO60 et de la section des nerfs vagues et du nerf grand splanchnique

I. Central neural mechanisms of vomiting

I. Mécanismes nerveux centraux du vomissement

Mechanisms and Control of Emesis. Eds A.L. Bianchi, L. Grélot, A.D. Miller, G.L. King. Colloque INSERM/ John Libbey Eurotext Ltd. © 1992, Vol. 223, pp. 3-9

An historical overview of emesis

Armand L. Bianchi and Laurent Grélot

Département de Physiologie et Neurophysiologie, URA CNRS 205, Faculté des Sciences et Techniques Saint-Jérôme, 13397 Marseille Cedex 13, France

Summary: Nausea and vomiting have been from time immemorial important concerns, not only in terms of their prevention and treatment, but also the induction of vomiting has been used at all times and under all civilizations as a therapeutic tool to fight against gastrointestinal or even more general sickness. It is possible to find writings or traces of such concerns not only in ancient treatises of Grecian and Roman Occidental Medicine, but also in oral traditions left by other Cultures. Nowadays, there is less concern with the induction of vomiting than with the treatment of nausea and vomiting during, for example, motion and space sickness, pregnancy sickness, and treatment of cancer patients. All these concerns together with the pharmacological aspects of their treatments have been presented and discussed during this Meeting. They are summarized in the chapters of these Proceedings, each of them being written by the best specialist in each field. Finally, neurophysiological and neuropharmacological aspects have been important topics of this Meeting as they have been for the last decades. Indeed, it is vital to discover the nervous mechanisms and the neurotransmitters involved in the induction of nausea and vomiting to maximize the chance to treat and control these symptoms in every circumstance.

Résumé: L'Etude du Vomissement à Travers les Ages. *L'apparition de nausées et de vomissements a été depuis des temps immémoriaux une préoccupation importante chez l'homme, bien entendu pour les prévenir ou les interrompre, mais c'est le déclenchement du vomissement qui a été de tout temps et sous toutes les civilisations un moyen thérapeutique pour lutter contre les troubles gastro-intestinaux, ou encore contre certaines maladies. On trouve des écrits ou des traces de telles préoccupations non seulement dans les vieux traités de médecine occidentale gréco-romaine, mais aussi dans les traditions orales laissées par d'autres cultures. De nos jours, ce sont moins les aspects inductions du vomissement que les problèmes soulevés par le traitement de la nausée et du vomissement qui sont restés préoccupants, que ce soit dans la vie de tous les jours, et c'est le cas du mal des transports et du mal de l'espace, ou encore des nausées induits par la grossesse, ou que ce soit pour atténuer ou prévenir les effets secondaires des traitements utilisés chez les malades atteints du cancer. Tous ces problèmes ainsi que les solutions pharmacologiques mises en oeuvre ont été présentés et discutés au cours de ce Colloque. Ils sont résumés dans les chapitres de cet ouvrage écrits par les meilleurs spécialistes de chacune des questions. Enfin, les aspects neurophysiologiques et neuropharmacologiques sont aussi à l'ordre du jour depuis ces dernières décennies, et ils ont été discutés au cours de ce Colloque. Il est en effet essentiel que les mécanismes nerveux ainsi que les neurotransmetteurs mis en jeu dans le déclenchement de la nausée et du vomissement soit bien compris pour pouvoir traiter et contrôler ces symptômes en toutes circonstances.*

It is likely that humans were aware of the existence of an alimentary canal even before the major anatomical discoveries of the 17th to 20th centuries. Abdominal pain, diarrhea and vomiting were always associated with the guts. In medical imagery throughout the centuries, vomiting (and diarrhea) was considered as a neurological syndrome which was the first sign of general poisoning, and was considered a detoxication phenomenon. Hence, vomiting was induced as part of a wide variety of therapies until the 20th century.

The emetic syndromes are described in writings of ancient Chinese medicine where it is said that when the spleen is sick it can no longer digest the aliments, and that food taken in the morning is vomit in the evening. The Chinese prescriptions are numerous, for example rhubarb (*Rheum officinalis*), hog or he-goat liver extracts are used for purgation (cited after Cocheton et al., 1987).

In America, medical data of ancient civilization are known through the reports of the first pioneers. The induction of vomiting was most often the result of therapy aimed at evacuation. Inca and Maya civilizations viewed vomiting and diarrhea as tools to purify the organism by clearing out the morbid agents which were in it, as did the physicians of the ancient Grecian and Roman civilizations, or of the Middle-Ages (cited after Cocheton et al., 1987).

Emetic agents played a major role in the therapy of native Americans. Hurons of Canada used holly (*Ilex vomitoria*) and other species of *Euphorbias* or, more simply, the swallowing of large quantities of hot water. Many other decoctions or mixtures to induce purgation by vomiting and diarrhea were used, but the most important and potent drug having emetic properties but used as an antidiarrheal substance was the *ipecacuanha* (*Uragoga* or *Cephaelis ipecacuanha*). The roots of *ipecacuanha* were mainly used by Amazonian Indians, and their use was described by European explorers during the 17th Century. The active constituent "emetin" was isolated in the 19th century (cited after Cocheton et al., 1987).

Figure 1 - Young man vomiting (unknown date, Vatican Museum, Roma)
cited after Penso (1984)

At the time of Hippocrates, the Grecians assumed that sickness could be explained by a disequilibrium in the four fundamental body-fluids, and vomiting was considered to result from an excess of one of these body-fluids. This belief was retained throughout the Middle-Ages until the 18th century (cited after Lyons and Petrucelli, 1978).

Celsus, an assumed physician from ancient Rome, (De Medicina around 100 A.D.) proposed the use of vomiting to solve digestive problems, but he considered that vomiting was more useful in winter than summer. His prescription was to drink a mixture of salty hot water and honey, or to use Hellebore (*Veratrum album*). Romans were hearty eaters, and they often had attacks of indigestion, or *cruditas*, which caused nausea: *crudates quae nauseum faciumt*, eructation, or *ructus*, hiccup or *singultus* and vomiting or *vomitiones* (Plinius, Historia naturalis, 23-79 A.D). For Galenus (De facultae naturalis, about 129-200 A.D.), vomiting was analogous to diarrhea: when the stomach was overloaded with food, the quantity or quality of which was not acceptable, it threw out its content (Fig. 1). Plinius also noted the existence of sea sickness (*nausea maris in navigationibus*) as part of stomach sickness (cited after Penso, 1984).

Textbooks of medicine of the 19th century mentioned "nervous emesis" as either a proper sickness or as a symptom of other unknown diseases. Pregnancy sickness was classified as this type of emesis (Vallein, 1850). To treat the emetic syndrome the physicians at this time used various kinds of drugs or mixtures such as opium, morphine, laudanum, quinquina decoction, gaseous mineral water, plant coal, or antispasmodic preparation of valerian. Rubbing Belladonna extracts against the abdomen were used to treat pregnancy sickness. Psychological approach was also a proposed method which could be compared to "positive attitude" in use today to fight against sickness in parallel with modern chemical therapy. Since all these methods in use during the 19th century gave weak results in treating emesis, physicians had a reasonable alternative: they often proposed that patients stop any drug treatment and food intake, and hopefully observed some cases of recovery (Vallein, 1850).

As discussed previously by Brizzee (1990), the early physicians and physiologists were greatly concerned with the physiological effects of nausea and vomiting, but not with the underlying mechanisms. For a long time, vomiting was thought to produced by contractions of the stomach. The first explanation of the mechanisms of vomiting appeared with Magendie's experiments in 1825 which demonstrated the essential role of the respiratory muscles in generating the abdominal pressure needed for expulsion of the stomach contents. Since then, numerous investigators have been interested in the mechanics of vomiting (see Brizze's minireview, 1990) and the basic pharmacological mechanisms of the emetic response (see Leslie et al., 1990).

A major advancement in the characterization of the neural mechanisms which control emesis was provided by Borison and Wang (1949 & 1953) (see also Borison's obituary in this Book). However, an interesting point which has attracted Neurophysiologists, concerns the reconfiguration of the motor output to the respiratory muscles during vomiting. The proposal is that the rhythmic pattern generator subserving ventilatory motor output is strongly inhibited during vomiting, and that another pattern generator directly drives the respiratory motoneurones at the spinal level. These different configurations of the motor output are able to induce either ventilation or vomiting, or any other pressure for expulsion.

Results from our Laboratory (Bianchi and Grélot, 1989) and others (Miller, 1990) have showed that the inspiratory bulbospinal neurones of both the dorsal and ventral respiratory groups, which drive the inspiratory spinal motoneurones during ventilation, are subjected to an intensive inhibition during vomiting. This inhibition suppresses the excitatory drive on inspiratory bulbospinal neurons. At the spinal level, the alternate periodic motor output subserving the expiratory and inspiratory muscles is thus remodulating to induce co-activation of both types of muscles now no longer involved in ventilation but in elevation of pressure in the abdomen and thorax to produce expulsion of gastric contents (Fig. 2). It is likely that this inhibition is coming from a pattern generator other than the one involved in ventilation. These results indicate that different pattern generators can drive the same muscles in different patterns to modify performance and fit circumstances. This question is not restricted to the respiratory-vomiting neuronal networks but can be taken at a more general point of view of the plasticity of a neural network (e.g., Marder, 1988).

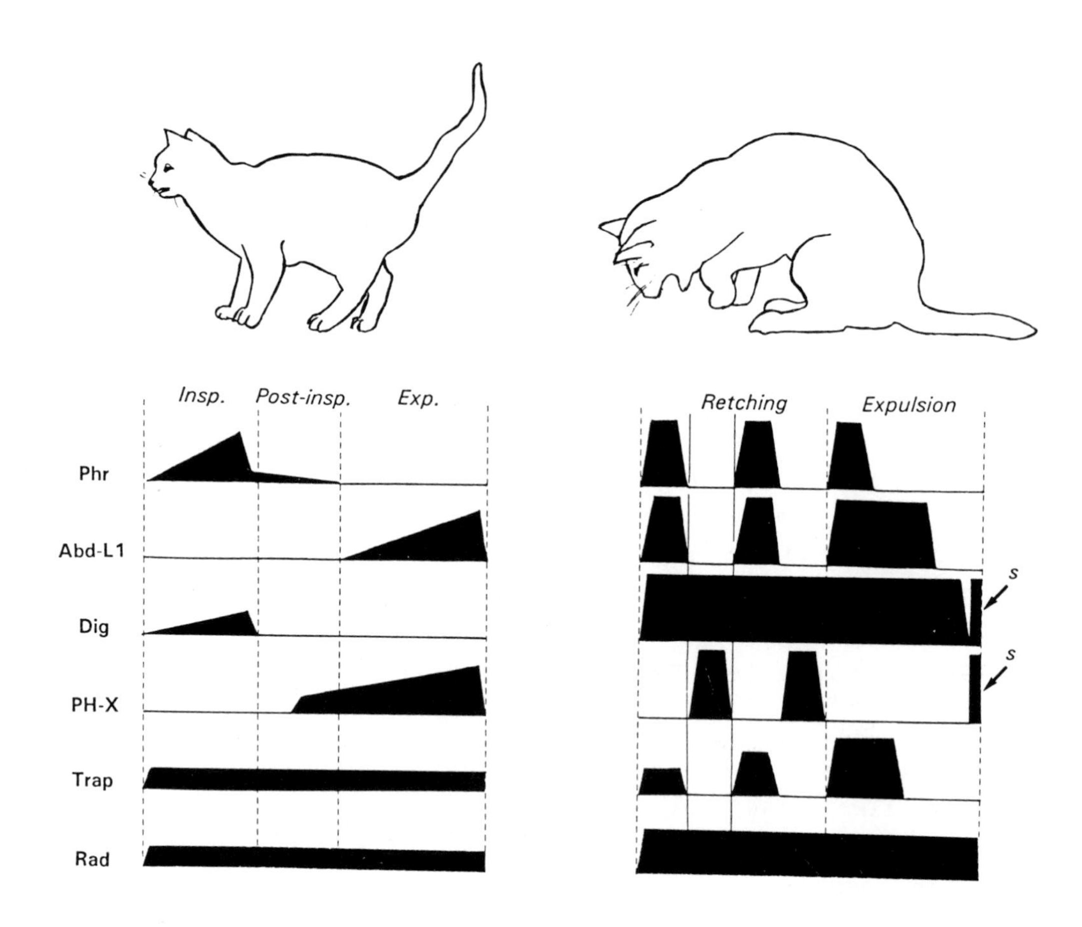

Figure 2 - Sketch of the pattern of activity of respiratory and non-respiratory nerves in the cat during vomiting (right) as compared to normal respiration and behavior (left). Left, vertical hatched line indicate the three respiratory phases. Insp., inspiration; Post-insp., post-inspiration; Exp., expiration. Right, vertical hatched lines indicate the two phases of vomiting (i.e. retching and expulsion); vertical filled lines in the retching phase indicate an interburst, a period during which the PH-X is activated. Note the buccopharyngeal stage of swallowing (arrows and *s*) identified in some nerves at the end of the expulsion phase.

Abbreviations: Phr, phrenic nerve; Abd-L1, abdominal (cranial iliohypogastric) nerve; PH-X, pharyngeal branch of the vagus nerve; Dig, digastric nerve; Tra, nerve to the trapezius; Rad, nerve to triceps brachii.

Regarding the mechanisms of neural control of vomiting, the challenge is now to elucidate where is the brain stem neural network driving the vomiting task of the respiratory muscles. How is this neural network activated by various kinds of afferents (visceral, vestibular, chemical etc...), directly or through the area postrema? What are the neurotransmitters involved? Insights to these unanswered questions will improve the treatment of emesis in different situations such as motion sickness, pathology or drug administration and therapy.

Acknowledgement: *We express our thanks to Mrs J. Roman for the preparation of illustrations, and to Mrs A.M. Poudevigne Chief Librarian at the Library of the Faculty of Medicine, La Timone, Marseille who facilitated access to books devoted to history of medicine. Our thanks are also directed to Professor J. Frexinos (CHU Toulouse) who sent me reprints of Medicine Textbooks of the 19th century dealing with emetic syndroms.*

References

Bianchi, A. L. and Grélot,L. (1989). Converse motor output of inspiratory bulbospinal premotoneurones during vomiting. Neurosc. Lett. 104, 298-302.

Borison, H.L. and Wang, S.C. (1949). Functional localization of central coordinating mechanism for emesis in cat. J. Neurophysiol. 12, 305-313.

Borison, H.L. and Wang, S.C. (1953). Physiology and pharmacology of vomiting. Pharmacol. Rev., 5, 193-230.

Brizzee, K. R. (1990) Mechanics of vomiting: a minireview. Can. J. Physiol. Pharmacol. 68, 221-229.

Cocheton, J.J., Guerre, J. and Pequignot,H. (1987). *Histoire illustrée de l'hépato-gastro-entérologie de l'Antiquité à nos jours.* Les Editions Roger Dacosta, Paris.

Magendie, F. (1825). *Précis élémentaire de Physiologie.* Méquignon-Marvis, Paris.

Marder, E. (1988). Modulating a neuronal network. Nature 335, 1-2.

Miller, A.D. Nonaka, S., Lakos, S.F. and Tan, L.K. (1990). Diaphragmatic and external intercostal muscle control during vomiting: behavior of inspiratory bulbospinal neurons. J. Neurophysiol. 63, 31-36.

Leslie, R.A., Sha,Y., Thejomayen,M., and Murphy, K.M. (1990) The neuropharmacology of emesis: the role of receptors in neuromodulation of nausea and vomiting. Can. J. Physiol. Pharmacol. 68, 279-288.

Lyons, A.S. and Petrucelli, R. J. (1978) *Medicine: an illustrated History.* Abrams Inc., N.Y. (French translation by Cottereau, J.P. et al., Presse de la Renaissance, Paris).

Penso, G. (1984). *La Médecine Romaine*. Les Editions Roger Dacosta, Paris.

Vallein, F. L. I. (1850) *Guide du médecin praticien: résumé général de pathologie interne et de thérapeutiques appliquées. Tome 2, maladies des voies digestives.* Baillière, Paris.

Mechanisms and Control of Emesis. Eds A.L. Bianchi, L. Grélot, A.D. Miller, G.L. King. Colloque INSERM/
John Libbey Eurotext Ltd. © 1992, Vol. 223, pp. 11-18

Neurotransmitter receptor subtypes related to vomiting

Dušan B. Beleslin

Department of Pharmacology, Medical Faculty, P.O. Box 662, 11 000 Belgrade, Serbia, Yugoslavia

SUMMARY

The objective of this paper is to summarize current knowledge in neurotransmitter receptor subtypes related to vomiting. Of 5-HT receptors 5-HT-3 binding sites have been found on vagal afferents, within the nucleus of the tractus solitarius, area postrema and dorsal nucleus of the vagus nerve, whereas 5-HT-1A receptors are associated at or near the vomiting centre. Alpha-2 adrenoceptors, dopamine D-2 receptors, histamine H-1 and H-2 receptors, muscarinic M-1 receptors, nicotinic receptors and opioid mi and delta receptors reflect the regulation of emesis within the area postrema. Muscarinic receptors, although it is not yet known which subtypes, participate in the motion-induced emesis at least in vestibular apparatus, in afferents at vestibular nucleus and in other brainstem areas. Finally, mi opioid receptor subtypes have been implicated in the regulation of emesis at vomiting centre. Of course, neurotransmitter receptor subtypes related to emesis vary across animal species.

Sous-types de récepteurs impliqués dans la médiation neurochimique du vomissement
Résumé: *Ce chapitre résume les connaissances actuelles portant sur les sous-types de récepteurs impliqués de mécanisme émétique. Les sites de fixation sérotoninergiques de type 5-HT-3 ont été trouvés sur les terminaisons sensorielles du nerf vague, alors que ceux de type 5-HT-1A sont présents dans la région du centre du vomissement. Les récepteurs adrénergiques alpha 2, dopaminergiques D-2, histaminiques H-1 et H-2, muscariniques M-1, nicotiniques et aux substances opiacées mu et delta, tous localisés dans l'area postrema, sont impliqués dans la régulation de l'activité émétique. Les récepteurs muscariniques, dont le sous-type n'est pas encore caractérisé, localisés dans l'appareil vestibulaire et dans certaines régions du tronc cérébral, sont impliqués dans le vomissement associé au mal des transports. Enfin, les récepteurs aux substances opiacées de type mu, présents au niveau du centre du vomissement, ont été impliqués dans la régulation du vomissement. Il est à noter que les sous-types de récepteurs impliqués dans les mécanismes de contrôle du vomissement varient selon l'espèce animale considérée.*

INTRODUCTION

The objective herein is to characterize the basic emetic control mechanism/s from both physiological and pharmacological point of view and relate the mechanism/s to neurotransmitter receptor subtypes to the extent that they are understood at present. The words "vomiting" and "emesis" in this work, are used synonymously.

The emetic reflex consists of detectors which identify the emetic stimuli and transmit impulses to the vomiting centre via afferents in which after the integration through effectors the vomiting is initiated. Neurotransmitter receptor subtypes related to emetic reflex are considered below.

AFFERENT SYSTEMS

Emesis may be initiated by stimulation of the gastrointestinal tract (pharynx, stomach, duodenum), from higher cortical and limbic regions of the brain, from supramedullary (labyrinth, diencephalon) and medullary (area postrema, nucleus of the tractus solitarius, vestibular complex) structures of the brain. The most important detectors are the gastrointestinal tract and the chemoreceptor trigger zone within the area postrema. Table 1 summarizes receptors, receptor subtypes and neurotransmitters subserving the emesis in afferent and efferent systems as well as in the vomiting centre.

Table 1. Receptors, Receptor-Subtypes and Neurotransmitters Subserving the Emesis at Afferent and Efferent Systems and at Vomiting Centre

SYSTEM/S	RECEPTOR/S	NEUROTRANSMITTER/S	ANTAGONIST/S	SPECIES
AFFERENT SYSTEMS				
Gastrointestinal tract	5-HT-3	5-HT	ondansetron tropisetron	ferret
Nucleus of the tractus solitarius	5-HT-3	5-HT	ondansetron tropisetron	man cat ferret
Vestibular complex	muscarinic	acetylcholine	atropine scopolamine	bovine
Labyrinth	muscarinic H-1	acetylcholine (?)	atropine scopolamine	monkey dog cat
Diencephalon	imidazoline (?)	clonidine	(?)	cat
VOMITING CENTRE				
	5-HT 5-HT-1	5-HT	reserpine	cat dog ferret
	alpha-adrenergic receptors	noradrenaline	reserpine	cat dog
EFFERENT SYSTEMS				
Gastrointestinal tract	5-HT-3 (?)	5-HT (?)	ondansetron tropisetron	man ferret
	D-2 (?)	dopamine (?)	neuroleptics	man ferret
	muscarinic (?)	acetylcholine (?)	atropine	cat

GASTROINTESTINAL TRACT

There are a number of different mechanisms by which stimuli arising from the gastrointestinal tract cause emesis. For instance, mechanical stimulation of the pharynx, ingested toxins, cell damage, degeneration, necrosis, inflammation, anticancer chemo- and radiation therapy induce emesis. Of many receptors found in the gastrointestinal tract, 5-HT receptors, most probably, play a key role in the initiation of emesis. The following observation support this view. 5-HT-3 (also known as M receptors) have been demonstrated on vagal afferents. The activation of 5-HT-3 receptors by 5-HT induces depolarization and increases nervous activity in the afferents. This effect is blocked by 5-HT-3 antagonists (Richardson ***et al.***, 1986). The cytotoxic drugs cause 5-HT release from the enterochromaffin cells and from the mucosa of the gastrointestinal tract and activate 5-HT-3 receptors on afferent vagal fibres. In ferrets, after cytotoxic drugs, stimulation of 5-HT-3 receptors induces abnormal discharge of the vagal fibres which evoke emesis. A combination of bilateral vagotomy and greater splanchnic nerve section as well as the administration of the 5-HT-3 receptor antagonist, BRL 24924, almost completely abolish the vomiting in response to cytotoxic drugs (Hawthorn ***et al.***, 1988).

MEDULLARY STRUCTURES

Of medullary structures the most important are nucleus of the tractus solitarius, the vestibular complex and the area postrema.

NUCLEUS OF THE TRACTUS SOLITARIUS. - Visceral afferents, mostly of vagal origin, act through the nucleus of the tractus solitarius to stimulate the vomiting centre, but vagal afferents also project to the area postrema. 5-HT-3 receptors which mediate emesis have been found within the nucleus of the tractus solitarius of mice, rats, ferrets, cats and humans (Pratt ***et al.***, 1990). In addition, alpha-2 adrenoceptors subserving emesis have been located in the fourth ventricle around the locus coeruleus of the cat (van Dongen, 1980).

VESTIBULAR COMPLEX. - Motion stimuli are transmitted via the brainstem reticular formation to the vomiting centre to induce emesis. The vestibular complex of the bovine brain contains muscarinic receptors (Pedigo & Brizzee, 1986), but it is not yet known of which subtypes. It is interesting to note that muscarinic M-1 receptors outside the cat's area postrema are involved in the emetic reflex (Beleslin & Nedelkovski, 1986).

AREA POSTREMA. - Area postrema is a circumventricular organ which lacks a typical blood-brain barrier. The chemoreceptor trigger zone is within area postrema (Borison & Wang, 1953). Its histological, vascular and neurochemical organization is adapted to the role of a detector (sensory) organ capable of sensing and transmitting the emetic stimuli either from the blood, the cerebrospinal fluid or from other brain regions to the vomiting centre. Chemoreceptor trigger zone responds to endogenous substances of pathophysiologic origin as well as to exogenous chemicals. Thus, the action on receptors within the chemoreceptor trigger zone does not necessarily demand the participation of a transmitter substance. On the other hand, within the vomiting centre a drug action affects synaptic transmission and must, therefore, involve one or more neurotransmitters (Costello & Borison, 1977). Neurochemical, pharmacological and radioligand binding studies revealed different types of receptors and neurotransmitters in the area postrema. The most interesting among them are catecholaminergic, cholinergic, nicotinic, histaminergic, opioid mechanisms and receptors, as summarized in Table 2.

Catecholaminergic Mechanisms and Receptors. - Area postrema of many species, including men, contains catecholamines and their receptors. Moreover, catecholamines and drugs acting on catecholamine receptors are known as very potent emetic agents. However, the relative significance of dopamine, noradrenaline and adrenaline in the regulation of emesis within the area postrema is not well understood. For instance, the emetic activity of catecholamines varies across animal species. Thus, it has been demonstrated that men and dogs are highly sensitive to dopamine agonists, whereas these agents are much less active in cats and virtually devoid of the emetic activity in monkeys (Samardžić & Beleslin, 1989). In addition, different catecholamines exhibit different emetic potencies in the same species. In cats the most active is adrenaline, whereas the least active is dopamine (Jovanović-Mićić ***et al.***, 1989). Interestingly, apart from catecholamines, predominantly alpha-1 adrenergic agonists, phenylephrine and methoxamine (Malobabić ***et al.***, 1989; Beleslin ***et al.***, 1990), as well as predominantly alpha-2 adrenoceptor agonists, clonidine, guanabenz and xylazine (Lucot & Crampton, 1986; Japundžić ***et al.***, 1989; Samardžić ***et al.***, 1992) produce emesis in cats.

Our knowledge about the adrenoceptors within the area postrema regulating emesis is still incomplete. The earliest report on adrenoceptors subserving emesis is that of Jenkins & Lahay (1971). Namely, in cats, drugs which act on central alpha adrenoceptors, but not on central beta adrenoceptors produce emesis. Later, detailed pharmacological studies have shown that the emetic response to noradrenaline, also in cats, is most effectively antagonized by drugs with marked alpha-2 adrenoceptor blocking activity. These alpha-2 adrenoceptors are located within the area postrema, since in cats with ablated area noradrenaline no longer produce emesis (Beleslin & Štrbac, 1987). Similarly, Lucot & Crampton (1986) provided evidence that xylazine, an alpha-2 adrenoceptor agonist, produces emesis via alpha-2 adrenoceptors in the area postrema of the cat. In this context, it is postulated that noradrenergic neurones might recognize a common site of confluence of different inputs subserving the emesis in the area postrema (Beleslin **et al.**, 1989b). According to Beleslin **et al.**, (1989b) noradrenergic neurones as well as cholinergic axon terminals within the area postrema are necessary for the emetic action of noradrenaline and muscarinic M-1 receptors subserve the cholinergic axon terminals. Furthermore, unexpected results in the experiments with dopamine in cats showed that the emetic responses to dopamine are most effectively suppressed by alpha-2 adrenoceptor blocking drugs, but not by dopamine antagonists. It appears, therefore, that central alpha-2 adrenoceptors rather than central dopamine receptors are associated with the emetic response to dopamine, at least in the cat (Samardžić et **al.**, 1986). In other species, the effect of dopamine agonists can be selectively blocked by dopamine D-2 receptor antagonist as well as by ablation of the area postrema. The presence of dopamine and dopamine D-2 receptors has been demonstrated in the area postrema of dogs and man (Stefanini & Clement-Cormier, 1981; Schwartz **et al.**, 1986).

Cholinoceptive Mechanisms and Receptors. - Muscarinic agonists in cats like carbachol and anticholinesterases induce intense behavioural excitation, whereas emesis has been only sporadically observed (Samardžić & Beleslin, 1989). On the other hand, pilocarpine, arecoline and muscarinic ganglionic stimulants like MCN-A-343 and AHR-602 evoke much less behavioural excitation in cats, while the emesis is more frequent (Beleslin & Samardžić, 1979). Of these drugs, pilocarpine and MCN-A-343, exhibit the most consistent emetic effect (Borison, 1959; Beleslin & Nedelkovski, 1988). The obvious differences in the behavioural and emetic effects of two groups of muscarinic agonists raised the question of uniformity of the central muscarinic receptors. The predominant selectivity of MCN-A-343 for the muscarinic M-1 receptors has been confirmed in experiments with cats in which the emetic effect of MCN-A-343 is more selectively blocked by the specific M-1 muscarinic antagonist, pirenzepine than by atropine (Beleslin & Nedelkovski, 1988). However, the site/s of the emetic action of the muscarinic drugs have not been completely localized, since the ablation of the area postrema significantly reduces, but does not entirely abolish the emetic response to MCN-A-343 (Beleslin & Nedelkovski, 1988) or to pilocarpine (Borison, 1959). In addition to these findings, Pedigo & Brizzee (1985) have described muscarinic receptors in the bovine area postrema. Cholinergic neurones have not been found in the area postrema, but the presence of cholinacetyltransferase suggests that cholinergic nerve terminals might be located in this structure of the medulla (Schwartz **et al.**, 1986).

Nicotinic Mechanisms and Receptors. - Nicotine and dimethylphenylpiperazinium (DMPP) evoke emesis by an action on the area postrema in cats and dogs (Laffan & Borison, 1957; Beleslin & Krstić, 1986, 1987). The emetic effects of nicotine and DMPP are dose-dependent and selectively blocked by ganglionic blocking agents. On the other hand, the neurochemical nature of neurones, at which nicotinic receptors producing emesis are located in the area postrema is still ill-understood (Beleslin & Krstić, 1986, 1987). More detailed investigation of central effects of nicotinic drugs revealed several discrepancies between nicotine and DMPP. For instance, nicotine is about 80 times more potent than DMPP, on the basis of ED_{50}, in inducing emesis. Intracerebroventricular (ICV) nicotine evokes hypotension whereas ICV DMPP has virtually no effect on the arterial blood pressure. Salivation is another symptom which occurs after ICV nicotine, but not after ICV DMPP (Samardžić & Beleslin, 1989). Thus, the differences in the emetic and central cardiovascular effects, as well as in the capacity to induce salivation, between ICV nicotine and DMPP may also reflect the existence of more than one subtype of nicotinic receptors, at least in the brain.

5-Hydroxytryptamine Mechanisms and Receptors. - 5-HT-3 receptor subtypes within the area postrema, at least in ferrets, participate in the central regulation of emesis (Barnes et **al.**, 1988). Moreover, 5-HT-3 receptors have been located in the area postrema of cats and humans (Pratt **et al.**, 1990), although there is no firm evidence that these receptors take part through the area postrema in the central regulation of emesis.

Histaminergic Mechanisms and Receptors. - The emetic action of histamine has been thoroughly investigated in men, monkeys and dogs. On the other hand, cats are resistant to the emetic action of histamine (Jovanović-Mićić **et al.**, 1992). Both histamine H-1 and H-2 receptors as well as histamine have been found in the area postrema of men and dogs (Bhargava **et al.**, 1976; Schwartz **et al.**, 1986). In this connection it should be mentioned that antihistamines attenuated the dopamine-induced emesis in cats (Beleslin ***et al.***, 1989a).

Table 2. Receptors, Receptor-Subtypes and Neurotransmitters Subserving Emesis within the Chemoreceptor Trigger Zone within the Area Postrema

RECEPTOR	NEUROTRANSMITTER	ANTAGONIST	SPECIES
D-2 D-2	dopamine dopamine	neuroleptics neuroleptics	man dog
alpha-adrenoceptors alpha-adrenoceptors alpha-2 adrenoceptors	noradrenaline noradrenaline noradrenaline	? ? yohimbine	man dog cat
alpha-adrenoceptors alpha-adrenoceptors alpha-adrenoceptors	adrenaline adrenaline adrenaline	? ? yohimbine	man dog cat
H-1 H-1	histamine histamine	antihistamines antihistamines	man dog
H-2 H-2	histamine histamine	? cimetidine	man dog
5-HT-3	5-HT	ondansetron tropisetron	man
5-HT-3	5-HT	ondansetron tropisetron	ferret
muscarinic	acetylcholine	atropine scopolamine	man
muscarinic M-1	acetylcholine	pirenzepine	cat
nicotinic	?	ganglionic blocking drugs	cat
opioid mi	morphine	naloxone nalorphine	man dog cat
opioid delta	enkephalins	naloxone nalorphine	dog cat

Opioid Mechanisms and Receptors. - It is well known that morphine produces emesis in all species, including man. In the area postrema enkephalins and opioid receptors have been found in many animal species, including humans, whereas beta-endorphin in this brain structure has been detected only in men (Schwartz ***et al.***, 1986). At present, mi and delta opioid receptors are of prevailing importance for the emetic action of opioids (Costello & Borison, 1977; Beleslin ***et al.***, 1981, 1982; Jovanović-Mićić ***et al.***, 1989).

Neuropeptides and Putative Amino-Acid Neurotransmitters. - A large number of neuropeptides have been detected in the area postrema of many animal species and men. However, there is evidence that of many neuropeptides only substance P, neurotensin, angiotensin II, VIP, TRH and gastrin evoke emesis via the area postrema in dogs (Carpenter ***et al.***, 1984). The emetic effect of neuropeptides is not easy to study because of rapid degradation by peptidases, as well as of the lack of specific agonists and antagonists.

Of putative amino-acid neurotransmitters glutamate has been reported to induce emesis. GABA has been detected in the area postrema, but there has been no evidence so far that this amino-acid participates in the regulation of emesis.

Alcohol and Receptors. - Recently it has been reported that alcohol has a selective inhibitory effect on noradrenaline- and nicotine-induced emesis in cats. In fact, differential responses to alcohol most probably reflect the microenvironment of alpha-noradrenergic and nicotinic receptors in the area postrema of cats (Beleslin ***et al.***, 1991).

SUPRAMEDULLARY STRUCTURES

The labirynth and the diencephalon are the most interesting brain structures in the central regulation of emesis.

LABYRINTH. - It is well known that motion elicits vomiting. The vestibular apparatus, which responds to motion stimuli, is apparently subserved by cholinergic neurones. The cholinergic mechanisms are also involved in afferents at vestibular nuclei as well as in other brainstem structures which participate in the motion sickness symptoms. Therefore, it is evident that muscarinic antagonists are very effective antiemetics. Antihistamines and drugs like chlorpromazine and prochlorpromazine are good antiemetics for the motion sickness-induced emesis. The antiemetic activity of these drugs is, at least, in part due to their antimuscarinic action. However, the most effective antimotion sickness drug is a muscarinic antagonist, scopolamine. The animals used in models of motion sickness usually include monkeys, dogs and cats (Pedigo & Brizzee, 1986).

DIENCEPHALON. - Several lines of evidence point to the involvement of diencephalon in the central regulation of emesis. In the earliest reports it was shown that vomiting is induced in the cat by electrical stimulation of the hypothalamus (Borison & Wang, 1953). Recently, it has been reported that among noradrenergic agonists tested (noradrenaline, clonidine, phenylephrine, methoxamine), only clonidine induces emesis when microinjected in the anterior hypothalamic preoptic area of the cat. Interestingly, the clonidine-induced emesis was resistant to the inhibitory effects of alpha-adrenoceptor blocking drugs, antimuscarinic substances, 5-HT, opioid and dopamine antagonists (Beleslin ***et al.***, 1987). The pharmacological nature of clonidine-induced emesis remains, thus, to be determined.

VOMITING CENTRE

The integration of the emetic stimuli and synchronization of the appropriate responses occurs in the lateral reticular formation of the brainstem, termed "vomiting centre". This region is not a rigidly defined anatomical and histological structure. The neurones involved in the vomiting centre are rather diffusely distributed within the region of lateral reticular formation of medulla (Borison & Wang, 1953), According to Costello and Borison (1977) the vomiting centre is polysynaptic and it is subserved by many neurotransmitters. It follows then that a drug affecting synaptic transmission within the vomiting centre involves more than one neurotransmitter. In good lines with this view are the results of Beleslin & Krstić (1986, 1987) and Beleslin & Štrbac (1987) who reported that of many drugs injected ICV only reserpine suppressed the activity of the vomiting centre. Reserpine, contrary to 6-hydroxydopamine, hemicholinium-3 and 5,6-dihydroxytryptamine, affects more than two neurotransmitter systems. It appears, therefore, that at least catecholaminergic and 5-hydroxytryptaminergic neurotransmitters and receptors subserve the polysynaptic transmission within the vomiting centre. Of these, most probably, dopamine, noradrenaline, adrenaline and 5-HT are the most important. Of course, at present, it is impossible to ascertain the receptor subtypes, although there is a report that postsynaptic 5-HT-1A receptors are involved in the central regulation of emesis at a convergent structure at or near the vomiting centre of the cat (Lucot & Crampton, 1989). Theleologically, polysynaptic transmission with many and various neurotransmitters is essential, because complex respiratory and somatic movements, autonomic phenomena and gastrointestinal movements are integrated and synchronized in vomiting centre to produce emesis. However, Costello & Borison (1977) reported that morphine and morphine-like drugs suppress the vomiting centre as well. Morphine acts pre- and postsynaptically and affects many neurotransmitter systems. It is possible, therefore, that morphine acts at one neurotransmitter system presynaptically, whereas postsynaptically at the other neurotransmitter system. Since the effect of morphine is antagonized by naloxone it follows that mi subtype of opioid receptors, most probably, are involved in the regulation of the emesis within the vomiting centre. Taken together, the present results suggest that the vomiting centre may be suppressed when more than one neurotransmitter systems are inhibited whereas only one neurotransmitter, arising in afferent pathway, may initiate emesis in vomiting centre.

EFFERENT SYSTEMS

Basically, vagus plays a prominent role in efferent systems. Dopamine and 5-HT-3 receptors as well as muscarinic cholinoceptors are the most important of many receptors in the gastrointestinal tract (Table 1). The ability of metoclopramide to facilitate gastric emptying has been considered to involve an antagonism at peripheral dopamine receptors (Akwari, 1983). Moreover, 5-HT-3 antagonists increase, also, the gastric emptying (Costall *et al.*, 1987). However, there is evidence that both metoclopramide and 5-HT-3 antagonists by increasing cholinergic activity, probably through the release of acetylcholine facilitate the gastric emptying (Sanger, 1987, 1984).

This work was supported by a grant of the Scientific Fund of Serbia.

REFERENCES

Akwari, O.E. (1983): The gastrointestinal tract in chemotherapy-induced emesis: a final common pathway. *Drugs* 25, Suppl. 1, 18-34.

Barnes, N.M., Costall, R.J., Naylor, F.D. & Tattersall F.D. (1988): Identification of $5\text{-}HT_3$ recognition sites in the ferret area postrema. *J. Pharm. Pharmacol.* 40, 586-588.

Beleslin, D.B. & Krstić, S.K. (1986): Dimethylphenylpiperazinium-induced vomiting: nicotinic mediation in area postrema. *Brain Res. Bull.* 16, 5-10.

Beleslin, D.B. & Krstić, S.K. (1987): Further studies on nicotine-induced emesis: nicotinic mediation in area postrema. *Physiol. Behav.* 39, 681-686.

Beleslin, D.B. & Nedelkovski, V. (1988): Emesis induced by 4-(m-chlorophenylcarbamoyloxy)-2-butyniltrimethylammonium chloride (MCN-A-343): evidence for a predominant central muscarinic M_1 mediation. *Neuropharmacology* 9, 949-956.

Beleslin, D.B. & Samardžić, R. (1979): Comparative study of aggressive behaviour after injection of cholinomimetics, anticholinesterases, nicotinic and muscarinic ganglionic stimulants into the cerebral ventricles of conscious cats: failure of nicotinic drugs to evoke aggression. *Psychopharmacology* 60, 147-153.

Beleslin, D.B. & Štrbac, M. (1987): Noradrenaline-induced emesis: alpha-2 adrenoceptor mediation in the area postrema. *Neuropharmacology* 26, 1157-1165.

Beleslin, D.B., Jovanović-Mićić, D., Nikolić, S.B. & Samardžić, R. (1991): Selective effect of ethanol on norepinephrine- and nicotine-induced emesis in cats. *Alcohol* 8, 409-501.

Beleslin, D.B., Jovanović-Mićić, D. & Samardžić, R. (1989a): The effect of histamine H-1 antaginists on dopamine-induced emesis. *Iugoslav. Physiol. Pharmacol. Acta* 25, 195-198.

Beleslin, D.B., Jovanović-Mićić, D., Samardžić, R. & Malobabić, Z.S. (1990): Studies on behavioural effects of phenylephrine in cats. *Iugoslav. Physiol. Pharmacol. Acta* 26, 17-21.

Beleslin, D.B., Krstić, S.K., Stefanović-Denić, K., Štrbac, M. & Mićić, D. (1981): Inhibition by morphine and morphine-like drugs of nicotine-induced emesis in cats. *Brain Res. Bull.* 6, 451-453.

Beleslin, D.B., Rezvani, A.H. & Myers, R.D. (1987): Rostral hypothalamus: a new neuroanatomical site of neurochemically-induced emesis in the cat. *Brain Res. Bull.* 19, 239-244.

Beleslin, D.B., Samardžić, R., Krstić, S.K. & Mićić, D. (1982): Differences in central effects of β-endorphin and enkephalins: β-endorphin, a potent psychomotor stimulant. *Neuropharmacology* 21, 99-102.

Beleslin, D.B., Štrbac, M., Jovanović-Mićić, D., Samardžić, R. & Nedelkovski, V. (1989b): Area postrema: cholinergic and noradrenergic regulation of emesis. A new concept. *Arch. Inter. Physiol. Biochem.* 97, 107-115.

Bhargava, K.P., Dixit, K.S. & Palit, G. (1976): Nature of histamine receptors in the emetic chemoreceptor trigger zone. *Br. J. Pharmacol.* 57, 211-213.

Borison, H.L. (1959): Effect of ablation of medullary emetic chemoreceptor trigger zone on vomiting responses to cerebral intraventricular injection of adrenaline, apomorphine and pilocarpine in the cat. *J. Physiol.* 147, 172-177.

Borison, H.L. & Wang, S.C. (1953): Physiology and pharmacology of vomiting. *Pharmacol. Rev.* 5, 193-230.

Carpenter, D.O., Briggs, D.B. & Strominger, N. (1984): Behavioral and electrophysiological studies of peptide-induced emesis in dogs. *Fed. Proc.* 43, 2952-2954.

Costall, B., Gunning, R.J. & Tyers, M.B. (1987): The effect of GR38032F, novel $5\text{-}HT_3$-receptor antagonist on gastric emptying in the guinea-pig. *Br. J. Pharmacol.* 91, 263-264.

Costello, D.J. & Borison, H.L. (1977): Naloxone antagonizes narcotic self-blockade of emesis in the cat. *J. Pharmacol. Exp. Ther.* 203, 222-230.

Hawthorn, J., Ostler, K.J. & Andrews, P.L.R. (1988): The role of the abdominal

visceral innervation and 5-hydroxytryptamine M-receptors in vomiting induced by the cytotoxic drugs cyclophosphamide and cis-platin in the ferret. *Quat. J. Exp. Physiol.* 73, 7-21.
Japundžić, N., Jovanović-Mićić, D. & Beleslin, D.B. (1989): Behavioural effects of clonidine in cats. *Iugoslav. Physiol. Pharmacol. Acta* 25, 289-293.
Jenkins, L.C. & Lahay, D. (1971): Central mechanisms of vomiting related to catecholamine response: anaesthetic implication. *Canad. Anaesth. Soc. J.* 18, 434-441.
Jovanović-Mićić, D., Japundžić, N. & Beleslin, D.B. (1989): Behavioural effects of ketocyclazocine in cats. *Iugoslav. Physiol. Pharmacol. Acta* 25, 305-308.
Jovanović-Mićić, D., Japunžić, N., Samardžić, R., Tomić-Beleslin, N. & Beleslin, D.B. (1992): Quantitative analysis of autonomic effects of intracerebroventricular histamine. *Iugoslav. Physiol. Pharmacol. Acta* 28, Suppl. 9, 83-86.
Jovanović-Mićić, D., Štrbac, M., Krstić, S.K., Japundžić, N., Samardžić, R. & Beleslin, D.B. (1989): Ablation of the area postrema and emesis. *Metab. Brain. Dis.* 4, 55-60.
Laffan, R.J. & Borison, H.L. (1957): Emetic action of nicotine and lobeline. *J. Pharmacol. Exp. Ther.* 121, 468-476.
Lucot, J.B. & Crampton, G.H. (1986): Xylazine emesis, yohimbine and motion sickness susceptibility in the cat. *J. Pharmacol. Exp. Ther.* 237, 450-455.
Lucot, J.B. & Crampton, G.H. (1989): 8-OH-DPAT suppresses vomiting in the cat elicited by motion, cisplatin or xylazine. *Pharmacol. Biochem. Behav.* 33, 627-631.
Malobabić, Z.S., Jovanović-Mićić, D., Japundžić, N. & Beleslin, D.B. (1989): Studies on behavioural effects of methoxamine in cat. *Iugoslav. Physiol. Pharmacol. Acta* 25, 355-359.
Pedigo, N.W. & Brizzee, K.R. (1985): Muscarinic cholinergic receptors in area postrema and brainstem areas regulating emesis. *Brain Res. Bull.* 14, 169-177.
Pratt, G.D., Bowery, N.G., Kilpatrick, G.J., Leslie, R.A., Barnes, N.M., Naylor, R.J., Jones, J.J., Nelson, D.R., Palacios, J.M., Slater, P. & Reynolds, J.M. (1990): Consensus meeting agrees distribution of 5-HT_3 receptors in mammalian hindbrain. *TiPS* 11, 135-137.
Richardson, B.P., Engel, G., Donatsch, P. & Stadler, P.A. (1985): Identification of serotonin M-receptor subtypes and their specific blockade by new class of drugs. *Nature* 316, 126-131.
Samardžić, R, & Beleslin, D.B. (1989): Neurochemical mechanisms in area postrema and emesis. *Iugoslav. Physiol. Pharmacol. Acta* 25, Suppl. 8, 133-153.
Samardžić, R., Japundžić, N., Terzić, A., Jovanović-Mićić, D. & Beleslin, D.B. (1985): Nature of vomiting produced by dopamine. In *Dopamine, Ageing and Diseases*, ed. J.Borsy, L.Kerecsen & L.Gyorgy, pp. 123-126. Budapest: Proc. 4th Cong. Hung. Pharmacol. Soc., 3.
Samardžić, R., Jovanović-Mićić, D. & Beleslin, D.B. (1992): Behavioural effects of guanabenz: vomiting and motor impairment. *Iugoslav. Physiol. Pharmacol. Acta* 28, Suppl. 9, 165-168.
Sanger, G.J. (1984): Mechanisms by which metoclopramide can increase gastrointestinal motility. In *Mechanisms of Gastrointestinal Motility and Secretion*, ed. A. Bennett & G. Velo, pp. 303-324. New York: Plenum Press.
Sanger, G.J. (1987): Increased gut cholinergic activity and antagonism of 5-hydroxytryptamine M-receptors by BRL 24924: potential clinical importance of BRL 24924. *Br. J. Pharmacol.* 91, 77-87.
Schwartz, J.C., Agid, Y., Bouthenet, M.L., Javoy-Agid, F., Llorens-Cortes, C., Martres, M.P., Pollard, H., Sales, N. & Taquet, H. (1986): Neurochemical investigations into the human area postrema. In *Nausea and Vomiting: Mechanisms and Treatment*, ed. J.C.Davis, G.V. Lake-Bakaar & Grahame-Smith, pp. 18-30. Berlin Heidelberg: Springer-Verlag.
Stefanini, E. & Clement-Cormier, Y. (1981): Detection of dopamine receptors in the area postrema. *Europ. J. Pharmacol.* 74, 257-260.
Van Dongen, P.A.M. (1980): Locus ceruleus region: effects of behavior of cholinergic, noradrenergic and opiate drugs injected intracerebrally into freely moving cats. *Exp. Neurol.* 67, 52-78.

Mechanisms and Control of Emesis. Eds A.L. Bianchi, L. Grélot, A.D. Miller, G.L. King. Colloque INSERM/ John Libbey Eurotext Ltd. © 1992, Vol. 223, pp. 19-27

Functional anatomy of the emetic circuitry in the brainstem

R.A. Leslie and D.J.M. Reynolds

Oxford University SmithKline Beecham Centre for Applied Neuropsychobiology, University Department of Clinical Pharmacology, Radcliffe Infirmary, Woodstock Road, Oxford OX2 6HE, UK

SUMMARY

The brainstem pathways involved in mediating nausea and emesis are still not fully understood. The neuropharmacology of these processes is complex, in that different, but poorly defined, neuronal groups appear to modulate distinct types of emetic stimuli. We have used a new functional neuronal mapping technique, c-fos immunocytochemistry, to see if it is possible to identify cells in the brainstem that are activated by particular emetic stimuli. The results indicate that distinct subgroups of neurons in the dorsal vagal complex may be involved in mediating emetic responses associated with cisplatin, loperamide, and ipecacuanha. The c-fos mapping technique has proved to be a valuable tool for studies of the pharmacology and anatomy of emetic processes.

Anatomie fonctionnelle du réseau nerveux du tronc cérébral engendrant l'activité émétique.

Résumé: *Les voies nerveuses impliquées dans la médiation de la nausée et du vomissement ne sont encore que partiellement connues. La neuropharmacologie de ces mécanismes est complexe car des groupes de neurones différents, bien que mal définis, modulent des types distincts de stimuli émétiques. Nous avons utilisé une nouvelle technique neuroanatomique : la détection immunocytochimique de la protéine c-fos, pour tenter de localiser dans le tronc* *cérébral les neurones activés par certains stimuli émétiques. Nos résultats indiquent que des sous-groupes distincts de neurones du complexe vagal dorsal pourraient être impliqués dans la médiation des réponses émétiques au cisplatine, au lopéramide et à la teinture d'ipéca. La technique de cartographie par révélation de la protéine c-fos s'avère être un outil efficace dans l'étude pharmacologique et neuroanatomique des mécanismes émétiques.*

INTRODUCTION

Despite the substantial research effort in recent years that has been devoted to understanding the brain circuitry responsible for mediating the emetic response, several fundamental questions remain unanswered. In particular, for different emetic substances, the relative contribution of central versus 'peripheral' mechanisms to the triggering of the emetic response can be very variable. Numerous attempts have been made to examine this question by performing specific vagal and splanchnic nerve lesions or ablation of the "chemoreceptive trigger zone" for vomiting (the area postrema; AP). This approach has been limited by a number of factors including species variability, difficulty in assuring specificity of the lesion (area postrema versus nucleus of the solitary tract, NTS, for example) and the apparent plasticity of the nervous pathways involved.

Functional mapping studies using the 2-deoxyglucose procedure (Sokoloff et al., 1977) have been problematic, to some extent, because of the relative lack of resolution of this technique in the very small brain nuclei involved. Over the last few years techniques have been developed to monitor the expression of the immediate-early gene c-fos as a sensitive marker of cellular activity. Within the brain, detection of c-fos expression using in situ hybridization and immunocytochemistry have been used increasingly frequently to map neuronal pathways. The c-fos gene encodes a 62 kDa transcriptional factor, Fos, which is rapidly and transiently expressed in response to a variety of stimuli including growth factors and neurotransmitters. Along with another immediate-early gene product (Jun), Fos acts as a transcriptional regulator. Although there remains much that is unclear about the details of such regulation, c-fos mapping has been demonstrated to be a reliable tool for studying neuronal activity in the intact brain (Sagar et al., 1988; Dragunow and Faull, 1989).

We have used the technique of immunocytochemistry of Fos protein in an attempt to identify metabolically active neuronal pathways in the caudal brainstem following emetic stimuli (Reynolds et al., 1991). The technique provides cellular resolution and gives some insight into the site of action of a variety of emetic substances. These studies have used mainly the ferret, an animal that is increasingly employed to study emetic physiology and pharmacology. The patterns of neuronal activity resulting from stimulation with substances thought to act centrally as emetic agents, as opposed to those presumed to have a peripheral site of action, have been compared. The patterns of Fos induction that were observed were specific to the type of emetic stimulus studied and we have demonstrated that the use of immediate-early gene expression to map sites of neuronal activity is a practical way of studying the neuropharmacology and anatomy of emetic circuitry.

Neurotransmitters involved with the emetic response

In recent years a plethora of neurotransmitter and neuromodulator compounds have been identified in brainstem nuclei known to mediate at least some aspects of the emetic response (for some recent reviews see Barnes, 1984; Leslie, 1985; Palkovits, 1985; Leslie and Reynolds, 1992). Biochemical, anatomical, pharmacological and physiological investigations have all played their part in helping to elucidate which neuroactive substances are important in initiating and modulating the complex physiological processes associated with emesis. Most of the classical neurotransmitters (acetylcholine, serotonin, dopamine, noradrenaline, glutamate, GABA, etc.) have been localized in the so-called "dorsal vagal complex" (DVC). This caudal rhombencephalic region forms the terminal field of most visceral afferent (vagal) fibres known to carry sensory information related to the generation and control of nausea and emesis. It also incorporates the dorsal motor nucleus of the vagus nerve which contains the somata of neurons supplying motor information to much of the thoracic and abdominal viscera. This region of the brain is rich in receptors specific to many of these transmitters. On top of this, many of the neuropeptide neuromodulatory compounds thus far discovered also occur in the DVC as well as their respective receptors.

It is possible to modify the consequences of different emetic stimuli using a wide variety of drugs from various pharmacological classes (Barnes, 1984). For example, it is well established that motion (and now space) sickness can be more or less successfully treated with antihistamine or anticholinergic (muscarinic) drugs. These drugs, however, are remarkably ineffective in alleviating the severe sickness associated with radio- or chemotherapy given to cancer patients. On the other hand, such patients can be very successfully treated, both prophylactically and post-hoc, with 5-HT3 receptor antagonists. So far it seems that these latter drugs are not effective in treating motion sickness or some other types of emesis, for example that associated with gastric irritation (ingestion of hyperosmotic fluids, for example). It seems apparent that the emetic response involves a complex matrix which may be activated at different points. As yet, no pharmacological agent has been found that can inhibit emesis under all conditions, suggesting a multiplicity of neurotransmitters and neuromodulators operating at different sites within the matrix.

MATERIALS AND METHODS

Adult male and female ferrets (Mustela putorius furo), weighing between 0.5 and 1.5kg were used in these experiments. Some comparative studies were performed with adult male Sprague-Dawley rats weighing 200-250g. All animals were fed and watered ad libitum. In all cases, when drug or saline vehicle was given, animals were continuously monitored for signs of nausea or emetic activity; times and numbers of retches and episodes of emesis were recorded. Animals given emetic drugs and exhibiting emetic activity were killed by an overdose of sodium pentobarbital (i.p.) and transcardiac perfusion with saline and fixative two hours after the onset of emesis. Control animals, or animals pretreated with antiemetic drugs, that did not vomit, were killed at the corresponding time interval. Some animals received unilateral cervical vagus nerve lesions nine to 14 days before drug challenge. To accomplish this, animals were deeply anaesthetized (ketamine, 10mg/kg i.m., halothane and N2O/O2) and under aseptic conditions, a unilateral nodose ganglion excision was performed. Incisions were sutured in layers and postoperative recovery was uneventful in all cases. The completeness of nerve excision was confirmed by histological examination of the excised ganglion. Some control animals received sham vagotomy operations.

Following perfusion fixation with 4% paraformaldehyde, brains were removed and processed for Fos immunocytochemistry. Sections (100μm) of the caudal medulla oblongata, including the dorsal vagal complex, were cut with a Vibrotome and incubated in primary antiserum (dilution 1:2000) raised in rabbit against a beta-gal-Fos fusion protein (Medac, Hamburg) or in sheep against residues 2-16 of the N-terminal region of the Fos molecule (Cambridge Research Biochemicals, UK). An avidin-biotin-HRP procedure (Vector, Peterborough, U.K.), using diaminobenzidine as a chromogen, was then performed.

The drugs used in these studies were as follows: atropine (Phoenix Pharmaceuticals), cisplatin (Lederle), granisetron (SmithKline Beecham), ipecacuanha (John Radcliffe Hospital, Oxford, UK), loperamide (Sigma), naloxonazine (Research Biochemicals Inc.).

RESULTS

Loperamide-induced emesis in the ferret

Loperamide has been used as a stimulus to study the emetic response in the ferret, and is thought to act by a direct action on opiate receptors on neurons within the central nervous system (Bhandari et al., 1992). We gave this drug to six animals (0.5mg/kg s.c.) and in all cases they vomited within 20min. When the animals were perfused and their brains processed for Fos immunocytochemistry, Fos-like immunoreactivity (FLI) was seen throughout the rostro-caudal extent of the dorsomedial NTS in all six brains (Fig. 2). The dorsomedial region of the NTS (i.e., dorsal and medial to the solitary tract) incorporates severa distinct subnuclei as defined by cytoarchitectonic studies, mainly performed in the cat (eg., Loewy and Burton, 1978). Between this regioj of the NTS and the AP is sandwiched the subnucleus gelatinosus (SNG) of the NTS which also extends rostral to the AP. Animals which received saline control injections showed little or no FLI in the brainstem (Fig. 1). Low levels of FLI were seen in the region of the nucleus ambiguus, but none was observed in any other brainstem region at the level of the DVC. Little or no FLI was observed in the AP or SNG (Fig. 2). Unilateral cervical vagotomy (in a further 4 animals) two weeks before drug challenge did not affect the FLI in their brainstems (Fig. 3). Pretreatment with the opiate antagonist naloxonazine (1mg/kg s.c.) prevented emesis and markedly reduced FLI in the DVC of all four animals tested (Fig. 4).

Effects of loperamide on Fos expression in the rat brainstem

It could be argued that the FLI in the ferret brainstem, following loperamide administration, was secondary to the physical stimulus of vomiting rather than the pharmacological effects of the drug. To study this, we performed similar experiments in the rat, an animal that does not vomit.

Two animals received loperamide (0.5mg/kg s.c.) 135min before being perfused and examined for FLI in the brainstem. Heavy staining was seen in the dorsomedial subnuclei of the NTS as in the ferret, but, in addition, there was lighter staining in the AP and SNG (Fig. 6). As with the ferrets, saline control injections resulted in very little or no FLI in the rat brainstem (Fig. 5).

Cisplatin-induced emesis in the ferret

Cisplatin is one of the most commonly used cytotoxic drugs in cancer chemotherapy; it is also highly emetic. A large proportion of the action of this drug is thought to be peripheral, and dependent upon activation of 5-HT3 receptors positioned on the distal terminals of gastric vagal afferent nerve fibres (Andrews et al., 1988). We administered cisplatin (10mg/kg, i.p.) to six ferrets, and all animals displayed emetic behaviour consistent with that reported in other studies.

Unilateral vagotomy (9-14 days previous to drug challenge) in a further six animals did not significantly affect the latency to retching and vomiting or the overall number of emetic episodes following the drug. Pretreatment with the 5- HT3 receptor antagonist granisetron (5 mg/kg s.c., n=4) abolished cisplatin- induced retching and vomiting in all animals. Pretreatment with the muscarinic antagonist atropine (0.4-0.6mg/kg, n=6) did not affect nausea and vomiting or the pattern of FLI in the DVC (Fig. 10). Control animals treated with saline alone, or granisetron followed by saline, did not retch or vomit. In control animals, basal levels of FLI were low or undetectable. In all unlesioned animals which had received saline followed by cisplatin, heavy FLI was observed in the AP and in the NTS (Fig. 7). The FLI extended throughout the AP, but was most pronounced on its lateral aspects. Cells exhibiting FLI within the NTS were scattered throughout that nucleus as well, but were not as densely packed as they were in the AP. The majority of labelled cells occurred in the dorsomedial subnuclei of the NTS, and in the SNG. A few scattered cells within the boundaries of the dorsal motor nucleus of the vagus nerve exhibited FLI. Granisetron given 30min before cisplatin challenge resulted in marked attenuation of FLI in the NTS bilaterally, but there was no obvious reduction of FLI in the AP (Fig. 8). In the animals with unilateral cervical vagus nerve lesions (all of which received saline followed by cisplatin) FLI in the ipsilateral NTS was greatly reduced when compared with the unlesioned animals or the contralateral sides of lesioned animals (Fig. 9). There was no clear attenuation of staining in the AP of lesioned animals.

Cisplatin effects in the rat

In control experiments, intraperitoneal injections (1ml/100g) of isotonic saline were made in six rats, and the effects on Fos immunoreactivity were assessed. All these animals showed low or no evidence of FLI in the brainstem. In contrast, following cisplatin administration in a further six rats, large amounts of FLI were observed in the DVC, in a pattern very similar to that seen in the ferret brain (Fig. 11). Pretreatment with granisetron (n=5) greatly reduced the FLI seen in the AP and the SNG and attenuated the FLI seen in other areas of the NTS (Fig. 12).

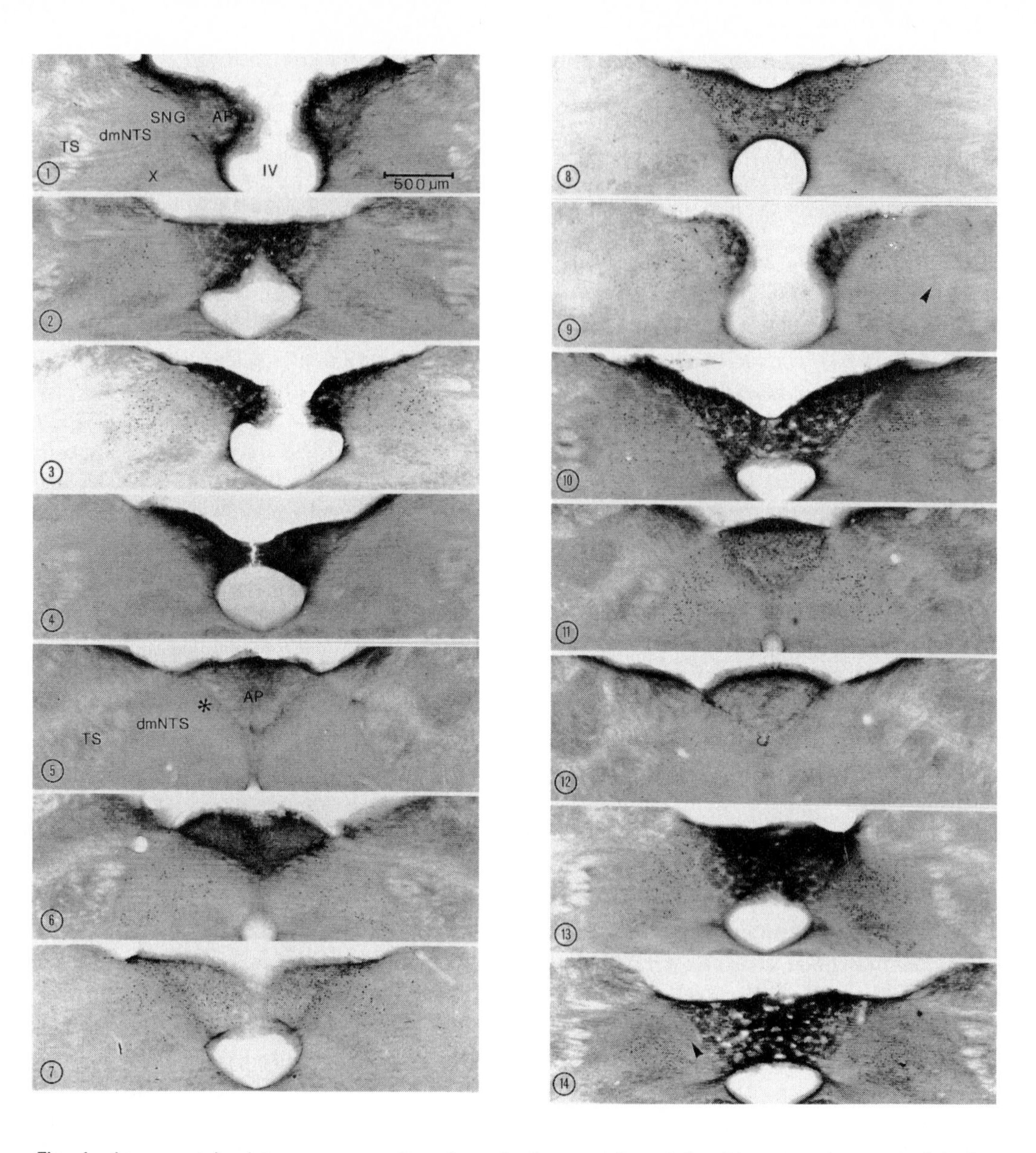

Fig. 1 Immunostained transverse section through the caudal medulla oblongata of a control (saline treated) ferret. AP = area postrema, dmNTS = dorsomedial subnuclei of the nucleus of the solitary tract, SNG = subnucleus gelatinosus of the NTS, TS = tractus solitarius, X = dorsal motor nucleus of the vagus, IV = fourth ventricle. Fig. 2 Loperamide treated ferret. Note the small, darkly stained Fos-positive cell nuclei throughout the dmNTS. Fig. 3 Loperamide treatment in a ferret with a previous left vagotomy (left side of figure). Note lack of effect of the lesion. Fig. 4 Ferret treated with naloxonazine followed by loperamide. Note the marked attenuation of FLI. Fig. 5 Control rat medulla (magnification as in Fig. 1). * = gelatinous region of the NTS. Fig. 6 Loperamide treated rat. Fig. 7 Cisplatin treated ferret. Note dense FLI in AP and SNG. Contrast with Fig. 2. Fig. 8 Ferret treated with granisetron followed by cisplatin. Note attenuation of FLI in NTS but not AP. Fig. 9 Cisplatin treatment in a ferret with a previous right vagotomy. FLI is reduced on the lesioned side (arrowhead). Fig. 10 Ferret treated with atropine followed by cisplatin; compare with Fig. 7. Note lack of effect of atropine on FLI. Fig. 11 Rat treated with cisplatin. Note similar distribution of FLI to that in ferret (Fig. 7). Compare with loperamide treated rat (Fig. 6). Fig. 12 Rat treated with granisetron followed by cisplatin. Note great reduction in FLI. Fig. 13 Ipecacuanha treated ferret. Fig. 14 Ferret treated with granisetron followed by ipecacuanha. Note the reduction in FLI in the SNG (arrowhead).

Ipecacuanha-induced emesis in the ferret

Syrup of ipecacuanha ("ipecac") has been used for many years as an emetic in the treatment of poisoning. The principal active agents in ipecacuanha are the alkaloids emetine and cephaeline. The mechanism of action is not well understood, but it is often assumed to be a gastric irritant and to cause emesis in this way. Emetine, however, can exert a central emetic effect which is unaffected by bilateral subdiaphragmatic vagotomy (Davis, 1988). We tested ipecacuanha in the ferret at a dose corresponding to that used in man; the drug was given as 1ml of paediatric syrup in 20ml of fresh milk presented in a bowl, and was readily consumed within a few minutes.

Vomiting occurred in all animals tested (n = 6) with a latency of 20min. Unilateral cervical vagotomy (two weeks prior to drug challenge, n = 4) did not affect the latency to vomiting or the number of emetic episodes. Pretreatment of the animals with granisetron (1mg/kg s.c., n = 6) abolished emesis due to ipecacuanha. Control animals received milk only, and showed no emetic activity.

FLI was observed in the brains of all animals given ipecacuanha. The densest staining occurred in the dorsomedial subnuclei of the NTS and the SNG, and lesser amounts were seen in the AP (Fig. 13). Pretreatment with granisetron prevented ipecacuanha-induced vomiting and markedly reduced the FLI in the SNG but did not affect FLI in the rest of the NTS (Fig. 14). Unilateral cervical vagotomy had no effect on the FLI in the dorsal vagal complex.

DISCUSSION AND CONCLUSIONS

These studies employed the immunocytochemical technique to monitor expression of the immediate-early gene c-fos in brains of animals challenged with emetic and anti-emetic drugs. The results showed both anatomical and pharmacological specificity, and indicate the usefulness of the technique for this type of neuropharmacology. Cells showing FLI were limited to brainstem nuclei known to be involved in CNS control of emesis, and the cellular resolution of the technique allowed precise mapping of activity that was specific for the different drugs employed. The maps represented neurotransmitter-mediated neural activity which was not a result merely of the physical act of retching or vomiting, because the same patterns of activity were seen in the brains of rats as well as ferrets. Rats do not have a vomiting response, but they do develop gastric stasis and conditioned taste aversion with many agents that cause emesis in other species. The FLI seen in the DVC of rats used in this study may, therefore, be related to these phenomena. C-fos gene induction was attenuated, or even totally prevented, in some cells by pretreatment of animals with specific antagonists of the emetic drugs under study whereas pretreatment of animals with antagonists ineffective against the emetic drug did not.

Treatment of experimental animals with the emetic loperamide resulted in FLI in the dorsomedial subnuclei of the NTS. This was attenuated by the mu opioid antagonist naloxonazine but not by vagus nerve section. These results are consistent with there being a central mode of action of this drug in initiating the emetic response. The absence of FLI in the

AP is interesting, as the AP has been implicated as the site of action of loperamide-induced emesis (Bhandari et al., 1992). Fos immunocytochemistry did, however, identify cell bodies in the dorsomedial NTS, so that it is possible that loperamide activates receptors located on dendrites of these NTS cells that extend into the AP (Morest, 1960).

In contrast, cisplatin resulted in FLI occurring in the AP and SNG of the NTS, and somewhat less in the dorsomedial subnuclei of the NTS. The specific 5-HT3 receptor antagonist granisetron, as well as unilateral vagal nerve lesion, had the effect of inhibiting this response in the subnuclei of the NTS but not in the AP. These results suggest that cisplatin exerts an effect through vagal pathways. The fact that neither 5-HT3 receptor antagonism nor vagus nerve lesion abolished FLI in the AP is interesting. It seems probable, in light of this, that cisplatin also has a direct effect on cells in the AP rather than one that is mediated only by vagal afferent fibres. The AP is implicated as a chemoreceptive trigger zone for vomiting; whether cisplatin-induced activity in cells of the AP is related to emesis, however, is unknown (for more detailed discussion see Reynolds et al., 1991).

Ipecacuanha-induced FLI, like that due to cisplatin, was heavy in the dorsomedial subnuclei of the NTS and the SNG of the ferret, and slightly less in the AP. Granisetron was effective in abolishing emesis associated with ipecacuanha administration, but only appeared to reduce FLI in the SNG. The dense FLI of the dorsomedial NTS was not affected by the 5-HT3 receptor antagonist. Vagus nerve lesion neither affected the vomiting response to ipecacuanha, nor the FLI. These results would be consistent with a central site of action of ipecacuanha, and a central site of action of granisetron in modulating the emetic response to this drug. It may be that the latter was due to an action of the 5-HT3 receptor antagonist on the dense population of 5-HT3 receptors that are situated on vagal afferent terminals located mainly within the SNG of the ferret (Leslie et al., 1990). These 5-HT3 receptors are lost after unilateral cervical vagotomy, and it is unclear, therefore, why treatment with a 5-HT3 receptor antagonist should reduce FLI, when unilateral vagotomy does not. Further work is underway to resolve this issue.

In summary, these studies with c-fos immunocytochemistry suggest that loperamide exerts its emetic action centrally, activating cells in the DVC of the brainstem. In contrast, cisplatin seems to act via a vagal pathway to cause emesis. Granisetron mimics the action of vagus nerve lesion in its effects on FLI in the brainstem resulting from the administration of cisplatin. The situation with ipecacuanha is not so clearcut, and requires further investigation. Taken together, the results of this study indicate that c-fos immunocytochemistry is a valuable technique for studying the neuropharmacology and anatomy of emesis.

ACKNOWLEDGEMENT

We are happy to thank J. Moorman, R. McQuade, N. Barber and H. Taylor for help with some aspects of this work.

REFERENCES

Andrews, P.L.R., Rapeport, W.G. and Sanger, G.J. 1988 Neuropharmacology of emesis induced by anti-cancer therapy. Trends Pharm. Sci. 9, 334-341.

Barnes, J.H. 1984 The physiology and pharmacology of emesis. Mol. Aspects Med. 7, 397-508.

Bhandari, P., Bingham, S. and Andrews, P.L.R. 1992 The neuropharmacology of loperamide-induced emesis in the ferret: the role of the area postrema, vagus, opiate and 5-HT3 receptors. Neuropharmacology, in press.

Davis, C.J. 1988 Neuropharmacological investigations into the mechanisms of emesis caused by cytotoxic drugs and radiation. D.Phil thesis, University of Oxford.

Dragunow, M. and Faull, R. 1989 The use of c-fos as a metabolic marker in neuronal pathway tracing. J. Neurosci. Meth. 29, 261-265.

Leslie, R.A. 1985 Neuroactive substances in the dorsal vagal complex of the medulla oblongata: nucleus tractus solitarius, area postrema and dorsal motor nucleus of the vagus. Neurochem. Internat. 7, 191-211.

Leslie, R.A., Reynolds, D.J.M., Andrews, P.L.R., Grahame-Smith, D.G., Davis, C.J. and Harvey, J.M. 1990 Evidence for presynaptic 5-HT3 recognition sites on vagal afferent terminals in the brainstem of the ferret. Neurosci. 38, 667-673.

Leslie, R.A. and Reynolds, D.J.M. 1992 Neurotransmitters and receptors in the emetic pathway. In: Neuropharmacology of emesis induced by anti-cancer therapy. Eds. P.L.R. Andrews and G.J. Sanger, Chapman and Hall, London.

Loewy, A.D. and Burton, H. 1978 Nuclei of the solitary tract: efferent projections to the lower brain stem and spinal cord of the cat. J. comp. Neurol. 181, 421-450.

Morest, D.K. 1960 A study of the structure of the area postrema with Golgi methods. Amer. J. Anat. 107, 291-303.

Palkovits, M. 1985 Distribution of neuroactive substances in the dorsal vagal complex of the medulla oblongata. Neurochem. Internat. 7, 213-219.

Reynolds, D.J.M., Barber, N.A., Grahame-Smith, D.G. and Leslie, R.A. 1991 Cisplatin-evoked induction of c-fos protein in the brainstem of the ferret: the effect of cervical vagotomy and the anti-emetic 5-HT3 receptor antagonist granisetron (BRL 43694). Brain Res. 565, 231-236.

Sagar, S.M., Sharp, F.R., and Curran, T. 1988 Expression of c-fos protein in brain: metabolic mapping at the cellular level. Science 240, 1328-1331.

Sokoloff, L. Reivich, M., Kennedy, C., Des Rosiers, M.H. Patlak, C.S., Pettigrew, K.D., Sakurada, O. and Shinohara, M. 1977 The [14C]deoxyglucose method for the measurement of local cerebral glucose utilization: theory, procedure, and normal values in the conscious and anaesthetized albino rat. J. Neurochem. 28, 897-916.

Mechanisms and Control of Emesis. Eds A.L. Bianchi, L. Grélot, A.D. Miller, G.L. King. Colloque INSERM/ John Libbey Eurotext Ltd. © 1992, Vol. 223, pp. 29-39

Activities of cranial and spinal respiratory-related motoneurons during vomiting

Laurent Grélot and Armand L. Bianchi

Département de Physiologie et Neurophysiologie, CNRS URA 205, Faculté des Sciences et Techniques Saint-Jérôme, 13397 Marseille Cedex 13, France

Summary: The present chapter is mainly devoted to the description of the activities of oropharyngeal, laryngeal, thoracic and abdominal motoneurons or muscles during vomiting in the decerebrate cat. Our results demonstrate that the not well localized neuronal network responsible for the generation and maintenance of vomiting exerts a potent influence on numerous motoneuronal pools at the cranial and spinal levels. All the motoneurons exhibiting a respiratory-related activity receive an excitatory or an inhibitory vomiting-related central drive which changes the time at which they are activated in relation to the other motoneurons. Their pattern of membrane potential profiles, and thus their firing properties also changes. Finally, preliminary results suggest that vomiting must also be accomplished with a postural adjustment through an activation of motoneurons innervating the muscles of the neck and the legs.

Résumé: Activité des motoneurones respiratoires pendant le vomissement. *Ce chapitre est consacré à la description du comportement des motoneurones oropharyngiens, laryngés, thoraciques et abdominaux pendant le vomissement chez le chat décérébré. Nos résultats démontrent que le réseau de neurones, encore mal localisé, engendrant l'activité émétique exerce une puissant emprise sur différentes populations de motoneurones spinaux et crâniens. Tous les motoneurones respiratoires reçoivent une commande excitatrice ou inhibitrice en relation avec le vomissement qui modifie leur moment d'activation par rapport aux autres motoneurones, mais aussi la trajectoire de leur potentiel de membrane, et donc leurs propriétés de décharge. Enfin, les résultats d'une étude préliminaire suggèrent qu'un ajustement postural concernant les muscles du cou et des pattes doit se réaliser pendant le vomissement.*

Introduction

Vomiting is defined as the violent expulsion of the alimentary bolus through the mouth. Under physiological conditions, this expulsion is thought to result from the synergist contractions of the main respiratory muscles (e.g. the diaphragm and the abdominal wall) but also non respiratory muscles (see the review of I.M. Lang in this book). During the last five years, much of the work of our laboratory has focused on the neural control of the striated muscles involved in vomiting. The present chapter will review our results in describing the behaviors of the respiratory-related and non respiratory-related muscles or motoneurons during vomiting.

Experimental designs and characterization of vomiting

All experiments were conducted on adult cats of either sex that were decerebrated. Animals were either paralyzed and artificially ventilated during experiments designed to record the electrical activities of neural elements, or non paralyzed and spontaneously breathing during electromyographic recording experiments. Sequences of vomiting were usually induced by electrical stimulation (continuous trains of 0.9 ms pulses, 25-33 Hz, 10-50 V) of the lower thoracic vagus nerves. Occasionally, vomiting was also elicited by administration of the emetic drugs lobeline sulfate (1-2 mg/kg) and naloxone (1-2 mg/kg).

We designed four sets of experiments in which we recorded during vomiting the electrical activities of either *i/* thoracic respiratory muscles, or *ii/* respiratory and non-respiratory nerves, or *iii/* single phrenic motor axons, or *iv/* somata of respiratory motoneurons. In the non paralyzed cats, electromyographic (EMG) activities of the diaphragm (costal part), abdominal (external oblique) and internal and external intercostal muscles were recorded with paired copper wires, insulated except at the tip, inserted into the muscles. In the paralyzed cats, the efferent activities of various respiratory and non-respiratory nerves were recorded with bipolar silver electrodes. Extracellular activities of phrenic motor axons were recorded with a bipolar platinum electrodes. Intracellular activities of motoneuronal somata were recorded with 10-25 megohm pipettes filled with saturated (3.0-3.5 M) KCl. All electrical signals were amplified, adequately filtered (DC,10 or 100 Hz to 10 KHz), displayed on a chart recorder and oscilloscope, and stored on tape.

In the non paralyzed cats, vomiting was characterized by a series of simultaneous EMG activities of the diaphragm and abdominal muscles (the so-called retching phase), culminating in an expulsion phase in which abdominal activity was prolonged both with respect to diaphragmatic discharge and to previous retching-related abdominal activities. In the paralyzed cats, fictive vomiting (Miller et al., 1987) was characterized by similar patterns of activity of the phrenic (C5 nerve rootlet) and the cranial iliohypogastric (L1 to L3 nerve rootlets) nerves which provide innervation to the diaphragm and abdominal muscles, respectively.

Activities of the oropharyngeal and laryngeal motoneurons.

The oropharyngeal and laryngeal patencies are dependent on the degree of contration of numerous muscles. Recording, during vomiting, of the nerves providing motor axons to these muscles permits speculations about the role of each component of that complex muscular apparatus. Our observations (Grélot et al., 1990) of laryngeal and oropharyngeal neural activities during fictive vomiting are summarized in Fig. 1.

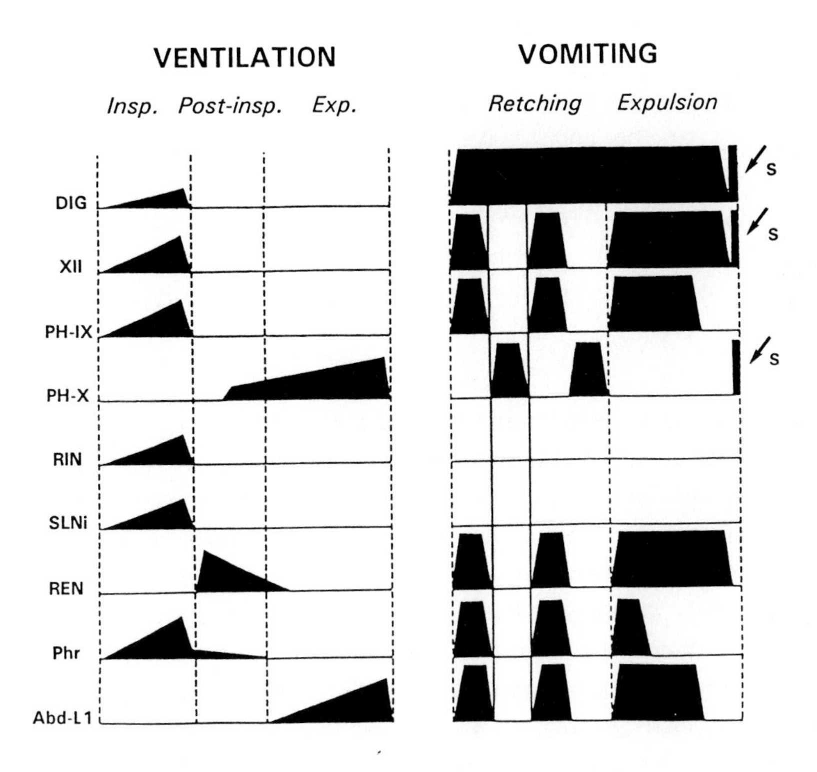

Figure 1: Schematic diagram depicting the activities of the oropharyngeal and laryngeal nerves versus phrenic and abdominal nerve activities in normal ventilation and during vomiting. **Left**, vertical hatched lines indicate the 3 respiratory phases. *Insp.*, inspiration; *Post-insp.*,post-inspiration; *Exp.*, expiration. **Right**, vertical hatched lines indicate the two phases of vomiting (i.e. retching and expulsion); vertical filled lines in the retching phase indicate a phrenic and abdominal interburst. Note the buccopharyngeal stage of swallowing (arrows and S) identified at the end of the expulsion phase. DIG, digastric nerve; XII, hypoglossal nerve; PH-IX, glossopharyngeal nerve; PH-X, pharyngeal branch of the vagus nerve; RIN, inspiratory branch of the recurrent laryngeal nerve; SLNi, inspiratory branch of the superior laryngeal nerve; REN, expiratory branch of the recurrent laryngeal nerve; Phr, phrenic nerve; Abd-L1, abdominal (cranial iliohypogastric) nerve.

The inhibition of the intrinsic and extrinsic laryngeal inspiratory nerves (RIN and SLNi) simultaneously with the potent activation of the intrinsic expiratory laryngeal nerve (REN) would cause closure of the glottis during both retching and expulsion. Concomitantly, the activation of the inspiratory glossopharyngeal (PH-IX) and hypoglossal (XII) nerves during both the retching and expulsion phases would increase the oropharyngeal patency, allowing an easier expulsion of the gastro-intestinal contents. At the same time, the expiratory pharyngeal nerve (PH-X) discharges during the inter-retch period and becomes silent throughout expulsion. This result suggests that the wall of the pharynx contracts rhythmically during the retching phase but in opposition with the abdominal strains, and then relaxes to facilitate the transit of the expelled bolus. In addition, the motoneurons providing motor innervation to the digastricus muscle are strongly activated during the emetic sequence. This activation would induce a depression of the jaw and thus an opening of the mouth during vomiting. Finally, at the end of the expulsion phase, buccopharyngeal stages of swallowing are observed on the digastric (DIG), the hypoglossal and expiratory pharyngeal vagus nerves. This swallowing activity, which cleans the oropharyngeal cavity after the transit of the expelled bolus, seems to be part of the motor program of vomiting since it persists in complete absence of sensory feedback from the oropharyngeal cavity.

Activities of the thoracic muscles and motoneurons

Although activities of the intercostal muscles have been investigated for 35 years, their real behavior during vomiting is still unclear. In an early study, Hukuhara et al., (1957) mentioned that, in the decerebrate dog, the external and internal intercostal muscles were co-activated during vomiting. Mc Carthy and Borison (1974), working on the decerebrate cat, invalidated these results, describing the external intercostal (eIC) muscle activity in synchrony with retches whereas the internal intercostal (iIC) muscle was seen to discharge between retches. Recently, in order to clarify the reasons of the discrepancies between the results of the two previous studies, Koga and Fukuda (1990) recorded, in the decerebrate and paralyzed dog, the activities of the intercostal nerves in different interspaces. Despite variable respiratory activities for a given nerve, they concluded that all mid-thoracic eIC nerves were activated during the inter-retches and all iIC nerves during the retches. Thus, their results appear totally opposite to those of Mc Carthy and Borison. Two additional (unpublished) studies, performed that year in the decerebrate cat by Miller and Yates (personnal communication) and Iscoe and Grélot, complicate our understanding of the vomiting-related behaviors the intercostals, since they present different results, and moreover, none of these results validate fully those of the previous studies. Indeed, recording external intercostal nerves (T6-T10), providing motor axons solely to eIC muscles, and the small branches of the internal intercostal nerves of the lower interspaces (T10-T13), supporting the innervation to the iIC muscles, Miller and Yates show that the former and the latter discharge during and between retches, respectively. Extrapoled to muscle activation, these behaviors are totally opposed to our (Iscoe and Grélot) EMG observations, since both eIC and iIC muscles of the lower interspaces (T10-T11) were seen discharging in phase with the diaphragm and abdominal retching-related bursts while both internal and external intercostals of mid-thoracic levels (T5-T6) were activated out of phase with these bursts. It is unlikely that the large discrepancies in all intercostal behaviors described above result from experimental artifacts (e.g., contamination between different intercostal muscles during EMG recordings or wrong identification of the real destination of the recorded nerves). It is more likely that these different behaviors are due to interspecific (cat versus dog) variations or drastic differences in the experimental procedures (i.e., the supine or prone position of the animal, cannulation of the trachea which reduces greatly the large intrathoracic pressure changes normally developed during a sequence of vomiting, pneumothorax which changes the position and the volume of the rib cage, or curarisation which suppresses the movement of the thorax and thus the sensory feed back from the intercostals). Hence, the intercostal muscle activity being strongly dependent on the segmental stretch reflex, it appears that the real behavior of these muscles could be elucidated only in freely moving animals.

Extracellular recordings of phrenic motor axons (Iscoe et al., 1990) allow a precise analysis of the firing pattern of the phrenic motoneurons during vomiting. During eupnea, almost half of all phrenic motoneurons spontaneously active in the decerebrate cat begin to fire action potentials during the first 10 per cent of the inspiratory period. Thereafter, recruitement of the remaining motoneurons continue throughout inspiration. During vomiting, recruitment times decrease such that all phrenic motoneurons fire action potentials in the first 20 per cent of the phrenic nerve activity (Fig. 2). This suggests that the central drive to the motoneuronal pool increases greatly during vomiting. Such a suggestion is corroborated by the result of the motoneuronal discharge frequency analysis which reveals that the phrenic motoneurons fire action potentials during vomiting at a frequency of approximately 90 spikes/s which is more than twice that observed during normal breathing. Moreover, this high discharge frequency is maintained throughout the vomiting episode.

Intracellular recordings of the somal membrane potential changes of phrenic motoneurons (Grélot et al., 1990) located in the ventral horn of the cervical (C4-C6) spinal cord has revealed the nature of the descending central drives to them during vomiting. The results are summarized in the Fig. 3. At the onset of each retch, the ramp-like depolarization, characteristic of the phrenic motoneurons during eupnea, is converted to an abrupt depolarization significantly greater than during normal inspiration. Then, the phrenic motoneurons exhibit a bell-shaped depolarization throughout the retch. During the inter-retch, their membrane potentials reach a level similar to that observed during normal expiration.

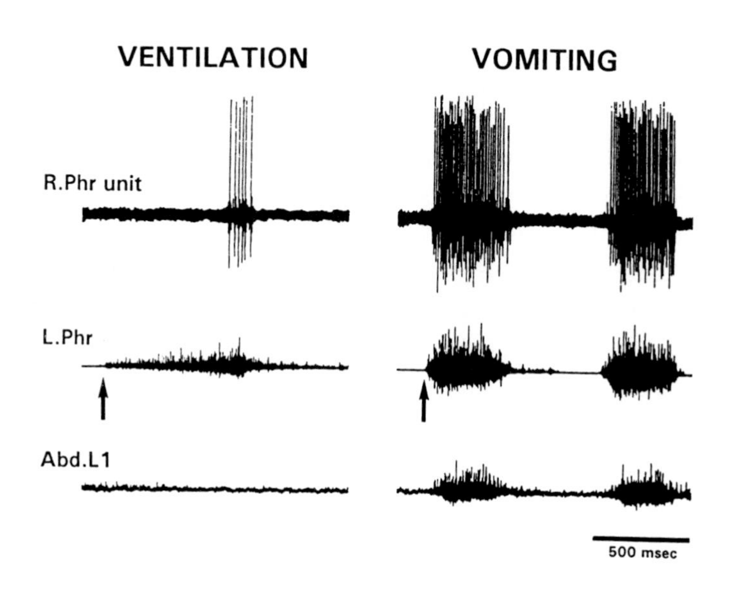

Figure 2: Extracellular recording of a phrenic motor axon (R. Phr unit) dissected in the right phrenic nerve during ventilation and vomiting. Note the decrease in recruitment time and increase in discharge frequency during vomiting. Arrows indicate the onset of the phrenic nerve activity during the two behaviors. L.Phr, left phrenic nerve; Abd.L1, abdominal nerve.

During the expulsion phase, the pattern is first the same, but after cessation of the phrenic discharge, their membrane potentials repolarize slowly until the end of the abdominal burst (e.g. the real expulsion). During that latter period, their membranes exhibit greater synaptic noise than during expiration, suggesting the existence of an active inhibitory mechanism. Such an hypothesis is confirmed by the effects of an intracellular injection of chloride ions, a technique currently used in Neurophysiology to reverse the waves of inhibitory postsynaptic potentials into depolarizations and thus to unmask the periods during which the motoneurons are actively inhibited. Such an intracellular chloride injection demonstrates that the phrenic motoneurons receive a weak inhibition during the inter-retch periods and a stronger one during the abdominal part of the expulsion. The behavior described above accounts for the phrenic motoneurons innervating the sternal and costal part of the diaphragm (Fig. 3A).

However, it is well known that the hiatal (periesophageal) part of the diaphragm relaxes during vomiting (Miller et al., 1988) to facilitates the gastro-oral reflux. The phrenic motoneurons innervating this hiatal part of the diaphragm exhibited a typical behavior during vomiting. They receive a central drive consisting of a hyperpolarization at the onset of the vomiting episode, and a depolarization with a firing activity during only the first half of each burst of both the retching and expulsion phases (Fig 3B).

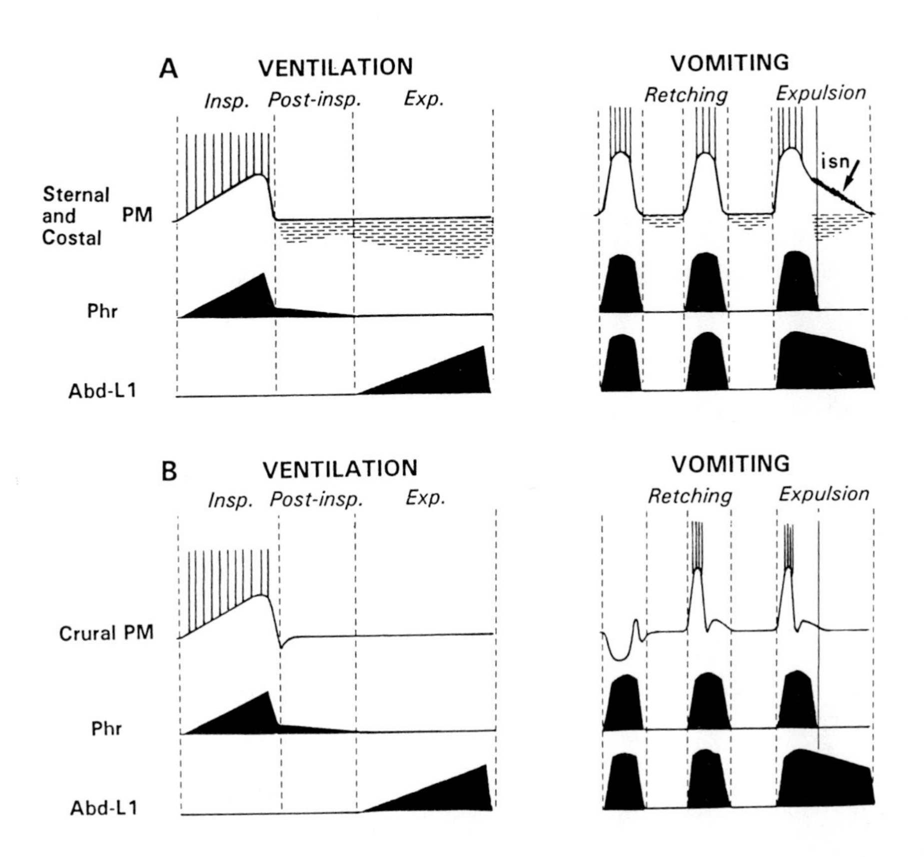

Figure 3: Schematic diagram depicting the membrane potential trajectories of the phrenic motoneurons (PM) during normal ventilation and vomiting. In each panel from top to bottom, membrane potentials of PMs with superimposed firing activity, phrenic (Phr) and abdominal (abd-L1) nerve activities (black areas). A: typical behaviors of PMs innervating the sternal and costal regions of the diaphragm. Horizontal hatched areas (in A) indicate the periods and patterns of active inhibition received by PMs; note the waves of postsynaptic inhibitions during the inter-retchs and the abdominal part of expulsion; arrow indicates a period of increased synaptic noise (isn) on motoneuronal membrane. B: behavior of PMs likely innervating the crural region of the diaphragm. Note the membrane hyperpolarization at the onset of the vomiting sequence. Period and pattern of postsynaptic inhibition are unknown on crural motoneurons.

Activities of the abdominal motoneurons

Intracellular recordings of the membrane potential changes of abdominal motoneurons (Grélot, Iscoe and Bianchi, unpublished preliminary results) located in the ventral horn of the lumbar spinal cord provide additional information concerning the nature of the descending vomiting-related drive. In the decerebrate cat, during normal breathing, the abdominal motoneuronal membrane exhibits very weak changes, if any, in relation the respiratory cycle. During vomiting, the membrane potentials exhibit a large bell-shaped depolarization throughout each retch, a pattern similar to that observed on the phrenic motoneurons. An intense firing activity (approximately 90 spikes/s) is produced during each retching-related depolarizations. A similar pattern of depolarization and firing, but longer, is observed during the expulsion phase. Intracellular chloride ionophoresis reveals that the abdominal motoneurons receive weak waves of synaptic inhibition during the inter-retch periods, and a stronger and brief one during the later part of the expulsion (Fig. 4). The EMG activity of these muscles expresses that during vomiting there is also a redistribution of the central drive to the postural muscles.

Activities of non respiratory motoneurons

Preliminary results (Grélot and Milano, unpublished observations) demonstrate that the motoneurons innervating the trapezius muscle in the neck and the triceps brachii (i.e. the extensor muscle of the elbow joint) are strongly activated during vomiting (Fig. 5). The motoneurons of the trapezius exhibit bursts of activity in phase with the phrenic and abdominal co-activations during both the retching and expulsion phase, while the motoneurons of the triceps brachii exhibit a tonic activity, sometime with a retch-related modulation, throughout the emetic episode.

Conclusions

The neuronal network responsible for the generation and maintenance of vomiting differs (totally or partly?, see Miller in this book) from that which drive the respiratory muscles during normal breathing (Bianchi and Grélot, 1989). Although, the localization of this neuronal network is still controversial (see Miller in this book), the nature of its potent command on the spinal and cranial motoneurons is quite well documented. Depending on the considered motoneuronal pool, this central drive was classically described as either a strong activation or a strong inhibition. However, fine electrophysiological studies have demonstrated that a given motoneuronal pool, for instance the phrenic one, receives both a strong activation but also an inhibition during, and at the end of the vomiting sequence.

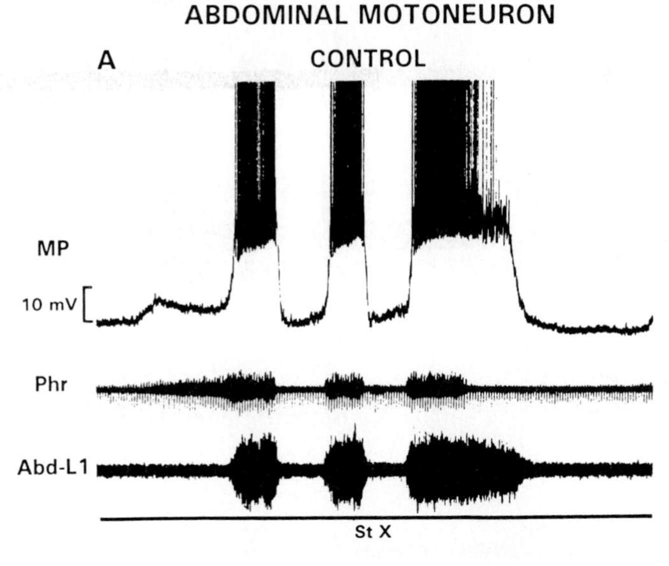

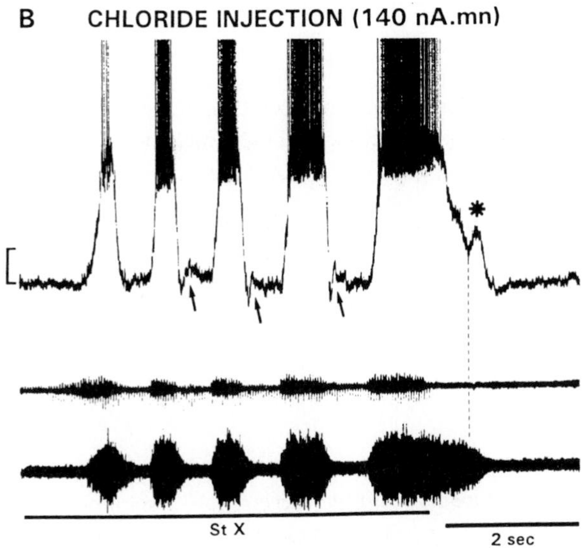

Figure 4: Membrane potential trajectories of an abdominal motoneuron during vomiting before (A) and after (B) intracellular chloride injection (140 nA.mn). In A and B the resting membrane potential is -74 mV. Note the weak reversals (arrows) of IPSPs between retches, and the stronger one (asterisk) during the late part of the expulsion phase (after the vertical hatched line). Current was on during recording (B). St X, electrical stimulation of the lower thoracic vagus nerves.

Further investigations are needed to elucidate whether these inhibitions are due to a direct descending inhibitory pathway to the motoneurons or, in opposition, an excitatory path to a local network of inhibitory interneurons. Preliminary results (Milano, Miller and Grélot, unpublished observations), indicate that spinal respiratory interneurons located in the phrenic motor nucleus receive a vomiting-related drive clearly different from that received by the motoneurons and could contribute to such inhibitory mechanisms.

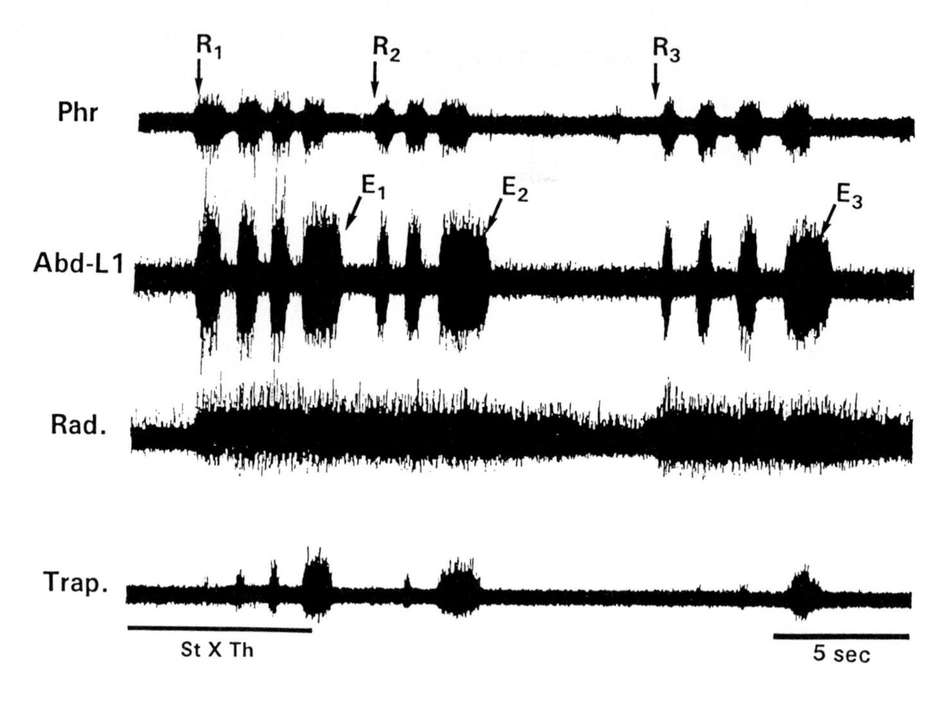

Figure 5: Activities of nerves providing motor axons to the trapezius (Trap.) and triceps brachii (Rad.) during a complex sequence of vomiting composed of 3 retching phases (arrows and R_1,R_2,R_3) all of them being terminated by an expulsion (arrows and E_1, E_2 and E_3). St X Th, electrical stimulation of the lower thoracic vagus nerves.

Acknowledgments

We thank Mrs Jocelyne Roman for the preparation of illustrations and Mr Michel Manneville for his technical assistance. This work was supported by grants from the *Direction des Recherches, Etudes et Techniques (DRET, 90/110)* and the CNRS (URA 205).

References

Bianchi, A.L. and Grélot, L. (1989): Converse motor output of inspiratory bulbospinal premotoneurones during vomiting. *Neurosci. Lett.*, 104: 298-302.

Grélot, L., Barillot, J.C. and Bianchi, A.L. (1990): Activity of respiratory-related oropharyngeal and laryngeal motoneurones during fictive vomiting in the decerebrate cat. *Brain Res.*, 513: 101-105.

Grélot, L., Miller, A.D., Milano, S., Portillo, F., and Bianchi, A.L. (1990): Patterns of membrane potentials of phrenic motoneurons during fictive vomiting and coughing in the decerebrate cat. In: *Proceedings of the International Conference on Modulation of Respiratory Pattern: Peripheral and Central Mechanisms, Lexington, KY*, p. 87.

Hukuhara, T., Okada, H. and Yamagami, M. (1957): On the behavior of the respiratory muscles during vomiting. *Acta Med. Okayama*, 11: 117-125.

Iscoe, S., Milano, S., Grélot, L. and Bianchi, A.L., (1990): Discharge patterns of phrenic motoneurons during vomiting in decerebrate cat. *Proceeding of the International Conference on Modulation of Respiratory Pattern: Peripheral and central Mechanisms.* Lexington, Kentuky USA, October 1990.

Koga, T. and Fukuda, H. (1990): Characteristic behavior of the respiratory muscles, esophagus, and external anal and urethral sphincters during straining, retching and vomiting in the decerebrate dog. *Jap. J. Physiol.*, 40, 789-807.

Lang, I.M. (1992): New perspectives on the mechanisms controlling vomitus expulsion. In: *New Vistas on Mechanisms and Control of Emesis. Ed. A.L. Bianchi, L. Grélot, A.D. Miller and G.L. King. Colloque INSERM/John Libbey Eurotext Ltd. vol 223.*

McCarthy, L.E. and Borison, H.L. (1974): Respiratory mechanics of vomiting in decerebrate cats. *Am. J. Physiol.*, 226: 738-743.

Miller, A.D. (1992): Physiology of brain stem emetic circuitry. In: *New Vistas on Mechanisms and Control of Emesis. Ed. A.L. Bianchi, L. Grélot, A.D. Miller and G.L. King. Colloque INSERM/John Libbey Eurotext Ltd. vol 223.*

Miller, A.D., Lakos, S.F., and Tan, L.K. (1988): Central motor program for relaxation of periesophageal diaphragm during the expulsive phase of vomiting. Brain Res. 456: 367-370.

Miller, A.D., Tan, L.K., and Suzuki, I. (1987): Control of abdominal and expiratory intercostal muscle activity during vomiting: role of ventral respiratory group expiratory neurons. *J. Neurophysiol.*, 57: 1854-1866.

Mechanisms and Control of Emesis. Eds A.L. Bianchi, L. Grélot, A.D. Miller, G.L. King. Colloque INSERM/
John Libbey Eurotext Ltd. © 1992, Vol. 223, pp. 41-50

Physiology of brain stem emetic circuitry

Alan D. Miller

Laboratory of Neurophysiology, The Rockefeller University, 1230 York Avenue, New York, NY 10021, USA

SUMMARY

This chapter reviews i) the role of the area postrema as a central chemoreceptor trigger zone for vomiting (emesis), ii) concepts regarding the organization of the brain stem circuitry that coordinates the vomiting response, and iii) the brain stem pre-motor circuitry that controls the major respiratory muscles which are primarily responsible for producing the motor act of vomiting. Lesions of the area postrema abolish vomiting induced by many, but not all, emetic drugs but do not prevent vomiting in response to motion or activation of abdominal vagal afferents. The involvement of the area postrema in radiation-induced vomiting is controversial. The central organization of the neural circuitry that coordinates the vomiting response remains unknown. Nevertheless, it is concluded that there is no compelling evidence for the existence of an anatomically well localized "vomiting center". The respiratory muscles are activated in different patterns during breathing and vomiting and are controlled in part by some of the same propriobulbar and bulbospinal respiratory neurons during these two behaviors. The central processes by which various sensory inputs can lead to the forceful and highly coordinated act of vomiting are only partially understood.

Physiologie des réseaux nerveux du tronc cérébral impliqués dans le mécanisme émétique.
Résumé: *Ce chapitre dresse une revue i/ du rôle de l'area postrema (AP) comme zone chémosensible de déclenchement du vomissement, ii/ des concepts portant sur l'organisation des réseaux nerveux du tronc cérébral qui coordonnent la réponse émétique et iii/ de l'activité des prémotoneurones du tronc cérébral qui commandent les muscles respiratoires responsables de l'accomplissement du vomissement. La lésion de l'AP supprime le vomissement induit par de nombreuses (pas toutes) drogues émétiques, mais n'abolit pas le vomissement associé au mal des transport ou à l'activation des afférences viscérales vagales. L'implication de l'AP dans le vomissement consécutif à l'irradiation est toujours controversée. L'organisation hodologique du réseau nerveux qui coordonne la réponse émétique est inconnue. Néanmoins, il n'existe pas de preuve irréfutable de l'existence d'une région bien déterminée anatomiquement constituant le "centre du vomissement". Pendant la respiration et le vomissement, les muscles respiratoires, activés différemment, sont contrôlés en partie par quelques neurones respiratoires propriobulbaires et bulbospinaux. Les mécanismes nerveux centraux par lesquels des informations sensitives variées conduisent à l'activité puissante et hautement coordonnée que constitue le vomissement ne sont que partiellement compris.*

INTRODUCTION

All the essential neuronal circuitry for producing vomiting, apart from sensory inputs and motor outputs, is located within the medulla of the brain stem. This conclusion is based on the results of a series of lesion experiments in experimental animals (Miller and Nonaka, unpublished observations). This of course does not mean that other parts of the brain are not involved in producing vomiting under certain circumstances, for example psychogenic vomiting (Wruble *et al.*, 1982). It is also known that vomiting can be elicited by electrical stimulation of certain rostral brain regions (e.g., olfactory tubercle, amygdala, septum, fornix, ventral anterior thalamic nucleus, supraoptic area of the hypothalamus) (Hess, 1957; Robinson and Mishkin, 1968), undoubtedly via subsequent excitation of medullary structures.

In addition to excitatory inputs that produce vomiting, neuroinhibition can play a role in the regulation of emesis (see chapter by Zabara). Furthermore, the response to emetic stimuli has the potential for plasticity as discussed in the chapter by Andrews.

THE AREA POSTREMA AS A CHEMORECEPTOR TRIGGER ZONE FOR VOMITING

The concept of the area postrema as a central chemoreceptor trigger zone for vomiting was developed by Borison, Brizzee, and Wang (Borison and Wang, 1953). Lesions of the area postrema prevent vomiting induced by many emetic drugs (reviewed in Borison, 1989). Included in this group is the cancer chemotherapeutic agent cisplatin (McCarthy and Borison, 1984), which as discussed elsewhere in these Proceedings probably initiates vomiting through a cascade of mechanisms involving both abdominal visceral afferents ar the area postrema. Substances that persist in inducing vomiting following area postrema lesions include the opiate antagonist naloxone (Costello and Borison, 1977) and the serotonin-3 receptor agonist phenylbiguanide (Miller and Nonaka, 1992). In addition, area postrema lesions do not prevent vomiting induced by electrical stimulation of abdominal vagal afferents (Miller and Nonaka, 1992) or, despite early reports, by motion (Borison and Borison, 1986; Fox *et al.*, 1990; Wilpizeski *et al.*, 1986). The role of the area postrema in radiation-induced vomiting is controversial. Most investigators report that area postrema lesions prevent the initial vomiting elicited by radiation (reviewed in Borison, 1989; King and Makale, 1991). Borison and colleagues, however, have shown that cats still vomit in response to radiation following area postrema lesions (Borison *et al.*, 1987a). They argue that the critical reflex pathways bypass the area postrema and run in nearby sensory vagal and dorsal column fibers, which might have been unintentionally damaged in other studies involving area postrema lesions (Borison *et al.*, 1987a, 1987b).

Neurons in the area postrema exhibit a characteristic response to local iontophoretic application of emetic agents. These neurons which are silent at rest (as recorded in anesthetized dogs) start to fire at very low rates (1-3 times per second) for long durations (30 seconds to many minutes) beginning 3-20 seconds after drug application (Carpenter *et al.*, 1988). Since vomiting was not elicited in these animals, the response of area postrema neurons in relation to an actual vomiting episode has not yet been determined. Furthermore, the central processes that transform this slow input signal (1-3

Hz) into the forceful and highly coordinated motor output that produces vomiting have yet to be explored.

COORDINATION OF THE EMETIC RESPONSE - IS THERE A VOMITING CENTER?

The concept of a "vomiting center" located in the dorsolateral reticular formation of the brain stem was developed by Borsion and Wang on the basis of two types of experiments. One investigation used electrical stimulation of the brain stem of decerebrate cats to produce vomiting (Borison and Wang, 1949). In the other study, lesions produced by chronic implantion of radon pellets into dogs' brain stems resulted in an impaired vomiting response to emetic drugs (Wang and Borison, 1951b). The "vomiting center" was envisioned to receive projections from all emetic sensory inputs and to project in turn to all the necessary motor output nuclei.

In 1983, Miller and Wilson attempted to repeat the electrical stimulation studies of Borison and Wang (1949) with the aim of determining a more localized region from which vomiting could be evoked. Instead, we were unable to elicit readily reproducible vomiting and argued that if a well localized "vomiting center" existed in this region of the brain stem, its activation by electrical stimulation should produce vomiting more reliably than we were able to obtain. It should be noted that both brain stem electrical stimulation and lesion affect not only cell bodies but also axons of passage. Thus, it seems likely that the results of Borison and Wang can be explained at least in part by effects on vagal sensory afferents and/or area postrema efferents. It has been known for some time that electical stimulation of abdominal vagal afferents can reproducibly evoke vomiting at short latencies (Derbyshire and Ferguson, 1938; Miller *et al.*, 1987; Zabara chapter), and it has recently been shown that vomiting can also be elicited by stimulation along the vagal sensory input pathway within the brain stem (Fukuda and Koga, 1991).

New studies have shown that large lesions in the lateral portion of the brain stem at the level of the retrofacial nucleus abolish vomiting in dogs (Fukuda and Koga, 1991). This result is consistent with findings obtained independently in our laboratory using cats (Miller and Nonaka, unpublished observations). Electrical stimulation in this region can elicit the vomiting response (Fukuda and Koga, 1991). Fukuda and Koga concluded that the region of the Bötzinger complex near the retrofacial nucleus contains the central pattern generator for vomiting. However, in my view, there is not enough evidence at present to justify this conclusion if the term "pattern generator" is used in the same context as "vomiting center". As discussed in the following section, there are pre-motor neurons located in this region that are involved in generating the pattern of respiratory muscle discharge during vomiting. However, this pre-motor respiratory-related circuitry is unlikely to function as a traditionally conceived "vomiting center" since it probably does not project to all the necessary effector nuclei that have to be activated to produce all the phenomena associated with vomiting. In order to demonstrate that a "vomiting center"-like "pattern generator" exists in this region, it would have to be determined, firstly, that the lesion and stimulation results were due to effects on neuronal cell bodies as opposed to axons passing through the region. Secondly, the effective lesion site needs to be better localized within the confines of the lesioned area. Thirdly, one would have to ensure that the results were not due to perturbation of pre-motor and motor output circuitry. In this context, it is important to note that, instead of monitoring the entire motor act of vomiting, both Fukuda and Koga (1991) and Miller and Nonaka (unpublished observations) used a characteristic pattern of respiratory muscle nerve discharge in paralyzed animals to determine the occurrence of fictive vomiting. Thus, it was not determined whether lesions in this region also abolish, for example, the gastrointestinal correlates of vomiting along with the respiratory muscle components. Finally, one would want to identify neurons within this region that display the appropriate discharge and have the appropriate connections to function as a "vomiting center" type of "pattern generator". Despite these cautions, the region around the retrofacial nucleus may be a promising site for future investigations of the neuronal mechanisms that coordinate vomiting.

Two new models of the organization of the central coordinating circuitry for vomiting have recently been proposed as alternatives to the traditional concept of a "vomiting center". Firstly, it has been suggested that vomiting may be produced by the sequential activation of a series of effector nuclei as opposed to these motor nuclei being activated in parallel by a "vomiting center" (Davis *et al.*, 1986). Secondly, it has been proposed that a paraventricular system of nuclei, defined by their connections with the area postrema and each other, can collectively account for most of the phenomena associated with nausea and vomiting (Lawes, 1990, 1991).

In summary, the central organization of the neuronal circuitry that coordinates the vomiting response remains unknown and controversial. It is my view that there is no compelling evidence for the existence of an anatomically well localized "vomiting center".

PRE-MOTOR AND MOTOR OUTPUTS

The changes in intrathoracic and intraabdominal pressures that primarily produce vomiting are generated by the coordinated action of the major respiratory muscles (McCarthy and Borison, 1974; McCarthy *et al.*, 1974). The importance of accompanying changes in gastrointestinal (G.I.) activity are discussed in the chapters by Miolan and Lang. These changes in G.I. activity are, however, not essential for vomiting, which can still occur following gut denervation (Wang and Borison, 1951a). This section will provide an overview of what is known about the brain stem circuirty that controls the major respiratory muscles during vomiting. Their pattern of activation is described in detail in the chapter by Grélot and Bianchi. In brief, during vomiting the diaphragm and external intercostal (inspiratory) muscles cocontract with the abdominal (expiratory) muscles in a series of bursts of activity that culminates in expulsion. The internal intercostal (expiratory) muscles, in contrast, contract out of phase with these muscles during retching (McCarthy and Borison, 1974).

The discharge patterns of individual brain stem neurons have been studied during "fictive vomiting" in paralyzed animals. Fictive vomiting can be identified by the same characteristic pattern of a series of bursts of coactivation of diaphragmatic (phrenic) and abdominal muscle nerves that would be expected to culminate in expulsion if the animals were not paralyzed (Miller *et al.*, 1987). A schema of the possible roles of different brain stem respiratory neurons during vomiting is illustrated in Fig. 1. The premotor neurons that activate spinal expiratory (abdominal and internal intercostal) motoneurons are now fairly well established. In contrast, the brain stem neurons that

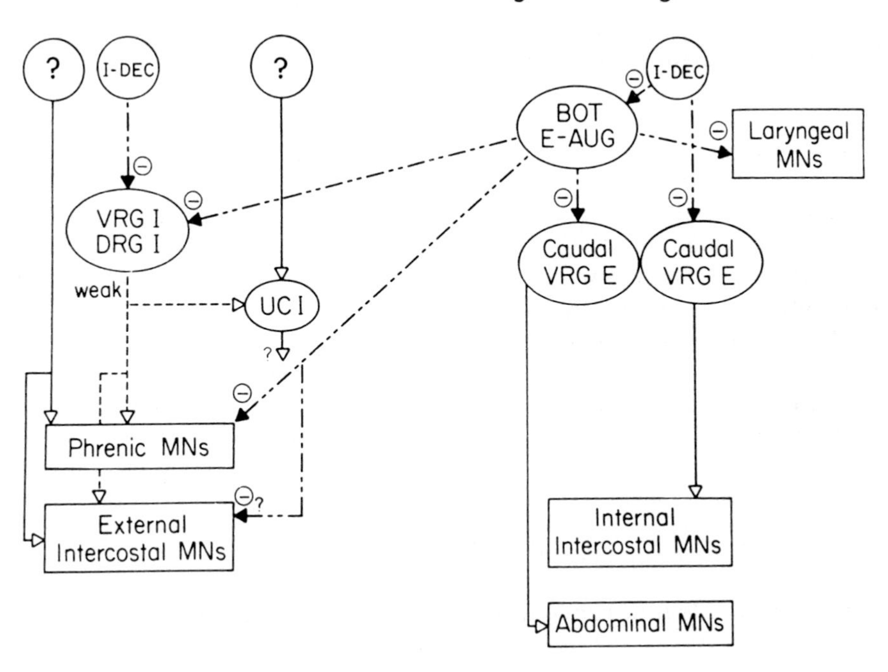

Fig. 1. Working hypothesis of the possible roles of brain stem respiratory neurons in the control of the major respiratory muscles during vomiting. Inspiratory spinal motoneurons are indicated on the left and expiratory ones on the right. The schema is based on patterns of single cell activity during (fictive) vomiting and on known or possible neuronal connections. Arrows do not distinguish between mono- and oligo-synaptic connections. Inhibitory connections are indicated by filled arrowheads. Modified with permission from Miller (1992). Abbreviations: BOT, Bötzinger; DRG, dorsal respiratory group; E, expiratory; E-AUG, augmenting expiratory; I, inspiratory; I-DEC, decrementing inspiratory; MNs, motoneurons; UC, upper cervical; VRG, ventral respiratory group.

activate spinal inspiratory (phrenic and external intercostal) motoneurons remain uncertain. Bulbospinal expiratory (E) neurons located in the portion of the ventral respiratory group (VRG) caudal to the obex (nucleus retroambigualis) make mono- or oligo-synaptic excitatory connections with abdominal and internal intercostal motoneurons (Feldman, 1986). During (fictive) vomiting, one subgroup of these neurons fires mainly during periods of abdominal nerve activation while another subgroup fires mainly between bursts of synchronous phrenic and abdominal discharge (Miller *et al.*, 1987) when internal intercostal motoneurons are activated (McCarthy and Borison, 1974). Cutting the axons of caudal VRG E neurons by a midsagittal section between C1 and the obex abolishes abdominal muscle nerve discharge during both expiration and fictive vomiting (Miller and Nonaka, 1990b). Possible effects on intercostal activity are not known. These observations from both cell recording and lesion studies are consistent with abdominal muscle activation during vomiting being mediated by caudal VRG E neurons.

During respiration, phrenic nerve discharge exhibits high frequency (50-100 Hz) oscillations (HFO) which are believed to originate from the brain stem inspiratory pattern generator. During (fictive) vomiting, this normal HFO is absent, indicating that inputs from the inspiratory pattern generator to phrenic motoneurons are shut off during vomiting (Cohen *et al.*, 1992). Phrenic and external intercostal motoneurons are activated during respiration via bulbospinal inspiratory (I) neurons located in the dorsal respiratory group (DRG) in the ventrolateral nucleus of the solitary tract and in the VRG rostral to the obex (nucleus para-ambiguus) (Feldman, 1986). In the cat, most (> 90%) of these bulbospinal I neurons are actively inhibited during (fictive) vomiting (Bianchi and Grélot, 1989) and either are mainly silent throughout the entire episode or fire only near the end of phrenic discharge (Miller *et al.*, 1990). Only a few neurons start firing soon after the onset of phrenic discharge, but even these cells could not *initiate* activation of spinal inspiratory motoneurons during vomiting. Another recent study using dogs has concluded that a higher fraction (one-third) of bulbospinal inspiratory neurons contributes to the discharge of spinal inspiratory motoneurons during (fictive) vomiting (Koga, 1991). It is not clear, however, how many of these neurons start firing soon enough to contribute to the initiation of motoneuronal firing. Given the increased phrenic and external intercostal discharge that occurs during vomiting (Grélot and Bianchi chapter; McCarthy and Borison, 1974), it seems likely that even in dogs other unknown brain stem neurons (not necessarily respiratory-related) are important for the control of the diaphragm and coactive external intercostal muscles during vomiting.

Many propriospinal I neurons located in the upper cervical (C1-3) spinal cord are active during (fictive) vomiting (Nonaka and Miller, 1991). These neurons have extensive projections to the thoracic cord and also send a smaller projection to the region of phrenic motoneurons and to the upper lumbar spinal cord (Hoskin *et al.*, 1988; Lipski and Duffin, 1986). Recent work, however, has shown that these neurons are not an essential relay for descending drive to spinal respiratory motoneurons since kainic acid injections into this cell group had no major effect on phrenic, intercostal, or abdominal discharge during (fictive) vomiting (Miller and Yates, unpublished observations). Kainic acid is known to produce dysfunction of neuronal cell bodies while sparing passing axons.

In addition to excitatory neurons, two types of inhibitory neurons with widespread connections are now known to play a role in controlling the discharge of medullary respiratory neurons during different phases of vomiting. One type is expiratory neurons that have an augmenting discharge pattern (E-AUG) and are located in the rostral portion of the VRG (Bötzinger (BOT) complex) in the vicinity of the retrofacial nucleus. The Bötzinger complex is defined functionally, rather than anatomically, as the region that contains certain expiratory neurons (Feldman, 1986). BOT E-AUG neurons make monosynaptic inhibitory connections with DRG (Merrill *et al.*, 1983) and VRG (Fedorko *et al.*, 1989) I neurons, caudal VRG bulbospinal E neurons (Jiang and Lipski, 1990), and laryngeal (Jiang and Lipski, 1990) and phrenic motoneurons (Merrill and Fedorko, 1984). During (fictive) vomiting, BOT E-AUG neurons discharge during the time period between synchronous phrenic and abdominal bursts and thus serve as a source of inhibitory input during that phase of the vomiting episode (Miller and Nonaka, 1990a). Another group of inhibitory neurons, inspiratory neurons with a decrementing firing pattern (I-DEC), is also located in the rostral VRG. These cells monosynaptically inhibit DRG and VRG bulbospinal I neurons, and bulbospinal E neurons in the caudal VRG and BOT (Ezure, 1990; Ezure *et al.*, 1989). About 1/2 of I-DEC neurons are active during synchronous phrenic and abdominal bursts during (fictive) vomiting, i.e. out of phase with the firing of inhibitory BOT E-AUG neurons. The remainder of the I-DEC neurons become silent (Miller and Ezure, 1992). Thus, DRG and VRG bulbospinal I neurons are thought to be inhibited by I-DEC and E-AUG neurons during different phases of the vomiting episode. The subgroup of caudal VRG E neurons that is active during abdominal discharge may be inhibited between abdominal bursts by BOT E-AUG neurons. Similarly, the subgroup of caudal VRG E neurons that is active between synchronous phrenic and abdominal bursts may be inhibited during these bursts by I-DEC neurons, which could also inhibit BOT E-AUG neurons.

Thus, respiratory muscles are controlled in part during vomiting by some of the same propriobulbar and bulbospinal respiratory neurons that are involved in their control during breathing. However, the identity of the neurons (not necessarily respiratory-related) that are responsible for activating phrenic and external intercostal motoneurons during vomiting remains uncertain. Better knowledge of these pre-motor circuits would be an important step for determining how various inputs, for example from abdominal vagal afferents, the area postrema, and the vestibular system, can lead to vomiting under different conditions.

ACKNOWLEDGMENT

The author's work is supported by grant NS20585 from the National Institute of Neurological Disorders and Stroke (U.S.A.).

REFERENCES

Bianchi, A.L. and Grélot, L. (1989): Converse motor output of inspiratory bulbospinal premotoneurones during vomiting. *Neurosci. Lett. 104*, 298-302.

Borison, H.L. (1989): Area postrema: chemoreceptor circumventricular organ of the medulla oblongata. *Prog. Neurobiol. 32*, 351-390.

Borison, H.L. and Borison, R. (1986): Motion sickness reflex arc bypasses the area postrema in cats. *Exp. Neurol. 92*, 723-737.

Borsion, H.L., McCarthy, L.E., Douple, E.B., Johnson, J., and Borison, R. (1987a): Acute radiation-induced vomiting in area postrema-ablated cats. *Radiat. Res. 109*, 430-439.

Borsion, H.L., McCarthy, L.E., and Johnson, J.R. (1987b): High dorsal column cordotomy plus subdiaphragmatic vagotomy prevents acute ionizing radiation sickness in cats. *Exp. Neurol. 98*, 645-658.

Borison, H.L. and Wang, S.C. (1949): Functional localization of central coordinating mechanism for emesis in cat. *J. Neurophysiol. 12*, 305-313.

Borison, H.L. and Wang, S.C. (1953): Physiology and pharmacology of vomiting. *Pharmacol. Rev. 5*, 193-230.

Carpenter, D.O., Briggs, D.B., Knox, A.P., and Strominger N. (1988): Excitation of area postrema neurons by transmitters, peptides, and cyclic nucleotides. *J. Neurophysiol. 59*, 358-369.

Cohen, M.I., Miller, A.D., Russell, B., and Shaw, C.-F. (1992): Weakness of short-term synchronization among respiratory nerve activities during fictive vomiting. *Am. J. Physiol.* in press.

Costello, D.J. and Borison, H.L. (1977): Naloxone antagonizes narcotic self-blockade of emesis in the cat. *J. Pharmacol. Exp. Ther. 203*, 222-230.

Davis, C.J., Harding, R.K., Leslie, R.A., and Andrews, P.L.R. (1986): The organisation of vomiting as a protective reflex. In *Nausea and Vomiting: Mechanisms and Treatment*, eds. C.J. Davis, G.V. Lake-Bakaar, and D.G.Grahame-Smith, pp. 65-75. Berlin: Springer-Verlag.

Derbyshire, A.J. and Ferguson, J.K.W. (1938): Studies on the vomiting reflex in cats and dogs. *Am. J. Physiol. 123*, 52-53.

Ezure, K. (1990): Synaptic connections between medullary respiratory neurons and considerations on the genesis of respiratory rhythm. *Prog. Neurobiol. 35*, 429-450.

Ezure, K., Manabe, M. and Otake, K. (1989): Excitation and inhibition of medullary inspiratory neurons by two types of burst inspiratory neurons in the cat. *Neurosci. Lett. 104*, 303-308.

Fedorko L., Duffin J., and England S. (1989): Inhibition of inspiratory neurons of the nucleus retroambigualis by expiratory neurons of the Botzinger complex in the cat. *Exp. Neurol. 106*, 74-77.

Feldman, J.L. (1986): Neurophysiology of breathing in mammals. In *Handbook of Physiology, The Nervous System IV, Intrinsic Regulatory Systems of the Brain*, ed. F.E. Bloom, pp. 463-524. Bethesda: American Physiological Society.

Fox, R.A., Corcoran, M., and Brizzee, K.R., (1990): Conditioned taste aversion and motion sickness in cats and squirrel monkeys. *Can. J. Physiol. Pharmacol. 68*, 269-278.

Fukuda, H., and Koga, T. (1991): The Bötzinger complex as the pattern generator for retching and vomiting in the dog. *Neurosci. Res. 12*, 471-485.

Hess, W.R. (1957): *The Functional Organization of the Diencephalon*, ed. J.R. Hughes. New York: Grune and Stratton.

Hoskin, R.W., Fedorko, L.M., and Duffin, J. (1988): Projections from upper cervical inspiratory neurons to thoracic and lumbar expiratory motor nuclei in the cat. *Exp. Neurol. 99*, 544-555.

Jiang, C. and Lipski, J. (1990): Extensive monosynaptic inhibition of ventral respiratory group neurons by augmenting neurons in the Bötzinger complex in the cat. *Exp. Brain Res. 81*, 639-648.

King, G.L. and Makale, M.T. (1991): Postirradiation emesis. In *Nausea and Vomiting: Recent Research and Clinical Advances*, eds. J. Kucharczyk, D.J. Stewart, & A.D. Miller, pp. 103-142. Boca Raton: CRC Press.

Koga, T. (1991): Discharge patterns of bulbar respiratory neurons during retching and vomiting in decerebrate dogs. *Jap. J. Physiol. 41,* 233-249.

Lawes, I.N.C. (1990): The origin of the vomiting response: a neuroanatomical hypothesis. *Can. J. Physiol. Pharmacol. 68,* 254-259.

Lawes, I.N.C. (1991): The central connections of area postrema define the paraventricular system involved in antinoxious behaviors. In *Nausea and Vomiting: Recent Research and Clinical Advances,* eds. J. Kucharczyk, D.J. Stewart, & A.D. Miller, pp. 77-101. Boca Raton: CRC Press.

Lipski, J. and Duffin, J. (1986): An electrophysiological investigation of propriospinal inspiratory neurons in the upper cervical cord of the cat. *Exp. Brain Res. 61,* 625-637.

McCarthy, L.E. and Borison, H.L. (1974): Respiratory mechanics of vomiting in decerebrate cats. *Am. J. Physiol. 226,* 738-743.

McCarthy, L.E. and Borison, H.L. (1984): Cisplatin-induced vomiting eliminated by ablation of the area postrema in cats. *Cancer Treat. Rep. 68,* 401-404.

McCarthy, L.E., Borison, H.L., Spiegel, P.K., and Friedlander, R.M. (1974): Vomiting: radiographic and oscillographic correlates in the decerebrate cat. *Gastroenterology 67,* 1126-1130.

Merrill, E.G. and Fedorko, L. (1984): Monosynaptic inhibition of phrenic motoneurons: a long descending projection from Bötzinger neurons. *J. Neurosci. 4,* 2350-2353.

Merrill, E.G., Lipski, J., Kubin, L., and Fedorko, L. (1983): Origin of the expiratory inhibition of nucleus tractus solitarius inspiratory neurones. *Brain Res. 263,* 43-50.

Miller, A.D. (1992): Vomiting: its respiratory components. In *Respiratory Control: Central and Peripheral Mechanisms,* eds. D.F. Speck, M.S. Dekin, W.R. Revelette, and T. Frazier. Lexington: University Press of Kentucky, in press.

Miller, A.D. and Ezure, K. (1992): Behavior of inhibitory and excitatory propriobulbar respiratory neurons during fictive vomiting. *Brain Res.,* in press.

Miller, A.D. and Nonaka, S. (1990a): Bötzinger expiratory neurons may inhibit phrenic motoneurons and medullary inspiratory neurons during vomiting. *Brain Res. 521,* 352-354.

Miller, A.D. and Nonaka, S. (1990b): Mechanisms of abdominal muscle activation during vomiting. *J. Appl. Physiol. 69,* 21-25.

Miller, A.D. and Nonaka, S. (1992): Mechanisms of vomiting induced by serotonin-3 receptor agonists in the cat: effect of vagotomy, splanchnicectomy or area postrema lesion. *J. Pharmacol. Exp. Ther. 260,* 509-517.

Miller, A.D., Nonaka, S., Lakos, S.F., and Tan, L.K. (1990:) Diaphragmatic and external intercostal muscle control during vomiting: behavior of inspiratory bulbospinal neurons. *J. Neurophysiol. 63,* 31-36.

Miller, A.D., Tan, L.K., and Suzuki, I. (1987): Control of abdominal and expiratory intercostal muscle activity during vomiting: role of ventral respiratory group expiratory neurons. *J. Neurophysiol. 57,* 1854-1866.

Miller, A.D. and Wilson, V.J. (1983): 'Vomiting center' reanalyzed: an electrical stimulation study. *Brain Res. 270,* 154-158.

Nonaka, S. and Miller, A.D. (1991): Behavior of upper cervical inspiratory propriospinal neurons during fictive vomiting. *J. Neurophysiol. 65,* 1492-1500.

Robinson, B.W. and Mishkin, M. (1968): Alimentary responses to forebrain stimulation in monkeys. *Exp. Brain Res. 4,* 330-366.

Wang, S.C. and Borison, H.L. (1951a): Copper sulfate emesis: a study of afferent pathways from the gastrointestinal tract. *Am. J. Physiol. 164*: 520-526.
Wang, S.C. and Borison, H.L. (1951b): The vomiting center: its destruction by radon implantation in dog medulla oblongata. *Am. J. Physiol. 166*: 712-717.
Wilpizeski, C.R., Lowry, L.D., and Goldman, W.S. (1986): Motion-induced sickness following bilateral ablation of area postrema in squirrel monkeys. *Laryngoscope 96*: 1221-1225.
Wruble, L.D., Rosenthal, R.H., and Webb. W.L. Jr. (1982): Psychogenic vomiting: a review. *Am. J. Gastroenterol. 77*: 318-321.

Mechanisms and Control of Emesis. Eds A.L. Bianchi, L. Grélot, A.D. Miller, G.L. King. Colloque INSERM/ John Libbey Eurotext Ltd. © 1992, Vol. 223, pp. 51-58

Cranio-mandibular disorders inducing nausea and vomiting

Francis Hartmann

Département des Sciences Anatomo-physiologique, Occlusodontique, Centre de Recherche et de Traitement de l'Appareil Manducateur, Faculté d'Odontologie, 27, boulevard Jean Moulin, 13385 Marseille Cedex 5, France

SUMMARY

Cranio Mandibular Disorders (CMD) often reflect a dysfunction of the Temporomandibular Joint (TMJ). They can occur after whiplash, difficult back teeth extraction and orthodontic procedures. The symptoms sometimes inclued nausea and /or vomiting. Clinical experiments combined with neuroanatomical labelling data have lead to the development accounting for the role of bruxism (clenching) in the genesis and continuation of these emetic symptoms in CMD.

Dysfonctions cranio-mandibulaires induisant nausées et vomissements.
Résumé : *Les dysfonctions craniomandibulaires (CMD) sont le plus souvent en corrélation avec une dysfonction de l'articulation temporomandibulaire (TMJ). A côté de phénomènes algiques, on peut observer des nausées voire des vomissements. L'expérimentation clinique fondée sur les données récentes de la neuroanatomie, permet d'élaborer un modèle neurophysiologique pour expliquer le rôle du bruxisme dans la genèse et l'entretien de certaines formes cliniques de nausées et de vomissements*

INTRODUCTION

Cranio Mandibular Disorders have recently been classified and subdivided by the American Academy Association of Cranio Mandibular Disorders, (Mac Neill, 1990) into two main categories, namely internal derangements (articular or arthrogenic disorders) and external derangements (muscular or myogenic disorders) of the Temporo Mandibular Joint (TMJ), (Hanson, 1988). Farrar & Mac Carthy (1982), have established that a dislocation of the TMJ meniscus can occur which is sometimes but not always susceptible to reduction. Patients suffering from this pathology have often undergone either whiplash effects in a motor accident, (Schwartz & Kendrick, 1984, Weinberg & Lapointe, 1987),, surgery under general anesthesia with intubation, difficult back tooth extraction or orthodontic procedures, (Farrar & Mac Carthy, 1982). But,the pathology of this joint is often misunderstood in the medical world (Farrar & Mac Carthy,1982). The main pathological signs resulting from the above etiological factors include limitation of mouth opening, deviation of the mandible and clicking at the level of the TMJ.

Patients suffering from internal derangement of the TMJ complain of headache, otalgia, pain in the pre-auricular area, behind the eye, and in the neck, shoulder or arm ; other symptoms can include vertigo, tachycardia, bruxism, and digestive problems (Farrar & Mac Carthy, 1982). We have attempted to etablish by questioning our patients what kind of digestive problems referred to by these authors actually involved. The result of our inquiry showed that the main symptoms of this type are nausea and vomiting. To our knowledge, the only relevant information available about problems of this kind is that in the study by (Lashley & Elder, 1982). These authors reported five case studies on patients with hyperemesis, migraine, bruxism and mixed headache who underwent clinical biofeedback treatment. The female patient with bruxism was referred for deep muscle relaxation training and EMG feedback. Her major complaint however was bruxism which had occurred mostly at night over the previous 15 years.

PATIENTS AND METHODS

The present study deals with 161 patients admitted to our Oro Facial Pain Center with TMJ dislocation, The diagnosis was etablished using the following procedures.

Questionning the patients

The patients reported that they suffered from pain in various regions (headache, otalgia, neck and shoulder pain), as well as from emesis, i.e., nausea and / or vomiting.

It was sometimes established only with some difficulty that some of the patients also had bruxism. In these cases the bruxism was mostly not of the teeth grinding but of the teeth clenching type. When no grinding occurs, there is no wearing of the dental enamel. Cases of bruxism involving only clenching therefore tend to be overlooked by physicians.

Tests applied

Endo-buccal palpation

Palpation of the lateral pterygoid muscle, (Travell & Simons, 1983, Bell,1985, Hartmann & Cucchi 1987, 1988, Hartmann & Sarat ,1988). This palpation nearly always induced hyperalgic effects. Here the palpation consisted of placing the small finger behind the superior maxillary tuberosity, working towards the ears. This palpation triggers the "jump sign" or "twitch response", (Travell & Simons, 1983). This nociceptive response indicates the state of contraction of the palpated muscle, although the diagnostic value of direct muscle palpation has sometimes been questioned, (Ash,1986), White, 1985).

When a physician palpates the Mac Burney point, he is actually palpating the region to which the nerves of the appendix project and probably not the appendix itself. Likewise, endo-buccal palpation applied to the pterygoid region, as described above, triggers "jump sign" nociceptive messages which reflect lateral pterygoid muscle dysfunction. This dysfunction has been found to accompany established cases of Cranio Mandibular Disorders (CMD).

Exo-buccal palpation

We systematically looked for three painful points which are often present in patients with CMD, (Hartmann & Cucchi, 1987 1988, Hartmann ***et al.,*** 1988), whether accompanied or otherwise by nausea and / or vomiting. We checked for pain in response to pressure applied to the sterno-cleido-mastoid muscle, the ipsilateral temporal muscle, and at the supra-internal angle of the orbital arcade. For these painful responses to consistute a valid diagnostic sign, it is indispensable that all three should be present at once. All these patients had been treated previously with drugs to combat nausea and vomiting, with no success.

Complementary tests

Tomography, arthrography

We systematically prescribed tomography for these patients. This often made it possible to detect malposition of the condyle in the glenoid cavity, which could be of variable extent and was sometimes reminiscent of a meniscal dislocation and therefore called for arthrography, (Helms & Katzberg, 1983). Out of the 161 arthrographies performed :

- a reducible meniscal dislocation was observed in 120 cases
- and a meniscal dislocation which was not reducible in 41 cases

Fonctional exploration of the trigeminal nerve

The trigeminal nerve was explored as previouly described by Papy & Hartmann (1989) involving :

- EMG of the temporal muscle
- Blink reflex test, involving interactions between the facial and trigeminal nerves
- Evoked somesthetic potential recordings on the trigeminal nerve

The treatment

First we always attempted to help the patient by counselling, where the following advice was given :

1 - to make a conscious effort not to clench their teeth.

2 - to clench their lips rather than their teeth, in agreement with data by Bratzlavsky (1972). This author has demonstrated that activation of the 7th facial nerve inhibits elevator muscle motoneurones.

3 - to put up red stickers around the house, car, and office reminding the patient that "clenching the teeth causes headache, pain, nausea and vomiting.

This procedure was most effective, and in two cases the counselling alone resulted in the disappearance of the vomiting. In the other patients, the counselling alone did not suffice and we therefore proceeded as follows :

Local myoresolution

Intramuscular injection of anesthetic without any vasoconstrictor such as mepivacaine or lidocaine (= xylocaine) into the two lateral pterygoid muscles using a method we have described previously (Hartmann ***et al.***, 1988). In addition to their anesthetic effects, mepivacaine or lidocaine exert a myoresolutive action (Bell, 1985 ; Gelb , 1977 ; Tanaka ***et al.***, 1981) at the level of the pterygoid muscles which were found to last for five to six days. Feinstein ***et al.*** (1969) ; Suko ***et al.*** (1976) Tanaka ***et al.*** (1981) have suggested that local anesthetics may interact with the Ca2+ -calmodulin complex and selectively inhibit the Ca2+-calmodulin enzyme activities. It has recently been suggested that the inhibitory effects of local anesthetics in the activation of the intra cellular calcium messenger system may be part of the pharmacological mechanism, whereby local anesthetics participate in cellular activities. (Ogawa 1990).

Experience has shown that it is necessary on average to perform these injections bilaterally into the pterygoid muscles once a week for eight weeks.

General myoresolution

Chloremezanon or *baclofen* were prescribed with a view to obtaining myoresolution. Both local and general myoresolution resulted in a satisfactory relaxation of the mandible elevator muscles.

RESULTS

The emetic symptoms of the 161 patients subjected to arthrography can be summarized as follows :

- 25 patients suffered from both nausea and vomiting
- 90 patients suffered from nausea and no vomiting
- the remaining patients did not complain of these symptoms.

Within two weeks generally, the nausea and vomiting had disappeared completely. The vomiting was the first symptom to be alleviated. Eight weeks of treatment were necessary before the other symptoms completely disappeared. The dislocation seemed to have no effect on the vomiting whether it was reducible or not.

A splint was placed on the mandible in some cases where neither the local or general myoresolution was sufficiently effective. This procedure is actually rarely used by us to treat nausea and vomiting but can often be necessary to deal with headache and neck pains.

We have previously noted that, after the second local anesthesia into the two lateral pterygoid muscles, the nausea and vomiting usually disappear. However, in some cases when a third injection is necessary, it is sometimes possible to observe an aggravation of all the symptoms after the injection, which can last for 24 to 36 hours. The nausea and vomiting subsequently disappear completely after this episode. The aggravation after the third injection is very well accepted by the patients if they are warned before treatment.

DISCUSSION

How are the links observed here between the masticatory system and nausea and vomiting to be accounted for ? Since the studies by Kerr (1962), it has been recognized that the trigeminal nerve is not the only source of sensory projections to the spinal nucleus of the trigeminal nerve. The Nucleus Tractus Solitarius (NTS) at the level of the obex, to which they convey messages from both the Area Postrema (AP) and peripheral afferents. The NTS is therefore a likely candidate as the site of interactions between the AP and peripheral afferent signals.

It has been clearly established on the basis of labeling experiments that vagal sensory projections extend to both sites of the AP and around neurons of the Dorsal Motor Nucleus (DMN). Kalia ***et al.,*** (1980) have reported that the NTS receives information from both the AP and peripheral afferents, from which they concluded that interactions may occur between these pathways, and that AP stimulation may facilitate the effects of solitary tract activation.

The NTS is known to be the primary relay of the peripheral cardiovascular, respiratory and gastrointestinal apparatus (Berger , 1979 ; Ciriello ***et al.,*** 1981 ; Jacquin ***et al.,*** 1982) On the other hand, intense substance P-like immonureactivity (SPLI) was observed in fiber bundles coursing between the spinal nucleus on the trigeminal nerve (South ***et al.*** ,1986 ; Wen-Bin ***et al.***, 1991) and the ventro lateral nucleus of the solitary tract at the level of the area postrema. Following unilaterally section of the trigeminal nerve, the SPLI-containing fiber bundles were absent ipsilaterally to the nerve section. These data indicated the presence of a trigeminal solitary projection which is composed of trigeminal sensory neurones containing substance P. These results suggest an anatomical route whereby substance P of trigeminal origin may modulate vagal or glossopharyngal sensory information (fig. **1**). According to Strand ***et al.,*** (1991), substance P can induce behavioral nociceptive responses (i.e. : biting). The continuation of this behavioural reponses may explain clenching.

During the day, these patients clenched their teeth quite moderately, whereas at night the force of the clenching was so strong that upon waking, the patients reported feeling fatigue and suffering from nausea and / or vomiting. The clenching played such a decisive role that the nausea and vomiting disappeared completely in three patients who had been encouraged by counselling to control their own clenching.

CONCLUSION

Via which pathway might dental afferents reach the area postrema ? The central projection targets of the periodontal mechanoreceptors are of two kinds (Hartmann et al., 1979 ; Van Willingen, 1986).

1 - The cell bodies of some dental afferents are located in the gasserian ganglion. Most of their central

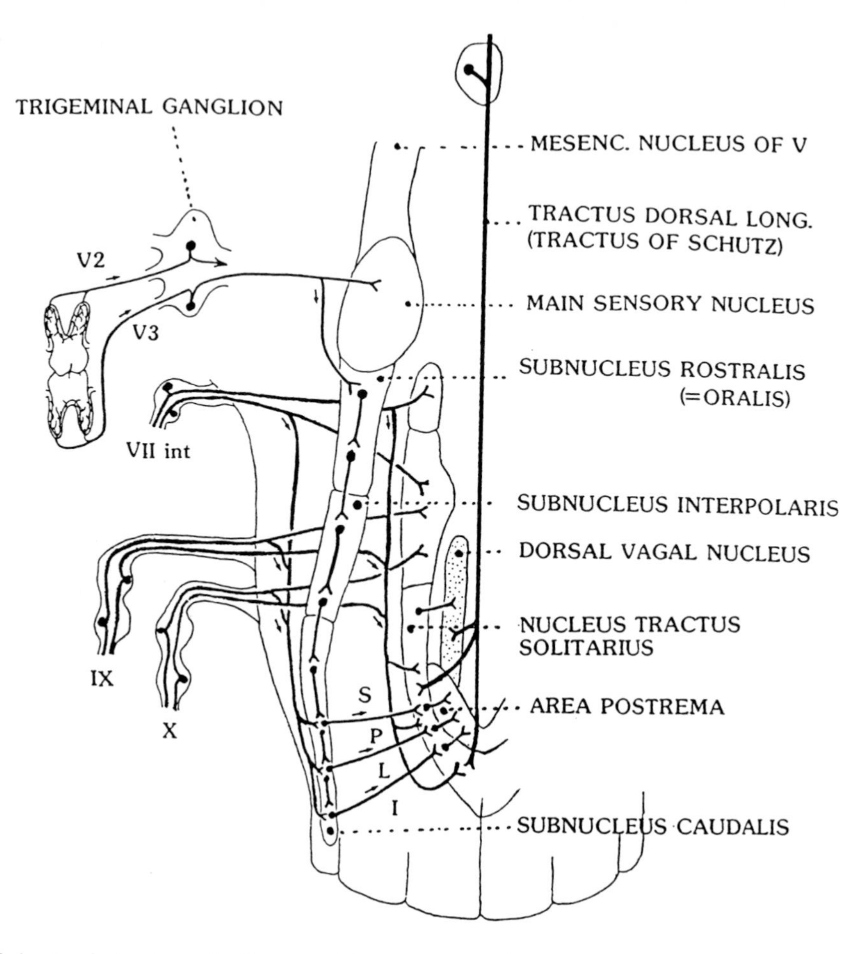

Fig. 1 Anatomical schematic diagram of the neurones projections of the cranial nerves and internuclear connectivity of the brainstem, drawn after Kerr (1962). Abbreviations : $\mathbf{V_2}$ Maxillary nerve ; V_3 Mandibular nerve ; $\mathbf{VII_{int}}$ Facial nerve (nervus intermedius) ; **IX** Glossopharyngeal nerve ; **X** Vagus nerve; SPLI, Subtance P like immunoreactivity

---

processes project to the spinal tract of the trigeminal nucleus (see figure **1**), which consists of a pars oralis, a pars interpolaris, and a pars caudalis an extends from the pons to the C 3 level.

On the other hand, Trub & Mei, (1991) have shown that periodontal mechanoreceptors project to the hypothalamus (VPM). Under these conditions, most of the periodontal mechanoreceptors are liable to activate the area postrema directly via the solitary tract and indirectly via the hypothalamus by the mean of the dorsal longitudinal tractus when clenching occurs. At the hypothalamic level, the dental afferents may be able to either enhance or reduce the activity of hypothalamic cells. The area postrema is known to receive abundant central projections from the parvocellular and paraventricular hypothalamic nuclei (Horst ***et al.*** 1984). The aim of our treatment was therefore to control the bruxism : if patients with cranio mandibular disorders could be prevented from clenching or grinding their teeth, it seems likely that their nausea and vomiting could be relieved.

Bilateral intramuscular injection of local anesthetic (lidocaine 3 %) seems to greatly inhibit the amount of proprioceptive and motor information conveyed to the mandibular elevator muscles when clenching occurs. Paradoxically, it is worth noting that the effects of the local anesthetic have been reported to last for five or seven days. It is therefore necessary to inject local anesthetic into the pterygoid muscles once a week for eight weeks. Incentally it was confirmed here that it is rarely necessary to have recourse to splints in order to control the emetic symptoms.

The results of the present study support the hypothesis that the area postrema (AP) may interact with periodontal mechanoreceptors (bruxism) to modulate NTS neurone activity.

REFERENCES

Ash, M.M. (1986) - Current concepts in the aetiology, diagnosis and treatment of TMJ and muscle dysfunction - *J. of Oral Rehabilitation*, **13** , 1-20

Bell, W.H. (1985) - Orofacial Pains: classification, diagnosis, management - 3rd edit., *Year Book Medical Pub., Inc.*, Chicago, 420 p

Berger, A.J. (1979) - Distribution of carotid sinus nerve afferent fibers to solitari tract nuclei of the cat using transganglioning transport of horseradish peroxidase.- *Neurosci. lett.*, **14**, 153-158

Bratzlavsky, M. (1972) - Pauses in activity of human jaw closing muscles - *Exp. Neurol.* ; **36,** 160-165

Ciriello, J., Calaresu, F.R. (1981)- Projections from buffer nerves to the nucleus of the solitary tract ; an anatomical and electrophysiological study in the rat.- *J. Autonom. Nerv. Syst.*, **3**, 299-310

Farrar, W.B., Mc. Carthy, W. (1982) - A clinical outline of T.M.J. : Diagnosis and treatment *Normandy Study Group for T.M.J. Dysfunction - 7 Ed. Montgomery Ed.* WALKER Co.

Feinstein, M.B., Paimre, M. (1969) - Pharmacological action of local anesthetics on excitation contraction coupling in striated anD smooth muscle - *Feder. Proceeding.*, **5**, 1643-1648

Gelb, H. (1977) - Clinical Management of Head, Neck and TMJ Pain and Dysfunction : A Multi-Disciplinary Approach to Diagnosis and Treatment.-*W.B. Saunders Co., Philadelphia, London, Toronto*, 547 p.

Hanson, T.L.(1988) - Craniomandibular disorders and sequencing their treatment - *Australian Prosthodontic Journal*, **2**, 9-15

Hartmann, F., Mei, N., & Al. (1979) - Bases neuro-physiologiques de l'occlusion - *Encycl.Medic. Chir., Paris, Stomato., 22008*,

Hartmann, F., Sarrat, P., & Al. (1988) - Muscle ptérygoïdien latéral, dissection anatomique et imagerie médicale. - Perspectives dans le traitement du S.A.D.A.M - *Act. Odont. Stomat.*,**163**, 545-566

Hartmann, F., Cucchi, G. (1988) - Le Syndrome de Costen : réévaluation du diagnostic *Médit. Medic.*, **376** : 3-12

Hartmann, F., Cucchi, G. (1987) - Muscle ptérygoïdien et S.A.D.A.M. : Diagnostic précoce et traitement - *Revue d'Odontostomatologie Tome XVI*, **3** : 209-218

Hay, M. & Bishop, V.S. (1991) - Interaction of area postrema and solitary tract in the nucleus tractus solitarius - *Am. J. Physiol.*, **260,** (Heart Circ. Physiol. 29) : H1466-H1473

Helms, C.A., Katzberg, R.W., & Al. (1983) - Internal Derangements of the T.M.J. - *Radiology Research and Education Foundation Edit.*, 231 p.

Horst, G.J., Luiten P.G.M. & Al. (1984) - Descending pathways from hypothalamus to dorsal motor vagus and ambiguus nuclei in the rat - *J. of the Auton. Nerv. Syst. ;* **11**, 59-75

Jacquin, M.F., Semba, K., & Al. (1982) - Trigeminal primary afferents project bilateraly to dorsal horn and ipsilateraly to cerebellum, reticular formation, and cunate, solitary, supra trigeminal and vagal nuclei, *Brain Research*, **246** : 285-291

Kalia, M., Melusam, M.M. (1980) - Brain Stem Projections of Sensory and Motor Components of the Vagus Complex in the Cat : I - The Cervical Vagus and Nodos Ganglions - *The Journal of Comparative Neurology*, 193 : 435-465

Kerr, W.L. (1962)- Facial vagal and glossopharyngal nerves in the cat - *Arch. Neurol.*, **6** , 264

Lashley, J. K., Elder, S.T. (1982) - Selected case studies in clinical bio feed back - *J. of Clinical Psychology*, **38**, 3, 530-540

Mac Neill, C. (1990) - Craniomandibular Disorders : Guidelines for evaluation ,diagnosis and management - *Quintessence Publishing*, **2**, 13-54

Ogawa, (1990) - Effect of local anesthetics on intracellular calcium messenger system - *J. Gifu. Dent. Soc.*, Vol. 17, **2**, 557-574

Papy, J.J., Hartmann, F., & Al. (1989) - Temporal muscle EMG and somatosensory investigation of trigeminal pathways in : "Electromyography of jaw reflexes in man" *D. van Steenberghe & A. De Laat Editors, Leuwen. Univ. Press.*, 409-2

Schwartz, H.C., Kendrick, R.W. (1984) - Internal derangements of the temporomandibular joint : description of clinical syndromes. - *Oral Surgery, Oral Medecine*, **58**, 1, 24-9

South, E.H., Ritter, R.C. (1986) - Substance P-containing trigeminal sensory neurones project to nucleus of the solitary tract - *Brain Research*, **372**, 283-289

Strand, F.L., Kenneth, J.R., & Al.,(1991) Antonnawich, F.S., Garret, L.Y. - Neuropeptides hormones as neurotrophic factors - *Physiological Reviews*, **71**, 4,1034-35

Suko, J., Winkler, F., & Al. (1976) - Aspects of the mechanism of action of local anesthetic on the sarcoplasmic reticulum of squelettal muscles - *Biochimica & Biophysica Acta*, **443**, 571-586

Tanaka, T., Hidaka, H.(1981) - Interaction of local anesthetics with calmodulin - *Bioch. & Biophys. Reas. Commun.*, **101**, 2, 447-453

Travell, J.G., Simmons, D.G. (1983) - Myofascial Pain and Dysfunctipon. The Trigger Point Manual - *Ed Williams &Wilkins, Baltimore*, 713 p

Trub, M., Mei, N. (1991) - Effects on periodontal stimulation on VMH neurones in anesthetized rats - *Brain Res. Bull.* **27**, 29-34

Van Willingen, J.D. (1986) - Motoriek van het trigeminus systeem. - In : VAN WILLIGEN J.D., Ed. Morfologie en functie van het orofaciale system. - *Utrecht : Bohn, Scheltema & Holkema*, 1983, 110

Wen-Bin- Zang, Ji-Shuo Li, & Al. (1991) - SP-Like Immuno reactivity in the primary trigeminal neurones projecting to the nucleus tractus solitarii - *Brain Research*, **558**, 87-89

Weinberg, S., Lapointe, H. (1987) - Cervical extension-flexion injury (whiplash) and internal derangement of the temporomandibualr joint - *J. Oral Maxillo-fac. Surg.*, **45** , 8 : 653-6

White, L.W. (1985) - The Lateral Pterygoïd Muscle : Fact and Fiction - *J. of Clinical Orthodontics*, **19** , 8 , 584-7

Mechanisms and Control of Emesis. Eds A.L. Bianchi, L. Grélot, A.D. Miller, G.L. King. Colloque INSERM/
John Libbey Eurotext Ltd. © 1992, Vol. 223, pp. 59-69

Neural control of the distal digestive tract responses associated with vomiting

J.P. Miolan

Département de Physiologie et Neurophysiologie, URA CNRS 205, Faculté des Sciences et Techniques Saint-Jérôme, 13397 Marseille Cedex 13, France

Summary: Emesis is a highly integrated physiological reflex involving somatic and autonomic motor events. The gastrointestinal motor components of the emetic reflex have been extensively described in the literature but the nervous mechanisms underlying these phenomena are poorly understood. In this review we discuss the mechanism by which gastrointestinal motor correlates of vomiting may be triggered. The activity of the vagal efferent fibers controlling the stomach has been recorded in conscious dog by using an indirect nerve suture technique. This study has provided evidence that the inhibitory phenomema occurring in the gastrointestinal tract prior to vomiting are due to a simultaneous and coordinated activation of excitatory and inhibitory vagal efferent pathways that usually control gastrointestinal motility. The excitatory mechanisms inducing the specific motor components of vomiting, i.e. the cholinergic retroperistaltic wave and the non-cholinergic motor contractions associated with emesis, are not induced by the nervous pathways referred to above and are likely due to the activation of specific excitatory vagal pathways.

Résumé: Contrôle nerveux de la motricité du tractus gastro-intestinal distal lors du vomissement.

Le vomissement est un acte physiologique complexe élaboré par les centres nerveux supérieurs et qui met en jeu des activités motrices diverses, contrôlées par les systèmes nerveux somatique et autonome. Les modifications de motricité gastro-intestinale qui se produisent lors du vomissement ont bien été décrites dans la littérature, mais les mécanismes nerveux qui contrôlent ces phénomènes sont mal connus. Dans cet article, nous envisagerons comment s'organise le message nerveux central qui pilote la motricité gastro-intestinale lors du vomissement. Nous avons enregistré chez l'animal éveillé l'activité unitaire des fibres vagales efférentes destinées à l'estomac distal grâce à une technique de suture nerveuse croisée hétérogène. Cette étude a montré que les phénomènes inhibiteurs se produisant lors du vomissement sont dus à la mise en jeu, simultanée et coordonnée, des voies vagales excitatrices et inhibitrices qui contrôlent de façon permanente la motricité gastrique. Quant aux phénomènes excitateurs se produisant lors du vomissement, à savoir l'onde rétropéristaltique et les contractions motrices non cholinergiques qui se déroulent au niveau intestinal, ils ne sont pas dus à l'activation des voies nerveuses vagales précédemment évoquées. Ces phénomènes résultent donc très vraisemblablement de l'activation de voies vagales spécifiques.

Introduction

The emetic reflex is a highly integrated physiological reflex involving precise temporal coordination between autonomic and somatic motor components. This reflex may be considered as part of a protective defense reaction.

The emetic reflex could be induced by various humoral factors acting on a chemoreceptor trigger zone located within the area postrema or by nerve afferents running mainly in the vagus nerve. All these stimuli converge on a "vomiting center" located within the reticular formation of the medulla oblongata (Wang and Borison, 1952; Borison and Wang, 1953). The current concept is that this center coordinates all the events in the emetic motor pattern i.e. the prodromal symptoms (salivation and licking), the changes in gastrointestinal motility and the profound modifications in respiratory musculature required to induce retching and vomiting (Wang and Borison, 1952; Miller and Wilson, 1983; Miller, 1990).

Among all the motor events occurring during emesis, the gastrointestinal component of this reflex is one of the protective mechanisms against ingested hazardous agents. The motor correlates of the digestive tract during vomiting had been investigated in particular since the 1970s by using cineradiographic (Smith and Brizzee, 1961), electromyographic (Weisbrodt and Christensen, 1972) and strain gauge force transducer techniques (Lang et al, 1986). These studies have resulted in a good understanding of the motor phenomena occurring in the digestive tract during vomiting, but the nervous mechanisms underlying these phenomena are as yet poorly understood.

The aim of this paper is to present the current state of knowledge on nervous control of the gastrointestinal tract responses associated with vomiting and on the mechanisms of their initiation and propagation.

I Gastrointestinal motor component of the emetic reflex.

Whatever the mode by which the emetic reflex is triggered, the gastrointestinal motor response is still identical in composition. In the stomach and in the small intestine the motor correlates of vomiting are characterized by inhibitory and excitatory phenomena appearing before retching and the expulsion phase.

The initial modifications of gastrointestinal motility during vomiting consist of a reduction or abolition of the contractile activity which is in progress. Electromyographic recordings have clearly shown that spike potentials associated with the muscle contraction of the distal part of the stomach or of the small intestine are suppressed (fig 1.). When emesis is induced in a

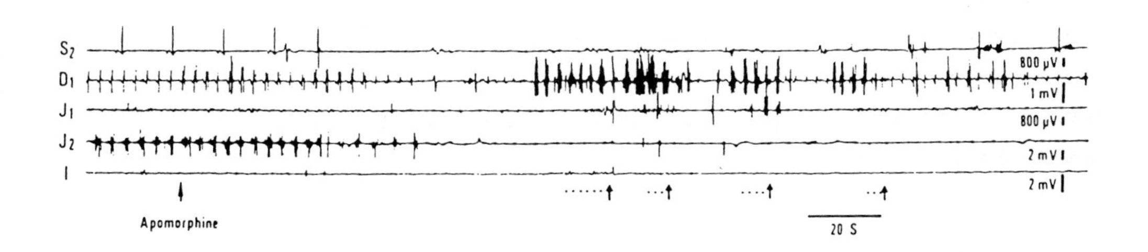

Fig 1: Modifications of gastrointestinal EMGs during vomiting induced by apomorphine in a fasting dog.
S2, D, J1, J2, I : EMGs recorded respectively on the stomach, the duodenum, the jejunum and the ileum. Vomiting induced by IV injection of apomorphine chlorhydrate. The dotted line indicates retching and arrows the expulsion of the gastric content.

fasting animal the regular spiking activity characteristic of phase III of the migrating myoelectric complex is abolished, whatever the location of this phase. The slow waves are also affected during this initial period of vomiting. The frequency of the slow waves is reduced at the different levels of the gastrointestinal tract but the main effects are observed in the proximal part of the gastrointestinal tract i.e. the antrum,the duodenum and the proximal jejunum. The amplitude of the slow waves also decreases greatly and drops below the threshold of detection. This lead to a disruption of the rhythmic oscillations for several seconds. All these observations indicate that a powerful inhibitory mechanism is initially acting to depress all motor events occurring from the stomach to the ileum prior to the appearance of the specific motor components of vomiting.

The first contractile event associated with vomiting occurs in the mid small intestine and is characterized by a single giant contraction which propagate orally to the gastric antrum (Lang et al, 1986). This retrograde giant contraction is well recorded by strain gauge force transducers oriented along the circular muscle axis of the gut and has an amplitude and a duration greater than those of contractions observed during phase III of a migrating myoelectric complex. The myoelectric response associated with the retrograde giant contraction has been characterized in some animals, such as the dog, as a single discrete spike potential (Lang et al, 1986) and in a few animals, such as the cat, by a high frequency low amplitude spike train (Weisbrodt and Christensen, 1972). The discrepancy between this inconspicuous electrical activity and the strong amplitude and long duration of the retrograde giant contraction raises the question of whether the electromechanical coupling of this contraction is the same as those involved during other contractile events. In addition, this fast electrical activity occurrs in the absence of slow waves, which at the level of the small intestine are absolutely necessary to give rise to a spike potential during peristaltic contractions.

After passage of the giant retrograde contraction a series of phasic contractions occurr within the small intestine for a few minutes (about 1 minute in the proximal small intestine, 3 to 5 minutes in the distal small intestine). The myoelectric correlates of these contractions are no different from those recorded during other phasic contractions i.e. each contraction is associated with a slow wave and there is a good correlation between the burst of fast activity and the strength of the contractions (Lang et al, 1986).

The visceral and somatic components of vomiting are generally linked but the visceral component may be activated alone. The inhibitory mechanism of the visceral components of vomiting could also be induced solely by small doses of apomorphine without activation of the motor excitatory component of this reflex. This indicates that the entire emetic response involves several nervous mechanisms activated successively. The link between the various components of vomiting may or may not be interrupted at each stage of this organization. As suggested by Davis et al (1986) the presence of a discrete "vomiting center" may not be absolutely necessary. In this case, the vomiting reflex could be organized in a series of nuclei activated sequentially, each of them controlling a particular aspect of the emetic response and triggering the following stage of emesis.

II Nervous control of the gastrointestinal motor changes during vomiting.

1) Efferent nervous structures involved.

It is now well known that the vagal efferent nerves play the predominant role in the control of the inhibitory and excitatory motor correlates of the gastrointestinal tract associated with vomiting (Gregory, 1947; Miolan et al, 1984; Lang et al, 1986).

Supradiaphragmatic vagotomy suppressed the powerful inhibitory mechanism producing the interruption of all gastrointestinal motility whereas retching and the expulsion phase of vomiting were still present. A slight reduction of gastric motor activity or a decrease of the slow wave frequency of the stomach are always present in vagotomized animals during the emetic reflex. This indicates that a weak non-vagal inhibitory component may play a part in inhibition of gastric motility during emesis. The nervous component involved in this inhibitory mechanism remains unexplored but the possible participation of the splanchnic nerves could be supposed

Sectioning the vagus nerves at the level of the diaphram eliminated all gastrointestinal contractile and myoelectric events occurring during the emetic reflex. The involvement of the vagus nerves in the control of the motor correlates of vomiting is therefore obvious.

2) Nature and function of the efferent vagal fibers involved in the motor correlates of vomiting.

All the efferent vagal fibers controlling the excitatory and inhibitory phenomena occurring during emesis are synaptically connected with intramural neurones. In the presence of a ganglionic blocking agent (hexamethonium), activation of these nervous pathways during vomiting is incapable of inducing any modifications of gastrointestinal motility (Miolan et al, 1984). The organization of these efferent vagal pathways is therefore from this point of view identical to that of other efferent parasympathetic pathways.

a) The vagal control of inhibitory response.

The inhibitory mechanism producing the reduction or the abolition of contractile activity in the upper gut is still effective in the presence of atropine. This indicates that the vagal preganglionic fibers probably excite intramural neurones mediating non-cholinergic non-adrenergic inhibition of the muscle. The final neurotransmitter responsible for this muscular inhibition is not yet perfectly understood. The vasoactive intestinal polypeptide may play at least a role in this inhibitory phenomenon.

We have recorded in conscious dog by an indirect nerve suture technique, the discharge of vagal preganglionic efferent fibers controlling the smooth muscle of the proximal and distal stomach (Miolan and Roman, 1974; Miolan and Roman, 1978). All the fibers recorded exhibit a spontaneous discharge whose frequency fluctuates with time and presents a direct or an inverse correlation with motor events occurring in the stomach. These studies have therefore provide direct evidence for a dual vagal efferent pathway activating either excitatory or inhibitory intramural neurones and permanently controlling gastric motility. We have recorded during vomiting the activity of 12 vagal efferent fibers. All these fibers presented a discharge frequency well correlated to motor events occurring in the distal part of the stomach. Their spontaneous discharge was also unaffected by swallowing, which indicates that these fibers are not involved in the receptive relaxation of the proximal stomach. For these reasons we have considered that these fibers were originally connected with intramural neurones in the distal stomach.
Eight out of 12 fibers had a spontaneous discharge whose frequency increased during each gastric contraction. These fibers probably

form synapses with excitatory intramural neurones and their activation may lead to an increase of gastric motility. About 30 seconds after the intravenous injection of apomorphine the discharge frequency of these fibers stopped abruptly (fig 2.). These fibers remained silent until the expulsion of gastric content. They fired again a few seconds after emesis and their firing reached values greater than those observed before injection of apomorphine.

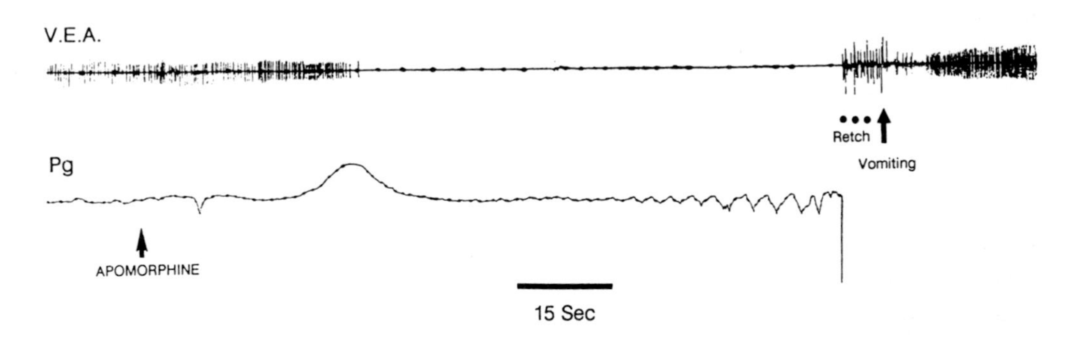

Fig 2: Discharge of a vagal efferent fiber supplying the stomach during vomiting.
V.E.A.: excitatory vagal efferent fiber recorded on the reinnervated diaphragm (see methods Miolan and Roman, 1978).
This fiber presented a discharge frequency directly correlated to motor events occurring in the distal stomach (see the increased discharge just before the gastric contraction indicated by the pressure recording).
Pg : endoluminal pressure recorded in the distal stomach.

Four out of the 12 vagal efferent fibers recorded had a discharge frequency conversely correlated with the contractile events occurring in the distal stomach. These fibers are probably connected with intramural inhibitory neurones and their activation leads to inhibition of gastric motility. Thirty to 45 seconds after the intravenous injection of apomorphine the spontaneous discharge of these fibers is greatly enhanced (fig 3.). This increased firing lasted until the expulsion phase.

The contrasting behaviour of these two types of vagal fibers during vomiting may explain the powerful inhibition occurring at the gastric level during the emesis reflex. The same patterns of discharge as those described for the gastric fibers could also be considered for fibers controlling the small intestine.

These results suggest that the simultaneous and coordinated activation of excitatory and inhibitory vagal efferent pathways that usually control gastrointestinal motility is also responsible for the suppression of motility occurring during the pre-expulsion phase of vomiting. We may conclude that the drive for the visceral inhibitory component of vomiting shares the common efferent pathways in the vagus.

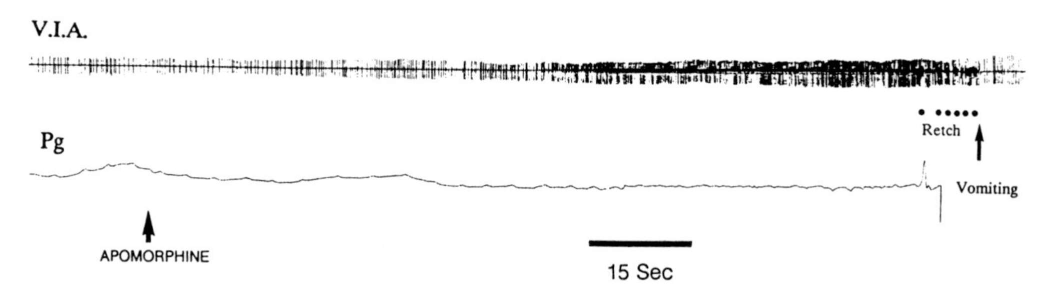

Fig 3: Discharge of a vagal efferent fiber supplying the stomach during vomiting.
V.I.A. : inhibitory vagal efferent fiber recorded on the reinnervated diaphragm. This fiber presented a discharge frequency conversely correlated to motor events occurring in the distal stomach.
Pg : endoluminal pressure recorded in the distal stomach.

b) The vagal control of excitatory responses.

- The vagal excitatory mechanisms inducing the specific motor components of vomiting are different in kind since the initial retroperistaltic wave is blocked by atropine whereas contractions following this antiperistalsis are still effective in the presence of this blocking agent.

The vagal cholinergic excitatory mechanism inducing the giant retrograde contraction does not seem to be organized by the vagal excitatory fibers whose activity we have recorded. The fibers whose activity increases spontaneously with each gastric contraction, and which are likely connected with cholinergic intramural neurones, exhibit a complete cessation of their firing when the retrograde contraction of vomiting reached the stomach. If this is in fact so, we must assume that specific vagal efferent activity is involved in the organization of the retroperistaltic wave. Unfortunately, it is not possible with our nerve suture technique to identify fibers which have no spontaneous discharge and which present only phasic bursting in phase with a motor event that is not easily reproductible such as vomiting. The antiperistaltic cholinergic wave occurring during vomiting might be triggered by a central nervous program organizing an ascending sequential activation of the gastrointestinal musculature. This hypothesis is corroborated by the fact that the retrograde peristaltic contraction can jump the gap created by transection of the gut. However the possible involvement of the enteric nervous system in the organization of the antiperistalsis occurring during vomiting cannot be entirely ruled out since Lang and coworkers (1988) have demonstrated convincingly that an intramural nervous circuitry activated by an intravenous injection of cholecystokinine octapeptide is capable of inducing, in the absence of the vagus nerves, an antiperistaltic contractile response of the small intestine similar in most respects to that found during the emetic response.

- With regard to the non cholinergic contractions occurring in the gastrointestinal tract during vomiting, it is tempting to speculate that a specific vagal pathway triggered these motor events. An intravenous injection of atropine in "normal" conditions of motility, i.e. during fasting or in a fed animal, induced the suppression of all gastrointestinal motor contractions. The non-cholinergic motor activity occurring in the digestive tact during vomiting seems therefore specific to particular physiological conditions. The presence of non cholinergic pathways in the vagus nerves has been reported for the gastric antrum, the small and large intestine (Collman et al, 1984). We have also shown that it is possible to induce "in vitro" an ascending non-cholinergic response by transmural nerve stimulation in the cat small intestine (Miolan and Niel, 1988) and that this non-cholinergic antiperistalsis is likely mediated by substance P (fig 4.). This response was obtained in cat, dog and ferret but we have failed to produce it in species which do not vomit such as rat and rabbit. Intravenous injection of cholecystokinine is also able to stimulate, in the absence of vagus nerves, a non cholinergic intramural circuitry inducing motor contractions (Lang et al, 1988).

Overall, these findings may suggest that there is during vomiting an activation of specific vagal excitatory pathways to override the functional polarization of the gut that ensures the normal peristaltic contractions. The main questions that arise are firstly to know why two different excitatory mechanisms are involved successively, and secondly, what the functional significance of the non-cholinergic contractions may be.

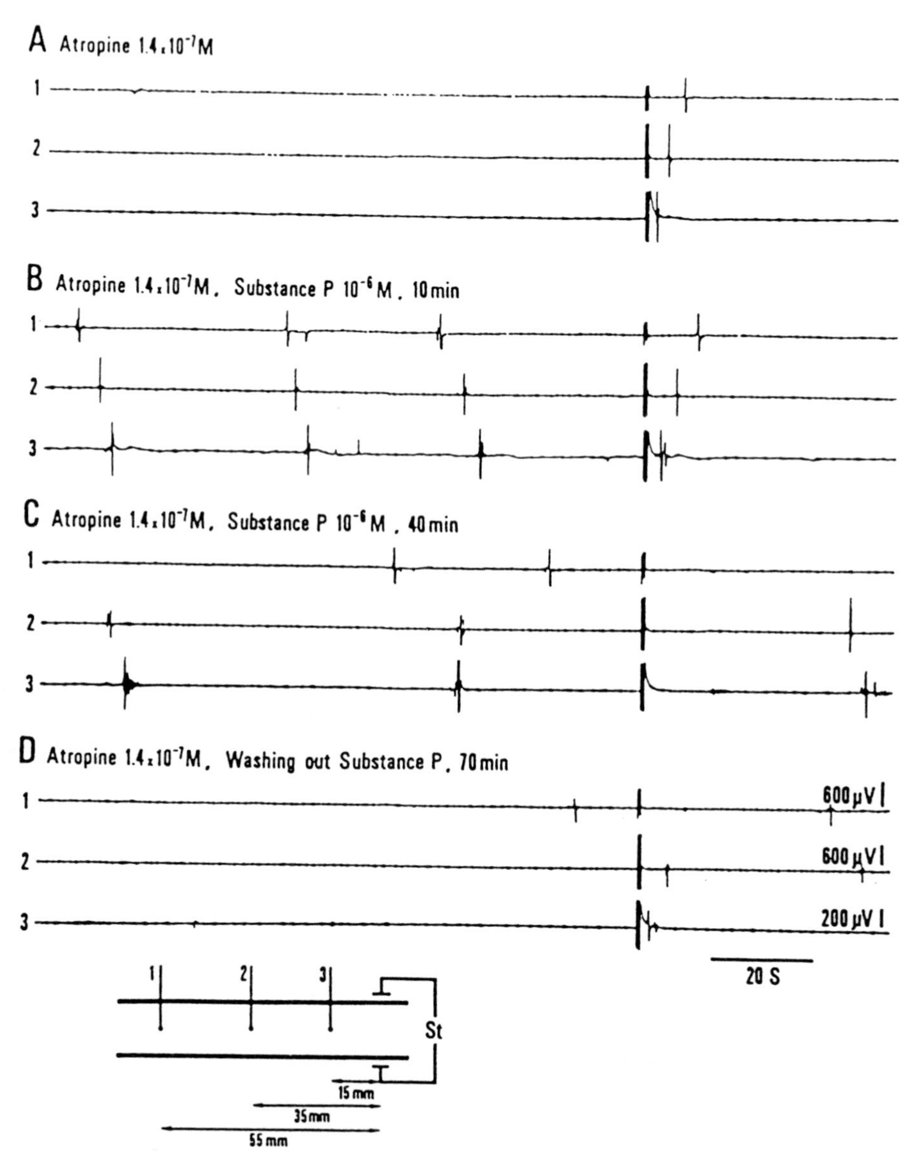

Fig 4 : Effect of substance P on the non-cholinergic ascending contraction induced by transmural nerve stimulation.
1, 2, 3 : E.M.Gs recordings.
In presence of atropine the nervous stimulation triggered a non cholinergic ascending excitation (A), 40 min after exposure to substance the stimulation became ineffective (C) (From Miolan and Niel 1988, with permission).

References.

Borison, H.L., and Wang, S.C. (1953): Physiology and pharmacology of vomiting. Pharmacol. Rev. 5: 193-230.

Brizzee, K.R.(1990): Mechanics of vomiting: a minireview. Can. J. Physiol. Pharmacol. 68: 221-229.

Collman, P.I., Grundy, D., Scratcherd, T. (1984): Vagal control of colonic motility in the anesthetized ferret: evidence for a non-cholinergic excitatory innervation. J. Physiol.,London. 348: 35-42.

Davis, C.J., Harding, R.K., Leslie, R.A., Andrews, P.L.R. (1986): the organization of vomiting as a protective reflex. In Nausea and vomiting: mechanisms and treatment, eds C.J. Davis, G.V. Lake-Bakaar, and D.G. Grahamme-Smith. pp 65-75. Berlin: Springer-verlag.

Gregory, R.A. (1947): The nervous pathways of intestinal reflexes associated with nausea and vomiting. J. Physiol.,London. 106:

Lang, I.M., Sarna, S.K., Condon, R.E. (1986): Gastrointestinal motor correlates of vomiting in the dog: Quantification and characterization as an independant phenomenon. Gastroenterology. 90: 40-47.

Lang, I.M., Marvig, J., Sarna, S.K. (1988): Comparison of gastrointestinal responses to CCK 8 associated with vomiting. Am. J. Physiol. 254: G254-G263.

Miller, A.D. (1990): respiratory muscle control during vomiting. Can. J. Physiol. Pharmacol. 68: 237-241.

Miller, A.D. and Wilson V.J. (1983): Vomiting center reanalyzed: an electrical stimulation study. Brain Res. 270: 154-158.

Miolan, J.P., and Roman, C. (1974): Décharge unitaire des fibres vagales efférentes lors de la relaxation réceptive de l'estomac du chien. J. Physiol., Paris. 68: 693-704.

Miolan, J.P., Lajard, A.M., Rega, P., Roman, C. (1974): Vagal control of gastrointestinal tract during vomiting. In Gastrointestinal motility, ed C. Roman. pp 167-176. Lancaster: MTP Press.

Miolan, J.P., and Roman, C. (1978): Discharge of efferent vagal fibers supplying gastric antrum: indirect study by nerve suture technique. Am. J. Physiol. 235: E366-E373.

Miolan, J.P., and Niel, J.P. (1988): Non cholinergic ascending excitatory response in the cat small intestine: possible involvement of substance P. Neuropeptides. 12: 243-248.

Smith, C.C., and Brizee, K.R. (1961): Cineradiographic analysis of vomiting in the cat: lower esophagus stomach and small intestine. Gastroenterology. 40: 654-664.

Wang, S.C., and Borison, H.L. (1952): A new concept of organization of the central emetic mechanism: recent studies on the sites of action of apomorphine, copper sulfate and cardiac glycosides. Gastroenterology. 22: 1-12.

Weisbrodt, N.W., and Christensen, J. (1972): Electrical activity of the cat duodenum in fasting and vomiting. Gastroenterology. 63: 1004-1010.

Mechanisms and Control of Emesis. Eds A.L. Bianchi, L. Grélot, A.D. Miller, G.L. King. Colloque INSERM/
John Libbey Eurotext Ltd. © 1992, Vol. 223, pp. 71-80

New perspectives on the mechanisms controlling vomitus expulsion

Ivan M. Lang

Departments of Surgery and Physiology, Medical College of Wisconsin, and Surgical Research Service, Zablocki VA Medical Center, Milwaukee, Wisconsin 53295, USA

SUMMARY

Vomitus expulsion has been described in prior studies as the result of strong contractions of the abdominal and respiratory muscles during elevation of the proximal stomach into the thoracic cavity and relaxation of the upper and lower esophageal sphincters and hiatal fibers of the diaphragm. These actions may not be sufficient to cause gastro-oral reflux because most of these motor events also occur during retching yet gastro-oral reflux occurs during vomiting only. The possibility that specialized pharyngoesophageal contractile events occur during vomiting but not retching to provide the final motive force for gastro-oral reflux was investigated using chronically instrumented dogs. It was found that during vomiting but not retching the geniohyoid muscle contracted strongly and a contraction of the cervical esophagus propagated retrogradely. These newly described events may be the primary motor events which distinguish a vomit from a retch and may account for projectile vomiting.

Nouvelles perspectives sur le mécanisme d'expulsion pendant le vomissement

Résumé: *L'expulsion du bol alimentaire lors du vomissement est classiquement décrite comme résultant de la puissante contraction des muscles respiratoires pendant l'élévation de l'estomac proximal dans la cavité thoracique et de la relaxation des sphincters oesophagiens et des fibres hiatalesdu diaphragme. Ces seuls mécanismes pourraient ne pas être suffisants pour provoquer un reflux gastro-oral puisqu'ils s'observent également pendant les périodes de haut-le-coeur non ponctuées par une expulsion. L'hypothèse selon laquelle des mécanismes moteurs pharyngo-oesophagiens, n'advenant que pendant le vomissement, constitueraient la force motrice finale du reflux gastro-oral a été testée chez le chien chronique. Nous avons observé pendant le vomissement, mais pas au cours du haut-le coeur, une forte contraction du muscle génio-hyoïdien accompagnée par une contraction rétrograde sur l'oesophage cervical. Ces derniers mécanismes semblent permettre de différencier le vomissement du haut-le-coeur, et pourraient expliquer le vomissement en fusée.*

INTRODUCTION

The vomiting process has been investigated scientifically for over 100 years and the basic physiologic mechanisms controlling this process are still not fully known (Lang and Sarna, 1989). This chapter will review the literature describing the mechanisms of vomitus expulsion and will incorporate recent findings which provide a new perspective to the understanding of this complex event.

METHODS

The new data presented in this manuscript are based on studies conducted in 20 awake, unanesthetized, and chronically instrumented dogs of both sexes weighing between 17 and 25 Kg. During aseptic surgery the animals were implanted with bipolar silver wire electrodes for recording myoelectric activity, and strain gauge force transducers for recording contractile activity. Myoelectric activity was recorded from the following muscles: mylohyoideus (MH), geniohyoideus (GH), thyrohyoideus (TH), thyropharyngeus (TP), cricopharyngeus (CP), esophagus (ESO) from upper esophageal sphincter (UES) to lower esophageal sphincter (LES), diaphragmatic dome (DD), and diaphragmatic hiatus (DH). Contractile activity was recorded from the LES, gastric fundus (F), gastric antrum (A), pylorus (P), duodenum (D), jejunum (J), and ileum (I). Recordings of esophageal length were made using sonomicrometry from ultrasonic crystals (2.5 mm diameter) embedded within the muscularis externa and placed 10 to 15 mm apart. The wires from the recording devices were connected to Amphenol plugs embedded in transcutaneous cannulas. Each animal was implanted with a catheter in the jugular vein, the opposite end of which was fitted with an intravenous catheter plug and placed subcutaneously for intravenous administration of emetic agents. In four animals the cervical vagosympathetic trunks were placed in loops of skin for subsequent local anesthetic blockade using 0.75 per cent bupivacaine. Vagal blockade was confirmed when the following criteria were met: heart rate at or above 200 bpm, absence of sinus arrythmia, absence of the gastrointestinal motor correlates of vomiting, and the presence of Horner's syndrome. Vomiting was activated using apomorphine, 2.5 to 15 ug/kg, i.v.

THE MECHANISMS CONTROLLING VOMITUS EXPULSION

The process of vomitus expulsion probably begins with the relaxation of the LES (Fig. 1.) and proximal stomach (Abrahamsson, 1973; Lefebvre et al., 1981; De Ponti et al.,1990). The LES and gastric fundus relax well before retching begins and these relaxations last for about 2 and 10 minutes respectively, which is sufficient time for the occurrence of retching and vomiting. The function of these responses may be to provide a receptacle for the reflux of intestinal contents caused by the RGC and to permit deformation of the proximal stomach during retching and vomiting (described in more detail below).

After esophago-gastric relaxation the cervical, but not thoracic (Figs. 1 and 3), esophagus and cricopharyngeus muscle, i.e. the UES (Lang et al., 1991), contract tonically (Fig. 2 and Table 1). This pharyngoesophageal contraction is probably directed in the longitudinal axis because radiological evidence in dogs indicates that

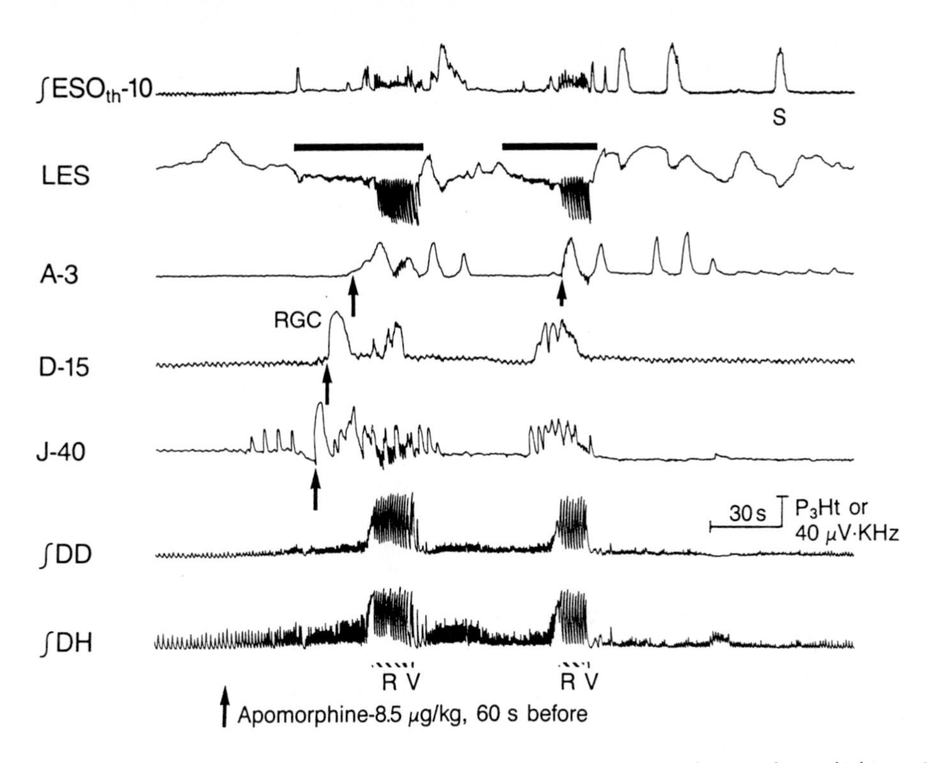

Fig.1. Temporal relationship of **LES relaxation** to RGC, retching and vomiting. S, swallowing; R, retching; V, vomiting; P_3Ht, mean maximum height of Phase 3 of the migrating motor complex; th, thoracic; and ∫, integrated EMG activity. See text for definition of symbols for recording devices. Numbers adjacent to recording device symbols indicate distance in cm from the pylorus for gastrointestinal devices and from the LES for esophageal devices. Solid bars indicate periods of LES relaxation associated with vomiting. Note the greater magnitude of LES relaxation associated with vomiting compared to swallowing.

about this time the LES and gastric cardia rise into the thoracic cavity (Johnson and Laws, 1966). In more direct evidence Torrance (1958) found that the striated muscle portion of the cat esophagus contracted longitudinally during vomiting. We correlated this pharyngoesophageal tonic contraction with changes in length between ultrasonic crystals sewn into the thoracic esophagus and found that the distance between crystals lengthened (about 8 mm) simultaneously with the pharyngoesophageal tonic contraction (Fig. 3). This effect was consistent with shortening of the pharynx and cervical esophagus. This longitudinal contraction of the pharynx and cervical esophagus pulls orad the already relaxed LES and proximal stomach eliminating the abdominal portion of the esophagus and deforming the proximal stomach into the shape of a funnel (Lumsden and Holden,1969; Smith and Brizzee, 1961). The function of this effect may be 1) to facilitate gastro-esophageal reflux by removing the acute angle the esophagus makes with the stomach and the fundic reservoir formed above the gastroesophageal junction, and 2) by preventing collapse of the esophago-gastric junction during retching and vomiting. Evidence supporting this function was found by Smith and Brizzee (1961) who reported that in 2 out of 7 cats gastroesophageal reflux of contrast material occurred just prior (30 seconds or less) to the first retch.

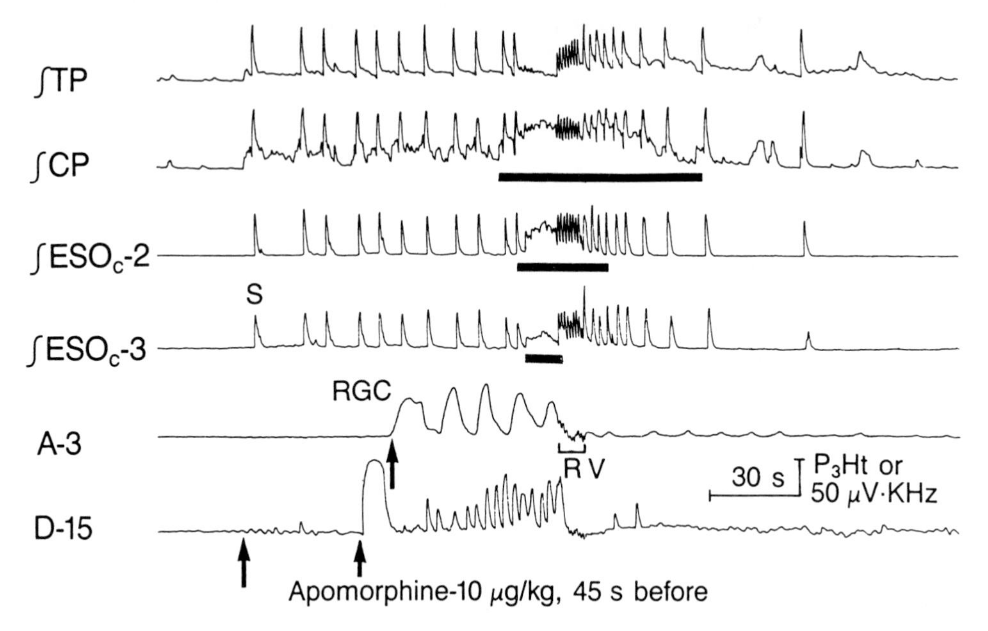

Fig. 2. Temporal relationship of the **pharyngoesophageal tonic contraction** to the RGC, retching and vomiting. See Fig.1 and text for definition of symbols. C, cervical. Numbers adjacent to recording device symbols indicate distance from the UES for esophageal electrodes. Solid horizontal bars indicate the period of pharyngoesophageal tonic contraction. Note the occurrence of pharyngoesophageal tonic contraction and increased swallow frequency before, during, and after retching and vomiting.

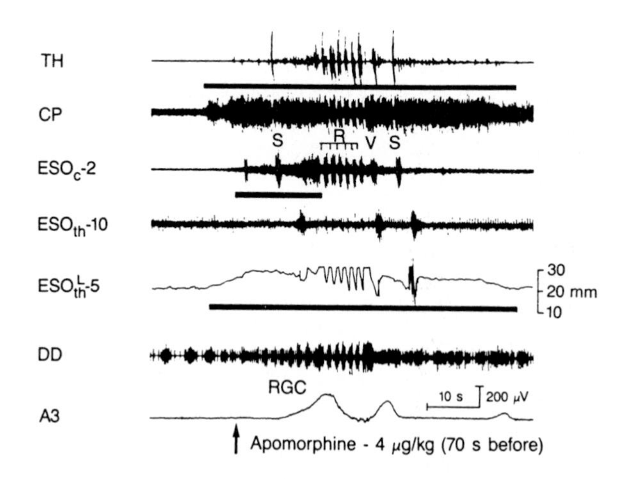

Fig. 3. Correlation of **thoracic esophageal stretch** with tonic pharyngoesophageal contraction. See Figs. 1 and 2 and text for definition of symbols. ESO^L, esophageal length gauge. Solid horizontal bars indicate period of pharyngoesophageal tonic contraction or thoracic esophageal stretch. Note that the thoracic esophagus stretches about 8 mm concomitant with the pharyngoesophageal tonic contraction, and that the thoracic esophagus remains relaxed throughout retching and vomiting.

The longitudinal pharyngoesophageal contraction is quickly followed by a series of retches produced by the simultaneous contraction then relaxation of the diaphragm, external intercostal muscles, and anterior abdominal muscles (Hukuhara et al., 1957; Jimenez-Vargas et al., 1967; McCarthy et al.,1974; Miller et al.,1987; Monges et al.,1978a). Retching occurs at a regular rhythm of about 1 Hz and each retch lasts about 0.5 s (Fig. 4 and Table 1). During each retch the abdominal pressure increases and the thoracic pressure decreases which creates a pressure gradient between abdomen and thorax (McCarthy and Borison, 1974). The force of contraction during retching increases progressively which in turn progressively increases this pressure gradient. The longitudinal tone of the pharynx and cervical esophagus, which increased prior to retching, relaxes and contracts 180 degrees out of phase with retching (Fig. 4; Monges et al., 1978b). The reciprocal action of the diaphragm and pharyngoesophageal muscles allows the herniated LES to move up and down with the diaphragm thereby maintaining a constant position in the thoracic cavity (Johnson and Laws, 1966). During each retch the gastric contents readily move up to the herniated LES (McCarthy et al., 1974; Johnson and Laws, 1966; Lumsden and Holden, 1969) because of the abdomino-thoracic pressure gradient and the funnelling of the proximal stomach. Gastric contents can also enter the esophagus during retching (Hesse, 1913; McCarthy and Borison, 1974) because the LES is relaxed (Fig.1.).

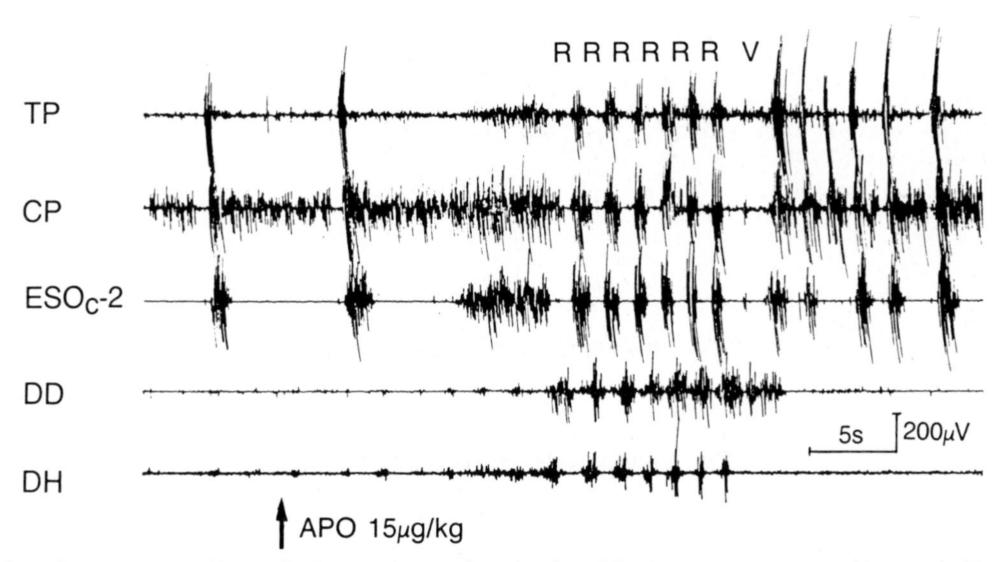

Fig. 4. EMG recording of the **reciprocal relationship** between contractile activity of the pharynx and cervical esophagus, and the diaphragm during retching and vomiting. See Figs. 1 and 2 and the text for definition of symbols. APO, apomorphine. Note the prolonged contraction of the diaphragmatic dome and concomitant relaxation of the pharynx, cervical esophagus and diaphragmatic hiatus during vomiting.

Between retches the esophageal contents fall back into the stomach (McCarthy et al., 1974; Johnson and Laws, 1966) as the abdomino-thoracic pressure gradient subsides and the pharyngoesophageal contraction returns. Thus, retching causes the repetitive movement of gastric contents into and out of the esophagus, and this effect increases progressively throughout the retching episode. The function of retching, therefore, may be to build up momentum in the vomitus in preparation for expulsion. This conclusion is consistent with recent studies by Andrews et al. (1990) who found that the number of retches per vomit was inversely related to the volume of fluid in the stomach. The increased mass of larger gastric volumes may require a lower velocity , i.e. fewer or less vigorous retches, to reach the critical momentum needed for expulsion. Although gastric contents can be propelled as far orad as the cervical esophagus during retching (Hesse, 1913) and the UES relaxes during each retch (Fig. 4; Monges et al., 1978b), orad evacuation does not occur until vomiting.

Vomitus expulsion occurs at the end of retching as a single maximal contraction of the rectus abdominis and diaphragmatic dome while the diaphragmatic hiatus relaxes (Fig. 4: Monges et al., 1978b). This action removes the final obstruction to gastro-esophageal reflux and allows a maximal reflux of gastric contents as well as a bulging of the proximal stomach into the thoracic cavity. These changes are reflected in a reversal of thoracic intravenous pressure from negative to positive. (McCarthy et al., 1974). It is unknown whether this increase in thoracic venous pressure represents a back pressure generated by restriction of flow in the descending aorta caused by the distended esophagus or an increase in intrathoracic pressure. We have found in acute studies of decerebrate cats that balloon distension of the thoracic esophagus can reduce flow in the descending aorta which significantly lowers femoral arterial pressure (Medda et al., 1991). Although the relaxation of the diaphragmatic hiatus during retching serves an important function, relaxation of the hiatus does not represent the primary motor event which results in gastro-oral evacuation. After all, gastric contents can be expelled into the esophagus as far orad as the UES (Hesse, 1913) during retching, but orad evacuation does not occur.

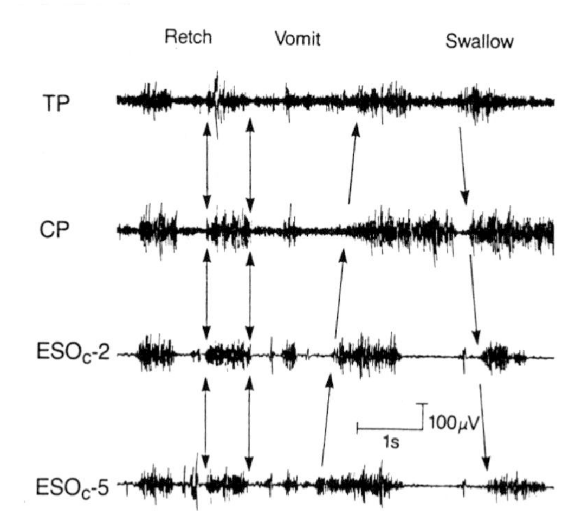

Fig. 5. Comparison of the EMG activities of the pharyngoesophageal region during retching, vomiting and swallowing: **The esophagopharyngeal retrograde contraction.** See Figs. 1 and 2 and the text for definition of symbols. Compare the simultaneous contraction between retches and the orthograde propagating contraction of swallowing to the retrograde propagating contraction after vomiting.

The final motor event necessary to produce gastro-oral reflux during vomiting is the retrograde contraction of the cervical esophagus (Fig. 5). During vomiting contraction of the rectus abdominis and diaphragmatic dome lasts about 1.5 s and this is accompanied by concurrent relaxation of the UES (Table 1). However, 0.5 to 1.0 s before the vomit-related contraction of respiratory muscles is complete the cervical esophagus about 5-10 cm from the UES contracts. This cervical esophageal contraction propagates orad at about 10 cm/s (Table 1) until it reaches the cricopharyngeus muscle. To further assist gastro-oral reflux the UES is forcefully opened by a strong contraction of the geniohyoideus (Fig. 6). Other hyoid or pharyngeal muscles remain relaxed throughout the vomit. For each vomit there is only one but occasionally (10%) two retrograde contractions of the cervical esophagus. The cervical esophageal retrograde contraction may represent one of the primary differences between retching and vomiting and may be responsible for projectile vomiting.

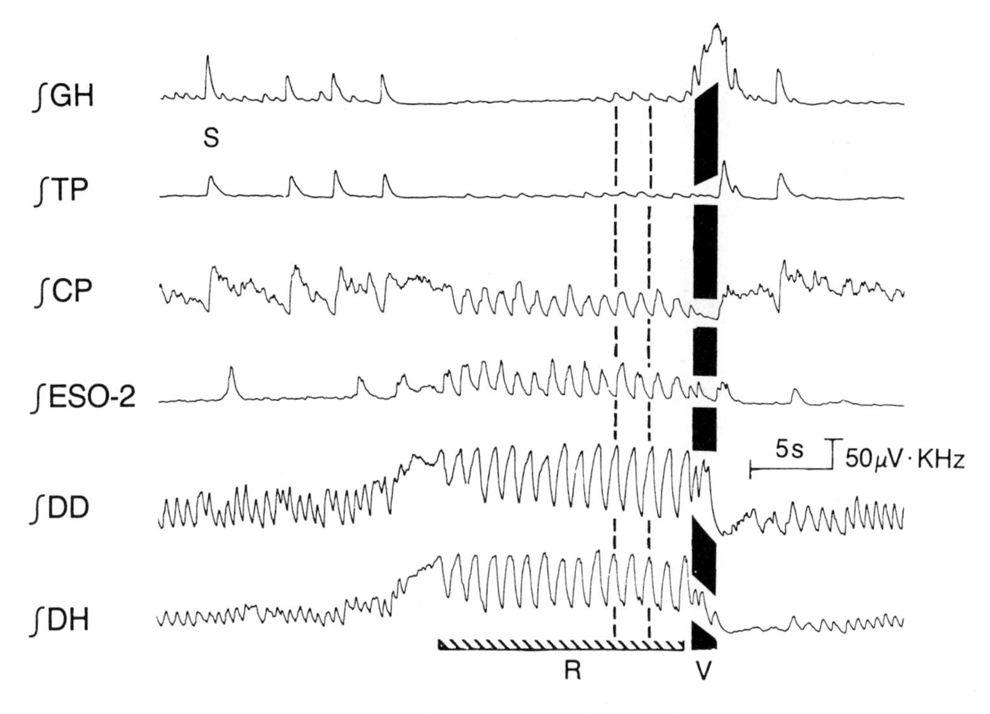

Fig. 6. Comparison of the myoelectric responses of the **geniohyoideus**, pharyngoesophageal region and diaphragm during retching and vomiting. See Figs. 1 and 2 and text for definition of symbols. Note the reciprocal relationship between contractile activity of the diaphragm and pharyngoesophageal region during retching (broken vertical lines) and the very large contraction of the geniohyoid muscle only during vomiting (solid vertical bar).

After vomitus expulsion, swallowing occurs at a high frequency (Fig.2). The stomach gradually returns to its normal position over the next few minutes (Smith and Brizzee, 1961; Johnson and Laws, 1966; McCarthy and Borison, 1974) as the tone of the pharynx and cervical esophagus slowly subsides and swallowing frequency decreases (Fig. 2).

THE ROLE OF THE VAGUS NERVES IN VOMITUS EXPULSION

Transection of the vagus nerves at the level of the diaphragm blocks the gastrointestinal motor correlates of vomiting but does not prevent retching or vomiting (Lang et al., 1986). In addition supradiaphragmatic vagotomy plus splanchnicectomy increase the number of retches per vomiting episode (Andrews et al., 1990). These results suggest that gastrointestinal afferents provide a negative feedback to the emetic center to limit the number of retches.

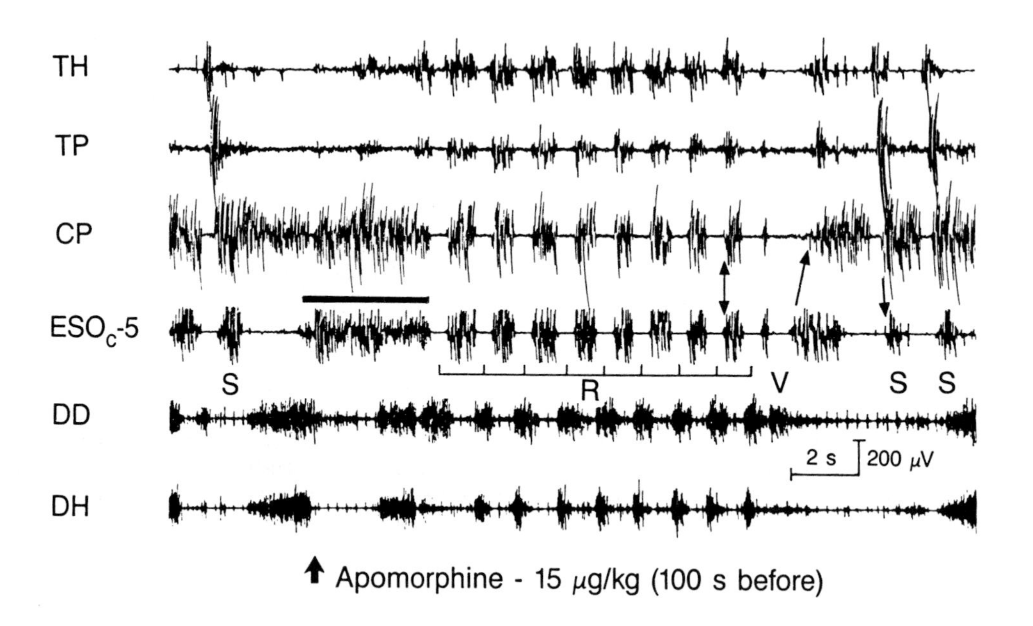

Fig. 7. The lack of effect of **cervical vagosympathetic nerve block** on the pharyngoesophageal responses associated with retching and vomiting. See Figs. 1 and 2 and text for definition of symbols. Note the presence of the pharyngoesophageal tonic contraction before retching (solid horizontal bar), the reciprocal contractions of the pharyngoesophageal region and diaphragm during retching and vomiting, and the esophagopharyngeal retrograde contraction after vomiting.

Vagal blockade at the cervical level does not alter the pharyngoesophageal responses associated with retching or vomiting and does not prevent vomitus expulsion (Fig. 7 and Table 1). Therefore, vagal reflexes of thoracic or abdominal origin or efferent fibers of the recurrent laryngeal nerves do not control these pharyngoesophageal motor responses. Rather these pharyngoesophageal responses are probably controlled centrally by emetic and motor nuclei through the pharyngoesophageal nerves which branch from the vagus nerves just rostral to the nodose ganglia (Evans and Christensen, 1979).

Table 1. Effect of cervical vagal anesthesia on esophagopharyngeal (EP) responses associated with vomiting.

Responses	Control	Vagal Block	P (t-test)
Duration of CP tone (s)	45 + 6 (9)	40 + 2 (4)	0.58
Duration of ESO tone (s)	9 + 1 (9)	9 + 2 (9)	0.93
Relaxation of CP during retching(ms)	524 + 35 (10)	519 + 59 (4)	0.94
Relaxation of CP during vomiting (s)	1.57 + .11 (10)	1.58 + .14 (4)	0.97
EP retrograde contraction velocity (cm/s)	11.3 + 1.0 (9)	8.8 + 1.4 (4)	0.17
Number of retches/vomit	9.2 + 1.3 (10)	9.0 + 1.9 (4)	0.93
Retch frequency (Hz)	1.0 + 0.0 (10)	1.0 + 0.1 (4)	0.38

Values listed are means + SEM. Numbers in parentheses indicate the number of animals per group. CP, cricopharyngeus; ESO, esophagus.

CONCLUSIONS

Three sets of responses are important for vomitus expulsion: 1) elimination of anatomical and physiological impediments to gastro-oral reflux, 2) orad directed momentum of the vomitus, and 3) an esophago-pharyngeal pump. The longitudinal contractions of the pharynx and cervical esophagus and the relaxation of the UES, LES and proximal stomach prior to or during retching and vomiting eliminate all anatomical and physiological impediments to gastro-oral reflux. Retching and the final heave of vomiting provide the necessary momentum to the vomitus. The cervical esophageal retrograde contraction and the forceful opening of the UES by the geniohyoid muscle provide the final necessary push to ensure gastro-oral reflux.

ACKNOWLEDGEMENTS

The technical assistance of Mr. Kenneth N. Schnepf and Ms. Margaret Steensrud was greatly appreciated. These studies were supported in part by Veterens Administration Merit Review Grant 5120-02P.

REFERENCES

Abrahamsson, H., Janssen, G., and Martinson, J. (1973): Vagal relaxation of the stomach induced by apomorphine in the cat. Acta Physiol. Scand. 88: 296-302.

Andrews, P.L.R., Bhandari, P., Garland, S., Bingham, S., Davis, C.J., Hawthorn, J., Davidson, H.I.M., Roylance, R., and Lane, S.(1990): Does retching have a function?: An experimental study in the ferret. Pharmacodyn. Ther. 9: 135-152.

De Ponti, F., Malagelada, J.-R., Azpiroz, F., Yaksh, T.L. and Thomforde, G.M. (1990): Variations in gastric tone associated with duodenal motor events after activation of central emetic mechanisms in the dog. J. GI Motil. 2: 1-11.

Evans, H.E. and Christensen, G.C. (1979): Miller's anatomy of the dog. Philadelphia: W.B. Saunders Company.

Hesse, O. (1913): Zur Kenntnis des Brechaktes. Nach Roentgenversuchen an Hunden. Pflueger's Arch. Gesamte Physiol. 152: 1-22.

Hukuhara, T., Okada, H. and Yamagami,M. (1957): On the behavior of the respiratory muscles during vomiting. Acta Med. Okayama 11: 117-125.

Jimenez-Vargas, J., Asiron, M., Voltas, J., Onaindia, J. (1967): Electromiografia de musculos respiratorios en la tos, en los reflejos de la glotis y en el vomito. Rev. Esp. Fisiol. 23: 65-74.

Johnson, H.D. and Laws, J.W. (1966): The cardia in swallowing, eructation, and vomiting. Lancet 2: 1268-1273.

Lang, I.M., Dantas, R.O., Cook, I.J. and Dodds, W.J. (1991): Videoradiographic, manometric, and electromyographic analysis of canine upper esophageal sphincter. Am.J.Physiol. 260: G911-G919.

Lang, I.M. and Sarna, S.K. (1989): Motor and myoelectric activity associated with vomiting, regurgitation and nausea. In Handbook of Physiology, Gastrointestinal Motility and Circulation, ed. J.D. Wood, pp. 1179-1198. Bethesda, MD: MTP Press Ltd.

Lang, I.M., Sarna, S.K., and Condon, R.E. (1986): Gastrointestinal motor correlates of vomiting in the dog: Quantification and characterization as an independent phenomenon. Gastroenterology 90: 40-47.

Lefebvre, R.A., Willems, J.L., and Bogaert, M.G. (1981): Gastric relaxation and vomiting by apomorphine, morphine and fentanyl in the conscious dog. Eur. J. Pharmacol. 69: 139-145.

Lumsden, K. and Holden, W.S. (1969): The act of vomiting in man. Gut 10: 173-179.

McCarthy, L.E. and Borison, H.L. (1974): Respiratory mechanisms of vomiting in decerebrate cats. Am. J. Physiol. 226: 738-743.

McCarthy, L.E., Borison, H.L., Spiegel, P.K., and Friedlander,R.M. (1974): Vomiting: radiographic and oscillographic correlates in the decerebrate cat. Gastroenterology 67: 1126-1130.

Medda, B.K., Lang, I.M., and Dodds, W.J. (1990): Control of UES tone by lung inflation reflexes. Gastroenterology 99: 1219.

Miller, A.D., Tan, L.K., and Suzuki, I. (1987): Control of abdominal and expiratory intercostal muscle activity during vomiting: role of ventral respiratory group expiratory neurons. J. Neurophysiol. 57: 1854-1866.

Monges, H., Salducci, J., and Naudy, B. (1978a): Dissociation between the electrical activity of the diaphragmatic dome and crura muscular fibers during esophageal distension, vomiting and eructation. J. Physiol. Paris 74: 541-554.

Monges, H., Salducci, J., and Naudy, B. (1978b): The upper esophageal sphincter during vomiting, eructation and distension of the cardia: an electromyographic study in the anesthetized dog. In Gastrointestinal motility in health and disease, ed. H.L. Duthie, pp. 575-583. Lancaster, England: MTP Press Ltd.

Smith, C.C. and Brizzee, K.R. (1961): Cineradiographic analysis of vomiting in the cat. I. Lower esophagus, stomach, and small intestine. Gastroenterology 40: 654-664.

Torrance, H.B. (1958): Studies on the mechanisms of gastroesophageal regurgitation. J. Royal Coll. Surg. Edinburgh 4: 54-62.

Mechanisms and Control of Emesis. Eds A.L. Bianchi, L. Grélot, A.D. Miller, G.L. King. Colloque INSERM/ John Libbey Eurotext Ltd. © 1992, Vol. 223, pp. 81-82

Identification of the abdominal neural pathway mediating the intestinal motor correlates of vomiting

Ivan M. Lang and Kenneth Schnepf

Departments of Surgery and Physiology, Medical College of Wisconsin, and Surgical Research Service, Zablocki VA Medical Center, Milwaukee, Wisconsin 53295, USA

In prior studies we found that the gastrointestinal motor correlates of vomiting were mediated by the thoracic vagus nerves (Lang et al., 1986), and that the mesenteric nerves mediated the initiation of these motor events locally (Lang and Sarna, 1989). However, the neural pathway from the thoracic vagus nerves to the mesenteric nerves is unknown. Anatomical evidence in rats (Berthoud et al., 1991) indicates that there are three abdominal branches of the vagus nerves: hepatic, gastric and celiac. All branches innervate the duodenum, but only the celiac branch innervates the jejunoileum. The aim of this study was to determine the role of the celiac branch of the abdominal vagus nerves in mediating the gastrointestinal motor correlates of vomiting.

METHODS

Three cats weighing between 3 and 5 kg were chronically instrumented with 6 strain gauge transducers on the gastrointestinal tract to record motor activity: gastric antrum (2 cm), duodenum (5 cm), and jejunoileum (30, 60, 90 and 120 cm), and 2 bipolar elctrodes to record myoelectric activity: antrum (1 cm) and jejunoileum (80-110 cm). The numbers in parentheses indicate the distance from the pylorus. Catheters were placed in the jugular vein and gastric corpus for subsequent nontraumatic administration of emetic agents intravenously or intragastrically. Emesis was activated by UK-14304 (2.5-10 ug/kg, i.v.), morphine (75 ug/kg, i.v.), or $CuSO_4$ (10-30 mg, i.g.). After obtaining control responses to the emetic agents, the celiac branch of the vagus nerves was ligated and transected in each cat. Each surgery was conducted using aseptic techniques and the cats were allowed 7-10 days recovery before resumption of experiments.

RESULTS

We found that all emetic episodes in all cats were accompanied by the gastrointestinal motor and myoelectric correlates of vomiting. Also, the retrograde giant contraction (RGC) began in the small intestine at 70 + 10 cm from the pylorus and propagated to the gastric antrum at 1.4 + 0.2 cm/s. After transection of the celiac branch of the vagus nerve in each cat, emesis was accompanied by a giant contraction of the gastric antrum only. No RGC's or other motor or myoelectric correlates of vomiting were observed in the duodenum, jejunum, or ileum (see figure below).

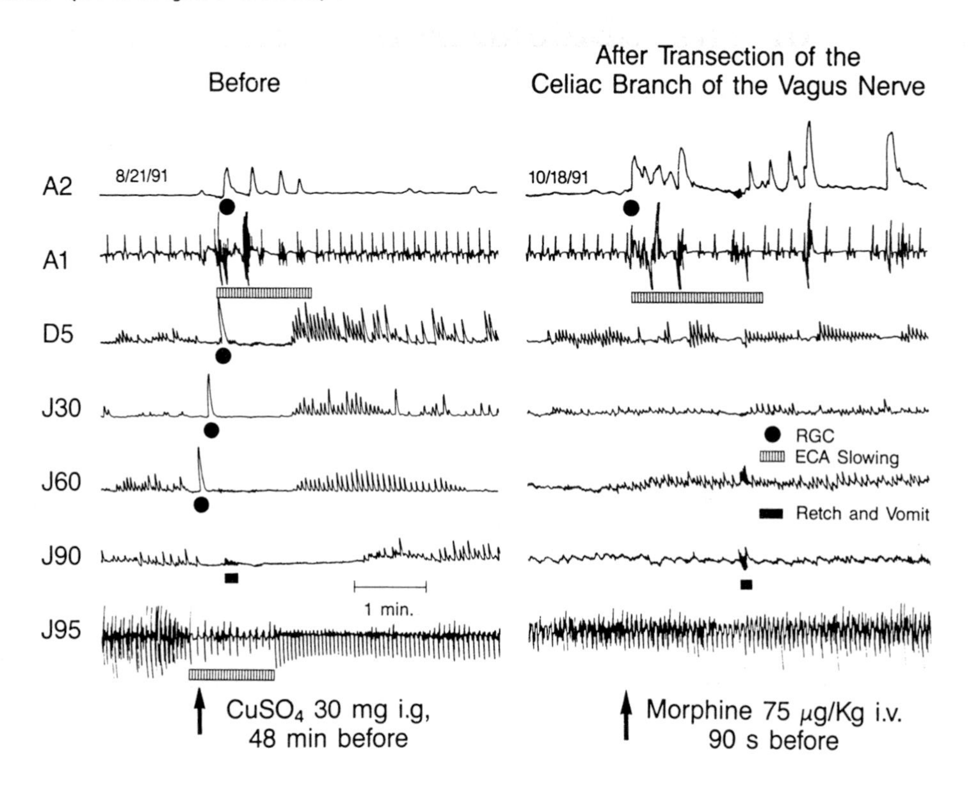

CONCLUSIONS

This study 1) indicates that the celiac branch of the vagus nerves mediates the intestinal motor correlates of vomiting, and 2) supports our prior conclusion that the central, rather than the enteric, nervous system controls the orad propagation of the retrograde giant contraction.

REFERENCES

Berthoud, H.-R., Carlson, N.R., and Powley, T.L. Topography of efferent vagal innervation of the rat gastrointestinal tract. (1991): AM. J. Physiol. 260: R200-R207.

Lang, I.M., and Sarna, S.K. (1989): Neural control of initiation and propagation of the retrograde giant contraction associated with vomiting. In Nerves and the Gastrointestinal Tract, pp. 726-731. Lancaster, England: MTP Press Ltd.

Lang, I.M., Sarna, S.K. and Condon, R.E. (1986): Gastrointestinal motor correlates of vomiting in the dog: Quantification and identification as an independent phenomenon. Gastroenterol. 90:40-47.

Mechanisms and Control of Emesis. Eds A.L. Bianchi, L. Grélot, A.D. Miller, G.L. King. Colloque INSERM/ John Libbey Eurotext Ltd. © 1992, Vol. 223, pp. 83-84

Brainstem distribution of neurons projecting axons to both phrenic and abdominal motor nuclei: a double fluorescent labeling study in the cat

F. Portillo, L. Grélot, S. Milano and A.L. Bianchi

Département de Physiologie et Neurophysiologie, CNRS URA 205, Faculté des Sciences et Techniques Saint-Jérôme, 13397 Marseille Cedex 13, France

In mammals, large increases in intra-abdominal pressure serving the realization of different behaviors such as vomiting, coughing, micturition, parturition or defecation are generated by the main respiratory muscles. In contrast to their respiratory patterns of activity, during vomiting or defecation, the diaphragm and the abdominal muscles are activated simultaneously. Recently, Bianchi and Grélot (1989) have shown in the decerebrate cat that during vomiting the medullary inspiratory premotor neurons, which normally drive the phrenic motoneurons during ventilation, are strongly inhibited. These results suggest that phrenic motoneurons receive during vomiting an excitatory input arising from neurons located in unidentified areas of the brainstem.

In order to localize, in the pons and the medulla, neurons which might be involved in the realization of the expulsive reflexes, we analyzed the distribution of brainstem neurons projecting axons to both phrenic and abdominal motor nuclei.

Two injections of retrograde fluorescent dyes were performed in the spinal cord of 20 cats. Diamidino Yellow (DY) was injected first, in the right or right and left ventral horns of the lumbar (L1-L3) spinal cord. Three weeks later, Fast Blue (FB) was injected in the right ventral horn of the cervical (C4-C6) cord. Animals were allowed to survive three additional weeks and then sacrificed. Brainstems were removed and cut in 50 μm thick slices which were examined with a microscope equipped with epifluorescence (excitation wavelength: 360 nm).

When the two fluorescent dyes were only applied to the same side of the lumbar and cervical cord, double labeled medullary neurons were located ipsilaterally in the nucleus retroambigualis and contralaterally in the dorsal aspect of the nucleus of the solitary tract and in the reticular formation. In the pons, doubly labeled neurons were located ipsilaterally in the parabrachial and Kölliker-Fuse nuclei. When DY was applied in both sides of the lumbar cord, doubly labeled neurons were found bilaterally in the retroambiguus and parambiguus nuclei, the dorsal and lateral aspects of the nucleus of the solitary tract (in the close vicinity of the inferior vestibular nucleus) and the raphe nucleus. In the pons, doubly labeled neurons were observed bilaterally in the parabrachial and Kölliker-Fuse nuclei.

The results of the present neuroanatomical study give evidence that pontine and medullary neurons are a source of descending pathways to both the phrenic and abdominal motor nuclei. Further investigations using electrophysiological recording techniques are necessary to establish the involvement of the neurons located in these different brainstem areas in the promotion of expulsive behaviors.

This work was supported by the Direction des Recherches, Etudes et Techniques (DRET France, grant 90/108).

Berman A.L. (1968): The brainstem of the cat. A cytoarchitectonic atlas with stereotaxic coordinates. The university of Wisconsin Press.

Bianchi, A.L. and Grélot, L. (1989): Converse motor output of inspiratory bulbospinal premotoneurones during vomiting. Neurosci. Lett., 104: 298-302.

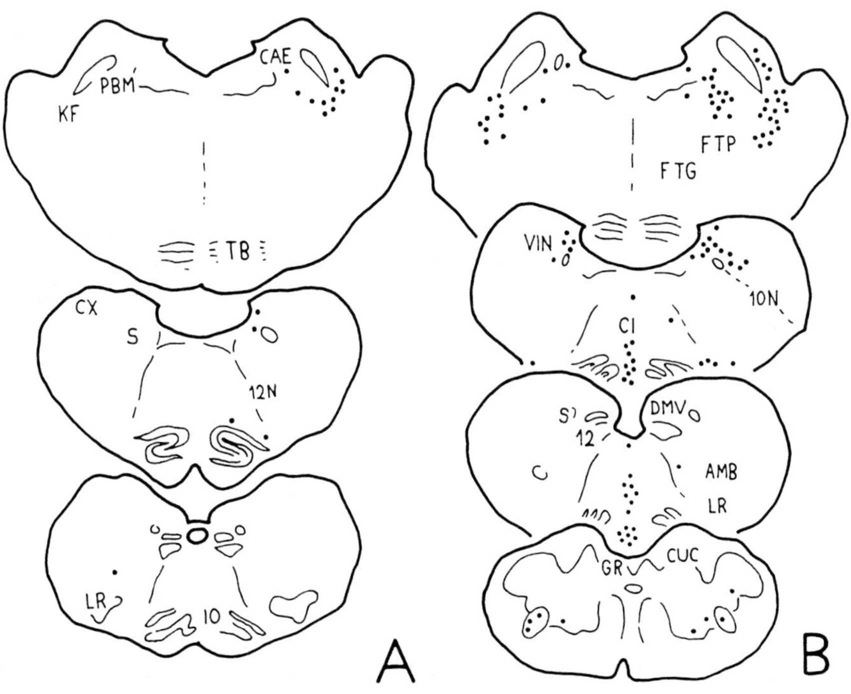

Figure legend: *Location, in the brainstem of two cats, of doubly labeled neurons following DY and FB injections on the right side of the spinal cord (A) or bilateral injections of DY in the lumbar cord (B) and unilateral (right) injection of FB in the cervical cord. Each dot is a doubly labeled neuron. Nervous structures are named according the nomenclature used by Berman. 10N, vagus nerve; 12, hypoglossal nucleus; 12N, hypoglossal nerve; AMB, nucleus ambiguus; CAE, nucleus caeruleus; CI, inferior central nucleus; CUC, caudal division of the cuneate nucleus; CX, external cuneate nucleus; DMV, dorsal motor nucleus of the vagus; FTG, gigantocellular tegmental field; FTP, paralemniscal tegmental field; GR, gracile nucleus; IO, inferior olive; KF, Kölliker-Fuse nucleus; LR, lateral reticular nucleus; PBM, nucleus parabrachialis lateralis; S, solitary tract; VIN, inferior vestibular nucleus.*

Mechanisms and Control of Emesis. Eds A.L. Bianchi, L. Grélot, A.D. Miller, G.L. King. Colloque INSERM/ John Libbey Eurotext Ltd. © 1992, Vol. 223, pp. 85-87

Cellular bases for a multifunctional role of nucleus tractus solitarii neurons

André Jean and Fabien Tell

Laboratoire de Neurobiologie Fonctionnelle, CNRS URA 205, Faculté des Sciences et Techniques Saint-Jérôme, 13397 Marseille Cedex 13, France

The nucleus tractus solitarii (NTS) has long been considered as only the primary sensory relay for gustatory and visceral afferent information, where the afferent impulses were thought to be processed by simple mechanisms of summation through neurons serving as threshold elements. It is worth noting, however, that premotor neurons have been shown to exist within the NTS, such as bulbospinal inspiratory neurons (BIANCHI, 1971; BERGER, 1977) or swallowing generator neurons (JEAN, 1972, 1990). Moreover, data obtained during the past ten years indicate that the NTS is a structure with a high degree of complexity, extensively connected with several central structures and containing an impressive diversity of neuroactive substances, which plays a key role in several integrative processes, such as autonomic and endocrine functions, emotional processes, hunger, thirst, pain mechanisms, level of consciousness... (see for reviews: SAWCHENKO, 1983; LESLIE, 1985; JEAN, 1991). Within the scope of this symposium, it is worth noting, although its role remains to be determined, that the NTS is undoubtedly involved in the control of emesis (MILLER and WILSON, 1983; CARPENTER, 1989; REYNOLDS *et al.*, 1991): the nucleus is the recipient of vagal afferents, it is extensively connected with the area postrema and also with the cerebellum; moreover, it contains a lot of neurotransmitter receptors concerned with emesis, in particular the 5-HT_3 subtype of serotoninergic receptors (see LESLIE, 1985; JEAN, 1991). Therefore, the NTS can no longer be considered as a simple relay. It is actually an integrative site which plays a dynamic role in the processing of afferent impulses. In this connection, it is puzzling that a structure of such a restricted size, with a small number of neurons, is involved in most mechanisms of major importance for the maintenance of life. Then a question arises: is a NTS neuron only involved in a fixed network controlling one function? or can a NTS neuron participate in the control and/or the generation of several functions?, as suggested by recent results obtained in invertebrates (MEYRAND *et al.*, 1991).

It is very likely that several complex mechanisms are involved in such a functional plasticity of NTS neurons. It is worth noting, however, that the electrophysiological properties of NTS neurons probably play a major role. *In vitro* results obtained from brainstem slices have shown that several ionic conductances other than the transient Na^+ current and the K^+ delayed rectifier do exist in NTS neurons. Indeed, TTX-resistant Ca^{++} currents and several types of K^+ currents have been identified in NTS neurons, in particular calcium-activated potassium currents ,I_{KCa}, a transient potassium current, I_A, and a muscarinic-sensitive potassium current, I_M (CHAMPAGNAT *et al.*, 1986; DEKIN and GETTING, 1987). Moreover, NTS neurons have been shown to exhibit pacemaker-like properties under bath application of NMDA or TRH (DEKIN *et al.*,1985; TELL and JEAN, 1990, 1991). Therefore, the existence of these different types of voltage-dependent and transmitter-gated conductances allows a NTS neuron to play a dynamic role in processing nerve impulses.

Recent results from our laboratory (TELL, 1991; TELL and JEAN, 1991) show that the interactions between the NMDA-gated and other voltage-dependent conductances play a key role in shaping the cell's discharge pattern. The pacemaker-like properties elicited by NMDA involve the voltage and Mg^{++}-dependence of the NMDA-gated conductances: the TTX-resistant cyclic depolarizations are induced only within a membrane potential range, between -60 mV and -85 mV. At more depolarized levels, NMDA elicits only a passive depolarization of the neuron. Moreover in Mg^{++}-free medium, the oscillatory activity is suppressed. Among the voltage-dependent conductances, I_{Ca} currents are required for the expression of the rhythmicity which vanishes in low Ca^{++}-concentration or cobalt-containing medium. I_{KCa} currents intervene also in the pattern of the cyclic depolarizations, their duration being highly increased under apamin. Of particular interest is the involvement of I_A current which is activated within the same range of membrane potentials where pacemaker-like properties are initiated by NMDA. The cyclic depolarizations show an initial ramp-shaped phase, the duration of which being more or less important depending on the level of membrane potential. Thus, the interactions between these different ionic conductances can induce different discharge patterns in the same NTS neuron. Under NMDA application, a neuron can exhibit a passive repetitive discharge when it is depolarized. This pattern is switched to a rhythmic bursting discharge when the neuron is slightly hyperpolarized, then to a rhythmic single discharge, which can occur at a higher frequency than that of the bursting activity, at more hyperpolarized level (see Figure 1).

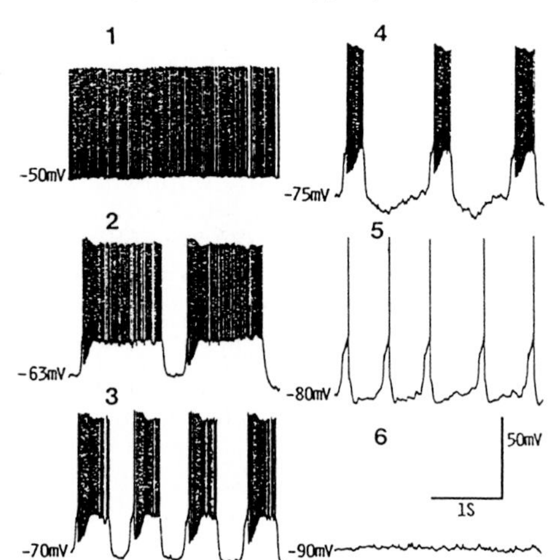

Figure 1: *Effects of NMDA application on a NTS neuron recorded* in vitro *from rat brainstem slices. NMDA (60 µM) induced depolarization associated with a repetitive firing pattern (trace 1). Depending on the amplitude of the hyperpolarization elicited by negative current injection, the neuron exhibited different rhythmic bursting patterns (traces 2, 3, 4) or a rhythmic single discharge (trace 5). These patterns are produced by interactions between the NMDA-gated conductances and voltage-dependent currents such as I_A and I_{KCa} in particular (from TELL and JEAN, 1991).*

Such endogenous properties of NTS neurons suggest that the same neuron may be involved in several behaviors, for example it might function as a sensory relay cell at a depolarized level or as a respiratory or a swallowing generator neuron at hyperpolarized levels (TELL, 1991; TELL and JEAN, 1991). It is worth noting that such a hypothesis fits well with preliminary *in vivo* results obtained from cat NTS neurons (GRELOT *et al.*, 1991). Therefore, as shown in invertebrates, it can be assumed that some NTS neurons may have a multifunctional role which appears particularly adapted in the case of the complex physiology of the NTS.

References:

BERGER, A.J. (1977). Dorsal respiratory group neurons in the medulla of cat: spinal projections, responses to lung inflation and superior laryngeal nerve stimulation. *Brain Res.*, **135**, 231-254.

BIANCHI, A.L. (1971). Localisation et étude des neurones respiratoires bulbaires. *J. Physiol. (Paris)*, **63**, 5-40.

CARPENTER, D.O. (1989). Central nervous system mechanisms in deglutition and emesis. In: *Handbook of Physiology, The Gastrointestinal System*, vol.I, Motility and circulation, J.D. Wood, ed., American Physiol. Soc., Bethesda, pp. 685-715.

CHAMPAGNAT, J., JACQUIN, T. and RICHTER, D.W. (1986). Voltage-dependent currents in neurones of the nuclei of the solitary tract of rat brainstem slices. *Pflügers Arch.*, **406**, 372-379.

DEKIN, M.S., RICHERSON, G.B. and GETTING, P.A. (1985). Thyrotropin-releasing hormone induces rhythmic bursting in neurons of the nucleus tractus solitarius. *Science*, **229**, 67-69.

DEKIN, M.S. and GETTING, P.A. (1987). In vitro characterization of neurons in the ventral part of the nucleus tractus solitarius. II. Ionic basis for repetitive firing patterns. *J. Neurophysiol.*, **58**, 215-229.

GRELOT, L., MILANO, S., PORTILLO, F. and BIANCHI, A.L. (1991). Behavior of neural elements of the respiratory network during reflexes involving respiratory muscles. In: *Neural nets and rhythms in vertebrates and invertebrates*, Minicolloque de la Société des Neurosciences, S33.

JEAN, A. (1972). Localisation et activité des neurones déglutiteurs bulbaires. *J. Physiol. (Paris)*, **64**, 227-268.

JEAN, A. (1990). Brainstem control of swallowing: localization and organization of the central pattern generator for swallowing. In: *Neurophysiology of the jaws and teeth*, A. Taylor, ed., Mc Millan Press, pp. 294-321.

JEAN, A. (1991). Le noyau du faisceau solitaire: aspects neuroanatomiques, neurochimiques et fonctionnels. *Arch. Int. Physiol. Bioch. Biophys.*, **99**, A3-A52.

LESLIE, R.A. (1985). Neuroactive substances in the dorsal vagal complex of the medulla oblongata: nucleus of the tractus solitarius, area postrema, and dorsal motor nucleus of the vagus. *Neurochem. Int.*, **7**, 191-211.

MEYRAND, P., SIMMERS, J. and MOULINS, M. (1991). Construction of a pattern generating circuit with neurons of different networks. *Nature*, **351**, 60-63.

MILLER, A.D. and WILSON, V.J. (1983). "Vomiting center" reanalyzed: an electrical stimulation study. *Brain Res.*, **270**, 154-158.

REYNOLDS, D.J.M., BARBER, N.A., GRAHAME-SMITH, D.G. and LESLIE, R.A. (1991). Cisplatin-evoked induction of c-fos protein in the brainstem of the ferret: the effect of cervical vagotomy and the anti-emetic 5-HT3 receptor antagonist granisetron (BRL 43694). *Brain Res.*, **565**, 231-236.

SAWCHENKO, P.E. (1983). Central connections of the sensory and motor nuclei of the vagus nerve. *J. Autonom. Nerv. Syst.*, **9**, 13-26.

TELL, F. and JEAN, A. (1990). Rhythmic bursting patterns induced in neurons of the rat nucleus tractus solitarii, in vitro, in response to N-methyl-D-aspartate. *Brain Res.*, **533**, 152-156.

TELL, F. (1991). Activité, propriétés endogènes et réponse au N-méthyl-D-aspartate des neurones du noyau du faisceau solitaire du rat adulte, étudiés in vitro. *Ph D. Thesis*, Université Aix-Marseille III, 152p.

TELL, F and JEAN, A. (1991). Activation of N-methyl-D-aspartate receptors induces endogenous rhythmic bursting activities in nucleus tractus solitarii neurons: an intracellular study on adult rat brainstem slices. *Eur. J. Neurosci.*, **3**, 1353-1365.

Mechanisms and Control of Emesis. Eds A.L. Bianchi, L. Grélot, A.D. Miller, G.L. King. Colloque INSERM/ John Libbey Eurotext Ltd. © 1992, Vol. 223, pp. 89-90

Substance P in the dorsal vagal nucleus: are preganglionnar cells directly connected by substance P-containing afferents?

F. Martini, A. Baude and J.J. Puizillout

CNRS-LNB1, 31, chemin Joseph Aiguier, 13402 Marseille Cedex 09, France

An outstanding feature in the vagal medullar area is the large amount and diversity of putative neurotransmitters which indicate the participation of neuropeptides, monoamines or amino-acids in integration of visceral information in terms of humoral or neuronal transmission. Of particular interest is the neuropeptide substance P (SP). Biochemical and histochemical data support the view that SP may have a leading part to assume vagal afferent neurotransmission in the lower brainstem as high density of SP-containing nerve terminals have been detected in the medullar area of the NST where vagal afferents are known to project. Pharmacological, morphological and electrophysiological studies were carried out in our laboratory to investigate the implication of SP in vagal functions.

First, the rôle of SP was analysed by observing the effects of local injections (into the 4th ventricle) of the peptide on the cardio-inhibitory reflex, evoked by stimulation of the aortic nerves or by i.v. administration of Phenylephrine. The results demonstrate that SP modifies the sensitivity of the reflex by increasing the bradycardia, providing evidence for a modulatory action of SP on the cardiovascular system. As this effect does not appear after bivagotomy, it is mediated essentially via the activation of the dorsal vagal nucleus (DNV) where are localized the majority of the cardioinhibitory neurons.

Secondly, we studied the endogeneous distribution of SP in the vagal system by immunohistochemistry. Substance P-immunoreactive (SP-ir) cell bodies and fibers were observed in the nodose ganglion. Numerous SP-ir terminals and fibers were localized throughout the caudo-rostral extend of the nucleus of solitary tract (NST) and in the DMN neuropile (1). After nodosectomy a large decrease of SP-ir was observed in the NST and also in the DMN (1). Using ultrastructural immunocytochemical procedures (2) SP-ir was observed in axon terminals and axon fibers which were mostly unmyelinated.

Quantitative data showed that at least 16% of axon terminals contained SP. Most (83%) of SP-containing terminals were seen to contact dendrites. Only 0.5% were observed to contact soma of interneurons. In 32.4% of cases SP-containing terminals were involved in synaptic contacts that were generally of the asymetrical Gray type 1. No axo-axonic synapses were observed in the DMN.

We also observed labelled terminals in contact with DMN neurons following axonal transport of wheat germ agglutinin labelled with horseradish peroxidase (WGA-HRP) previously injected in sensitive component of the vagus nerve, which demonstrate direct vago-vagal interactions. In support of these data we also showed that a unilateral nodose excision was followed by an ipsilateral increase in SP binding in the NST (200%) and also in the DMN (300%) (3). This SP receptor density up-regulation might be linked to the existence of vagal projections of nodose neurons directly to the DMN and interpret as a possible compensatory mechanisms for the decreased concentration of SP induced by the deafferentation.

Finally, SP was applied by superfusion to neurons of the DMN in slice preparations of the medulla oblongata. Intracellular recordings showed that neurons were depolarized with an increase in membrane input resistance. Others were hyperpolarized with a decrease of input resistance. Both effects were reversible and persisted after blockade of synaptic transmission. These results support the hypothesis that SP found in the DMN originates partly from vagal afferents and is involved in integrative processes of the central regulation of cardiovascular system and more generally in direct modulation of visceral functions mediated by vagal preganglionnar neurons.

1- BAUDE, A., LANOIR, J., VERNIER, P. et PUIZILLOUT, J.J., 1989, Substance P immunoreactivity in the dorsal medial region of the medulla in the cat. Effects of nodosectomy. J. chem. Neuroanat., 2: 67-81.

2- BAUDE,A., COURAUD,J.Y. and PUIZILLOUT, J.J., 1992, Fine distribution of Substance P-like immunoreactivity in the dorsal nucleus of the vagus nerve in cats. J. Chem. Neuroanat., in press.

3- SEGU,L., LANOIR, J. and PUIZILLOUT, J.J., 1991, Up-regulation of substance P binding sites in the vagus nerve projection area of the cat brainstem after nodosectomy. A quantitative autoradiographic study. J. Chem. Neuroanat., Vol.4, 447-459.

Mechanisms and Control of Emesis. Eds A.L. Bianchi, L. Grélot, A.D. Miller, G.L. King. Colloque INSERM/
John Libbey Eurotext Ltd. © 1992, Vol. 223, pp. 91-92

Spike properties of amyelinic neurons in rabbit nodose ganglia. Serotonin effects

C. Ducreux, J.C. Reynaud and J.J. Puizillout

CNRS, LNB1, 31, chemin Joseph Aiguier, 13402 Marseille Cedex 09, France

The nodose ganglion contains the major part of the sensitive cell bodies of the vagus nerve. From these ganglionar cell bodies emerges an axon which divides near the soma in two processes. The peripheral process (PP) innervates the viscera. The central process (CP) terminates in the nucleus of solitary tract. The ganglion was rapidly removed with its two processes and transferred in a chamber superfused with oxygenated Krebs's solution at 20°. The recordings were performed with classical intracellular electrodes (30-40 MΩ). The stimulations were applied on each process using two platinium wires embedded in vaseline. Our study concerns the unmyelinated neurons of type C. They were identified by the conduction velocity of their axons and by their spike duration. The neurons were divided in two groups: C1, which exhibited a spike with a fast after-hyperpolarization (F-AHP), and C2, which developped an additional slow after-hyperpolarization (S-AHP). The spike duration was 3.7 ± 1.2 ms for C1 (n=34), and 3.1 ± 0.8 ms for C2 neurons (n=20). The conduction velocities were similar for the two groups, but were different for the two processes: 0.59 ± 0.14 m/s for PP stimulation (n=45) and 0.25 ± 0.09 m/s for CP stimulation (n=25). The S-AHP lasted 9.2 ± 2.9 s (n=18) with an amplitude of 5.6 ± 2.6 mV.

Using steady hyperpolarizing currents, the S-AHP could be either reversed or, in most cells, nulled but not reversed (1). We measured the spike duration under the same experimental conditions and we found that the spike duration decreased with hyperpolarization in non reversing S-AHP neurons and that it remained constant in the others. To exclude any interferences with membrane potential variations, we recorded S-AHP at the resting potential. For that, the spikes were triggered just at the end of an hyperpolarizing pulses (duration: 80 ms). In these conditions the S-AHP amplitude could be easily related to the spike duration: when the spike duration remained constant with hyperpolarization the S-AHP amplitude was constant; when the spike duration decreased the S-AHP progressively decreased. In the case of spike decreasing duration neurons, when a spike was evoked by a depolarizing direct current following different conditionning hyperpolarized levels, we observed that the spike latency increased with the hyperpolarisation. This response is produced by a A-type potassium current which is activated before the inward current of the spike (2). With orthodromic stimulation this A current had no effects on the spike latency but it probably decreases the spike durations and consequently decreases the inward calcium current. The slow potassium calcium-dependant current cannot be activated and the S-AHP disappears.

The collision tests using a double shock, ortho and antidromic,showed that the block of conduction of the antidromic spike was produced at the level of the two processes branching and that the invasion of the soma was not necessary for the orthodromic propagation of the spike on the central process.

The local application of 5-HT (10-4 M) near the recorded neuron, induced a depolarization, a decrease in membrane input resistance and a block of spike conduction. Phenylbiguanide (PBG), a specific agonist 5-HT3, could induce either a depolarizing effect, or, in other neurons depolarized by 5HT, an hyperpolarization. The membrane of C neurons contains probably several 5HT receptors, some inducing depolarization, other hyperpolarization. These effects of PBG are complex and could imply different subtypes of 5HT3 receptors triggering different effectors.

1- FOWLER J.C., GREENE, R., and WEINREICH D., (1985), Two calcium-sensitive spike after-hyperpolarizations in visceral sensory neurones of the rabbit. J. Physiol. (Lond.), 365: 59-75.

2- GOLA, M. and ROMEY, G., (1971), Réponses anomales à des courants sous-liminaires de certaines membranes somatiques (neurones géants d' Helix pomatia). Pflügers Arch., 327: 105-131.

Mechanisms and Control of Emesis. Eds A.L. Bianchi, L. Grélot, A.D. Miller, G.L. King. Colloque INSERM/
John Libbey Eurotext Ltd. © 1992, Vol. 223, pp. 93-94

Interaction between central pattern generators for breathing and swallowing in the cat

Thomas E. Dick, Yoshitaka Oku, J. Richard Romaniuk and Neil S. Cherniack

Departments of Medicine, Neuroscience, and Physiology and Biophysics School of Medicine, Case Western Reserve University, Cleveland, Ohio 44106-5000, USA

We examined the interaction between central pattern generators for respiration and deglutition in decerebrate, vagotomized, paralyzed and ventilated cats (n=10), by recording activity from the following nerves: hypoglossal, phrenic, thyroarytenoid, and triangularis sterni. Fictive breathing was induced by increasing carbon dioxide in the inspired gas above apneic threshold (endtidal $PCo2$ 32 ± 4 mmHg) and fictive swallowing was induced by stimulating the internal branch of the superior laryngeal nerve (SLN) continuously (0.2 ms pulse duration, 10 Hz pulse frequency).

In all animals, three distinct phases of respiration were evident: phrenic nerve activity representative of respiration, thyroarytenoid nerve activity indicative of Stage-I expiration, and triangularis sterni activity indicative of Stage-II expiration. Stimulation of the SLN evoked short bursts of thyroarytenoid and hypoglossal nerve activity representative of the buccopharyngeal stage of fictive swallowing. Respiration was inhibited completely during deglutition in 2 of 10 animals. However, in the other eight animals, fictive breathing and swallowing occurred repetitively and simultaneously.

Changes in the breathing pattern were evident even with the current of the SLN stimulus pulse below threshold for eliciting swallowing. The respiratory rhythm decreased and integrated nerve activity changed as well. The duration of inspiration did not change but the duration of expiration especially Stage-II expiration increased. The rate of rise and peak amplitude of integrated phrenic nerve activity decreased. Peak amplitude of thyroarytenoid and Stage-I expiratory activity of the hypoglossal nerve increased. Triangularis sterni activity was suppressed completely, thus Stage-II expiration was measured as the absence of phrenic and thyroarytenoid activity. However if inspired carbon dioxide was increased, then triangularis sterni activity partially remained during SLN stimulation.

At the minimal stimulus intensity that evoked swallowing, one swallow occurred per breath initially. The fictive swallowing bursts occurred only at the respiratory phase transitions. In four animals, fictive swallows occurred at the transition between Stage-II expiration and inspiration; in two animals, at the transition between inspiration and Stage-I expiration; and in two other animals, at the transition between Stage-I and -II expiration. Thus, the patterns of interaction were consistent for each animal but varied across animals.

The response to SLN stimulation accommodated during the stimulus train. Accommodation was evident in both the interswallow interval (ISI) which lengthened and the pattern of interaction between breathing and swallowing in which fewer swallows occurred per breath. We plotted the next ISI (n+1) against the previous ISI (n) to show the dependence of the duration of ISI on the previous ISI. These plots were constructed for hypocapnic and eucapnic ventilated animals. With accommodation, ISI, n+1, increased as n increased. In addition, points overlapped for hypo- and eu-capnic conditions indicating that the swallowing frequency predominated over breathing frequency. However, separate clusters of points during eucapnic ventilation were evident indicating an interaction between breathing and swallowing central pattern generators. These separate clusters were most apparent later during the stimulus train when the pattern of interaction shifted from one swallow per breath to two swallows per breath. During this transition from one swallow per breath to one swallow per two breaths, inspiration could be prematurely terminated.

In contrast to the ISI, neither amplitude nor duration of the short burst of thyroarytenoid nerve activity changed. These variables appeared constant and were distributed over a narrow range through the period of evoked swallowing. Thus, the fictive swallowing event itself showed a fixed action pattern.

We conclude that the central pattern generators for swallowing and breathing can interact. The pattern of interaction is most evident at threshold stimulus current for evoking swallowing and supports the three phase theory of respiration. In particular the occurrence of a swallow could co-incide with any of the three phase transitions.

We gratefully acknowledge the financial support of National Institutes of Health (HL-25830) and the technical support of Philip Martinak.

Mechanisms and Control of Emesis. Eds A.L. Bianchi, L. Grélot, A.D. Miller, G.L. King. Colloque INSERM/
John Libbey Eurotext Ltd. © 1992, Vol. 223, p. 95

Chemosensitivity of intestinal mechanoreceptors: involvement in vomiting

S. Lucchini, N. Mei, L. Garnier, M.H. Michelucci

Laboratoire de Neurobiologie, CNRS, 31, chemin Joseph Aiguier, 13402 Marseille Cedex 9, France

It has been clearly demonstrated that the vagal nerves supply a rich sensory innervation to the small intestine. Therefore several kinds of mechano, thermo and chemosensitive afferents have been described at this level .(1)

Using the microelectrode technique, we recorded unitary vagal activities within nodose ganglia in anaesthetized cats. Only the responses involving intestinal receptors located both in muscular layers and in mucosa were selected in this work. After identification of receptors (distension, mucosal stroking etc.),the local arterial administration of C C K, substance P and a serotoninergic agonist (phenyl diguanide) was tested. Out of the 80 neurones involved in this study, 70 were activated by these three substances. The 10 last ones responded only to one substance (2 neurones) or two substances (8 neurones).
This activation was due to a direct effect on the nerve ending and not to an indirect effect due to motor changes in intestinal muscle since atropine did not affect the responses elicited by these substances. The chemosensitive responses problably involve a special part of the ending, or a particular mechanism since calcium channel blockers (cadmium, dihydropyridines) suppressed or notably reduced these responses whereas they were inefficient on the mechanosensitive responses.

It is concluded that the intestinal mechanoreceptors are certainly implicated in chemotherapy - induced vomiting because serotonin is involved in this phenomenon.

(1) MEI N. Intestinal chemosensitivity . Phsiol. Rev. 1985, 65, 211 - 237

Herbert L. Borison lecture

Conférence Herbert L. Borison

Mechanisms and Control of Emesis. Eds A.L. Bianchi, L. Grélot, A.D. Miller, G.L. King. Colloque INSERM/ John Libbey Eurotext Ltd. © 1992, Vol. 223, pp. 99-101

In memorial
Herbert Leon Borison (1922-1990)

Walter M. St John

Department of Physiology, Dartmouth Medical School, Hanover, NH, USA

In the Department of Pharmacology and Toxicology at Dartmouth Medical School, the laboratory in which Rosaline Borison had worked was named in her honor after her death in 1984. Ros, an exceptionally kind and warm person, had been Herb's wife for forty years and his research assistant for many of those years. She personified what were the two important elements for Herb: his family and his work.

The year 1944 was of great importance in Herb's life. In that year, he and Ros were married, and he completed his wartime work with the U.S. Army Signal Corps. Herb had been born in New York on May 20, 1922. At the age of nineteen, he obtained his Bachelor of Science degree from the City College of New York. Herb continued his education at New York University, from which he obtained a Master of Science Degree in 1942.

Scientifically, 1944 had great significance for Herb began his graduate studies at the College of Physicians and Surgeons of Columbia University in New York with a new assistant professor, S.C. Wang. Wang, who was to become a legendary figure in neurophysiology and neuropharmacology, had himself recently completed a number of years of work with S.W. Ranson at the Institute of Neurology of Northwestern University. The breadth and depth of Wang's scientific interests and his intensity and energy would become well known over the years. However, these attributes were already manifested to his earliest students. Herb commented on those days in a symposium held after Wang's retirement from Columbia on June 30, 1978: " ...the newly turned assistant professor decided to take me under his wing. From then on, there was no time for self-doubt or hesitation. If it had to be done, S.C. did it and you did it....As it turned out, the research path on which S.C. steered me in those delicious days remains unbroken even now" (Borison, 1980a).

The research path upon which Herb embarked would ultimately lead to a detailed characterization of brainstem mechanisms underlying the chemodetection of many emetic agents and the coordination of emesis, per se. Herb detailed the background of these discoveries in the

Wang symposium noted above. In brief, prior to his studies, chemodetection and coordination of emesis were considered to be controlled exclusively by the dorsal vagal nucleus. However, such an exclusive role was incompatible with the observation that emesis could still be induced by gastrointestional irritants in dogs with chronic lesions of the dorsal vagal nucleus. This incompatibility was seized upon by Borison and Wang, and the control of emesis was studied with their typical intensity. The relatively new procedure of electrical stimulation and lesions using stereotaxic techniques, which Wang had mastered with Ranson, was brought to bear on this problem. Herb summarizes their results as follows: "We formulated the bold concept that a specialized chemosensor for vomiting, having no coordinating function of its own, exists as a definitive anatomical entity in the fourth ventricle and, obversely, that a center for the coordination of vomiting, having no chemosensory function of its own, exists in the lateral reticular formation of the medulla oblongata" (Borison, 1980b).

Herb remained at Columbia for two years as an Instructor after having obtained his degree in 1948. Thirteen papers were published during his years with Wang. Most were related to emesis, but manuscripts concerning the control of cardiovascular and ventilatory activities also appeared.

In 1950, Herb accepted a position as Instructor of Pharmacology at the University of Utah College of Medicine. Thus, he and Ros made the dramatic geographical switch from Manhattan to Salt Lake City. They were to spend the next twelve years in Utah with Herb rising to Associate Professor Also, during these years, their two children, Ellen and Adam, were born.

Work on emesis continued with the "chemoreceptor trigger zone" being localized to the area postrema. The site of action of numerous emetic agents upon this structure was established, and the effectiveness of a number of anti-emetic agents was tested. With typical thoroughness, Herb also reported that the chemoreceptor trigger zone is not a unique receptor site for all emetic agents with some, such as veratrum alkaloids, acting at other loci. Acknowledgment of the quality of Herb's work came with the awarding of the 1953 John Jacob Abel Prize from the American Society of Pharmacology and Experimental Therapeutics. Herb also continued his work on the regulation of cardiovascular and ventilatory activities. Finally, in his last years at Utah, Herb established a scientific collaboration with Larry McCarthy, which was to continue for the rest of his career.

In 1962, Robert Gosselin offered Herb the position of professor in the Department of Pharmacology and Toxicology at Dartmouth Medical School. Herb and his family thus made another dramatic geographic switch to the Northern New England town of Hanover, New Hampshire. Work continued unabated with perhaps the most important results being a complete characterization of the respiratory mechanics of emesis. These studies with Larry McCarthy used combined pressure measurements in the thorax and abdomen along with electromyographic and cineradiographic recordings to document the retching and expulsion phases. Numerous studies of emetic and anti- emetic agents were also performed with the emetic actions of radiation and anti-neoplastic agents and the anti-emetic actions of the cannabinoids

receiving particular attention. Many manuscripts concerning the control of the ventilatory and cardiovascular systems were also published. However, fittingly, the last of the 141 manuscripts and chapters which Herb published was titled: "Area postrema: chemoreceptor circumventricular organ of the medulla oblongata."
The documentation of Herb's life and work does not provide insights into the man himself. Unfortunately, it is not uncommon to find those who are simultaneously insolent to inferiors and sycophantic to superiors. Herb was almost unique in that he reversed these traits. To students and junior colleagues, Herb was exceptionally warm, supportive and understanding. Any public criticism of the performance of a student was non-existent. However, public praise of achievements was common and extended. To colleagues, Herb was a selfless source of help and advice, not only concerning neuropharmacology and neurophysiology but also neuroanatomy, of which he had an extraordinary knowledge. Discussions of conflicting results were always professional with the important question being why were the results different, not who is correct.

To administrators at any local, national or international level, Herb was a formidable adversary. When injustice or unfairness was suspected, Herb did not move cautiously but rather charged forward. As Herb had noted concerning S.C. Wang,: "there was no time for self-doubt or hesitation."

Herb died in Hanover during the first week of December, 1990. As befit his devotion to family and work, his body was discovered in the laboratory which had been named in memory of Rosaline Borison. I believe that Herb's tribute to S.C. Wang should equally be applied to himself. Herbert Leon Borison: "We, who know you and have benefited from your work, your teaching and your counsel, salute you!"

[1] This paper was prepared by Walter M. St. John, Department of Physiology, Dartmouth Medical School, Hanover NH

References:

Borison, H.L. (1980a). Tribute to S.C. Wang. In Central control mechanisms and related topics (in honor of S.C. Wang), ed. H.H. Wang, M.R. Blumenthal and S.H. Ngai, pp.xxvii - xxxii. Mount Kisco, NY:Futura Publishing Company.

Borison, H.L. (1980b). Vomiting updated. In Central control mechanisms and related topics (in honor of S.C. Wang), ed. H.H. Wang, M.R. Blumenthal and S.H. Ngai, pp. 1-6. Mount Kisco, NY:Futura Publishing Company.

Mechanisms and Control of Emesis. Eds A.L. Bianchi, L. Grélot, A.D. Miller, G.L. King. Colloque INSERM/ John Libbey Eurotext Ltd. © 1992, Vol. 223, pp. 103-111

The blood-brain barrier and its penetration

Milton W. Brightman, Shoichiro Ishihara and Lisa Chang

National Institutes of Health, Laboratory of Neurobioloy, NINDS, 9000 Rockville Pike, Bethesda, MD 20892, USA

SUMMARY

Subregions of circumventricular organs (CVO), areas outside of the blood-brain barrier (BBB), have fenestrated, permeable vessels that enable the CVO to monitor blood constituents. CVO access to blood can be mimicked by skeletal muscle autografts inserted into the IV ventricle, so placed to test a current hypothesis that target tissue, rather than the source of vessels, determines the type of vessel growing into the target. However, we find that in rats with bilateral superior cervical ganglionectomy, some new vessels in the grafts are not of the muscle type but rather, fenestrated. This possible relation between innervation and vessel permeability awaits exploration. Most brain vessels do have a BBB which is penetrated, constitutively, by the glucose and transferrin transporters, for example, and, manipulatively, by altering solute properties.

La barrière hémato-encéphalique et sa pénétration.

Résumé: *Les régions circumventriculaires (CVO), des régions situées hors de la barrière hémato-encéphalique (BBB), sont fenêtrées, avec des vaisseaux perméables qui permettent aux CVO de revevoir les constituants du sang. L'accès des CVO au sang peut être simulé par des autogreffes de muscles squelettiques insérées dans le IVème ventricule, ainsi placées pour vérifier une hypothèse actuelle selon laquelle le tissu cible détermine le type de vaisseaux y aboutissant plutôt que l'origine de ces vaisseaux. Cependant, nous avons trouvé que chez le rat ayant subi une ablation bilatérale du ganglion cervical supérieur, certains nouveaux vaisseaux du greffon ne sont pas de type musculaire mais plutôt de type fenêtré. Cette relation possible entre l'innervation et la perméabilité des vaisseaux attend d'être explorée. La plupart des vaisseaux du cerveau doivent avoir une BBB qui, par constitution, est pénêtrée par le glucose et les transporteurs de la transferrine, par exemple, et, expérimentalement, en altérant les propriétés des solutés.*

The body of experimental evidence put forward by Borison and collaborators (1984) on the participation of the area postrema (AP) as a chemosensitive trigger zone in the emetic reflex, provided the first compelling inference for a function ascribable to a circumventricular organ (CVO). Accordingly, this discussion will emphasize CVO which lie outside of the blood-brain barrier. Before describing how the barrier may be influenced by its perivascular environment and how the barrier may be circumvented, a definition of what constitutes the barrier is presented first. The endothelial structure accounting for the passive blood-brain barrier to solutes enables that endothelium to act selectively. The passive diffusion of ions and hydrophilic solutes between blood and interstitial fluid (IF) of the central nervous system in mammals is prevented by the zonular or circumferential occlusion of the clefts between endothelial cells and by the lack of endocytotic transfer of most solutes across these cells. Consequently, the IF is not flooded by plasma solutes, the concentrations of which can then be regulated by both the endothelium and perivascular astrocytes (Brightman, 1989). In this way, homeostasis of the brain and spinal cord is achieved.

CIRCUMVENTRICULAR ORGANS (CVO)

In contrast to ion regulation, systemic, visceral, homeostasis is effected, not by barrier vessels, but rather by the permeable ones of the CVO. These fenestrated vessels apparently permit the neurons within CVO subregions to "sample" blood constituents so that appropriate, autonomic adjustments can be made. The participation of one of these CVO, the area postrema (AP), in emetic reflexes and visceral homeostasis has long been proposed by Borison and colleagues who have critically and thoroughly considered the possible roles of the AP from structural, physiological and pharmacological vantages. They came to regard the AP neurons, bathed by blood - derived constituents, as chemoreceptors that transduce chemical signals into neural impulses that need travel for only a short distance before reaching a hypothetical coordinating center within the medullary reticular formation (reviewed by Borison, 1989).

A consistent, heterogeneity of vascular structure and function within CVO has recently been revealed by correlating morphometry with quantitative autoradiography. Gross and colleagues have thus been able to resolve, within CVO, regions supplied by fenestrated, permeable vessels, next to subregions with comparatively impermeable, barrier vessels and intervening, transitional zones (Gross et al., 1986). An example of this subregional resolution, that may be relevant to emetic reflexes, is the dorsal vagal complex consisting of one CVO, the area postrema (AP), and two medullary nuclei : the nucleus of the tractus solitarius (NTS) and the dorsal motor nucleus of the vagus. The density and structure of the microvessels differ between these three structures and within them as well (Shaver et al., 1991). In the AP, the blood volume is about 3 - 4 times higher than it is in the barrier vessels of medullary gray matter. These differences correlate well with the higher glucose utilization in the AP. An even more remarkable difference is the blood-to-tissue transfer of a neutral amino acid, α– aminoisobutyric acid, a tracer with, as Gross points out, physicochemical properties similar to hormones . The product of the (permeability) x (surface area) of the capillary bed is about 100 - 400 times greater in the AP and 20 - 59 times greater in the NTS subregions than in the medullary gray matter. Another notable AP feature is the slow transit time for blood flowing through the AP capillaries which, as the authors note, would extend the opportunity for the AP to monitor blood constituents passing through it (Gross et al., 1991).

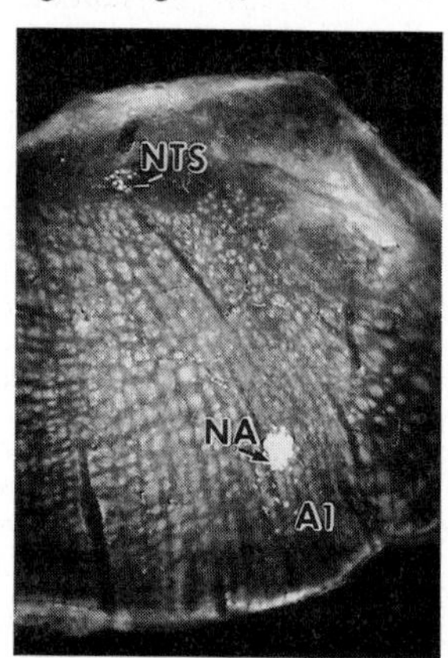

Figure 1. Transverse section through the medulla oblongata of a mouse after intravenous infusion of HRP 24 h prior to fixation. The nucleus of the tractus solitarius (NTS) has become labeled, presumably by retrograde transport of the HRP along NTS axons that project to the area postrema. Also labeled are the A1 adrenergic neurons and nucleus ambiguus (NA). (Broadwell & Brightman, 1976). X 26

The NTS is thought to be participate in the regulation of a variety of autonomic activities, such as respiratory and gustatory, by way of afferent fibers from cranial nerves IX and X and its reciprocal connections with the hypothalamus, amygdala and cerebral cortex (Van der Kooy et al., 1984). An indirect participation of the NTS in the emetic reflex may be through its neural connection or its vascular connection with the AP (Borison, 1989).

However, a more direct involvement of the NTS may be by way of one of its subdivisions, which is itself supplied by permeable, fenestrated capillaries (Gross et al., 1991). When large amounts of HRP are infused intravenously and sufficent time allowed for the retrograde transport of this protein within axons, neurons within the NTS and other nuclei in the brain stem (Fig. 1) become labeled by the HRP (Broadwell & Brightman, 1976). The fenestrated vessels in a portion of the NTS, however, may signify that, in addition to the indirect, axoplasmic route from the AP, blood constituents could be sampled directly by the NTS. The nucleus ambiguus is labeled retrogradely, presumably from pharyngeal and laryngeal muscles via the axons of cranial nerve IX, while the adrenergic A1 neurons might receive some of their HRP from the median eminence.

In addition to tracer proteins, the fenestrated vessels of CVO are also passively permeable to amino acids. Olney and associates have repeatedly demonstrated that dicarboxylic acids, such as glutamate and aspartate, when infused into systemic blood, are preferentially incorporated by CVO but not by the rest of the brain. These neuroexcitants are eventually toxic to neuroendocrine cells in both immature and mature brains. Like the protein, horseradish peroxidase (HRP), the much smaller amino acid molecules diffuse rapidly and readily into the adjacent cerebral neuropil. Thus, circulating, exogenous, aspartic acid rapidly enters the CVO : median eminence, and from there, into the contiguous arcuate nucleus, which lies within the blood-brain barrier. Aspartate simultaneously enters other CVO, for example, the subfornical organ; the remainder of the brain, within the barrier, incorporates very little (Price et al., 1984). According to their measurements of aspartate within subregions of the two CVO and contiguous brain areas mentioned, the penetration of the amino acid follows a diffusion gradient away from the CVO. Once the exogenous amino acid enters the brain's IF, the uptake of aspartate by brain cells would be regulated by a dicarboxylic acid transport mechanism that is active and saturable (Price et al., 1984). In the same way, the size and electric charge of an emetic agent within the IF, and its uptake by brain cells, would determine its concentration gradient in a particular region of the brain.

Like the IF spaces around fenestrated capillaries in other tissues, those around the fenestrated capillaries of CVO are considerably larger than the perineuronal and periglial clefts of the cerebral parenchyma (Fig. 2). The dimensions of the interstitial spaces and the parameters of blood flow, capillary permeability and transit time of blood within the subfornical organ and AP have been measured by Gross and associates. The large perivascular space is conducive to a rapid, free mixing of relatively large volumes of blood derived fluid and agents bathing the sensory neurons and neurites within and adjacent to the spaces, as alluded to previously (Gross, 1991).

INDUCTION OF PERMEABLITY FEATURES IN ENDOTHELIUM

How fenestrated capillaries are induced to form during development or tumorigenesis is unknown. This question relates to the important concept of Stewart and Wiley (1980), that the type of vessel supplying an organ is determined by that organ rather than the source of the vessels. They based the hypothesis on their observations that when vessels, permeable to large hydrophilic solutes, invaded developing brain tissue, the vessels took on the characteristics of vessels having a blood-brain barrier. Conversely, when brain vessels entered peripheral, mesenchymal tissue, they assumed the features typical of permeable capillaries. Some component of the brain apparently influenced ingrowing, permeable endothelium to change its phenotype to one of a barrier cell. The cell within the central nervous system most likely to influence the endothelium is its nearest neighbor, the perivascular astrocyte. There is some evidence that this cell does affect the degree of permeability presented by endothelium. When brain endothelial cells are co-cultured with astrocytes, the structure of the tight junctions between endothelial cells, viewed in freeze-fracture replicas with electron microscopy, become more frequent and continuous than do the junctions of solo endothelial cultures (Tao-Cheng et al., 1987; Arthur et al., 1987). The junctions in the co-cultures resemble more closely what would be expected of a barrier junction. Brain endothelial cells in solo culture lose their γ - glutamyl transpeptidase activity, responsible for amino acid transport across the blood-brain barrier. When brain endothelial cells are co-cultured with the cells from a C-6 glioma cell line, the activity of this enzyme is re-expressed (DeBault & Cancilla, 1980). An astrocytic influence on endothelial permeability to ions has been demonstrated by the high electrical resistance of ~ 600 Ω · cm² across an endothelial layer, when endothelial cells are cultured either with astrocytes (Meresse et al., 1989) or their conditioned medium containing agents that raise cAMP levels (Rubin et al., 1991).

The induction of barrier characteristics in brain endothelial cells might involve neurons as well as astrocytes. The addition of plasma membrane fractions of C6 glioma cells or of cortical neurons, to endothelial cells in vitro, brings about a modest increase in γ - glutamyl transpeptidase activity (Tontsch & Bauer, 1991). The C6 glioma cell membrane fraction also raises the activity of Na^+, K^+ - ATPase but the neuronal fraction, apparently, does not. Cell contact is probably required for the stimulations because either glial or neuronal conditioned medium, i.e., soluble factors, does not enhance enzymatic activity. The modest stimulation of one enzyme by neuronal cell membranes does suggest a neuronal influence on endothelial barrier properties, but such an influence would be more convincing if there were a greater effect on more than one enzyme.

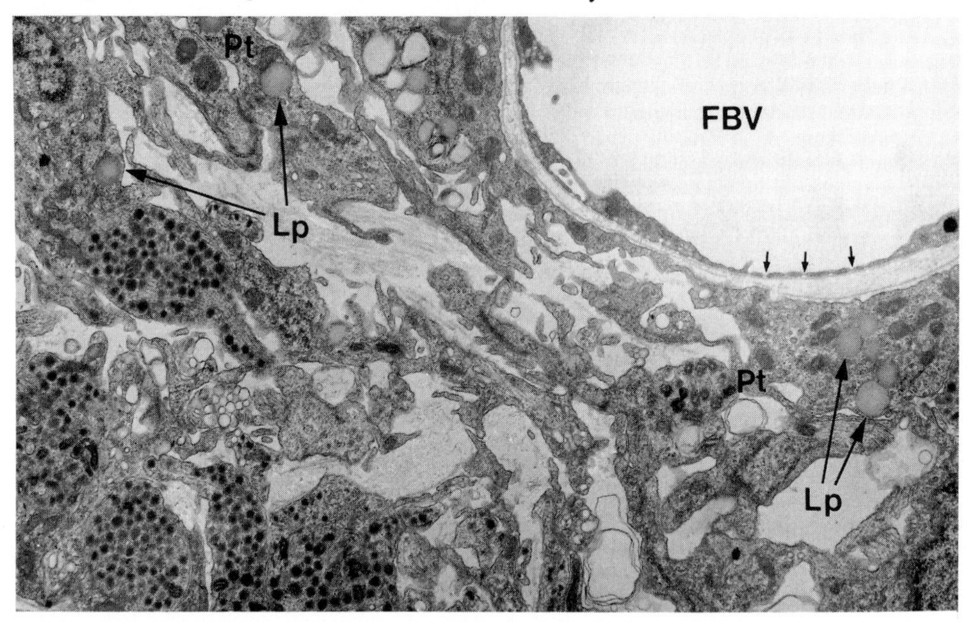

Figure 2. Like intact neural lobe, this grafted neural lobe that had been transplanted to the hypothalamus, contains many blood vessels (FBV) with fenestrae (arrows). Pituicytes (Pt) are astrocyte-like cells, recognized by their lipid droplets (LP) and content of glial fibrillary acidic protein. The pituicytes, like astrocytes, abut perivascular basal lamina but have not converted fenestrated capillaries into ones with barrier features. (Kadota et al., 1990). X 11, 200.

Notwithstanding these data, there are a number of experimental reports and inductive reasons for questioning the role of astrocytes on endothelial permeability. (1) Brain endothelial cells, cloned in solo culture in the absence of astroglia, form so tightly joined a cell layer that the electrical resistance across it may be of the order of 150 - 780 Ω · cm² (Rutten et al., 1987). (2) In situ, astrocytes may be situated close to blood vessels that do not have a passive barrier to the passage of solutes. The pituicyte of the pituitary gland's neural lobe has a number of astrocytic features, yet all of the vessels that it confronts are fenestrated (Fig. 2) and permeable (Kadota et al., 1990). (3) In some elasmobranchs, the barrier role of endothelium and astroglia is reversed: the endothelial junctions are open and permeable to circulating protein, whereas the subjacent, periendothelial layer of astrocytes is closed by tight junctions that block the entry of protein from the periendothelial space into the brain's IF (Brightman et al., 1971; Bundgaard & Cserr, 1981). (4) Conversely, certain vessels, like those of the subarachnoid space, have a blood-brain barrier but, rather than being surrounded by astroglial processes, are much nearer to pial cells and considerable extracellular matrix.

With these doubts in mind, the hypothesis that it is the target which determines the vessel type, is currently being tested in vivo by means of a "pseudo-CVO". This CVO simulation is created by inserting pieces of skeletal muscle upon the floor of the IV ventricle anterior to the area postrema. In this way, the location and permeability of CVO is mimicked by nuchal muscle autografts upon or near the choroid plexus of the ventricle. The blood-brain barrier (BBB) is thus circumvented permanently and focally as it is at CVO. When allografts of superior cervical ganglion (SCG) are used, their vessels rapidly anastomose with those of the surrounding brain and survival of the grafts is assured. The permeability of the grafts' vessels to an amino acid, as measured by quantitative autoradiography, is much higher than that of the surrounding barrier vessels but considerably less than some CVO (Tsubaki et al. 1989). When autografts of skeletal muscle are placed in the IV ventricle, the type of vessel supplying the grafts is concordant with the hypothesis : the capillaries within the muscle graft resemble those of normal muscle but not the barrier vessels of the subjacent brain with which they anastomose (Wakai et al., 1986). However, we have been finding that in

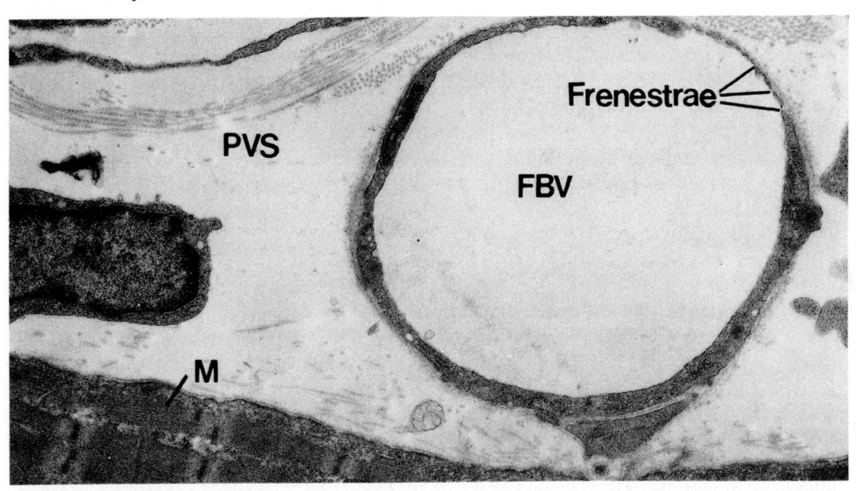

Figure 3. Skeletal muscle autograft, 4 w old, in the IV ventricle of a rat with bilateral superior cervical ganglionectomy, is vascularized by fenestrated blood vessels (FBV), that lie adjacent to muscle cells (M), rather than by a muscle type of vessel. The FBV here is probably a branch from adjacent choroid plexus vessels. FBV and large perivascular spaces (PVS) are also features of CVO. (Unpublished observations) X 12, 500

mature rats from which the SCG have been removed bilaterally 2 - 3 weeks prior to graft insertion, many of the vessels lying between muscle cells of the graft are fenestrated (Fig. 2) . Such vessels, evident at 2 days, 1 week and 4 weeks after grafting, are characteristic of choroid plexus and other CVOs, but not of skeletal muscle. Muscle grafts also resemble CVO in their generous perivascular spaces (Fig. 2) that may facilitate exchange of blood constituents with those of the IF bathing CVO neurons (Gross et al, 1991). Comparison of muscle graft vessels with those of allografts from 18 day old fetal brains placed in the IV ventricle of ganglionectomized rats is underway.

It is unknown how fenestrated capillaries come to supply muscle grafts in ganglionectomized rats. We propose that autonomic innervation may influence the development of the structure and permeability of certain blood vessels. Thus, nor-epinephrine or some other secretory product of SCG, might inhibit either the develpoment of fenestrated endothelium or the formation of fenestrae in proliferating capillary sprouts of choroid plexus or of skeletal muscle grafts. However, the barrier is normally penetrated, without external manipulation, in several specific ways (Table 1).

One such intrinsic route across the barrier is by way of endothelial carriers or transporters, special sites on the cell membrane that actively bring substances into and, in some cases, across the capillary endothelium to the IF (Table 1). The transferrin transporter carries this ligand from blood across brain capillaries to oligodendrocytes and other brain cells (Fishman et al., 1987). The constant, high requirement for glucose by the CNS is normally satisfied by its endothelial transporter which has been immunohistochemically identified in both barrier epithelium and barrier endothelium within the central nervous system and its extension, the retina (Pardridge, et al., 1990a ; Harik et al., 1990). So predictable is the presence of glucose transporters in brain vessels and its absence from the permeable, fenestrated vessels, of the CVO, that the demonstration of this carrier has been used to distinguish a barrier epithelium or endothelium from a non-barrier, permeable, endothelium (Pardridge et al., 1990a; Harik et al., 1990). The more recent localization of the transporter on non-barrier types of vessels, for example, on the endothelium of testicular vessels and the fetal side of the placental trophoblast capillaries (Farrell et al., 1992), however, raises the caveat that the glucose transporter is not necessarily accompanied by a barrier of zonular tight junctions.

CATIONIC SOLUTES

Like the plasma membrane of many other cell types, the luminal surface of brain endothelial cells bears numerous negatively charged groups to which cationized molecules can bind (Schmidley & Wissig 1986). Negatively charged protein, e.g., native serum albumin (pI~4) does not bind to the endothelial surface but is, instead, incorporated by fluid phase endocytosis and digested in lysosomes (reviewed by Broadwell, 1989). Adsorptive transcytosis of tracers has been demonstrated in the permeable, though non-fenestrated, endothelium of other tissues. Such adsorptive transcytosis across brain endothelium probably accounts for the barrier penetration of hydrophilic, cationic molecules to be described below, but the actual demonstration of this kind of transport brain capillaries is another matter (Broadwell, 1989).

Unlike the fenestrated vessels of CVO, the continuous vessels of almost all of the brain parenchyma are relatively impervious to hydrophilic substances except for the few types of solutes carried across the barrier by transporters. Although the passive barrier can be opened non-specifically to many solutes by a variety of intrusive methods (Table 1), a more selective approach is being developed by Pardridge and his associates. This method of overcoming the barrier, without in any way disturbing the brain or its vasculature, does so by rendering the solutes that are to be injected into blood, cationic. Native protein, such as serum albumin, does not cross the blood-brain barrier in appreciable amount. However, when serum albumin is made cationic by conjugating it to hexamethylenediamine, there is a marked uptake of the possitively charged protein by brain tissue (Smith & Borchardt, 1989; Pardridge et al., 1990b). The more cationic the albumin, the greater its incorporation into the brain of the awake rat. Considerably more albumin at pI ~ 11 is incorporated by brain at 6 - 18 minutes after its intravenous infusion, than is albumin at pI ~ 8 are (Shimon-Hophy et al., 1991). The mechanism of entry into brain is not clear. Mere electrostatic binding of the cationic protein to the negatively charged groups on the luminal face of the endothelium does not account for the 10 fold lower uptake by a cationic polymer with a molecular mass of 62 kDa, comparable to that of albumin's 67 kDa. Binding to albumin receptors is an alternative possibility (Triguero et al., 1989). Glycosylated serum albumin also crosses barrier vessels in vitro, presumably by adsorptive transcytosis (Smith & Borchardt 1989). If the binding of cationic ligands is coulombic or due to some kind of affinity, the protein would then be internalized by endocytosis and transported across the endothelial cells in a membrane - bounded, vesiculotubular system to the opposite, abluminal portion of the cell membrane. The electrostatic bond or affinity between the cationized peptide or protein and vesicle membrane would then have to be broken in order for these ligands to be freed for entry into the perivascular interstitial space. This event has not been directly demonstrated.

By cationizing the antibody, immunoglobulin G, it too has been brought across the barrier (Triguero et al., 1989). An extrapolation of cationizing proteins is to use them as vectors for bringing other protein or peptide into brain. A peptide β-endorphin, excluded by the barrier, has been covalently conjugated to cationic albumin by means of a disulfide containing coupling reagent. Having been ferried on the cationized albumin across the barrier endothelium, the disulfide reductases of brain cells cleave the conjugate so that the β-endorphin is released and made available to the brain cells (Pardridge, et al., 1990a). Such strategies hold exciting promise for the unintrusive delivery into brain of other peptides and of proteins with retention of their biological activity.

Table 1

Blood - Brain Barrier Penetration

Intrinsic	Imposed *
• (i) Transporters saturable carriers e.g., glucose	• (i) Infusion into CSF [c]
• (ii) Receptor Mediated [a] some proteins e.g., transferrin	• (ii) Hyperosmotic Blood [d] so as to open tight junctions (reversible)
• (iii) Cranial Nerves Project to regions with permeable vessels.	• (iii) Hypertension [e] e.g., metaraminol (reversible)
• (iv) CVO permeable vessels, large perivasc. space	• (iv) Radiocontrast dye I - V [f]
• (v) Solute Lipophilicity [b] Solute entry 1/α to its lipid solubility.	• (v) Endothelial Cationization [g] e.g., protamine infusion
	• (vi) Solute Cationization e.g., peptides, proteins
	• (vii) Fatty Acid I - V [h] e.g., oleic acid specific (reversible)
	• (viii) Non-CNS Grafts e.g.,muscle (permanent)

(i) & (ii) ------ highly selective

(iii) & (v) ----- specific

(iv) ------------- non - specific

* Non- Pathological States

References listed below are for those methods not discussed in the text.

• (a) Fishman et al., 1987; Broadwell ,' 1989 • (b) Oldendorf et al., 1972

• (c) Brightman, 1967; Borison et al., 1980; Rennels et al., 1985 • (d) Rapoport, 1970

• (e) Häggendal & Johansson, 1974 • (f) Numaguchi et al., 1984 • (g) Nagy et al., 1983

• (h) Sztriha & Betz, 1991.

REFERENCES

Arthur, F.E., Shivers, R.R. & Bowman, P.D. (1987) : Astrocyte - mediated induction of tight junctions in brain capillary endothelium : an efficient in vitro model. Develop. Brain Res. 36, 155 - 159.

Borison, H.L., Borison, R. & McCarthy, L.E. (1980) : Brain stem penetration by horseradish peroxidase from the cerebrospinalfluid spaces in the cat. Exper. Neurol. 69, 271 - 289.

Borison, R. & McCarthy, L.E. (1984) : Role of the area postrema in vomiting and related functions. Federation Proc. 43, 2955 - 2958.

Borison, H.L. (1989) : Area Postrema : Chemoreceptor circumventricular organ of the medulla oblongata. Progr. Neurobiol. 32, 351 - 390.

Brightman, M.W. (1965) : The distribution within the brain of ferritin injected into cerebrospinal fluid compartments. II. Parenchymal distribution. Am. J. Anat. 117, 193 - 219.

Brightman, M. (1989) : The anatomical basis of the blood-brain barrier. In The Clinical Impact of the Blood-Brain Barrier and its Manipulation. ed. E.A. Neuwelt, pp. 53-83. New York: Plenum Press.

Brightman, M.W., Hori, M., Rapoport, S.I., Reese, T.S. & Westergaard, E. (1973) : Osmotic opening of tight junctions in cerebral endothelium. J. Comp. Neurol. 152, 317 - 326.

Brightman, M.W., Reese, T.S., Olsson, Y., & Klatzo, I. (1971) : Morphological aspects of the blood-brain barrier to peroxidase in elsamobranchs. Progr. Neuropathol. 1, 146-161.

Broadwell, R.D. (1989) Transcytosis of macromolecules through the blood-brain barrier : a cell biological perspective and critical appraisal. Acta Neuropathol. 79, 117 - 128.

Broadwell, R.. & Brightman, M. (1976): Entry of peroxidase into neurons of central and peripheral nervous systems from extracerebral and cerebral blood. J. Comp. Neurol. 166, 257-280.

Bundgaard, M. & Cserr, H.F. (1981) : A glial blood-brain barrier in elasmobranchs. Brain Res. 226, 61 - 73.

DeBault, L.E. & Cancilla, P.A. (1980) : Gamma-glutamyl transpeptidase in isolated brain endothelial cells: Induction by glial cells in vitro. Science 207, 653 - 655.

Farrell, C.L., Yang, J. & Pardridge, W. M. (1992) : GLUT - 1 glucose transporter is present within apical and basolateral membranes of brain epithelial interfaces and in microvascular endothelia with and without tight junctions. J. Histochem. Cytochem. 40, 193 - 199.

Fishman, J.B., Rubin, J.B., Handrahan, J.V., Connor, J.R. & Fine, R.E. (1987) : Receptor-mediated transcytosis of transferrin across the blood-brain barrier. J. Neurosci. Res. 18, 299 - 304.

Gross, P.M., Sposito, N.M, Pettersen S.E. & Fenstermacher, J.D. (1986) : Differences in function and structure of the capillary endothelium in gray matter, white matter and a circumventricular organ of rat brain. Blood Vessels 23, 261 - 270.

Gross, P.M., Wall, K.M., Wainman, D.S. & Shaver, S.M. (1991) : Subregional topography of capillaries in the dorsal vagal complex of rats : II. Physiological properties. J. Comp. Neurol. 306, 83 - 94.

Häggendal, E. & Johansson, B. (1972) : Effect of increased intravascular pressure on the blood-brain barrier to protein in dogs. Acta Neurol. Scand. 48, 271 - 275.

Harik, S., Kalaria, r., Whitney, P., Andersson, L., Lundahl, P. Ledbetter, S.L. & Perry, G. (1990) :Glucose transporter are abundant in cells with "occluding" junctions at the blood-eye barriers. Proc. Natl. Acad. Sci. USA 87, 4261-4264.

Kadota, Y., Pettigrew, K.D. & Brightman, M.W. (1990) : Regrowth of damaged neurosecretory axons to fenestrated vessels of implanted peripheral tissues. Synapse 5, 175 - 189.

Meresse, S., Dehouck, M-P., Delorme, P.M., Bensaid, J-P., Tauber, C., Delbart, C., Fruchart, J-C. & Cecchelli, R. (1989) : Bovine brain endothelial cells express tight junctions and monoamine oxidase activity in longterm culture. J. Neurochem. 53, 1363 - 1371.

Nagy, Z., Peters, H. & Hüttner, I. (1983) : Charge-related alterations of cerebral endothelium. Lab. Investigation 49, 662 - 671.

Numaguchi, Y., Fleming, M.S., Hasuo, K., Puyau, F.A. & Nice, C.M. (1984) : Blood-brain barrier disruption due to cerebral arteriography : CT findings. J. Comp. Assist. Tomogr. 8, 936-939.

Oldendorf, W.H., Hyman, S., Braun, L. & Oldendorf, S.Z. (1972) : Blood-brain barrier : Penetration of morphine, codeine, heroin and methadone after carotid injection. Science

178, 984 - 986.
Öztas, B. & Sandalci, U. (1984) : Reversibility of blood-brain barrier dysfunction in acute hypertension induced by angiotensin. Exper. Neurol. 84, 666 - 670.
Pardridge, W.M., Boada, R.J. & Farrell, C.R. (1990a) : Brain-type glucose transporter (GLUT-1) is selectively localized to the blood-brain barrier. J. Biol Chem. 265, 18035 - 18040.
Pardridge, W.M., Triguero, D., Buciak, J. & Yang, J. (1990b): Evaluation of cationized rat albumin as a potential blood-brain barrier drug transport vector. J.Pharmacol.Exp.Therap. 255, 893 - 899.
Pardridge. W.M., Triguero, D. & Buciak, J.L. (1990c) : β-Endorphin chimeric peptides : transport through the blood-brain barrier in vivo and cleavage of disulfide linkage by brain. Endocrinology 126, 977 - 984.
Price, M.T., Pusateri, M.E., Crow, S.E., Buchsbaum, S., Olney, J. & Lowry, O.H. (1984) : Uptake of exogenous aspartate into circumventricular organs but not other regions of adult mouse brain. J. Neurochem. 42, 740 - 744.
Rapoport, S. I. (1970) : Effect of concentrated solutions on blood-brain barrier. Am. J. Physiol. 219, 270 - 274.
Rennels, M.L., Gregory, T.F., Blaumanis, O.R., Fujimoto, K. & Grady, P.A. (1985) : Evidence for a "paravascular" fluid circulation in the mammalian central nervous system, provided by the rapid distribution of tracer protein throughout the brain from the subarachnoid space. Brain Res. 326, 47 - 63.
Rubin, L.L., Hall, D.E., Porter, S., Barbu, K. Cannon, C., Horner, H.C., Janatpour, M, Liaw, C.W., Manning, K., Morales, J., Tanner, L.I., Tomaselli, K.J. & Bard, F. (1991) : A cell culture method of the blood-brain barrier. J. Cell Biol. 115, 1725 - 1735.
Rutten, M.J, Hoover, R.L. & Karnovsky, M.J. (1987) : Electrical resistance and macromolecular permeability of brain endothelial monolayer cultures. Brain Res. 425, 301 - 310.
Schmidley, J.W. & Wissig, S.L. (1986) : Anionic sites on the luminal surface of fenestrated and continuous capillaries of the CNS. Brain Res. 363, 265 - 271.
Shaver, S.W., Pang, J.J., Wall, K.M., Sposito, N.M. & Gross, P.M. (1991) : Subregional topography of capillaries in the dorsal vagal complex of rats. I Morphometric properties. J. Comp. Neurol. 306, 73-82.
Shimon-Hophy, M., Wadhwani, K.C. Chandrasekaran, K., Larson, D., Smith, Q.R. & Rapoport, S.I. (1991) : Regional blood-brain barrier transport of cationized bovine serum albumin in awake rats. Am. J. Physiol. 261, R478 - R483.
Smith, K.R. & Borchardt, R.T. (1989) : Permeability and mechansim of albumin, cationized albumin and glycosylated albumin transcellular transport across monolayers of cultured bovine brain capillary endothelial cells. Pharmaceut. Res. 6, 466 - 473.
Sposito, N.M. & Gross, P.M. (1987) : Topography and morphometry of capillaries in the rat subfornical organ. J. Comp. Neurol. 260, 36 - 46.

Stewart, P.A. & Wiley, M.J. (1981) : Developing nervous tissue induces formation of blood-brain characteristics in invading endothelial cells : A study using quail - chick transplantation chimeras. Devel. Biol. 84, 183-192.
Sztriha, L. & Betz, A.L. (1991) : Oleic acid reversibly opens the blood-brain barrier. Brain Res. 550, 257 - 262.
Tao-Cheng, J-H., Nagy, Z. & Brightman, M.W. (1987) : Tight junctions of brain endothelium in vitro are enhanced by astrocytes. J. Neurosci. 7, 3293 - 3299.
Tontsch, U. & Bauer, H-C. (1991) : Glial cells and neurons induce blood-brain barrier related enzymes in cultured cerebral endothelial cells. Brain Res. 539, 247 - 253.
Triguero, D., Buciak, J.D. & Pardridge, W.M. (1989) : Blood-brain barrier transport of cationized immunoglobulin G. Enhanced delivery compared to native protein. Proc. Natl. Acad. Sci. *U.S.A.* 86, 4761 - 4765.
Tsubaki, S., Brightman, M.W., Nagakawa, H., Owens, E. and Blasberg, R.G. (1987) : Local blood flow and vascular permeability of autonomic ganglion-transplants in the brain. Brain Res. 424, 71-83.
Van der Kooy, D., Koda, L.Y., McGinty, J.F., Gerfen, C.R. & Bloom, F.E. (1984) : The organization of projections from the cortex, amygdala and hypothalamus to the nucleus of the solitary tract in rat. J. Comp. Neurol. 224, 1 - 24.

II. Cancer chemotherapy- and radiation-induced emesis: mechanisms and treatments

II. Vomissements induits par la chimiothérapie anti-cancéreuse et l'irradiation: mécanismes et traitements

Mechanisms and Control of Emesis. Eds A.L. Bianchi, L. Grélot, A.D. Miller, G.L. King. Colloque INSERM/ John Libbey Eurotext Ltd. © 1992, Vol. 223, pp. 115-127

Mechanisms of chemotherapy-induced vomiting: involvement of 5-HT_3 receptors

Robert J. Naylor and John A. Rudd

The School of Pharmacy, University of Bradford, Bradford, West Yorkshire, BD7 1DP, UK

Abstract

There is clear evidence that 5-HT_3 receptor antagonists such as ondansetron and granisetron are highly effective to prevent the emesis induced by chemotherapy in animals and man. The 5-HT_3 receptors are located in high density on the vagus nerve terminals in the gut and centrally in the area postrema and nucleus tractus solitarius. These sites probably represent the most important antiemetic sites of action. The evidence that 5-HT is involved in emesis and the nature of the pathways mediating chemotherapy induced emesis are critically reviewed.

Mécanisme du vomissement induit par la chimiothérapie: implication des récepteurs sérotoninergiques 5-HT3.

Résumé: Il est clairement établi que les antagonistes des récepteurs sérotoninergiques de type 5-HT3, tels que l'ondansetron et le granisetron, sont hautement efficaces dans la prévention du vomissement induit par la chimiothérapie chez l'animal et l'homme. Les récepteurs 5-HT3 sont localisés en haute densité sur les terminaisons sensorielles vagales dans le tube digestif, et centralement dans l'area postrema et le noyau du faisceau solitaire. Ces différents sites représentent probablement les sites d'action antiémétiques les plus importants. L'implication de la 5-HT dans le vomissement et la nature des voies nerveuses mises en jeu pendant le vomissement induit par la chimiothérapie sont discutées.

Introduction

Clinical success in cancer chemotherapy is not only dependent on the discovery of effective new chemotherapeutic drugs, but is also dependent on controlling their toxic side-effects to improve the therapeutic index. Chemotherapy is well known to have a wide range of side-effects (eg. dehydration, electrolyte imbalance, impaired renal function, malnutrition and periods of anxiety and depression) leading in total to a decreased quality of life. But to the patient nausea and vomiting is one of the most distressing, in some cases being so severe as to discourage some patients from future potential life saving therapies (Laszlo & Lucas, 1981). Of the chemotherapeutic agents that are used, cisplatin (cis-diamminedichloroplatinum II) has the greatest potential to induce emesis, compromising some 60-100% of patients within approximately 2 hrs of administration (see Bremmer, 1991). It is to this end that the search for new antiemetic treatments commenced and this chapter attempts to review the possible mechanisms by which chemotherapy induces emesis and where the 5-HT_3 receptor antagonists act to achieve their antiemetic effects.

The Clinical Success of the 5-HT_3 Receptor Antagonists

Before the discovery of the 5-HT_3 receptor antagonists, high-dose metoclopramide was considered to be the most useful drug in controlling the emetic side effects induced by cancer chemotherapy (Triozzi and Laszlo, 1987), although its use was frequently associated with unwanted extrapyramidal side-effects (Indo and Ando, 1982; Leopold, 1984). The effectiveness of metoclopramide was initially attributed to its dopamine receptor antagonist properties (Niemegeers, 1982), but unlike other dopamine receptor antagonists, only high-dose metoclopramide was known to be effective at antagonising cisplatin-induced emesis (Alphin *et al.*, 1986; Costall *et al.*, 1986, 1987; Miner *et al.*, 1986). These observations suggested that metoclopramide may have an additional action other than its dopamine receptor antagonist properties to antagonise cisplatin-induced emesis.

An intuitive leap by Fozard and co-workers (1979) was made on the observations that metoclopramide could antagonise the actions of 5-HT at the 'M' receptor on the rabbit heart, and subsequently this lead to the development of the selective 5-HT_3 receptor antagonist MDL 72222 (Fozard, 1984) and the more potent and selective 5-HT_3 receptor antagonist ICS 205-930 (Richardson *et al.*, 1985). Since then, a number of relatively potent and selective 5-HT_3 receptor antagonists have been developed including ondansetron (GR 38032F; Butler *et al.*, 1988), granisetron (BRL 43694; Sanger and Nelson, 1989) and zacopride (Smith *et al.*, 1988b), presenting as effective antiemetics against chemotherapy- and radiation-induced emesis in both the human and animal models (see Bremer, 1991; King, 1990b). Indeed, the 5-HT_3 receptor antagonists represent a much improved treatment for chemotherapy-induced nausea and vomiting, causing a complete or major inhibition of emesis without the unwanted sedation and extrapyramidal side-effects associated with the clinical use of metoclopramide (see Bremer, 1991).

The Importance of Preclinical Studies

The antiemetic spectrum of action of the 5-HT_3 receptor antagonists against chemotherapy induced emesis was first shown in animals and has an impressive breadth. The emetic effects of actinomycin D, adriamycin, cisplatin, darcarbazine, and mechloroethamine are all successfully antagonised by the 5-HT_3 receptor antagonist zacopride in the dog (Smith *et al.*, 1988b; Smith *et al.*, 1989) and in the ferret, emesis induced by cisplatin has been controlled by ondansetron (Butler *et al.*, 1988; Endo *et al.*, 1990; Stables *et al.*, 1987), ICS 205-930, zacopride (Costall *et al.*, 1987, 1990), granisetron (Bermudez *et al.*, 1988), MDL72222 (Miner and Sanger, 1986), BRL24924 (Miner *et al.*, 1987) and in the *Suncus murinus* by ICS 205-930 (Torii *et al.*, 1990). The emesis induced by cyclophosphamide has been antagonised by ondansetron (Andrews *et al.*, 1987; Endo *et al.*, 1990) and granisetron (Bermudez *et al.*, 1988). There are few studies in the cat, but ICS 205-930 has been demonstrated to prevent cisplatin-induced emesis (Lucot, 1989). Therefore, there is little doubt that the 5-HT_3 receptor antagonists can inhibit chemotherapy-induced emesis in a number of animal models.

The current understanding of emetic mechanisms has been mainly derived from animal experimentation, with probably the most significant advances in emesis research being pioneered by Hatcher & Weiss (1923) and Borison & Wang (1949, 1953) many years ago. In particular, the distinction was made between a "vomiting centre" in the reticular formation of the medulla of the hindbrain which co-ordinates or represents the temporal activation of effector nuclei necessary to generate the forces required for emesis to occur, and the emetic detection sites which input to the vomiting centre to trigger the emetic reflex. This distinction has formed the bases of many hypotheses to explain emesis induction and antagonism. Today however, the "vomiting centre" is probably more wisely viewed as a collection of effector nuclei in the medulla of the hindbrain (see Fukuda & Koga, 1991; Miller and Wilson, 1983), with the area postrema (the proposed site of the "chemoreceptor trigger zone", see Borison and Brizzee, 1951; King, 1990b) and the gastrointestinal tract (in particular its neuronal connections with the brainstem via the vagal and splanchnic nerves) forming the most investigated areas in emesis research to determine the mechanisms by which chemotherapeutic agents induce emesis.

The Role of the Vagus in Chemotherapy-Induced Emesis: Relevance of 5-HT_3 Receptors

The physiological significance of the vagus nerve as the possible neuronal link between the gastrointestinal tract and the central mechanisms controlling emesis has been highlighted by Derbyshire and Ferguson (1938) who demonstrated that electrical stimulation of the ventral vagus in decerebrate cats and dogs could produce vomiting. This effect was more recently reported by Milano *et al.* (1990) using decerebrate cats, Fukuda & Koga (1991) using decerebrate dogs, and by Andrews *et al.* (1990) reporting emesis as a consequence of stimulating the abdominal vagus in conscious ferrets and urethane-anaesthetised ferrets (Andrews *et al.*, 1985).

Chemotherapy-induced emesis in the ferret is known to be partially mediated by the vagus and splanchnic nerves and could be the result of a possible disruptive action in the gastrointestinal tract (see Andrews *et al.*, 1988, 1990) Cisplatin- and cyclophosphamide-induced emesis has been prevented by a combination of bilateral vagotomy and splancthectomy. Retching to cisplatin is not abolished by either a single abdominal vagotomy or splancthectomy (see Andrews and Hawthorn, 1987; Hawthorn *et al.*, 1988).

There is evidence that injections of 5-HT or 2-methyl-5-HT into the abdominal aorta of urethane-anaesthetised ferrets can evoke a discharge of the abdominal vagus, the discharge being sensitive to 5-HT_3 receptor antagonism (Davison and Andrews, 1988). 5-HT_3 receptors are known to exist on the afferent vagal fibres (see Kilpatrick *et al.*, 1990; Round and Wallis, 1986) and activation of the vagus nerve *in vitro* by 5-HT, or the selective 5-HT_3 receptor agonist 2-methyl-5-HT, can also evoke a depolarisation which is sensitive to 5-HT_3 receptor antagonism (Davison and Andrews, 1988; Paintal, 1973). Therefore, the possibility exists that a mechanism could facilitate the emesis induced by chemotherapeutics by activation of 5-HT_3receptors at peripheral sites on vagal afferent fibres in the gastrointestinal tract.

The emetic response to stimulation of the central end of the vagus is not however blocked by 5-HT_3 receptor antagonists in the ferret (Andrews *et al.*, 1990), or in the cat (Milano *et al.*, 1990). This has tempted the above workers to conclude that the 5-HT_3 receptors involved in the suppression of emesis induced by agents such as cisplatin are probably not located at central sites and therefore, must be located at peripheral sites. A major failing of this hypothesis is that the vagus is also important in mediating other forms of emesis. The vagal afferents and splanchnic nerves are known to be important in the early phases of copper sulphate-induced emesis. Bilateral lesion of both the vagal afferents and splanchnic nerves abolishes the early retching and vomiting induced by copper sulphate, even at lethal doses (Wang & Borison, 1951, 1952). Thus, intragastric copper sulphate-induced emesis is not prevented by the 5-HT_3 receptor antagonists ICS 205-930 and ondansetron in the ferret (Costall et al., 1990; Buchheit *et al.*,1990) and zacopride in the dog (Smith *et al.*,1989). However, high dose ondansetron (Endo *et al.*, 1991) and ICS 205-930 (Bhandari & Andrews, 1991) have been reported to antagonise copper sulphate-induced emesis. The discrepancies may arise from the different doses of copper sulphate used to induce emesis and/or may indicate that a component of copper sulphate induced emesis may be mediated by a 5-HT_3 receptor mechanism. This may account for some of the similarities between the pathways utilised by copper sulphate and chemotherapy-induced emesis. However, reserpine and fenfluramine are ineffective antiemetic pretreatments against copper sulphate-induced emesis in the ferret (Rudd *et al.*, 1990) but prevent cisplatin-induced emesis (Costall *et al.*, 1988) indicating a basic difference between the mechanisms mediating cisplatin- and gastric irritation-induced emesis.

In addition and also overlooked, is the inability of bilateral vagotomy to prevent cisplatin-induced retching, suggesting that other inputs into the "vomiting centre" may have important 5-HT_3 receptors located on their afferents at central and/or peripheral sites. The other input could be partially mediated by the splanchnic nerves, and indeed, recent evidence has been presented to indicate that the splanchnic nerves may influence central 5-HT_3 receptors, based on a decrease in 5-HT_3 binding sites in the dorsal motor nucleus of the vagus nerve after splancthectomy (Leslie *et al.*, 1990).

The hypothesis that 5-HT_3 receptors located on the peripheral vagus in the gut are important sites for the 5-HT_3 receptor antagonists to exert their antiemetic effects has also been based on the ability of cisplatin to cause cell death in the intestines (Rosenberg, 1985; Lieberman *et al.*, 1970) and alter the 5-HT synthesis/turnover in the mucosa following treatment in the ferret (Endo *et al.*, 1990; Stables *et al.*, 1987). Unfortunately however, in both studies samples were removed at a time after the emetic response had ceased, i.e. on the second day of a repeated administration of cisplatin (9-10 mg/kg), 3 hours after the last administration. The results from the two studies did, however, clearly demonstrate that 5-HT levels become elevated in the ileal mucosa, but whereas one study found that the levels of 5-HIAA, the main metabolite of 5-HT was elevated, with no changes in noradrenaline levels (Stables *et al.*, 1987), the other reported a decrease in 5-HIAA levels and indicated that noradrenaline levels were elevated (Endo *et al.*, 1990). The discrepancies make it difficult to assess whether the metabolism of 5-HT is either increased or decreased. Nevertheless, mucosal damage was reported in the former studies, and it is known that cisplatin accumulates within the mucosa (Rosenberg, 1985) and has been reported to induce small intestinal toxicity in the mouse, reducing the crypt cell production rate and crypt to villus ratio (Allan and Smyth, 1986).

A further difficulty in such studies is that 5-HT is present in large amounts in the gut (Erspamer,1966) and even a modest change in 5-HT levels may only present as a small fraction of the total 5-HT content making changes difficult to detect. In addition, any depletion in 5-HT levels in the mucosa, under normal conditions, would be rapidly replaced. In the rat, the total content of 5-HT in the GI tract is completely renewed within 8-9 hours after its depletion, and the half life of 5-HT in the dog gastrointestinal tract is approximately 6-8 hours, and in man it is approximately 7-12 hours (see Erspamer and Testini, 1959). Therefore it would be virtually impossible to detect small increases in 5-HT metabolism, unless the synthesising capacity of the enterochromaffin cells is dramatically compromised by cisplatin. It is also difficult to determine if cisplatin directly caused the changes in 5-HT metabolism *per se* or if the changes were a consequence of physical changes in gastric motility and physical disruption by the consequent retching and vomiting movements.

Nevertheless, cisplatin has been reported *in vitro* to facilitate a release of 5-HT from the guinea pig small intestine, the release being antagonised by ondansetron, hexamethonium, tetrodotoxin, and scopolamine (Racke and Schworer, 1991), suggesting that cisplatin facilitates 5-HT release by a neuronal mechanism. Again, the relevance of this work is difficult to extrapolate to the situation in the ferret and human since not only is the guinea pig an animal incapable of vomiting, but only ondansetron of the treatments tested, is known to effectively control cisplatin-induced emesis.

5-HT is well known to be synthesised and stored in the enterochromaffin cells of the gastrointestinal tract (Verbeuren, 1989) and its release may be stimulated by agonism of beta-adrenoceptors, muscarinic and nicotinic receptors, and inhibited by agonism of alpha-adrenoceptors, $GABA_A$ and $GABA_B$ receptors, histamine, receptors, VIP, and somatostatin, suggesting that pharmacological intervention is possible (see Racke and Schworer, 1991). Curiously however, stimulation of the peripheral end of the vagus and/ or splanchnic nerves have been reported to induce a release of 5-HT from the enterochromaffin cells (Ahlman and Dahlstrom, 1983; Larsson *et al.*, 1979), and this may indicate a mechanism of action whereby cisplatin could facilitate 5-HT release. However, this also seems unlikely since propranolol can antagonise the 5-HT release from vagal stimulation (see Racke and Schworer, 1991), but is an ineffective pretreatment to inhibit cisplatin-induced emesis (Tattersall, 1988). It is possible to speculate that vagotomy and splancthectomy could play a dual role to prevent emesis, ie. to reduce the information reaching the "vomiting centre" and to reduce the peripheral release of 5-HT. It is also possible to speculate that alterations in the intrinsic activity of the gastrointestinal tract following vagotomy/ splancthectomy may play an independent role in reducing the intensity of the emetic response in isolation from the inability to convey information to the vomiting centre following such a surgical procedure.

The Role of the Area Postrema and Associated Brainstem Nuclei in Chemotherapy Induced Emesis: Relevance of 5-HT_3 Receptors

There are many neuronal afferent and efferent connections between the area postrema and various other brain structures thought to be involved in the emetic circuits (see Leslie and Gwyn, 1984). Efferent projections are known to project to the parabrachial region of the pons in both the cat and rat (Loewy and Burton, 1978; Shapiro and Miselis, 1985), the nucleus of the spinal trigeminal nerve, the nucleus intercalatus, the nucleus prepositus hypoglossi, the hypoglossal nucleus, the locus coeruleus, and the superficial layers of the colliculi in the rat (Vigier and Portalier, 1979; Vigier and Rouviere, 1979). Efferent projections from the area postrema also extend to the subnucleus gelatinosus (also referred to as the area subpostrema, see Gwyn and Wolstencroft, 1968) and regions of the nucleus tractus solitarius (Gwyn and Leslie, 1979; Gwyn *et al.*, 1982; Leslie and Gwyn, 1982; Morest, 1967). Afferent neuronal connections to the area postrema have been reported to arise from the cranial nerves (V, IX, X), the hypothalamus, the nucleus tractus solitarius (particularly the subnucleus gelatinosus), the parabrachial area and the dorsal motor nucleus of the vagus (Leslie, 1986, Brizzee and Mehler, 1986). Other visceral afferent inputs into the area postrema have been reported to arise from the dorsal and lateral columns of the spinal cord (Morest, 1967).

The nucleus tractus solitarius (NTS) and subnucleus gelatinosus are important brain areas in emesis control since they are brainstem areas that directly underlay the area postrema, and are the site of termination for many of the vagal afferents arising from the gastrointestinal tract (Gwyn *et al.*, 1979, 1982). 5-HT_3 receptor recognition sites have been identified in high density within the area postrema, NTS, subnucleus gelatinosus and in lower density in the dorsal motor nucleus of the vagus nerve and the spinal trigeminal tract of a variety of species including man (Barnes *et al.*, 1990; Kilpatrick *et al.*, 1989; Leslie *et al.*, 1990b; Palacious *et al.*, 1991; Pratt and Bowery, 1989; Radja *et al.*, 1991; Reynolds *et al.*, 1991b; Waeber *et al.*, 1988). Vagal afferents are also reported to terminate in the area postrema, the dorsal motor nucleus of the vagus (Beckstead and Norgren, 1979; Gwyn *et al.*, 1979; Odekunle and Bower, 1985) and the reticular formation (Norman and Bower, 1982). The disappearance of 5-HT_3 receptor binding sites after vagotomy in the NTS suggests that they modulate the activity of the vagus before consequent input to the "vomiting centre" (Leslie *et al.*, 1990). 5-HT is present in neurones in the AP (see Leslie, 1985, 1986) and release from this site may facilitate or sensitise the vagus nerve. The 5-HT_3 receptor antagonists could easily be visualised to exert their antiemetic effects at such a site in the NTS and subnucleus gelatinosus.

The area postrema, site of the 'chemoreceptor trigger zone', classically defined by the abilities of lesions to abolish the emetic response to apomorphine and also to a host of other emetogens (Borison and Brizzee, 1951; see King 1990b for a review) can evoke vomiting on electrical stimulation (Iwase, 1971; Ikeda and Yamanaka 1970). It is however generally accepted that emetogens that have their major mechanism of action via the area postrema are unaffected by pretreatment with 5-HT_3 receptor antagonists eg. the 5-HT_3 antagonists are ineffective at abolishing the retching and vomiting induced by apomorphine (Bermudez *et al.*, 1988; Costall *et al.*, 1990; Miner *et al.*, 1987; Smith *et al.*, 1989) and loperamide

(Andrews *et al.*, 1990).

Functional evidence to support a central site facilitating the inhibition of emesis by the 5-HT_3 receptor antagonists has been provided by Higgins *et al.* (1989) who antagonised cisplatin-induced emesis in ferrets by the direct central injection of 5-HT_3 receptor antagonists ondansetron, GR 65630 and MDL 72222, into the vicinity of the area postrema/NTS. In addition, ablation of this area in the cat (McCarthy and Borison 1984; Miller &Wonaka, 1992) and dog (Bhandari *et al.*, 1989) prevents cisplatin-induced emesis, further implicating the area postrema in cisplatin-induced emesis. It is also known that cisplatin administered into the cerebroventricular system of cats (0.3 mg) can induce emesis (Smith *et al.*, 1988a). However the emesis induced via this route of administration was of rapid onset of 4 minutes compared to the latency of approximately 100 minutes following the intravenous injection of 7.5 mg/kg, and was blocked by zacopride (Smith *et al.*, 1988a). Since cisplatin administered intravenously does not evoke emesis with such a short latency of onset, the results in the cat are a peculiarity. A similar situation exists in the ferret, with 100-600 μg of cisplatin injected i.c.v. inducing emesis, but in these studies emesis occurred after a latency of approximately 100 min, compared to the normal latency of 70 min for a intravenous dose of 10 mg/kg i.v. (Tattersall, 1988). Nevertheless, both sets of results indicate that cisplatin has a capability to induce emesis centrally, albeit at reduced intensity (in terms of retches and vomits), possibly at the level of the area postrema.

The Involvement of 5-HT in Emesis

The ability of the 5-HT_3 receptor antagonists to inhibit chemotherapy induced emesis (see above) has implicated 5-HT in the emetic response (Andrews *et al.*, 1988). However, the role of 5-HT in the emetic reflex remains far from clear. Evidence is available that the precursor of 5-HT, 5-hydroxytryptophan (5-HTP), when administered intravenously to man can induce emesis within 30-120 min (Chadwick and *et al.*, 1974; Magnussen and Nielsen-Kudsk, 1979), and when administered orally induces nausea, further implicating a rise in 5-HT function as a causative factor for emesis (Alexander *et al.*, 1963; Carroll *et al.*, 1970; Greenwood *et al.*, 1975). Emesis induced by the intraperitoneal administration of 5-HTP has also been observed in cats and dogs, and intravenous infusions of 5-HT have produced retching and vomiting in dogs (Bogdanski *et al.*, 1958; Cahen, 1964). Although these studies may indicate that the emesis may be occurring due to a peripheral action, 5-HTP can penetrate the blood brain barrier, and it is possible that the emesis induced by 5-HTP is of a central origin (Moir and Eccleston, 1968; Wurtman *et al.*, 1981) The 5-HT receptor subtype(s) involved in the emesis evoked in the cat and dog from these studies are unknown and may even involve a direct or indirect release of catecholeamines (Cahen, 1964). A more recent study by Miller & Nanaka (1992) found that 2-methyl-5-HT (3.7 mg/kg i.p.) and another 5-HT_3 receptor agonist phenylbiguanide (2.0-8.0 mg/kg i.p.) reliably induced emesis in the cat, the emesis to phenylbiguanide being prevented by MDL 72222. The threshold doses of phenylbiguanide to induce emesis in the cat were increased after vagotomy and particularly after splancthectomy but were not affected by area postrema lesion.

A lack of emetic activity has been reported to exist with 2-methyl-5-HT in the ferret when administered i.v. (3 mg/kg) or orally (King, 1990a). Conversely, a study by Sancilio and co-workers (1991) indicated that both 2-methyl-5-HT and phenylbiguanide, when administered orally at high doses (10 mg/kg) could induce emesis in the ferret, the emesis being prevented by 5-HT_3 receptor antagonism with ICS 205-930 and zacopride. Emesis has also been evoked by the intravenous, subcutaneous and intraperitoneal injection of 5-HT (2.5-10 mg/kg), and by the subcutaneous administration of 2-methyl-5-HT (0.63-10 mg/kg) in the *Suncus murinus*, the emesis being prevented by vagotomy or pretreatment with ICS 205-930 (Torii *et al.*, 1991). Curiously however, central injection of the 5-HT_3 receptor agonist, 2-methyl-5-HT into the ventricles of the ferret does not convincingly induce emesis (Higgins *et al.*, 1989;

Tattersall, 1988) and a retching response was only recorded in 1/5 animals. As the excitatory responses of the area postrema to 5-HT are quite rapid (Carpenter, 1983), it would be expected that if the 5-HT_3 receptors at the level of the area postrema actually produce emesis on activation then 5-HT or the 5-HT_3 receptor agonists studied would induce emesis with a short latency of onset. Clearly this is not the case in animal models, and may indicate a need to investigate the effect of 5-HT infusion over longer time periods.

The above studies tend to indicate that the 5-HT_3 receptors located in the periphery, possibly in the gut, have the capacity to induce emesis and this may reflect a mechanism by which cisplatin induces emesis ie. by a localised release of 5-HT. However, the studies by Miller & Nonaka (1992) uncovered an important difference between cisplatin- and 5-HT_3 receptor agonist-induced emesis. Thus whilst the abdominal visceral nerves are important to some extent in mediating the emesis induced by both cisplatin and phenylbiguanide (based on the increases in thresholds and delays in the onset of emesis), the area postrema is crucial to cisplatin-induced emesis, but does not effect phenylbiguanid- induced emesis.

The Involvement of 5-HT in Chemotherapy Induced Emesis

If 5-HT is released from stores such as the enterochromaffin cells of the gastrointestinal tract during treatment with cisplatin, then it does not seem unreasonable to assume that 5-HT would become elevated in the plasma and perhaps exert an action at additional sites. In the human, cisplatin based chemotherapy only dramatically increased the plasma levels of 5-HT in 4/10 patients (Barnes *et al.*, 1990). It is interesting to note from this study that in some patients that did experience breakthrough emesis 5-HT levels in the plasma were not elevated, even in the samples that were taken during vomiting episodes. Those patients that were observed to have an increase in plasma 5-HT levels may be those in which 5-HT_3 receptor antagonists are effective. 5-HT_3 antagonists are effective in 50-80 % of patients treated with chemotherapy (Chevallier 1990; Cupissol *et al.*, 1990; Marty; 1990; Marty *et al.*, 1990), and it is tempting to speculate that the patients that do not exhibit increases in plasma 5-HT are those patients that are not protected from emesis by 5-HT_3 receptor antagonists. It is possible that in these patients, emesis occurs via unspecified neurotransmitter systems. Nevertheless, an important finding of the study was that patients would request additional antiemetics in the absence of increases in plasma 5-HT which may tend to indicate that nausea operates independently of elevations of plasma 5-HT. Contrasting with this study are results obtained in the ferret where an emetogenic dose of cisplatin failed to affect plasma 5-HT, 5-HTP or 5-HIAA levels (Rudd *et al*, 1992). This discrepancy may be the result of a species difference and is conflicting with the notion that there is a gross release of 5-HT and could indicate that the role of 5-HT in the emesis induced by cisplatin is more subtle. Indeed the ability of 5-HT synthesis inhibition to prevent cisplatin-induced emesis in the ferret (Barnes *et al.*, 1988) may indicate that the 5-HT system is important in emesis but does not need to be increased to facilitate the emesis.

A detailed study by Cubeddu and colleagues (1990) reported that the nausea and vomiting in response to cisplatin in man closely parallelled urinary increases in 5-HIAA excretion. These increases were thought indicative of an increase in 5-HT release from the enterochromaffin cells, and occurred in all patients. Cubeddu and colleagues (1990) used the excretion of creatinine to correct the changes of 5-HIAA with variation in urinary output, and although this approach is attractive, it may be flawed by the ability of cisplatin to cause damage to kidney function and reduce creatinine clearance (see Rosenberg, 1985). Unfortunately, the study did not record the status of 5-HIAA levels in the urine after the emesis induced by cisplatin had subsided, so it is not possible to know whether the levels of 5-HIAA return to baseline in the absence of nausea and vomiting, or if the increases were a consequence of kidney damage, in which case the return to baseline would be expected to be slower. Another problem that may arise from relying urinary levels of 5-HIAA as an indicator of 5-HT function during treatment with chemotherapeutic agents that are toxic to the kidney is that 5-HT is itself synthesised in the kidney (Sole *et al.*, 1986) and therefore non -specific kidney damage may release 5-HT from this site. This possibility was not anticipated and therefore it is difficult to directly correlate the increases in urinary 5-HIAA levels with 5-HT release from the enterochromaffin cells of the gastrointestinal tract.

Anatomical Location of the 5-HT_3 Receptors Important for the Antiemetic Effects of the 5-HT_3 Receptor Antagonists

A few studies have attempted to pharmacologically separate the peripheral and central 5-HT_3 receptor sites, in order to visualise the site of action for the 5-HT_3 receptor antagonists. These studies utilised quaternary derivatives of potent and selective 5-HT_3 receptor antagonists, with known antiemetic actions against cisplatin-induced emesis. A study in the ferret found that quaternarised ICS 205-930 could antagonise the retching and vomiting induced by cisplatin, and it was concluded that the 5-HT_3 receptors responsible for the antiemetic effects of the 5-HT_3 receptor antagonists are located peripherally (Buchheit *et al.*, 1990). This study overlooked the possibility that the quaternarised compound could have been antagonising emesis at the level of the area postrema, as this structure has an incomplete blood-brain-barrier. Contrasting with the results obtained in the ferret, the quaternary 5-HT_3 receptor antagonist LY 191617, failed to protect against cisplatin-induced emesis in the dog (Robertson *et al.*, 1990), suggesting that the site of the 5-HT_3 receptors involved in mediating the emetic response evoked by cisplatin is not at the level of the area postrema, or at other peripherally located sites. Overall, the studies in the dog and ferret may indicate a true species difference in the location of the emetic detection mechanisms, or that there are differences between the lipophilicity of the quaternarised compounds used.

As already indicated, 5-HT_3 receptor recognition sites have been demonstrated to exist on vagal afferents in the nucleus tractus solitarius, particularly in the rostral regions (Leslie *et al.*, 1990b). Treatment of ferrets with cisplatin has been observed to increase c-fos protein activity in this region and in the area postrema, suggesting that cisplatin induces an increase in neurotransmitter-receptor activation in these areas (Reynolds *et al.*, 1990a). The increase in c-fos activity in the NTS was reduced by vagotomy, or by pretreatment with granisetron, but the activity remained unchanged in the area postrema. The area postrema may have been stimulated by other substances circulating in the blood, or indeed by cisplatin itself. It is also known that stimulation of the abdominal vagus also results in an increase in glucose utilisation in the area postrema, NTS, dorsal motor nucleus of the vagus, and the hypoglossal nucleus (Andrews *et al.*, 1990) However, the pharmacological relevance of this to the emesis induced by cisplatin is obscure.

Conclusion

From a consideration of all the above evidencé, it is possible to hypothesise that the 5-HT_3 receptors, which are located both within the gut and within the dorsal vagal complex, may play an important and perhaps pivotal role in the emetic mechanism of action of chemotherapeutic agents. It seems possible that activation of the area postrema, or other input (possibly cortical), has the ability to facilitate release of a substance which directly or indirectly stimulates the 5-HT_3 receptors located within the dorsal vagal complex. This interaction could then facilitate or sensitise the effects of the vagal and splanchnic nerve inputs, before the information is relayed to the "vomiting centre". Indeed, the hypothesis accommodates the observations that both the vagal and splanchnic afferents are important in the reflex, as is the integrity of the area postrema. Furthermore, activation of the area postrema need not necessarily be the mechanism involved in the sensitisation process, as a non-specific increase in 5-HT_3 receptor function in the region of the NTS and/or subnucleus gelatinosus could fulfil the criteria. This hypothesis is also suited to the possibility that the vagus and splanchnic nerves could be activated by 5-HT and/or other substances. Since vagal afferents also communicate with the area postrema, it could be that reverberation within a feedback-loop may allow the area postrema and the visceral afferent inputs to sensitise each other's effects (see fig. 1.0.). The identification of the various endogenous emetogens provides a crucial future challenge both for an understanding of the mechanisms involved in emesis and the development of therapeutic interventions.

However, caution in all the above studies must be exercised when collectively viewing the evidence from the dog, cat, monkey and ferret in attempts to identify the site of action of the 5-HT_3 receptor antagonists for the treatment of radiation- and cisplatin-induced emesis. The emetic control mechanisms of each species are different with respect to the detection sites used. For example, the inputs into the "vomiting centre" mediating the effects of radiation-induced emesis have been studied more extensively than for the effects of chemotherapy. In the dog, lesion of either the vagus and/or the splanchnic nerves only slightly delays radiation-induced emesis, although there is a tendency for the emesis to be reduced by approximately 30 %, whereas area postrema lesions completely abolish the emesis (Carpenter *et al.*, 1986; Harding *et al.*, 1985; Wang *et al.*, 1958), at least the early emesis. Delayed emesis to radiation can appear in dogs after either area postrema or vagal and splanchnic nerve lesions, but a combination of both is effective at abolishing both stages of emesis (Wang *et al.*, 1958). As regards the monkey, both single area postrema or vagal lesions are effective to prevent the emesis (Brizzee 1956). In contrast, area postrema lesions in the cat are ineffective at abolishing the early phases of radiation induced emesis (Borison *et al.*, 1987), as are lesions of the vagus and/or splanchnic nerves (Wang, *et al.*, 1958). Vagotomy and/or splancthectomy does, however, delay the onset to emesis. Whereas the area postrema does not appear to be important in the vomiting response of cats to radiation, it is essential in the emetic actions of cisplatin (McCarthy and Borison, 1984; Miller & Nonaka, 1992), thus highlighting important differences in the mechanisms of action of radiation and cisplatin-induced emesis in the cat.

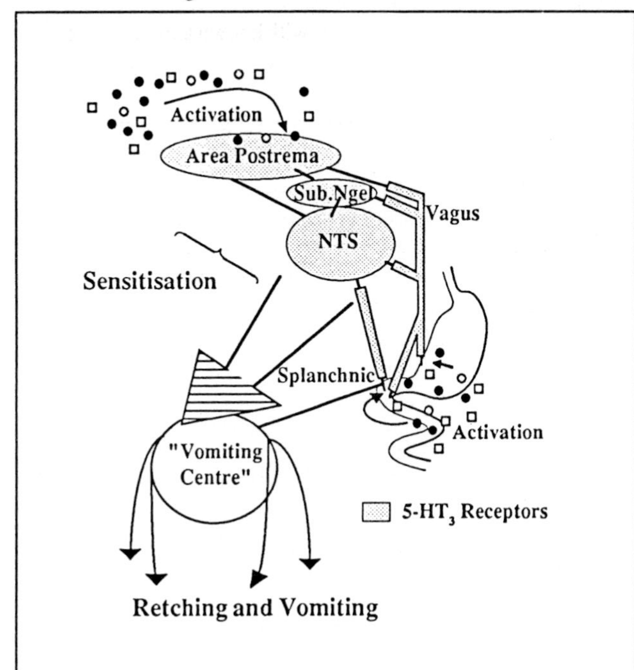

Figure 1.0. The major emetic circuts involved in the emetic response to chemotherapy and the possible sites of action for the 5-HT_3 receptor antagonists. Sub.Ngel: subnucleus gelatinosus; NTS: nucleus tractus solitarius.

It remains a possibility that the emetic pathways utilised for the expression of cisplatin-induced emesis and those used by 5-HT could be different based on the ability of 5-HT to interact with other 5-HT receptor subtypes. A general rise in 5-HT would be anticipated to be emetic by an agonist action at the 5-HT_3 receptor whilst be antiemetic by an agonist action at the 5-HT_{1A} receptor (Lucot & Crampton, 1988). The role of 5-HT interaction at the putative 5-HT_4 receptor awaits further research but may be indicated as being emetic via vagal pathways (Bhandari & Andrews, 1991).

References

Ahlman, H. and Dahlstrom, A. (1983) Vagal mechanisms controlling serotonin release from the gastrointestinal tract and pyloric motor function. *J. Auton. Nerv. Syst.* 9: 119-140.

Alexander, F., Curtis, G. C., Sprince, H. and Crosley, A. P. (1963) L-methionine and L-tryptophan feeding in non-psychotics and schizophrenics with and without tranylcypramine. *J. Nerv. Ment. Dis.* 137: 135-142.

Allan, S. G. and Smyth, J. F. (1986) Small intestinal mucosal toxicity of cis-platinum - comparison of toxicity with platinum analogues and dexamethasone. *Br. J. Cancer* 53: 355-360.

Alphin, R. S., Proakis, A. G., Leonard, C. A., Smith, W. L., Dannenburg, W. N., Kinnier, W. J., Johnson, D. N., Sancilio, L. F. and Ward, J. W. (1986) Antagonism of cisplatin-induced emesis by metoclopramide and dazopride through enhancement of gastric motility. *Dig. Dis. Sci.* 31: 524-529.

Andrews, P. L. R. and Hawthorn, J. (1987) Evidence for an extra-abdominal site of action for the 5-HT_3 receptor antagonist BRL24924 in the inhibition of radiation-evoked emesis in the ferret. *Neuropharmacology* 26: 1367-1370.

Andrews, P. L. R., Bingham, S. and Davis, C.J. (1985) Retching evoked by stimulation of abdominal vagal afferents in the anaesthised ferret. *J. Physiol.* 358: 103P.

Andrews, P. L. R., Davis, C. J., Bingham, S., Davidson, H. I. M., Hawthorn, J. and Maskell L. (1990) The abdominal visceral innervation and the emetic reflex: pathways, pharmacology, and plasticity. *Can. J. Physiol. Pharmacol.* 68: 325-345.

Andrews, P. L. R., Hawthorn, J. and Sanger, G. J. (1987) The effect of abdominal visceral nerve lesions and a novel 5-HT-M receptor antagonist on cytotoxic and radiation induced emesis in the ferret. *J. Physiol.*382: 47P.

Andrews, P. L. R., Rapeport, W. G. and Sanger, G. J. (1988) Neuropharmacology of emesis induced by anti-cancer therapy. *TIPS* 9: 334-341.

Barnes, J. M., Barnes, N. M., Costall, B., Naylor, R. J. and Tattersall, F. D. (1988) Reserpine, para-chlorophenylalanine and fenfluramine antagonise cisplatin-induced emesis in the ferret. *Neuropharmacology* 27: 783-389.

Barnes, J. M., Barnes, N. M., Costall, B., Naylor I. L., Naylor, R. J. and Rudd, J. A. (1990) Topographical distribution of 5-HT_3 receptor recognition sites in the ferret brain stem. *Naunyn-Schmied. Arch. Pharmacol.* 342: 17-24.

Barnes, N.M., Ge., J., Jones, W.G., Naylor, R.J. & Rudd, J.A. (1990) Cisplatin-induced emesis: preliminary results indicative of changes in plasma levels of 5-hydroxytryptamine. *Br. J. Cancer.* 62, 862-864.

Beckstead, R. M. and Norgren, R. (1979) An autoradiographic examination of central distribution of the trigeminal, facial, glossopharyngeal and vagal nerves in the monkey. *J. Comp. neurol.* 184: 455-472.

Bermudez, J., Boyle, E. A., Miner, W. D. and Sanger, G. J. (1988) The anti-emetic potential of the 5-$hydroxytryptamine_3$ receptor antagonist BRL 43694. *Br. J. Cancer* 58: 644-650.

Bhandari, P. & Andrews, P.L.R. (1991) Preliminary evidence for the involvement of the putative 5-HT_4 receptor in zacopride and copper sulphate-induced vomiting in the ferret. *Eur. J. Pharmacol.* 204, 273-280.

Bhandari, P, Gupta, Y.K., Seth, S.D. & Chugh, A. (1989) Cisplatin-induced emesis: Effect of chemorecepter trigger zone ablation in dogs. *Asi Pacific Journal of Pharmacol.* 4, 209-211.

Bogdanski, D. F., Weissbach, H. and Udenfriend, S. (1958) Pharmacological studies with the serotonin precusor, 5-hydroxytryptophan. *J. Pharmacol. Exp. Ther.* 122: 182-194

Borison, H. L. and Brizzee, K. R. (1951) Morphology of emetic chemoreceptor trigger zone in cat medulla oblongata. *Proc. Soc. Exp. Biol. Med.* 77: 38-43.

Borison, H. L. and Wang, S. C. (1949) Functional localization of the central coordinating mechanism for emesis in cat. J. *Neurophysiol.* 12: 304-313.

Borison, H. L. and Wang, S. C. (1953) Physiology and pharmacology of vomiting. *Pharmac. Rev.* 5: 193-230.

Bremer, K. (1991) 5-Hydroxytryptamine (serotonin) subtype 3 antagonists, a major step in prophylaxis and control of cytostatic and radiation-induced emesis. *J. Canser Res. Clin. Oncol.* 117: 85-87.

Brizzee, K. R. and Mehler, W. R. (1986) The central nervous connections involved in the vomiting reflex. In *Nausea and Vomiting: Mechanism and Treatment.* (Eds. Davies, C. J., Lake-Bakaar, G. V. and Grahame-Smith, D. G.) Springer-Verlag, Berlin, pp.31-55.

Buchheit, K. H., Buscher, H. H. and Gamse, R. (1990) The antiemetic profile of the 5-HT_3 receptor antagonist, ICS205-930, and its quaternary derivative. *The 2nd IUPHAR Satellite Meeting on Serotonin*, Bazel, Switzerland, July 11-13, P148.

Butler, A., Hill, J. M., Ireland, S. J., Jordon, C. C. and Tyers, M. B. (1988) Pharmacological properties of GR38032F, a novol antagonist at 5-HT_3 receptor. *Br. J. Pharmacol.* 94: 397-412.

Cahen, R. L. (1964) On the mechanism of emesis induced by 5-hydroxytryptamine. *P.S.E.B.M.* 116: 402-404.

Carpenter, D. O., Briggs, D. B. and Strominger, N. (1983) Responses of neurons of canine area postrema to neurotransmitters and peptides. Cell. Molec. *Neurobiol.* 3: 113-126.

Carroll, B. J., Mowbray, R. M. and Davies, B. M. (1970) Sequential comparison of L-tryptophan with ECT in severe depression. *Lancet* i: 967-969.

Chadwick, D., Reynolds, E. H. and Marsden, C. D. (1974) Relief of action myoclonus by 5-hydroxytryptophan. *Lancet* i: 111-112.

Chevallier, B. (1990) Efficacy and safety of granisetron compared with high-dose metoclopramide plus dexamethasone in patients receiving high-dose cisplatin in a single-blind study. *Eur. J. Cancer* 26 [Suppl 1]: S.33-S.36.

Costall, B., Domeney, A. M., Naylor, R. J., Owera-Atepo, J. B., Rudd, J. A. and Tattersall F. D. (1990) Fluphenazine, ICS 205-930 and *dl*-fenfluramine differentially antagonise drug-induced emesis in the ferret. *Neuropharmacol.* 29: 453-462.

Costall, B., Domeney, A. M., Naylor, R. J. and Tattersall F. D. (1986) 5-Hydroxytryptamine M-receptor antagonism to prevent cisplatin-induced emesis. *Neuropharmacolgy* 25: 959-961.

Costall, B., Domeney, A. M., Naylor, R. J. and Tattersall F. D. (1987) Emesis induced by cisplatin in the ferret as a model for the detection of anti-emetic drugs. *Neuropharmacology* 26: 1321-1326.

Cubeddu, L. X., Hoffmann, I. S., Fuenmayor, N. T. and Finn, A. L. (1990a) Efficacy of ondansetron (GR 38032F) and the role of serotonin in cisplatin-induced emesis. New Eng. J. Med. 322: 810-816.

Cupissol, D. R., Serrou, B. and Caubel, M. (1990) The efficacy of granisetron as a prophylactic anti-emetic and intervention agent in high-dose cisplatin-induced emesis. *Eur. J. Cancer 26* [Suppl 1]: S.23-S.27.

Davison, H. I. M. and Andrews P. L. R. (1988) Vagal efferent activation mediated via 5-HT_3 receptors. *Symposium on Nausea and Vomiting* : a multidisplinary perspective, Ottawa, November A12 (Astract).

Derbyshire, A. J. and Ferguson, J. K. W. (1938) Studies on the vomiting reflex in cats and dogs. Am. J. Physiol. 123: 52-53.

Endo, T., Minami, M., Monma, Y., Yoshioka, M., Saito, H., Kinami, J., Toshimitsu, Y. and Parvez, H. (1990) Effect of GR38032F on cisplatin- and cyclophosphamide-induced emesis in the ferret. *Biogenic Amines* 7: 525-533.

Erspamer, V. (1966) Peripheral physiological and pharmacological actions of indole alkylamines. In: *Handbook of Experimental Pharmacology: 5-Hydroxytryptaminie and Related Indolealkylamines,* Vol 14 (Ed V Erspamer) Springer-Verlag, Berlin, pp.245-359

Erspamer, V. and Testini, A. (1954) Observations on the release and turnover rate of 5-hydroxytryptamine in the gastrointestinal tract. *J. Pharm.* 11: 618-623.

Fozard, J. R. (1984) MDL 72222: a potent and highly selective antagonist at neuronal 5-hydroxytryptamine receptors. *Naunyn-Schmied. Arch. Pharmacol.* 329: 36-44.

Fukuda, H. & Koga, T. (1991) The botzinger complex as the pattern generator for retching and vomiting in the dog. *Neurosci. Res.* 12, 471-485.

Greenwood, M. H. and Lader, M. H. (1975) The acute effects of oral (-)-tryptophan in human subjects. *Br. J. Clin. Pharmacol.* 2: 165-172.

Gwyn, D. G. and Leslie, R. A. (1979) A projection of vagus nerve to the area subpostrema in the cat. *Brain Res.* 161: 335-341.

Gwyn, D. G. and Wolstencroft, J. H. (1968) Cholinesterases in the area subpostrema. A region adjacent to the area postrema in the cat. *J. Comp. Neurol.* 133: 289-308.

Gwyn, D. G., Leslie, R. A. and Hopkins, D. A. (1979) Gastric afferents to the nucleus of the solitary tract in the cat. *Neurosci. Lett.* 14: 13-17.

Gwyn, D. G., Wilkinson, P. H. and Leslie, R. A. (1982) The ultrastructural identification of vagal terminals in the solitary nucleus of the cat after anterograde labelling with horseradish peroxidase. *Neurosci. Lett.* 28: 139-143.

Hatcher, R. A. and Weiss, S. (1923) Studies on vomiting. J. Pharmacol. Exp. Ther. 22: 139-193.

Hawthorn, J. Ostler, K. J. and Andrews, P. L. R. (1988) The role of the abdominal visceral innervation and 5-hydroxytryptamine M-receptors in vomiting induced by the cytotoxic drugs cyclophosphamide and *cis*-platin in the ferret. *J. Exp. Physiol.* 73: 7-21.

Higgins, G. A., Kilpatrick, G. J,. Bunce, K. T., Jones, B. J. and Tyers, M. B. (1989) 5-HT_3 Receptor antagonists injected into the area postrema inhibit cisplatin-induced emesis in the ferret. *Br. J. Pharmacol.* 97: 247-255.

Ikeda, M. and Yamanaka, Y. (1967) Electric stimulation study on localization of the vomiting centre. *J. Physiol. Soc. Jap.* 29: 129-130.

Indo, T. and Ando, K. (1982) Metoclopramide-induced parkinsonism: clinal characteristics of ten cases. *Archs. Neurol.* 39: 494.

Iwase, Y. (1971) Pathophysiology of vomiting. *J. Physiol. Soc. Jap.* 33: 567-577.

Kilpatrick, G. J., Jones, B. J. and Tyers, M. B. (1989) Binding of the 5-HT_3 ligand [^{3}H]GR65630 to rat area postrema, vagus nerve and the brains of several species. *Eur. J. Pharmacol.* 159: 157-164.

Kilpatrick, G. J., Bunce, K. T. and Tyers, M. B. (1990) 5-HT_3 receptors. *Medicinal Res. Rev.* 10:441-475.

King, G. L. (1990a) Emesis and defecation induced by the 5-hydroxytryptamine (5-HT_3) receptor antagonist zacopride in the ferret. *J. Pharmacol. Exp. Ther.* 253: 1034-1041.

King, G. L. (1990b) Animal models in the study of vomiting. *Can. J. Physiol. Pharmacol.* 68: 260-268.

Larsson, I., Ahlman, H., Bhargava, H. N., Dahlstrom, A., Pettersson, G. and Kewenter, J. (1979) The effects of splanchic nerve stimulation on the plasma levels of serotonin and substance P in the portal vein of the cat. *J. Neural. Trans.* 47: 89-98.

Laszlo, J. and Lucas, V. S. Jr. (1981) Emesis as a critical problem in chemotherapy. *New. Eng. J. Med.* 305: 948-949.

Leopold, N. A. (1984) Prolonged metoclopramide-induced dyskinetic reaction. *Neurology* 34: 238.

Leslie, R. A. (1986) Comparative aspects of the area postrema: fine-structural considerations help determine its function. *Cell. Molec. Neurobiol.* 6: 95-120.

Leslie, R. A. and Gwyn, D. G. (1984) Neuronal connections of the area postrema. *Fed. Proc.* 43: 2941-2943.

Leslie, R. A., Reynolds, D. J. M., Andrews, P. L. R., Grahame-Smith, D. G., Davis, C. J. and Harvey, J. M. (1990b) Evidence for presynaptic 5-hydroxytryptamine$_3$ recognition sites on vagal afferent terminals in the brainstem of the ferret. *Neurosci.* 38: 667-673.

Leslie, R. A., Shah, Y., Thejomayen, M., Murphy, K. M. and Robertson, H. A. (1990a) The neuropharmacology of emesis: the role of receptors in neuromodulation of nausea and vomting. *Can. J. Physiol. Pharmacol.* 68: 279-288.

Lieberman, M. W., Verbin, R. S., Landay, M., Liang, H., Farber, E., Lee, T.-N. and Starr, R. (1970) A probable role for protein synthesis in intestinal epithelial cell damage induced *in vivo* by cytosine arabinoside, nitrogen mustard, or X-irradiation. *Cancer Res.* 30: 942-951.

Loewy, A. D. and Burton, H. (1978) Nuclei of the solitary tract: Efferent projections to the lower brain stem and spinal cord of the cat. J. Comp. Neurol. 181: 421-450.

Lucot, J. B. (1989) Blockade of 5-hydroxytryptamine$_3$ receptors prevents cisplatin-induced but not motion- or xylazine-induced emesis in the cat. *Pharmacol. Biochem. Behav.* 32: 207-210.

Lucot, J. B. and Crampton, E. H. (1988) 8-OH-DPAT suppresses vomiting in the cat elicited by motion, cisplatin or xylazine. *Pharmacol. Biochem. Behav.* 33: 627-631.

Magnusson, I. and Nielsen-Kudsk, F. (1979) Pharmacokinetics of intravenously administered L-5-hydroxytryptophan in man. *Acta. Pharmacol. et. Toxicol.* 44: 308-314.

Marty, M. (1990) A comparative study of the use of granisetron, a selective 5-HT$_3$ antagonist, versus a standard antiemetic regimen of chlorpromazine plus dexamethasone in the treatment of cytostatic-induced emesis. *Eur. J. Cancer* 26 [Suppl 1]:S.28-S.32.

Marty, M., Pouillart, P,. Scholl, S., Droz, J. P., Azab, M., Brion, N., Pujade-Lauraine, E., Paule, B., Paes, D. and Bons, J. (1990) Comparison of the 5-hydroxytryptamine$_3$ (serotonin) antagonist ondansetron (GR 38032F) with high-dose metoclopramide in the control of cisplatin-induced emesis. *N. Eng. J. Med.* 322: 816-821.

McCarthy, L. E. and Borison, H. L. (1984) Cisplatin-induced vomiting eliminated by ablation of the area postrema in cats. *Cancer Treat. Rep.* 68: 401-404.

Milano, S., Grelot, L., Chen, Z. and Bianchi, A. L. (1990) Vagal-induced vomiting in decerebrate cat is not suppressed by specific 5-HT$_3$ receptor antagonists. *J. Auton. Nerv. Syst.* 31: 109-118.

Miller, A.D. & Nonaka, S. (1992) Mechanisms of vomiting induced by serotonin-3 receptor agonists in the cat: effect of vagotomy, splanchnicectomy or area postrema lesion. *J. Pharmacol. Exp. Ther.* 260, 509-517

Miller, A. D. and Wilson, V. J. (1983) 'Vomiting centre' reanalyzed: an electrical stimulation study. Brain Res. 270: 154-158.

Miner, W. D. and Sanger, G. J. (1986) Inhibition of cisplatin-induced vomiting by selective 5-hydroxytryptamine M-receptor antagonism. *Br. J. Pharmacol.* 88: 497-499.

Miner, W. D., Sanger, G. J. and Turner, D. H. (1986) Comparison of the effects of BRL 24924, metoclopramide and domperidone on cisplatin induced emesis in the ferret. *Br. J. Pharmacol.* 88: 274P.

Miner, W. D., Sanger, G. J. and Turner, D. H. (1987) Evidence that 5-hydroxytryptamine-3 receptors mediate cytotoxic drug and radiation evoked emesis. *Br. J. Cancer* 56: 159-162.

Moir, A. T. B. and Eccleston, D. (1968) The effects of precursor loading in the cerebral metabolism of 5-hydroxyindoles. *J. Neurochem.* 15: 1093-1108.

Morest, D. K. (1967) Experimental study of the projections of the nucleus of the tractus solitarius and the area postrema in the cat. *J. Comp. Neurol.* 130: 277-300.

Niemegeers, C. J. E. (1982) Antiemetic specificity of dopamine antagonists. Psychopharmacology 78: 210-213.

Norman, P. and Bower, A. J. (1982) An autoradiography study of the brain stem projections of vagal visceral afferent fibres in the domestic hen. *J. Anat.* 134: 583-589.

Paintal, A. S. (1973) Vagal sensory receptors and their reflex effects. *Physio. Rev.* 53: 159-227.

Palacios, J. M. P., Waeber, C., Mengod, G. and Hoyer, D. (1991) Autoradiography of 5-HT receptors: a critical appraisal. *Neurochem. Int.* 18: 17-25.

Pratt, G. D. and Bowery, N. G. (1989) The 5-HT$_3$ receptor ligand [^{3}H]BRL 43694, binds to presynaptic sites in the nucleus tractus solitarius of the rat. *Br. J. Pharmacol.* 97: 414.

Racke, K. and Schworer, H. (1991) Regulation of serotonin release from the intestinal mucosa. Pharmacol. Res. 23: 13-25.

Radja, F., Laporte, A.-M., Daval, G., Verge, D., Gozlan, H. and Hamon, M. (1991) Autoradiography of serotonin receptor subtypes in the central nervous system. *Neurochem. Int.* 18: 1-15.

Reynolds, D.J.M., Barber, N.A., Grahame-Smith, D.G. & Leslie, R.A. (1991a) Cisplatin-evoked induction of I protein in the brainstem of the ferret: the effect of vagotomy and the antiemetic 5-HT$_3$ receptor antagonist granisetron (BRL 43694). *Brain Res.* 565, 231-236.

Reynolds, D. J. M., Leslie, R. A., Grahame-Smith, D. G. and Harvey, J. M. (1991b) Autoradiographic localization of 5-HT$_3$ receptor ligand binding in the cat brainstem. *Neurochem. Int.* 18: 69-73.

Richardson, B. P., Engel, G., Donatsch, P., Stadler, P. A. (1985) Identification of serotonin M-receptor subtypes and their specific blockade by a new class of drugs. *Nature* 316: 126-131.

Robertson, D. W., Cohen, M. L., Krushinski, J. H., Wong, D. T., Parli, C. J. and Gidda, J. S. (1990) LY191617, a 5-HT_3 receptor antagonist which does not cross the blood brain barrier. *The 2nd IUPHAR Satellite Meeting on Serotonin*, Bazel, Switzerland, July 11-13, P149.

Rosenberg, B. (1985) Fundamental studies with cisplatin. *Anticancer Chemotherapy* 55: 2303-2316.

Round, A. and Willis, D. I. (1986) The depolarising action of 5-hydroxytryptamine on rabbit vagal afferent and sympathetic neurones *in vitro* and its selective blockade by ICS 205-930. *Br. J. Pharmacol.* 88: 485-494.

Rudd, J.A., Costall, B., Naylor, R.J. & Tattersall, F.D. (1990) The emetic action of copper sulphate in the ferret. *Eur. J. Pharmacol.* 183, 1213.

Rudd, J.A., Bunce, K.T., Cheng, C.H.K. & Naylor, R.J. (1992) The effect of cisplatin on plasma 5-HT, 5-HIAA and 5-HTP levels during emesis in the ferret. *Br. J. Pharmacol.* 105, 274P.

Sancilio, L. F., Pinkus, L. M., Jackson, C. B. and Munson, H. R. (1991) Studies on the emetic and antiemetic properties of zacopride and its enantiomers. *Eur. J. Pharmacol.* 192: 349-353.

Sanger G. J. and Nelson D. R. (1989) Selective and functional 5-$hydroxytryptamine_3$ receptor antagonism by BRL 43694 (granisetron). *Eur. J. Pharmacol.* 159: 113.

Shapiro, R. E. and Miselis, R. R. (1985) The central neural connections of the area postrema of the rat. *J. Comp. Neurol.* 234: 344-364.

Smith, W. L., Alphin, R. S., Jackson, C. B. and Sancilio, L. F. (1989) The emetic profile of zacopride. *J. Pharm. Pharmacol.* 41: 101-105.

Smith, W. L., Callaham, E. M. and Alphin, R. S. (1988a) The emetic activity of centrally administered cisplatin in cats and its antagonism by zacopride. *J. Pharm. Pharmacol.* 40: 142.

Smith, W. L., Sancilio, L. F., Owera-Atepo, J. B., Naylor, R. J. and Lambert, L. (1988b) Zacopride a potent 5-HT_3 receptor antagonist. *J. Pharm. Pharmacol.* 40: 301-302.

Sole, M.J., Madapallimattam, A. & Baines, A.D (1986) An active pathway for serotonin synthesis by renal proximal tubules. *Kidney Int.*, 29, 689-694.

Stables, R., Andrews, P. L. R., Bailey, H. E., Costall, B., Gunning, S. J., Hawthorn, J., Naylor, R. J. and Tyers M. B. (1987) Antiemetic properties of the 5-HT_3-receptor antagonist, GR38032F. *Cancer Treat. Rev.* 14: 333-336.

Tattersall, F. D. (1988) 5-Hydroxytryptamine control of emesis and gastrointestinal activity. Ph.D. Thesis, University of Bradford.

Torii, Y., Saito, H. and Matsuki, N. (1990) Selective blockade of cytotoxic drug-induced emesis by 5-HT_3 recpetor antagonists in Suncus-Murinus. *Jap. J. Pharmacol.* 55: 107-113.

Torii, Y., Saito, H. and Matsuki, N. (1990) 5-Hydroxytryptamine is emetogenic in the house musk shrew, *Suncus murinus*. *Naunyn-Schmiedeberg's Arch Pharmacol.* 344, 564-567.

Triozzi, P. L. and Laszlo, J. (1987) Optimum management of nausea and vomiting in cancer chemotherapy. Drug 34: 136-149.

Verbeuren, T. J. (1989) Synthesis, storage, release and metabolism of 5-hydroxytryptamine in peripheral tissues. In: *Peripheral Actions of 5-Hydroxytryptamine*. (Ed. Fozard, J.R.) Oxford: Oxford University Press 1989: pp1-25.

Vigier, D. and Portalier, A. (1979) Efferent projections of the area postrema demonstrated by autoradiography. *Arch. Ital. Biol.* 177: 308-324.

Vigier, D. and Rouviere, A. (1979) Afferent and efferent connections of the area postrema demonstrated by the horseradish peroxidase method. *Arch. Ital. Biol.* 177: 325-339.

Waeber, C., Dixon, K., Hoyer, D. and Palacios, J. M. (1988) Localization by autoradiography of neuronal 5-HT_3 receptos in the mouse CNS. *Eur. J. Pharmacol.* 151: 351-352.

Wurtman, R. J, Hefti, F. and Melamed, E. (1981) Precursor control of neurotransitter synthesis. *Pharmacol. Rev.* 32: 315-335.

Mechanisms and Control of Emesis. Eds A.L. Bianchi, L. Grélot, A.D. Miller, G.L. King. Colloque INSERM/
John Libbey Eurotext Ltd. © 1992, Vol. 223, pp. 129-139

Clinical trials in acute cancer chemotherapy-induced vomiting

Mark G. Kris, Leslie B. Tyson, Lorraine Baltzer and Katherine M.W. Pisters

Thoracic Oncology Service, Division of Solid Tumor Oncology, Department of Medicine, Memorial Sloan-Kettering Cancer Center, New York, NY 10021, USA

SUMMARY

Clinical trials have identified high-dose intravenous metoclopramide and dexamethasone as safe and effective medications for controlling vomiting caused by anticancer drugs. Insights gained through the empiric testing of these agents have advanced our understanding of the physiology of emesis and led to the identification of the newest class of antiemetics, the 5-HT3 antagonists. The trial methodology developed over the last 15 years reviewed in this article allowed the rapid testing and quick acceptance of ondansetron as the new antiemetic standard worldwide. Combinations of antiemetics can prevent cisplatin-induced emesis in the majority of patients. Current research focuses on identifying better antiemetic drugs and the development of more convenient and effective schedules, dosage forms, and combinations.

Résumé: Essais cliniques dans le vomissement aigu induit par la chimiothérapie anticancéreuse.

Des essais cliniques ont montré que de fortes doses intraveineuses de métoclopramide et de dexaméthasone sont des médications efficaces et sans problème pour contrôler le vomissement induit par les drogues anticancéreuses. Une meilleure compréhension obtenue grâce aux tests empiriques de ces agents a permis d'avancer dans notre connaissance de la physiologie de la réponse émétique, et conduit à l'identification de nouvelles classes d'antiémétiques, les antagonistes 5-HT3. La méthodologie d'essai développée depuis ces 15 dernières années, et revue dans cet article, a permis le test et l'acceptation rapide de l'Ondansetron comme le nouvel antiémétique standard à usage mondial. Des combinaisons d'antiémétiques peuvent prévenir chez une majorité de malades le vomissement induit par l'administration de cisplatine. La recherche actuelle s'efforce d'identifier de meilleures drogues antiémétiques et de développer des périodes, des modalités de dosage et des combinaisons plus faciles d'emploi et plus efficaces.

INTRODUCTION

When patients express their concerns about cancer treatment, nausea and vomiting lead the list (Coates et al. 1983). These fears are well founded, as commonly used anticancer drugs such as cisplatin can cause a median of eleven vomiting episodes during the first twenty-four hours following its administration (Gralla et al. 1981b). Unfortunately, our understanding of the pathophysiology and prevention of chemotherapy-induced vomiting did not parallel developments in anticancer therapy, and in fact, the magnitude and severity of chemotherapy-induced vomiting was the trigger for antiemetic research. The empiric testing of antiemetic drugs in patients with cancer has driven this investigative effort.

Clinical trials have identified several safe and effective antiemetic drugs including metoclopramide and dexamethasone. Their use alone and in combination has led to the control of acute chemotherapy- induced emesis in most patients and prevention in the majority (Kris et al. 1987). The observation that metoclopramide, a less potent and non-specific inhibitor of serotonin, controlled emesis at high intravenous doses but was less effective at lower doses suggested that enhanced blockade of serotonin receptors may play a role in chemotherapy-induced emesis. This observation, coupled with the development of specific agonists and antagonists of serotonin receptor subtypes, has led to the improvement of both antiemetic control and our understanding of emesis through the development of the 5-HT3 antagonists such as ondansetron. The testing of antiemetic drugs in cancer patients receiving cisplatin has led to the current animal model for the study of this condition, the control of cisplatin-induced emesis in the ferret (Costall et al. 1987, Florczyk et al. 1982). This report will review current study designs, discuss the results of completed clinical trials and examine areas for further research.

TRIAL DESIGN

Initially, few trials specifically examined a drug's antiemetic effects with chemotherapy. Drug doses and schedules were often not tested in Phase I trials evaluating an agent's antiemetic effects with chemotherapy. Study endpoints were not precisely defined. Several of these reports were patient or physician anecdotes attesting to the benefits of the drugs tested. Although several trials had shown "significant" results, the clinical impact was negligible.

The development of high-dose intravenous metoclopramide by Gralla marked a distinct change in this pattern and the study designs utilized to evaluate this agent for the control of acute chemotherapy- induced emesis have become standard. Doses, schedules and toxicities for the candidate agent when used as an antiemetic are defined in a Phase I trial (Gralla et al. 1981a). These same doses are then tested in formal efficacy trials. It is here that trial design is critical. A standard emetic stimulus must be chosen that produces a predictable degree and pattern of vomiting following its administra- tion. Cisplatin was initially chosen and remains the current standard for this purpose since it is available worldwide, enjoys wide usage, is a vital component of potentially curative chemotherapy regimens, and it has been shown in trials using placebo antiemetics to produce severe vomiting in all patients (Gralla et al. 1981b, Homesley et al. 1982). Cisplatin's emetic potential is both schedule and dose-related. Three dose ranges have emerged as emetic stimuli for antiemetic trials: Low dose: 20 - 40 mg/m2, moderate dose: 50 - 80 mg/m2, high dose: >90 mg/m2. The length of the cisplatin infusion also correlates with the severity of vomiting caused by this agent (Jordan et al. 1985). This parameter must also be standardized for clinical trials. An infusion duration of two hours or less is generally used.

Objective Endpoints

Antiemetic trials initially focused on the need to obtain objective data to establish the drugs effective- ness for this indication. The primary endpoint for these early studies was the determination of the number of emetic episodes measured by the direct observation of an investigator during the 24 hours following cisplatin. This twenty-four hour observation period was chosen after determining the pattern of vomiting following cisplatin administration. An emetic episode was defined as any vomiting of stomach contents or from one to five "dry" heaves during any five minute period (Gralla et al. 1981b). In addition, based on the severity of vomiting observed following cisplatin with no or inadequate antiemetic protection, vomiting control has been graded as complete (no emetic episodes) or major (0,1 or 2 emetic episodes). As antiemetic control has improved, the percentage of patients having no emetic episodes, i.e., vomiting prevention, has become the primary study endpoint.

Expected adverse effects (such as sedation, diarrhea, and acute dystonic reactions anticipated in the metoclopramide trials) need to be prospectively identified, and their occurrence was also documented and graded by direct observation. Sedation has been graded from 0 to 3+ using the following scheme: none (0); mild (1+) patient lethargic but aroused by verbal stimuli and completely oriented to time, place, and person when awakened; moderate (2+) patient aroused only by physical stimuli and completely oriented when awakened; and marked (3+) (patient aroused only by physical stimuli and disoriented when awakened). The maximum degree of sedation observed during the 24 hour study period is usually reported. Diarrhea is graded from 0 to 2+ as follows: Grade 0--zero to three loose bowel movements during a 24 hour period; Grade 1--four loose bowel movements during a 24 hour period; Grade 2--five or more loose bowel movements during a 24 hour period. Again, the maximum grade observed during the 24 hour study period is usually reported. The concepts addressed in efficacy trials are summarized in Table 1.

Table 1. Methodological Issues in Antiemetic Efficacy Trials (Phase II)

- Candidate Drug
  Dose and schedule when used as an antiemetic established in Phase I trials
- Standard Emetic Stimulus
  Defined dose and schedule of cisplatin administration
- Direct Observation
- Defined Study Period - Usually 24 hours
- Primary Endpoint
  Complete Control of Vomiting and Retching
- Number and Time of Emetic Episodes Recorded
- Side-Effects Defined, Recorded and Graded

At the conclusion of Phase II trials, the efficacy and toxicity data were then critically examined to see if Phase III comparison trials are warranted. A decision was then made as to what is the appropriate "standard therapy." At the time of the initial trials of high dose metoclopramide, no therapy was either approved or clinically accepted for the control of cisplatin-induced emesis, therefore, a placebo infusion was most appropriate (Gralla et al. 1981b). Using a double-blind, randomized study design, Gralla compared high-dose intravenous metoclopramide (given at the dose and schedule tested in the Phase I and Phase II trials and using the same study design considerations) to placebo, and intramuscular prochlorperazine (an antiemetic in common use at the time) and dronabinol (Gralla et al. 1984). Homesley conducted a second randomized trial comparing high-dose intravenous metoclopramide to placebo (Homesley et al. 1982). Following these studies and several non-randomized trials (Kris et al. 1985, Strum et al. 1982), metoclopramide gained regulatory approval for this indication in the United States and became the "standard" for the control of acute chemotherapy- induced emesis. New agent development focused on the identification of agents that had either improved effectiveness or fewer adverse effects than metoclopramide.

Following the demonstration that high-dose, intravenous metoclopramide was safe and superior to placebo in two randomized trials testing its use for the control of acute emesis following cisplatin, the use of placebos for this indication has been unnecessary and unethical. The adverse effects of available antiemetics are always mild and rarely, if ever, treatment-limiting, and the possible occur- rence of side-effects is not a justification for the use of placebos in antiemetic trials. Since effective antiemetics identified have been shown to lessen or prevent emesis regardless of the anticancer drug administered, the use of placebos is inappropriate no matter what the emetic stimulus studied.

As the first 5-HT3 antagonists entered Phase III trials, metoclopramide remained the standard and several trials have been concluded comparing ondansetron to metoclopramide (DeMulder et al. 1990, Hainsworth et al. 1991, Marty et al. 1990). Since ondansetron proved superior to intravenous metoclopramide in each of these trials and it is used extensively worldwide, it has now become the standard against which new antiemetics will be compared.

Subjective Endpoints

Once several safe and effective antiemetic drugs were identified using the objective study methods described above, it became both relevant and important to measure subjective parameters as outlined in Table 2.

Table 2. Subjective Endpoints of Antiemetic Trials

Nausea
Vomiting
Sedation
Comfort
Satisfaction
Anxiety
Patient Preference

The first attempts to quantify these outcomes simply measured the presence or absence of each parameter. However, except for patient preference where individuals compared each of the treatments they received, this "yes/no" approach proved inexact. Research in the area of pain research has already established the 100 millimeter visual analogue scale as a feasible, reliable and valid system of measurement for subjective variables (Scott & Huskisson 1976). One hundred millimeter visual analogue scales like the one for nausea presented in Table 3 have been shown to be feasible, reliable and valid in antiemetic studies (Clark et al. 1985, Kris et al. 1985, Kris et al. 1987, Kris et al. 1989).

Table 3. Visual Analogue Scale Used to Measure Nausea

How much nausea did you have during the treatment period?

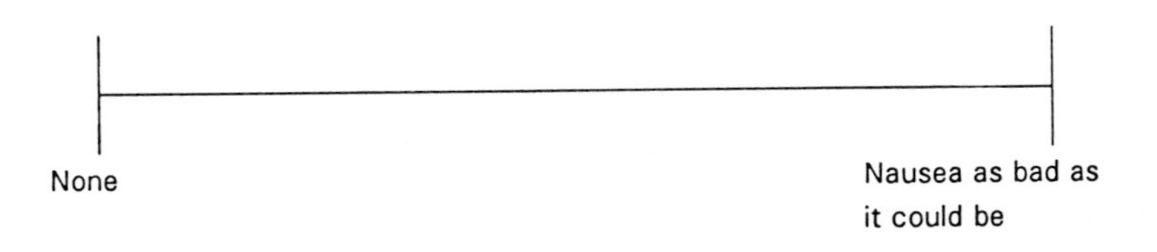

Convergent validity was established comparing the visual analogue scale results for vomiting and sedation to the observed number of vomiting episodes and degrees of sedation. Although no objective means of assessing nausea is possible, nausea scores correlated with the directly observed numbers of vomiting episodes. These scales have been successfully employed in a number of antiemetic trials, and in all cases, they have worked well in terms of their accuracy, their convenience and relevance for both patients and research staff.

Patient Characteristics

Three patient characteristics have been found to influence the severity of vomiting observed after the administration of cisplatin: age, sex, and alcohol use. Investigators have documented the decreased severity of emesis following cisplatin in patients with a history of chronic alcohol use (D'Acquisto et al. 1986, Sullivan et al. 1983). In these reports, individuals with a history of long-term high alcohol use displayed a decreased severity of vomiting or an increased degree of complete and major control when effective antiemetics were used when results in these individuals were compared to similar patients with no history of alcohol use. Vomiting was still always observed among patients with high alcohol use, and these individuals still require the optimal antiemetic therapy recommended for each type, dose, and schedule of chemotherapy. Women, especially those under the age of 50, appear to experience more emetic episodes and lower rates of complete control than men treated in a similar fashion (Roila et al. 1987, Roila et al. 1989). It is important to note the percentage of women and individuals with a history of chronic high alcohol use when evaluating the results of efficacy trials of antiemetics. In randomized trials, consideration should be given to the stratification of study subjects based on age, sex, and alcohol use to assure a balanced allocation of patients to each study arm.

CURRENT STATUS OF ANTIEMETIC THERAPY

Single Agents

The commonly used antiemetics that have been shown to be effective and safe for the control of chemotherapy-induced emesis are displayed in Table 4.

Table 4. Commonly Used Drugs Given with Anticancer Chemotherapy

Drug	Reference
ANTIEMETICS	
Ondansetron	(Kris et al. 1989, Marty et al. 1990)
Metoclopramide	(Gralla et al. 1981b, Homesley et al. 1982)
Dexamethasone	(Cassileth et al. 1983, Markman et al. 1984)
Granisetron	(Addelman et al. 1990, Warr et al. 1991)
Haloperidol	(Grunberg et al. 1984)
Dronabinol	(Frytak et al. 1979)
Nabilone	(Einhorn 1982, Herman et al. 1979)
High-dose Intravenous Prochlorperazine	(Carr et al. 1987)
ADJUNCTIVE AGENTS	
Lorazepam	(Kris et al. 1987, Laszlo et al. 1985)
Diphenhydramine	(Kris et al. 1987)
Midazolam	(Potanovich et al. 1989)

Worldwide, ondansetron, dexamethasone and metoclopramide are the most widely used. In phase II single agent trials, ondansetron controls high dose cisplatin-induced emesis in 42% of patients (Kris et al. 1989) and metoclopramide in 39% (Kris et al. 1985).

In a recent multicenter, randomized trial comparing these two agents in patients receiving cisplatin ≥100 mg/m2, ondansetron prevented emesis in 40% of patients and metoclopramide 30% (Hainsworth et al. 1991). Ondansetron was equivalent to dexamethasone in a randomized trial among patients receiving moderately emetogenic chemotherapy (Jones et al. 1991). The single agent results of dexamethasone with cisplatin have been less impressive. This agent's greatest use and study have been in combination with metoclopramide as discussed below. Granisetron is the second specific 5-HT3 antagonist to gain regulatory approval in several countries. It has undergone less investigation than ondansetron and no formal single-agent comparison trials with ondansetron have yet been reported. Haloperidol, dronabinol, nabilone and high-dose intravenous prochlorperazine are all less widely used and, in general, have lower effectiveness and/or more severe adverse effects than the other agents mentioned.

Lorazepam has been extensively employed as an adjunct to antiemetic drugs to lessen anxiety, restlessness and extrapyramidal symptoms caused by cancer and cancer therapy. No trial clearly documents its antiemetic effectiveness. It has been shown to lessen anxiety and akathisia more effectively than diphenhydramine when used in combination with dexamethasone and metoclopramide (Kris et al. 1987). Lorazepam employed at a dose of 1.5 mg/m2 has been given safely with the combination of ondansetron and dexamethasone with similar results (Tyson et al. 1992). The use of diphenhydramine has been shown to lessen the incidence of extrapyramidal effects when given with metoclopramide (Allen et al. 1985). No trials have specifically addressed its use as an antiemetic. Midazolam has undergone only limited testing for this indication. Preliminary studies suggest its use is safe and that it can provide satisfactory sedative and antianxiety effects of short duration to permit its use in an outpatient setting (Potanovich et al. 1989).

Combination Antiemetics

Emesis is a complex reflex controlled by multiple neurotransmitters. Each antiemetic agent devel- oped to date is only partially effective. Theoretically, combinations of antiemetic agents can block more neurotransmitter receptor types and block them more completely and thereby improve anti- emetic control. A series of trials combining metoclopramide with corticosteroids have demonstrated enhanced effects with the combination (Allan et al. 1984, Grunberg et al. 1986, Kris et al. 1985, Roila et al. 1987, Strum et al. 1985). When metoclopramide was combined with dexamethasone and lorazepam using optimal schedules and doses for each drug in the combination, vomiting was prevented in 63% of patients given cisplatin ≥100 mg/m2 with lessened side-effects and only four drug administrations over a two hour period (Kris et al. 1987). Roila has combined ondansetron with dexamethasone and tested it in patients receiving moderate or high-dose cisplatin (Roila et al. 1991). Vomiting was prevented in 91% of patients with a regimen requiring four antiemetic drug infusions over a four hour period. Combination antiemetics are the current standard therapy for the control of chemotherapy-induced emesis. These two regimens are described in detail in Table 5 below.

Table 5. Standard Combination Antiemetics

Metoclopramide	3 mg/kg, IV, 30 min before and 90 mins
-plus-	after chemotherapy
Dexamethasone	20 mg IV 40 min before chemotherapy
-plus-	
Lorazepam	1.5 mg/m2 45 min before chemotherapy
	(Kris et al. 1987)
Ondansetron	0.15 mg/kg 30 min before and 90 and
-plus-	210 min after chemotherapy
Dexamethasone	20 mg IV 40 min before chemotherapy
	(Roila et al. 1991)

AREAS OF RESEARCH

New Agents

Several new serotonin antagonist antiemetics have been identified. Tropisetron (ICS 205-930), RG 12915 and MDL 73147EF are currently the subject of active investigation. Although each agent has a distinct chemical structure and pharmacokinetic profile, all have shown substantial antiemetic effec- tiveness and no dose-limiting side-effects. No trials directly comparing the efficacy and side-effects of the serotonin antagonists have been initiated. These trials will dominate antiemetic research for several years to come.

Combinations, Alternate Schedules and Dosage Forms

The success with metoclopramide and dexamethasone programs has spurred combination antiemetic research with ondansetron. Results to date show that ondansetron can be safely given with dexa- methasone with enhanced levels of antiemetic protection (Roila et al. 1991, Smith et al. 1991, Tyson et al. 1991). The addition of ondansetron to the combination of metoclopramide, dexamethasone and lorazepam is currently under study (Tyson et al. 1992). Recent trials have demonstrated that ondansetron maintains its effectiveness when given as a single intravenous dose for some doses of cisplatin (Beck et al. 1992, Marty & d'Allens 1990). A single intravenous dose may not be equally effective for cisplatin doses ≥ 100 mg/m2 (Kris et al. 1992). Oral forms of antiemetic medications appear equally efficacious when compared to the intravenous route. Even patients receiving cisplatin have equivalent protection when given oral ondansetron (Smith et al. 1991). Oral RG 12915 is currently being compared to intravenous ondansetron in patients receiving cisplatin. Oral formulations are more convenient, less expensive and preferred by patients, and therefore are the optimal dosage form. The determination of the doses and schedules for oral formulations of each available antiemetic for each emetic situation and drug are an appropriate subject for future trials.

CONCLUSIONS

Clinical trials have identified safe and effective antiemetic drugs and drug combinations. The method- ological groundwork for the evaluation of antiemetic agents to prevent vomiting following anticancer chemotherapy has been established, and candidate drugs can now be accurately and quickly evaluated as potential therapies for this indication. Using available combinations of antiemetic agents, vomiting can be prevented in two-thirds of patients and lessened in virtually all patients receiving potent emesis-causing drugs like high-dose cisplatin. Using the methodology now developed, future trials will test the usefulness of new agents and develop more convenient and effective dosage forms, schedules and combinations of available drugs.

REFERENCES

Addelman, M., Erlichman, C. et al. 1990. Phase I/II trial of granisetron: A novel 5-hydroxytryptamine antagonist for the prevention of chemotherapy-induced nausea and vomiting. J Clin Oncol 8 (2) : 337-341.

Allan, S.G., Cornbleet, M.A. et al. 1984. Dexamethasone and high dose metoclopramide: efficacy in controlling. Br Med J 289 (6449) : 878-9.

Allen, J.C., Gralla, R. et al. 1985. Metoclopramide: dose-related toxicity and preliminary antiemetic studies in children receiving cancer chemotherapy. J Clin Oncol 3 (8) : 1136-41.

Beck, T.M., Madajewicz, S. et al. 1992. A double blind, stratified, randomized comparison of intravenous (IV) ondansetron administered as a multiple dose regimen versus two single dose regimens in the prevention of cisplatin-induced nausea and vomiting. Proc Am Soc Clin Oncol 11 : 378.

Carr, B.I., Blayne, D.W. et al. 1987. High doses of prochlorperazine for cisplatin-induced emesis. A prospective, random dose-response study. Cancer 60 : 2165-2169.

Cassileth, P.A., Lusk, E.J. et al. 1983. Antiemetic efficacy of dexamethasone therapy in patients receiving cancer chemotherapy. Arch Intern Med 143 (7) : 1347-9.

Clark, R., Tyson, L. et al. 1985. A correlation of objective (OBJ) and subjective (SUBJ) parameters in assessing antiemetic regimens (AER). Oncol Nurs Forum (Suppl) 12 : 96.

Coates, A., Abraham, S. et al. 1983. On the receiving end - patient perception of the side effects of cancer chemotherapy. Eur J Cancer Clin Oncol 19 : 203-208.

Costall, B., Domeney, A.M. et al. 1987. Emesis induced by cisplatin in the ferret as a model for the detection of anti-emetic drugs. Neuropharmacology 26 (9) : 1321-6.

D'Acquisto, R., Tyson, L.B. et al. 1986. The influence of a chronic high alcohol intake on chemotherapy-induced nausea and vomiting. Proc Am Soc Clin Oncol 5 : 257.

DeMulder, P.H., Seynaeve, C. et al. 1990. Ondansetron compared with high-dose metoclopramide in prophylaxis of acute multicenter, randomized, double-blind, crossover study. Ann Intern Med 113 (11) : 834-40.

Einhorn, L. 1982. Nabilone: an effective antiemetic agent in patients receiving cancer chemotherapy. Cancer Treat Rev 9 : 55-61.

Florczyk, A.P., Schurig, J.E. et al. 1982. Cisplatin-induced emesis in the ferret: a new animal model. Cancer Treat Rep 66 (1) : 187-9.

Frytak, S., Moertel, C.G. et al. 1979. Delta-9-Tetrahydrocannabinol as an antiemetic for patients receiving cancer chemotherapy. Ann Intern Med 91 : 825-830.

Gralla, R.J., Braun, T.J. et al. 1981a. Metoclopramide: initial clinical studies of high dose regimens in cisplatin-induced emesis. In The treatment of nausea and vomiting induced by cancer chemotherapy. Edited by Poster, D. 167-176. New York: Masson.

Gralla, R.J., Itri, L.M. et al. 1981b. Antiemetic efficacy of high-dose metoclopramide: randomized trials with placebo and prochlorperazine in patients with chemotherapy-induced nausea and vomiting. N Engl J Med 305 (16) : 905-9.

Gralla, R.J., Tyson, L.B. et al. 1984. Antiemetic therapy: a review of recent studies and a report of a random assignment trial comparing metoclopramide with delta-9-tetrahydrocannabinol. Cancer Treat Rep 68 (1) : 163-72.

Grunberg, S.M., Akerly, W.L. et al. 1986. Comparison of metoclopramide and metoclopramide plus dexamethasone for complete protection from cisplatinum-induced emesis. Cancer Invest 4 (5) : 379-385.

Grunberg, S.M., Gala, K.V. et al. 1984. Comparison of the antiemetic effect of high-dose intravenous metoclopramide and high-dose intravenous haloperidol in a randomized double-blind crossover study. J Clin Oncol 2 : 782-787.

Hainsworth, J., Harvey, W. et al. 1991. A single-blind comparison of intravenous ondansetron, a selective serotonin antagonist, with intravenous metoclopramide in the prevention of nausea and vomiting associated with high-dose cisplatin chemotherapy [see comments]. J Clin Oncol 9 (5) : 721-8.

Herman, T.S., Einhorn, L.H. et al. 1979. Superiority of nabilone over prochlorperazine as an antiemetic in patients receiving cancer chemotherapy. N Engl J Med 300 : 1295-1297.

Homesley, H.D., Gainey, J.M. et al. 1982. Cisplatin chemotherapy and emesis in patients given metoclopramide and controls. The New England Journal of Medicine 307 : 250.

Jones, A.L., Hill, A.S. et al. 1991. Comparison of dexamethasone and ondansetron in the prophylaxis of emesis induced by moderately emetogenic chemotherapy. Lancet 338 : 483-7.

Jordan, N.S., Schauer, P.K. et al. 1985. The effect of administration rate on cisplatin-induced emesis. J Clin Oncol 3 (4) : 559-561.

Kris, M.G., Clark, R.A. et al. 1992. Phase II trial of a single intravenous dose of ondansetron in patients receiving cisplatin >100 mg/m2. Am J Clin Oncol : (in press).

Kris, M.G., Gralla, R.J. et al. 1989. Phase II trials of the serotonin antagonist GR38032F for the control of vomiting caused by cisplatin. J Natl Cancer Inst 81 (1) : 42-6.

Kris, M.G., Gralla, R.J. et al. 1985. Consecutive dose-finding trials adding lorazepam to the combination of metoclopramide plus dexamethasone: improved subjective effectiveness over the combination of diphenhydramine plus metoclopramide plus dexamethasone. Cancer Treat Rep 69 (11) : 1257-62.

Kris, M.G., Gralla, R.J. et al. 1987. Antiemetic control and prevention of side effects of anti-cancer therapy with lorazepam or diphenhydramine when used in combination with metoclopramide plus dexamethasone. A double-blind, randomized trial. Cancer 60 (11) : 2816-22.

Kris, M.G., Gralla, R.J. et al. 1989. Controlling delayed vomiting: double-blind, randomized trial comparing placebo, dexamethasone alone, and metoclopramide plus dexamethasone in patients receiving cisplatin. J Clin Oncol 7 (1) : 108-14.

Kris, M.G., Gralla, R.J. et al. 1985. Improved control of cisplatin-induced emesis with high-dose metoclopramide and with combinations of metoclopramide, dexamethasone, and diphenhydramine. Results of consecutive trials in 255 patients. Cancer 55 (3) : 527-34.

Laszlo, J., Clark, R.A. et al. 1985. Lorazepam in cancer patients treated with cisplatin: a drug having antiemetic, amnestic, and anxiolytic effects. J Clin Oncol 3 : 864-869.

Markman, M., Sheidler, V. et al. 1984. Antiemetic efficacy of dexamethasone. Randomized double-blind crossover study with prochlorperazine in patients receiving cancer chemotherapy. N Engl J Med 311 (9) : 549-52.

Marty, M. & d'Allens, H. 1990. A single daily dose (SD) of ondansetron (OND) is as effective as a continuous infusion (CI) in the prevention of cisplatin (DDP)-induced nausea (N) and vomiting (V). Ann Oncol (Suppl) 1 : 112.

Marty, M., Pouillart, P. et al. 1990. Comparison of the 5-hydroxytryptamine3 (serotonin) antagonist ondansetron (GR 38032F) with high-dose metoclopramide in the control of cisplatin-induced emesis. N Engl J Med 322 (12) : 816-21.

Potanovich, L.M., Kris, M.G. et al. 1989. Midazolam as an adjunct to antiemetics in patients receiving cancer chemotherapy: a phase I trial. Proc Am Soc Clin Oncol 8 : 342.

Roila, F., Tonato, M. et al. 1987. Antiemetic activity of high doses of metoclopramide combined with methylprednisolone versus metoclopramide alone in cisplatin-treated cancer patients: a randomized double-blind trial of the Italian Oncology Group for Clinical Research. J Clin Oncol 5 (1) : 141-149.

Roila, F., Tonato, M. et al. 1989. Protection from nausea and vomiting in cisplatin-treated patients: high-dose metoclopramide combined with methylprednisolone versus metoclopramide combined with dexamethasone and diphenhydramine: a study of the Italian Oncology Group for Clinical Research. J Clin Oncol 7 (11) : 1693-1700.

Roila, F., Tonato, M. et al. 1991. Prevention of cisplatin-induced emesis: a double-blind multicenter randomized crossover study comparing ondansetron and ondansetron plus dexamethasone. J Clin Oncol 9 (4) : 675-8.

Scott, J. & Huskisson, E.C. 1976. Graphic Representation of pain. Pain 2 : 175-184.

Smith, D.B., Newlands, E.S. et al. 1991. Comparison of ondansetron and ondansetron plus dexamethasone as antiemetic prophylaxis during cisplatin-containing chemotherapy. Lancet 338 : 487-90.

Strum, S.B., McDermed, J.E. et al. 1985. High-dose intravenous metoclopramide versus combination high-dose metoclopramide and intravenous dexamethasone in preventing cisplatin-induced nausea and emesis: a single-blind crossover comparison of antiemetic efficacy. J Clin Oncol 3 (2) : 245-251.

Strum, S.B., McDermed, J.E. et al. 1982. Intravenous metoclopramide an effective antiemetic in cancer chemotherapy. JAMA 247 (19) : 2683-2686.

Sullivan, J.R., Leyden, M.J. et al. 1983. Decreased cisplatin-induced nausea and vomiting with chronic alcohol ingestion. N Engl J Med 309 : 796.

Tyson, L.B., Kris, M.G. et al. 1991. Combining ondansetron with dexamethasone: a randomized antiemetic trial comparing two ondansetron schedules in patients receiving cisplatin. Proc Am Soc Clin Oncol 10 : 341.

Tyson, L.B., Kris, M.G. et al. 1992. Combining antiemetics that block dopamine and serotonin receptors: trial of metoclopramide + ondansetron + dexamethasone + lorazepam (MODL) in patients given high dose cisplatin (>100 mg/m2). Proc Am Soc Clin Oncol 11 : 400.

Warr, D., Willlan, A. et al. 1991. Superiority of granisetron to dexamethasone plus prochlorperazine in the prevention of chemotherapy-induced emesis. J Natl Cancer Inst 83 (16) : 1169-1173.

Mechanisms and Control of Emesis. Eds A.L. Bianchi, L. Grélot, A.D. Miller, G.L. King. Colloque INSERM/
John Libbey Eurotext Ltd. © 1992, Vol. 223, pp. 141-146

Pharmacological treatment of delayed emesis

Matti S. Aapro

Centre Anticancéreux, B.P. 44, 1261 Genolier and Division d'Onco-Hématologie, Hôpital Cantonal, 1211 Genève 14, Switzerland

SUMMARY

Nausea and vomiting occurring 24 hours after the initial emetogenic insult (delayed emesis) are an important clinical problem. These symptoms appear in up to 89% of cisplatin treated patients and can affect 50% of patients initially controlled by 5-HT_3 antagonists. There are presently no clear indications for the use of these newer agents in the control of delayed emesis. A combination of steroids and metoclopramide has been shown to have somme efficacy in this setting.

Traitement pharmacologique des vomissements différés

Résumé: *Les nausées et vomissements apparaissant 24 heures après l'événement émétogène (vomissements différés) sont un problème clinique important. Ces symptômes touchent jusqu'à 89% des patients traités au cisplatine et peuvent atteindre 50% des malades initialement contrôlés par les antagonistes de la 5-HT_3. Il n'y a actuellement pas d'indication claire à l'usage de ces nouveaux agents pour le contrôle des vomissements différés. Une combinaison de stéroïdes et metoclopramide a été démontrée efficace dans ce cas.*

INTRODUCTION

Most studies on the effect of antiemetic agents have looked at the first 24 hours after the emetogenic insult. Delayed emesis, defined as nausea or vomiting occurring after this initial observation period has received minimal attention. The present progress in antiemetic treatments has however created an interest among more investigators for this problem, which detracts considerably from the overall efficacy of emetic control. Delayed emesis will contribute to the development of anticipatory nausea and vomiting (a conditioned behaviour), and can severely affect the quality of life of cancer patients.

FACTORS INFLUENCING DELAYED EMESIS

Type of chemotherapy

Cisplatin-based chemotherapy, particularly when high-doses of this agent are used, universally produces delayed side-effects. However, many other agents are associated with delayed symptoms, in particular high-dose intravenous cyclophosphamide. A review of recent studies where 5-HT_3 antagonists were used to control acute emesis indicates that up to 50% of the patients who had not suffered emesis on day 1 will complain of nausea or vomiting during the subsequent 2 to 7 days (Aapro, 1991).

Dose of cisplatin.

The incidence of delayed emesis in cisplatin treated patients varies according to the dose of this chemotherapeutic agent. In patients treated at doses below 90 mg/m2 the incidence is 22% to 50% (Roila et al,1991, Schneider et al,1991), while it is much higher in those treated at higher doses of cisplatin, ranging between 43 and 89% (Kris et al ,1989, Moreno et al, 1991, Roila et al, 1991, Schneider et al, 1991).

Initial control.

Several groups have noticed that patients who do not experience nausea and vomiting during the first 24 hours of observation tend to do better during follow-up. However, two large data sets indicate that even complete initial emetic control will not avoid the appearance of delayed symptoms in 26 to 47% of respectively 110 and 532 patients (Roila et al, 1991, Schneider et al, 1991, Shinkai et al, 1989). Patients who had vomited during the acute phase do poorly, with 53 to 88% of them experiencing delayed symptoms.

Gender.

In a fashion similar to that observed for control of acute emesis, female patients do worse also during the delayed phase, with respectively 39 and 76 percent of delayed symptoms in males and females respectively (Roila et al, 1991).

Table 1

PREDICTING DELAYED EMESIS

Chemotherapy
High versus low dose cisplatin.
Cyclophosphamide (i.v.) combinations.
Absence of control during acute phase.

Sex
Females do worse

CAUSES

In spite of the importance of the problem, and of all the observations cited above, little is known about the physiology of these symptoms. It is quite remarkable to notice that in spite of continuation of effective acute phase anti-5HT3 treatment, patients will experience delayed emesis (Sorbe et al, 1990). This points to mecanisms different from the action of serotonin. Among the possibilities are the noxious effects of toxin released from chemotherapy injured gut cells, transmitted via other neuro-effectors, possibly via dopamine-related pathways.

CONTROL OF DELAYED EMESIS

Phase II studies

Many non-controlled studies have looked at this question, and provide no answer except as to the tolerability of the agents used.

Phase III studies with steroids or metoclopramide

Randomised studies have been conducted by a few groups and give some indication as to the limited efficacy of presently available means to control chemotherapy related delayed emesis.

Adrenocorticotropic-hormone(ACTH) has been studied in 60 patients undergoing cisplatin based chemotherapy. During the acute phase all patients received metoclopramide and dexamethasone and were then randomised to ACTH or placebo for 4 days. Complete protection from delayed emesis was seen in 33% of the placebo treated patients and in 57% of those receiving ACTH (Passalacqua et al, 1988).

Continuation over several days of an i.v. regimen of metoclopramide and dexamethasone, a difficult treatment for out patients, has been shown to considerably increase the protection from delayed emesis in 42 cisplatin-treated patients. Those patients who were on placebo had no emesis in 50% of the cases, while 75% of those on the active drugs had no emesis (Shinkai et al, 1989).

Along the lines of the above study, two other groups have evaluated the efficacy of metoclopramide and/or dexamethasone in the control of delayed symptoms. Oral metoclopramide 20 mg (four times a day = q.i.d.) has been compared to dexamethasone (1mg q.i.d.) and placebo (q.i.d.) over 7 days in 120 patients treated with higher-dose cisplatin therapy. These authors report a 52% protection from nausea with metoclopramide, 69% with dexamethasone, and both are superior to placebo (27% patients without nausea). This study failed to show statistically significant advantage for protection from emesis, where protection rates are 69%, 65% and 57% respectively (Roila et al, 1991).

Ninety-one patients on 120 mg/m2 of cisplatin received initially a combination of dexamethasone, metoclopramide and lorazepam and were then randomised to one of three treatment regimens: placebo; oral dexamethasone 8 mg q.i.d. for 2 days, then 4 mg q.i.d. for 2 days; or dexamethasone as above with oral metoclopramide 0.5 mg/Kg q.i.d. for 4 days. Fifty-two percent of the patients receiving the combination treatment had no delayed womiting, while only 35% were protected by dexamethasone and 87% vomited when receiving placebo (Kris et al, 1989).

Table 2

RANDOMISED STUDIES OF
STEROIDS OR METOCLOPRAMIDE FOR DELAYED EMESIS

Agent	*Protection rate (CR)*	*Comparator (CR)*	
ACTH	57%	Placebo	33%
MCP + DEX i.v.	75%	Placebo	50%
MCP p.o.	69%	Placebo	57%
DEX p.o.	65%	Placebo	57%
DEX p.o.	35%	Placebo	13%
MCP + DEX p.o.	52%	Placebo	13%

ACTH = adrenocorticotropic-hormone
MCP = metoclopramide
DEX = dexamethasone
CR = complete response

Phase III studies with 5-HT_3 antagonists

Three studies have evaluated the newer 5-HT3 antagonists in the particular setting of delayed nausea and vomiting.

Gandara (1991) has reported on 48 patients, who had had less than three episodes of acute emesis and were then randomised to continue on ondansetron 16 mg three times a day or placebo for 4 days. On the days of observation, 39 to 50% of patients on placebo had no further vomiting versus 57 to 78% of those on ondansetron. Control of nausea was however poor in both groups.

Kaizer et al (1992) evaluated three groups of patients receiving low-dose ciplatin and non-cisplatin chemotherapies. Arm A (125 patients) received 10 mg dexamethasone i.v. and 8 mg ondansetron i.v. followed by 8 mg ondansetron p.o. every 12 hours for 9 doses. Arm B (50 patients) received a higher 16 mg ondansetron i.v. dose along with dexamethasone and then placebo p.o. Arm C (126 patients) received the same i.v. treatment as Arm A and then 8 mg ondansetron p.o. once, followed by placebo. Acute protection was similar in arms A + C (79% no emesis) and B (73% no emesis).

The authors report that in arm A 65% of the patients had no emesis over the 5 days of observation, whereas only 45% ($p=0.02$) of the patients had no emesis over 5 days on arm C.
They conclude that oral ondansetron is more effective than placebo in reducing delayed nausea and vomiting. However, (J. Pater, personal communication) arm B patients also experienced a 5 days protection rate similar to arm A. It is thus premature to conclude that oral ondansetron is really an effective agent, compared to placebo, for control of delayed emesis.

A further study has looked at ondansetron compared to dexamethasone in patients undergoing non-cisplatin based chemotherapy. These authors report a 72% protection rate from delayed emesis with dexamethasone compared to 60% with ondansetron. The figures are 52% and 43% for protection from nausea, indicating that dexamethasone, a much cheaper treatment, is at least as effective in this group of patients as ondansetron (Jones et al, 1991). Similar results have been recently reported in patients undergoing CMF type chemotherapy (Levitt et al, 1992), where ondansetron was compared to metoclopramide.

Table 3

RANDOMISED STUDIES OF ORAL 5-HT_3 ANTAGONISTS AND DELAYED EMESIS

Agent	*Protection rate (CR)*	*Comparator (CR)*
Ondansetron	57-78%	Placebo 39-50%
Ondansetron	65%	Placebo 45-65%
Ondansetron	60%	Dexamethasone 72%
Ondansetron	70%	Metoclopramide 70%

CONCLUSION

Presently available data show that delayed emesis continues to be a significant clinical problem. Although there are no studies comparing the best available combination (dexamethasone and oral metoclopramide) to the newer antiemetics, the role of 5-HT_3 antagonists in this setting remains questionable.

REFERENCES

Aapro M.S. (1991): 5-HT_3 Receptor antagonists: An overview of their present status and future potential in cancer therapy-induced emesis. Drugs 42 (4), 551-568.

Gandara D.R. (1991): Progress in the control of acute and delayed emesis induced by cisplatin. Eur. J. Cancer, Vol 27, suppl. 1, S9-S11.

Jones A.L, Hill A.S, Soukip M et al (1991): Comparison of dexamethasone and ondansetron in the prophylaxis of emesis induced by moderately emetogenic chemotherapy. Lancet: 338, 483-87.

Kaizer L, Warr D, Hoskins P et al (1992): The effect of schedule and maintenance on the antiemetic efficacy of ondasetron (ond) combined with dexamethasone (dex) in patients receiving moderately emetogenic chemotherapy. Proc Am soc clin oncol: 11, 381.

Kris MG, Gralla RH, Tyson LB et al (1989): Controlling delayed vomiting: double blind, randomised trial comparing placebo dexamethasone alone and metoclopramide plus dexamethasone in patients receiving cisplatin. J. Clin Oncol: 7, 108-114.

Levitt M, Warr D, Yelle L et al (1992) : The anti-emetic effect of ondansetron (Ond) is not superior to dexamethasone plus metoclopramide (DXM/MCP) in CMF chemotherapy (chemo) for breast cancer: A phase III study by the National Cancer Institute of Canada, clinical trials group (NCIC CTG). Proc Am soc clin oncol 11: 388.

Moreno I, Rosell R, Abad-Esteve A, et al (1991): Randomized trial for the control of acute vomiting in cisplatin treated patients: High dose Metoclopramide with dexamethasone and lorazepam as adjuncts versus high-dose alizapride plus dexamethasone and lorazepam. Oncology 48, 397-402.

Passalacqua R, Bella M, Monici L et al (1988): Double-blind randomised trial for the control of delayed emesis: Comparison of placebo versus adrenocorticotropic hormone (ACTH). Proc Am Soc clin oncol: 9, 1270.

Roila F, Boschetti E, Tonato M, et al (1991): Predictive factors of delayed emesis in cisplatin-treated patients and antiemetic activity and tolerability of metoclopramide or dexamethasone. Am J clin oncol (CCT) 14 (3), 238-242.

Schneider M. on behalf of the granisetron study group (1990): Incidence of delayed cisplatin-induced emesis following acute anti-emetic prophylaxis with granisetron. Presented at the symposium "Advances in emesis control" 15th UICC, Hamburg.

Shinkai T, Saijo N, Eguchi K et al (1989): Control of cisplatin induced delayed emesis with metoclopramide and dexamethasone: a randomised controlled trial. Japan J Clin Oncol: 19, suppl.1, 40-44.

Sorbe B, Frankendal B, Glimelius B et al (1990) : A multicentre randomised study comparing the anti-emetic effects of the 5-HT3 antagonist ICS 205-930 with a metoclopramide-containing anti-emetic cocktail in patients receiving cisplatin chemotherapy. Abstract W9:17 XVth ESMO Congress, Copenhagen.

Mechanisms and Control of Emesis. Eds A.L. Bianchi, L. Grélot, A.D. Miller, G.L. King. Colloque INSERM/ John Libbey Eurotext Ltd. © 1992, Vol. 223, pp. 147-155

Is all radiation-induced emesis ameliorated by 5-HT_3 receptor antagonists?

Bernard M. Rabin [1] and Gregory L. King [2]

[1] Behavioral Sciences and [2] Physiology Departments, Armed Forces Radiobiology Research Institute, Bethesda, Maryland, USA; and [1] Department of Psychology, University of Maryland Baltimore County, Baltimore, Maryland, USA

SUMMARY

Exposing ferrets to gamma rays or X-rays produces vomiting that can be attenuated by 5-HT_3 receptor antagonists and by subdiaphragmatic vagotomy. The present experiments evaluated the effectiveness of these treatments on emesis evoked by exposure to other types of radiation, fast neutrons from a nuclear reactor and high-energy protons (200 MeV), which differ in the relative effectiveness with which they produce vomiting. The results indicated that higher doses of 5-HT_3 receptor antagonists Eusatron (0.03 and 0.30 mg/kg, s.c.) and Ondansetron (0.10 and 0.30 mg/kg, s.c.) prevented emesis following neutron irradiation. Lower doses of these 5-HT_3 receptor antagonists and subdiaphragmatic vagotomy attenuated neutron-induced emesis, increasing the latency and decreasing the severity of the emetic episodes. Ondansetron (0.50 and 1.00 mg/kg, s.c.) completely prevented vomiting following exposure to high-energy protons. The results are interpreted as indicating that similar 5-HT_3-dependent mechanisms mediate emesis produced by exposure to different types of radiation, despite differences in their relative effectiveness.

Tout vomissement radio-induit est-il amélioré par les antagonistes des récepteurs 5-HT_3?

Résumé: *L'exposition de furets aux rayons gamma ou aux rayons X produit des vomissements qui peuvent être atténués par les antagonistes des récepteurs 5-HT3 et par la vagotomie sous-diapragmatique. Les expériences présentées ont évalué l'efficacité de ces traitements sur la réponse émétique évoquée par l'exposition à d'autres types de radiation, comme les neutrons rapides provenant d'un réacteur nucléaire et les protons à haute énergie (200 MeV), qui diffèrent dans leur efficacité relative à produire des vomissements. Les résultats ont montré que de fortes doses d'antagonistes des récepteurs 5-HT3 Eusatron (0,03 et 0,30 mg/Kg, s.c.) et d'Ondansetron (0,10 et 0,30 mg/Kg, s.c.) empêchent la réponse émétique qui suit l'irradiation neutronique. Des doses plus faibles de ces antagonistes et la vagotomie sous-diaphragmatique atténuent la réponse émétique induite par les neutrons, en augmentant leur latence et en diminuant leur sévérité. L'Ondansetron (0,50 et 1,00 mg/Kg s.c.) bloque le vomissement induit par l'exposition aux protons à haute énergie. Les résultats sont interprétés en indiquant que des mécanismes semblables à ceux dépendant des récepteurs 5-HT3 provoquent la réponse émétique produite par l'exposition aux différents types de radiation, en dépit de différences dans leur efficacité relative.*

INTRODUCTION

Exposure to sublethal doses of ionizing radiation can produce nausea and emesis. For the most part, studies of radiation-induced emesis have utilized exposure to X-rays (Andrews & Hawthorn, 1987; Miner *et al.*, 1987) or gamma rays (King, 1988). Pretreating ferrets with serotonin type-3 ($5\text{-}HT_3$) receptor antagonists or performing bilateral subdiaphragmatic vagotomy reliably attenuates the emetic response to these types of radiation, causing significant increases in latency to the first response and ameliorating the severity of the episode (Andrews & Hawthorn, 1987; Miner *et al.*, 1987; King & Landauer, 1990).

In addition to gamma rays and X-rays, emesis can be produced by exposure to other types of ionizing radiation, including neutrons and protons. However, the relative effectiveness of these types of radiation in producing emesis differs from that of gamma rays (Fig. 1). Working with a suprathreshold dose of fast neutrons from a nuclear reactor, Young (1986) reported that increasing the proportion of neutrons in a mixed neutron/gamma field increased the number of

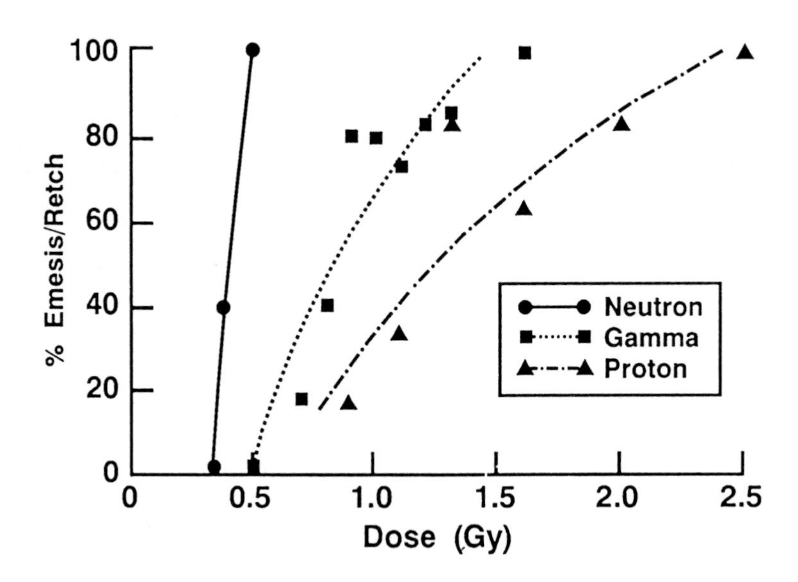

Fig. 1. Dose-response curves for emesis in ferrets following exposure to mixed neutron/gamma radiation (midline neutron dose:total dose ratio = 0.86), gamma rays (cobalt-60), and protons (200 MeV). The ED_{50}s and 95% confidence limits were: neutrons, 40 cGy (confidence limits could not be calculated because there was only a single dose with other than a 0% or 100% response); gamma rays, 85 cGy, 59/98 cGy; protons, 123 cGy, 86/153 cGy. Data redrawn from Rabin *et al.* (1992a; 1992b) and King (1988)

bouts of vomiting in an individual monkey, but did not increase in the total number of monkeys that vomited. Similarly, Rabin *et al.* (1992a) have shown that exposure to mixed fast neutron/gamma radiation from a nuclear reactor (midline neutron dose:dose ratio, 0.86) evokes emesis at lower doses than exposure to cobalt-60 gamma rays. In contrast, exposure to protons is significantly less effective in producing emesis than is exposure to gamma rays (Rabin *et al.*, 1992b). Both the threshold dose and the ED_{100} for proton-induced emesis are greater than required for gamma ray-induced emesis.

Because neutron irradiation can cause significantly greater tissue damage and gastrointestinal effects than gamma rays, Young (1986) has suggested that different mechanisms may mediate neutron-induced emesis than those that mediate emesis following exposure to gamma rays. Similarly, the observation that protons are significantly less effective in eliciting emesis than gamma rays may also imply the involvement of different mechanisms. Because $5\text{-}HT_3$ receptor antagonists are not equally effective in disrupting emesis produced by all types of emetic stimuli (Andrews & Hawthorn, 1987; Costall *et al.*, 1990; Lucot, 1989), it is possible that $5\text{-}HT_3$ receptor antagonists may not be effective in preventing neutron- or proton-induced emesis.

The present experiments were undertaken to evaluate the effectiveness of $5\text{-}HT_3$ receptor antagonists in preventing emesis in ferrets produced by exposure to two different types of radiation: fast neutrons from a nuclear reactor and high-energy protons. For the studies of neutron-induced emesis, the relative effectiveness of two different $5\text{-}HT_3$ receptor antagonists, Ondansetron and Eusatron, was evaluated using procedures designed to determine the ED_{50} of each compound. For proton-induced emesis, only Ondansetron was tested using doses that had been previously established to be effective against cisplatin-induced emesis (Higgins *et al.*, 1989). In addition, the effect of bilateral abdominal vagotomy was also tested against emesis evoked by exposure to neutrons in order to provide a comparison with previous research using gamma rays (Andrews & Hawthorn, 1987; Miner *et al.*, 1987; King & Landauer, 1990).

METHODS

Subjects: The subjects for all experiments were male fitch ferrets weighing 1.0 to 1.5 kg obtained from Marshall Farms (North Rose, NY). They were castrated and descented by the supplier. The ferrets were maintained in AAALAC-accredited animal facilities at the Armed Forces Radiobiology Research Institute (AFRRI) and at Brookhaven National Laboratory (BNL). Food and water were continually available.

Drugs: Both Ondansetron (Glaxo Res., Inc., Research Triangle Park, NC) and Eusatron (Rhone-Poulenc Rorer, King of Prussia, PA) were made fresh using 0.9% NaCl as the vehicle and given in a final volume of less than 1 cc. Both were gifts intended for research use.

Neutron Experiments:

Surgery: For laparotomy (n = 4) or bilateral abdominal vagotomy (n = 4), all animals were medicated, anesthetized, and surgically manipulated as previously described (King and Landauer, 1990). In order for the results to be comparable with those of other experiments (Andrews and Hawthorn, 1987), animals were allowed a 7-10 day postoperative recovery period prior to irradiation.

Procedure: Twenty min prior to irradiation, ferrets were given an s.c. injection of either the compounds or vehicle. They were individually placed in a well-ventilated plastic tube and mechanically transferred to and from the exposure room through an extractor tube. The transfer took approximately 2 min in each direction. Following exposure, the ferrets were placed in a large, well-ventilated clear plastic box and behaviors observed and recorded for 2 hr, as previously described (King and Landauer, 1990). Behaviors were recorded on a personal computer. For those animals receiving 5-HT_3 receptor antagonists, the doses of Ondansetron ranged between 0.003 and 0.30 mg/kg (n = 18), and for Eusatron, between 0.001 and 0.30 mg/kg (n = 17). Test doses of these compounds were based on the method of Golub and Grubbs (1956) that can provide an ED_{50}.

Radiation and Dosimetry: Exposure to a mixed field of neutron and gamma radiation was carried out by placing the ferrets in shielded containers and exposing them to a fixed total dose of 2.0 Gy in the AFRRI TRIGA reactor. Prior to animal irradiation, the dose rate at the midline was established in a lucite phantom (which approximated the size and shape of the ferret) by using the paired-ion chamber technique (Goodman, 1985). All experiments were carried out unilaterally and the doses reported as mid-tissue dose (MTD). Corresponding values of dose-rates used in the neutron-to-total dose ratios were 1 Gy/min and 0.86 (neutron/gamma ≈ 6), respectively. Along the length of the ferret the MTD values were found to vary: the head and tail ends of the animal recorded MTDs of 93% and 85% of the midpoint MTD, respectively. Representative free-in-air photon and neutron spectra information is contained in Verbinski *et al*. (1981).

Data Analysis: For these experiments, latency to the first event was measured from the time that the irradiation ended. The individual values for the various emetic parameters obtained for each group were compared by ANOVA or the Kruskall-Wallis Rank Sum test, as appropriate. Further comparison among the groups was done with the Dunn's test or the Newman-Keul's multiple range test.

Proton Experiments:

Procedure: Thirty min prior to exposure, ferrets were given an s.c. injection of Ondansetron. The doses were 0.5 mg/kg (n = 4) and 1.0 mg/kg (n = 7). These doses were selected because previous research showed that they produced a relatively complete disruption of emesis evoked by exposure to X-rays or gamma rays (Higgins *et al*., 1989). For exposure, the ferrets were placed in a well-ventilated plastic tube. Following exposure, the ferrets were placed in large, well-ventilated clear plastic cages where their behavior was monitored for 1.5-2.0 hr.

Radiation and Dosimetry: Exposure to protons was performed using the linear accelerator at BNL. Ferrets were placed in the center of a 35 cm diameter field perpendicular to the proton beam and given whole-body exposures of 2.5 Gy of 200 MeV protons using 50 μsec pulses with a pulse rate of 0.333 pulses/sec. At this energy, there is a uniform dose-depth distribution through the ferret. This dose was selected because it was the lowest dose that produced emesis in 100% of the untreated subjects. The dose rate was 1.0-2.0 Gy/min. Dosimetry was performed using a 0.05 cc ionization chamber located in an acrylic phantom placed in the center of the proton field. The midline dose to the phantom was determined according to a standard protocol (Vinckier *et al.*, 1991).

RESULTS

Neutron Exposure:

The preliminary results (Table 1) show that all neutron-irradiated animals (intact, laparotomized, and vagotomized) retched and or vomited postirradiation. As reported in the table, however, the vagotomized animals responded significantly later and with significantly fewer retches than did the intact or laparotomized animals. The overall duration of the episode (from first to last retching event) was significantly less for the vagotomized animals than for those receiving laparotomy.

TABLE 1

Effect of Subdiaphragmatic Vagotomy on Neutron-Induced* Emesis

Pretreatment	n	Latency to 1st Episode (min)**	Episode Duration (min)	No. Retches
Intact	4	15.6 ± 6.6	59.4 ± 3.9	97.8 ± 34.8
Surgery				
Laparotomy	4	10.1 ± 1.5	83.8 ± 15.2[b]	133.3 ± 32.7
Vagotomy	4	51.4 ± 4.9[a]	12.8 ± 7.7[b]	17.0 ± 8.8[a]

* 2.0 Gy, mixed neutron/gamma radiation; neutron:gamma ratio ≈ 6:1
** All values are mean ± S.E.M.
[a] Significantly different from intact and laparotomy, $p < 0.05$.
[b] Significantly different from one another, $p < 0.05$.

As shown in Table 2, pretreating ferrets with Eusatron (0.03 and 0.30 mg/kg) and Ondansetron (0.1 and 0.3 mg/kg) was generally effective in preventing vomiting following exposure to a suprathreshold dose of reactor neutrons. Preliminary data (data not shown; n = 2/compound) using lower doses of Eusatron (0.01 mg/kg) and Ondansetron (0.056 mg/kg) indicate that at these doses the $5\text{-}HT_3$ receptor antagonists did not prevent the emetic response to 2.0 Gy of neutron irradiation, although there were clear reductions in the values of several emetic parameters for the treated animals compared with untreated controls. Both $5\text{-}HT_3$ receptor antagonists increased the latency to vomiting following exposure and ameliorated the severity of the episode, decreasing both the duration of the episode and the number of retches observed during the episode.

Proton Exposure:

The effects of pretreatment with the 5-HT_3 receptor antagonist Ondansetron on proton-evoked emesis are summarized in Table 2. Both doses of Ondansetron completely prevented emesis following exposure to 2.5 Gy of high-energy protons for the entire observation period of 1.5-2.0 hr.

Table 2

Effect of 5-HT_3 Receptor Antagonists on Neutron*- and Proton**-Induced Emesis

	Dose (mg/kg)	Number Vomiting	Number Tested
Neutron			
Eusatron	0.03	0	3
	0.30	0	2
Ondansetron	0.10	1	4
	0.30	0	2
Proton			
Ondansetron	0.00	6	6
	0.50	0	4
	1.00	0	7

*2.0 Gy, mixed neutron/gamma radiation
**2.5 Gy, 200 MeV protons

DISCUSSION

The present results indicate that 5-HT_3 receptor antagonists were effective treatments against the emesis evoked by exposure to fast neutrons from a nuclear reactor and high-energy protons in ferrets. These preliminary experiments suggest that pretreating ferrets with low doses of the 5-HT_3 receptor antagonists Ondansetron and Eusatron delayed the onset of emesis and ameliorated the severity of emesis following exposure to fast neutrons. However, from these preliminary data we have not yet established ED_{50} values for the two compounds in order to compare their efficacy. The higher doses of both Eusatron and Ondansetron more completely disrupted neutron-evoked emesis, with only 1 of 11 ferrets vomiting. Similarly, pretreatment with higher dose Ondansetron was equally effective in preventing emesis following exposure to high-energy protons within the 1.5- to 2-hr observation period. In addition, bilateral subdiaphragmatic vagotomy caused a significant attenuation of the emesis evoked by exposure to fast neutrons, both delaying the onset of the response and attenuating the severity of the episodes.

Despite the fact that fast neutrons from a nuclear reactor are more effective in evoking emesis in ferrets than are gamma rays while exposure to high-energy protons are significantly less effective (Rabin *et al.*, 1992a; 1992b), pretreatment with 5-HT_3 receptor antagonists was effective in preventing the vomiting produced by exposure to either type of radiation. The present results parallel the results obtained following exposure to X-rays and gamma rays (Andrews & Hawthorn, 1987; Miner *et al.*, 1987; King & Landauer, 1990). With these types of radiation, lower doses of 5-HT_3 receptor antagonists and bilateral subdiaphragmatic vagotomy increase the latency of the emetic response following irradiation and attenuate the severity and duration of vomiting. Higher doses of 5-HT_3 receptor antagonists, on the other hand, are more effective in preventing radiation-induced emesis. Because the present results fast neutrons and high-energy protons show the same pattern of effects, these results do not support the hypothesis that different mechanisms mediate emesis produced by exposure to different types of radiation (Young, 1986). Rather, the present results are consistent with the hypothesis that similar mechanisms mediate the emetic response to the different types of radiation.

While these results indicate that similar 5-HT_3-dependent and vagal mechanisms mediate emesis following exposure to different types of ionizing radiation, the nature of those mechanisms needs further clarification. Andrews and Hawthorn (1987) have proposed a dual mechanism for radiation-induced emesis: an early phase that is dependent upon vagal innervation and a later phase that is dependent upon a circulating emetic agent, possibly 5-HT, which may act upon 5-HT receptors in the area postrema, the chemoreceptive trigger zone. Previous research using X-rays (Andrews & Hawthorn, 1987) and gamma rays (King & Landauer, 1990) as well as the present results with fast neutrons supports that hypothesis, showing that administration of low doses of 5-HT_3 receptor antagonists or bilateral subdiaphragmatic vagotomy disrupts the early emetic response to ionizing radiation without producing an equivalent disruption of the later emetic response. Also supporting the hypothesis of dual mechanisms mediating radiation-induced emesis in ferrets is the observation by King & Landauer (1990) that the combined treatment with the 5-HT_3 receptor antagonist zacopride and subdiaphragmatic vagotomy is more effective in disrupting emesis following irradiation than is either procedure by itself.

In the ferret, serotonergic neurons are found in the gut and in abdominal visceral afferents (Andrews *et al.*, 1988) as well as in a variety of brain stem structures, including the area postrema, dorsal vagal complex and nucleus of solitary tract (Barnes *et al.*, 1988; Higgins *et al.*, 1989; Kilpatrick, *et al.*, 1989; Leslie *et al.*, 1990; Pinkus *et al.*, 1989). Bilateral subdiaphragmatic vagotomy eliminates the binding of 5-HT_3 receptor antagonists in the dorsal vagal complex, where the majority of afferent vagal fibers terminate (Leslie *et al.*, 1990). Thus, exposing ferrets to ionizing radiation may produce immediate effects on the gut and on vagal afferents to produce short-latency vomiting. The longer latency emetic response following irradiation may result from the excitation of brain stem structures by radiation-released peripheral serotonin or an emetic toxin that affects brain stem serotonergic systems, either in the area postrema or elsewhere. Higher doses of 5-HT_3 receptor antagonists may disrupt serotonergic transmission at these brain stem structures, in addition to affecting the peripheral release of serotonin from the gut, thereby causing a more complete blockage of radiation-induced vomiting.

In summary, the present results show that administration of 5-HT_3 receptor antagonists are as effective in disrupting emesis evoked by exposure to fast neutrons from a nuclear reactor and to protons as they are with X-rays and gamma rays, despite the differences in the effectiveness with which the different types of radiation elicit vomiting. Also, the results on the effects of subdiaphragmatic vagotomy on emesis evoked by exposure to fast neutrons are similar to those obtained following exposure to X-rays and to gamma rays. These results, therefore, support the hypothesis that similar mechanisms mediate the emetic response to different types of radiation.

REFERENCES

Andrews, P. L. R., & Hawthorn, J. (1987): Evidence for an extra-abdominal site of action for the 5-HT_3 receptor antagonist BRL24924 in the inhibition of radiation-evoked emesis in the ferret. *Neuropharmacology* 26, 1367-1370.

Andrews, P. L. R., Rapeport, W. G., & Sanger, G. J. (1988): Neuropharmacology of emesisinduced by anto-cancer therapy. *Trends Pharmacol. Sci.* 9, 334-341.

Barnes, N. W., Costall, B., Naylor, R. J., & Tattersall, F. D. (1988): Identification of 5-HT_3 recognition sites in the ferret area postrema. *J. Pharm. Pharmacol.* 40, 586-588.

Costall, B., Domeney, A. M., Naylor, R. J., Owera-Atepo, J. B., Rudd, J. A., & Tattersall, F. D. (1990): Fluphenazine, ICS 205-930 and *dl*-fenfluramine differentially antagonise drug-induced emesis in the ferret. *Neuropharmacology* 29, 453-462.

Golub, A., & Grubbs, F. E. (1956): Analysis of sensitivity experiments when the levels of stimulus cannot be controlled. *J. Amer. Statistical Assoc.* 51, 257-265.

Goodman, L. J. (1985): A practical guide to ionization chamber dosimetry at the AFRRI reactor. AFRRI Contract Report #CR85-1.

Higgins, G. A., Kilpatrick, G. J., Bunce, K. T., Jones, B. J., & Tyers, M. B. (1989): 5-HT_3 receptor antagonists injected into the area postrema inhibit cisplatin-induced emesis in the ferret. *Br. J. Pharmacol.* 97, 247-245.

King, G. L. (1988): Characterization of radiation-induced emesis in the ferret. *Radiat. Res.* 114, 599-612.

King, G. L., & Landauer, M. R. (1990): Effects of Zacopride and BMY25801 (Batanopride) on radiation-induced emesis and locomotor behavior in the ferret. *J. Pharmacol. exp. Ther.* 253, 1026-1033.

Kilpatrick, G. J., Jones, B. J., & Tyers, M. B. (1989): Binding of the 5-HT_3 ligand [^{3}H]GR65630, to rat area postrema, vagus nerve and the brains of several species. *Eur. J. Pharmacol.* 159, 157-164.

Leslie R. A., Reynolds, D. J. M., Andrews, P. L. R., Grahame-Smith, D. G., Davis, C. J., & Harvey, J. M. (1990): Evidence for presynaptic 5-hydroxytryptamine$_3$ recognition sites on vagal afferent terminals in the brainstem of the ferret. *Neuroscience* 38, 667-673.

Lucot, J. B. (1989): Blockade of 5-hydroxytryptamine receptors prevents cisplatin-induced emesis but not motion- or xylazine-induced emesis in the cat. *Pharmacol. Biochem. Behav.* 32, 207-210.

Miner, W. D., Sanger, G. J., & Turner, D. H. (1987): Evidence that 5-hydroxytryptamine$_3$ receptors mediate cytotoxic drug and radiation-evoked emesis. *Br. J. Cancer* 56, 159-162.

Pinkus, L.M., Sarbin, N.S., Barefoot, D.S., and Gordon, J.C. (1989): Association of [^{3}H]zacopride with 5-HT$_3$ binding sites. *Eur. J. Pharmacol.* 168, 355-362.

Rabin, B. M., Hunt, W. A., Wilson, M. E., & Joseph, J. A. (1992): Emesis in ferrets following exposure to different types of radiation: A dose-response study. *Aviat. Space Environ. Med.* 63, in press. (a)

Rabin, B. M., Joseph, J. A., Hunt, W. A., Kandasamy, S. B., & Ludewight, B. (1992): Behavioral endpoints for radiation injury. Presented at the World Space Congress, Washington, DC. (b)

Verbinski, V., Cassapakis, C., Hagan, W., Ferlic, K., & Daxon, E. (1981): Calculation of the neutron and gamma ray environment in and around the AFRRI TRIGA reactor. DNA Contract Report # DNA 5793F-2, v. 2.

Vinckier, S., Bonnet, D. E., & Jones, D. Y. L. (1991): Code of practice for clinical proton dosimetry. *Radiother. Oncol.* 20, 53-63.

Young, R. W. (1986): Mechanisms and treatment of radiation-induced nausea and vomiting. In *Nausea and Vomiting: Mechanisms and Treatment*, ed C. J. Davies, G. V. Lake-Bakaar, & D. G. Grahame-Smith, pp. 94-109. Berlin: Springer-Verlag.

ACKNOWLEDGMENTS

This research was supported by the Armed Forces Radiobiology Research Institute, Defense Nuclear Agency, under work units 00157 and 00107. Views presented in this paper are those of the authors; no endorsement by the Defense Nuclear Agency has been given or should be inferred. The authors wish to thank J. Weatherspoon, T. K. Dalton and S. B. Kandasamy, for their assistance in these experiments. GLK wishes to express his gratitude to Mr. T. Lively for writing the software used to record the behavioral events.This research was conducted according to the principles described in the Guide for the Care and Use of Laboratory Animals prepared by the Institute of Laboratory Animal Research, National Research Council.

Mechanisms and Control of Emesis. Eds A.L. Bianchi, L. Grélot, A.D. Miller, G.L. King. Colloque INSERM/ John Libbey Eurotext Ltd. © 1992, Vol. 223, pp. 157-165

Clinical trials in the prevention and control of emesis induced by therapeutic radiation

T.J. Priestman and S.G. Priestman

The Radiotherapy Department, The Royal Hospital, Cleveland Road, Wolverhampton, WV2 IBT, UK

SUMMARY

Emesis causes distress to a small but significant minority of patients undergoing radiotherapy for malignant disease. Established anti-emetic drugs, such as metoclopramide and prochlorperazine, offer only limited symptom control. Recent studies with the 5HT3 receptor antagonist, ondansetron, have shown a clear superiority for this drug in the prevention and control of radiation induced emesis, with the abolition of vomiting and retching in more than 90% of patients at high risk of developing sickness, and complete relief of nausea in approximately 80% of these patients. Further trials with 5HT3 antagonists are indicated to fully define their role in the managementof sickness induced by therapeutic radiation.

Essais cliniques dans la prévention et le contrôle du vomissement induit par la radiothérapie.

Résumé: *Le vomissement conduit à une détresse chez un nombre réduit mais non négligeable de malades au cours de la radiothérapie anticancéreuse. L'usage de drogues anti-émétiques, telles que la métoclopramide et la prochlorperazine, n'offre qu'un contrôle limité des symptômes. Des études récentes avec l'Ondansetron, un antagoniste des récepteurs 5-HT3, ont nettement montré la supériorité de cette drogue dans la prévention et le contrôle du vomissement radio-induit par la suppression de tout vomissement et de tout haut-le-coeur chez plus de 90% des patients à haut risque, et une guérison complète chez approximativement 80% de ces patients. Des essais complémentaires avec les antagonistes des récepteurs 5HT3 sont indiqués pour définir pleinement leur rôle dans le contrôle des malaises induit par la radiothérapie.*

INTRODUCTION

Although the majority of patients undergoing radiotherapy as part of their cancer treatment will not experience sickness there remains a substantial minority for whom nausea and vomiting will occur as distressing side-effects during their irradiation. For those patients who do develop problems, the degree of emesis varies considerably but is generally less severe than that associated with cisplatin-based chemotherapy. The duration of radiation-induced sickness may, however, be considerably longer than that associated with chemotherapy - since a course of radiotherapy may involve 30 to 40 fractions (treatments) over a period of 6 to 8 weeks and, if untreated, sickness could persist throughout this period. Thus whilst the emesis associated with therapeutic irradiation is not as severe or predictable as that seen with many cytotoxic drug regimens, the symptoms are still upsetting for the patient and require treatment.

The pathophysiology of radiation-induced emesis remains unclear but in purely practical terms a number of factors have been identified which help predict the likelihood of sickness developing during treatment. These include:

1. Site

Patients having radiotherapy to the upper abdomen are most at risk of developing symptoms. Surprisingly although this problem has been recognised since the earliest days of therapeutic irradiation the actual incidence of emesis in this situation has never been accurately quantified, although in one series of patients undergoing hemi-body irradiation it was noted that following single doses of 8 Gy, with no anti-emetic prophylaxis, 91% of those having upper body irradiation and 33% receiving lower body treatment experienced significant emesis ((Danjoux et al, 1979). Animal studies have shown that such irradiation causes the release of emetic substances, such as methionine, catecholamines, prostaglandins, dopamine and enkephalin from the first part of the small bowel which stimulate the chemoreceptor trigger zone in the hind brain. Direct stiumlation of the chemoreceptor trigger zone via neural pathways from the upper gastro-intestinal tract has also been implicated (Harding, 1988). Despite these logical explanations it is still the case that a small but significant proportion of patients undergoing radiotherapy to other sites of the body, where such mechanisms cannot be involved, still experience considerable emesis.

2. Field size

In general terms the greater the volume of tissue being irradiated the greater the risk of sickness developing. The most obvious example of this is total-body irradiation for patients with leukaemias and lymphomas.

3. Dose per fraction

The greater the dose given at each treatment the greater the risk of emesis. Most curative radiotherapy involves courses of daily treatment (5 days per weeek) for between 3 to 8 weeks with average daily doses of 1.8 to 3 Gy. Palliative radiation often comprises single exposure treatments with doses of 8 to 15 Gy, greatly increasing the risk of emesis for these patients.

4. Age

It has been suggested that children are less susceptible to radiation-induced emesis than adults (Westbrook et al, 1987).

5. Anxiety

Although not well documented it has also been suggested that anxiety and apprehension may increase the likelihood of sickness in radiotherapy patients.

Despite the long-standing recognition if the problem of radiation-induced emesis there have been very few published studies regarding its control or prevention. This is in marked contrast to the now very extensive literature on chemotherapy related sickness. A discussion of those trials which have been reported may be conveniently divided into two categories: series using established anti-emetics and series using the new generation of anti-emetics - the 5HT3-antagonists.

STUDIES WITH ESTABLISHED ANTI-EMETICS

In Britain at the present time metoclopramide is almost certainly the most widely used anti-emetic for the control of radiation-induced emesis. Despite this pre-eminence there are only three published studies on its efficacy in this indication other than recent comparative trials with 5HT3-antagonists, these latter results are considered below. In the former series an initial study looked at patients receiving upper abdominal radiotherapy during a fractionated course of treatment with daily doses of 2 Gy. All patients received metoclopramide 10mgs tds orally from the beginning of their treatment. Of the 30 patients evaluated 14 had no nausea or vomiting throughout their course. Of the remainder 10 experienced minor emesis but did not require a change in therapy and six had symptoms controlled by metoclopramide for an average of six days but then developed more severe emesis and were given the cannabinoid nabilone as an alternative anti-emetic, this controlled their sickness but gave rise to some toxicity (Priestman & Priestman, 1984).

This initial evaluation led to a randomized double-blind cross-over study where patients who developed emesis during a fractionated course of radiotherapy, and still had five or more treatments before completing their course, were given either metoclopramide 10mgs tds orally or nabilone 1mg bd (with a placebo tablet at midday). 52% of those given nabilone felt they achieved good symptom control compared to 48% who received metoclopramide. A further 24% and 36% respectively felt that control was adequate and that they did not wish for any additional anti-emetic therapy. These results obviously showed no significant difference in efficacy between the two drugs but nabilone caused significantly more toxicity than metoclopramide, which was well-tolerated (Priestman & Priestman, 1987). These results would suggest that appproximately 80% of patients who experience radiation-induced emesis will achieve good or adequate symptomatic relief with oral metoclopramide.

The third study randomised 89 patients who developed emesis during a course of radiotherapy to receive either metoclopramide 100mg 4 hourly, prochlorperazine 10mg 4 hourly or a placebo. Surprisingly assessments based on the number of vomits and a rating scale for nausea showed no significant differences between the three arms (although no precise figures for response were quoted). Less surpisingly there was extensive toxicity with metoclopramide at this high dose, 21 of 28 (75%) patients experiencing side-effects, which were principally neurological (Sokol et al, 1986).

Phenothiazine derviatives are also extensively employed, probably the most popular agent being prochlorperazine. Once again, however, apart from the series cited above and one other (small) study the only published results with this drug in this indication come from randomized trials with 5HT3-antagonists. The former (small) trial was a randomized cross-over comparison with the cannabinoid tetrahydrocannabinol in patients undergoing fractionated irradiation. Only eleven patients were randomized, however, and of these only seven were evaluable; of these 4 of 7 noticed an improvement in symptoms with the cannabinoid and 3 with prochlorperazine (Ungerleider et al, 1984).

A less frequently used phenothiazine, chlorpromazine, was evaluated in a randomized comparison with the cannabinoid levonantrodol (Lucraft & Palmer, 1982). In this series patients received either 25mg of chlorpromazine or 0.5 or 0.75 mg of levonantrodol 30 minutes before single exposure treatments of 10 to 15 Gy to the thoracic/lumbar spine or hypochondrium. 43 patients were entered, 7 of 14 (50%) in the chlorpromazine group vomited within 4 hours of irradiation compared with 17 of 29 (59%) given the cannabinoid. Although the numbers were small and no details on the severity of emesis were given the authors final conclusion that neither drug proved particularly effective was probably valid.

Cannabinoids enjoyed a brief vogue during the mid-1980s in the treatment of radiation-emesis and the three published studies assessing their efficacy are described above. Although nabilone appeared relatively active in this indication its considerable toxicity resulted in its being generally abandoned in favour of less troublesome agents.

Domperidone is the only other agent to have recieved any attention in the literature in this situation. A review of unpublished data has reported on seven patients given a course of abdominal irradiation, 17 who received throacic radiotherapy and six who underwent total body irradiation. All patients had developed sickness during treatment and were given the drug at a dose of 10 to 20 mgs tds. Only 14 (47%) had complete relief of symptoms and 6 (20%) had no benefit whatsoever (Reyntjens, 1979).

STUDIES WITH 5HT3 ANTAGONISTS

These may be conveniently divided into trials based on conventional radiotherapy and those involving total body irradiation.

Trials with conventional radiotherapy

Two prospective double-blind randomised studies, both from Britain, have been reported comparing established anti-emetics with a 5HT3 anatagonist.

The first of these was based on single-exposure high-dose palliative treatments. Patients who were to receive single doses of 8 to 10 Gy to fields of at least 100cm^2 to the upper abdomen (centred between T10 to L1) were randomised to receive either ondansetron 8mg tds for 5 days or metoclopramide 10mgs tds for a similar period. Both drugs were started one hour prior to irradiation and given orally. Assessment of emesis was by diary cards, completed by the patient, and responses in terms of emesis were graded as complete (no episodes of retching or vomiting), major (1-2 episodes), minor (3-5 episodes) or failure (more than five emetic episodes). Nausea was graded into four categories: none, mild, moderate or severe, based on the patients' own assessments.

Originally it had been planned to recruit 160 patients to this trial but the protocol specified that an interim analysis would be carried out after approximately half that total had been reached and the study would be terminated if highly significant differences were apparent. In fact 97 patients had entered the trial at the time of the interim assessment, 84 of whom were evaluable. The results showed that in the first 24 hours after irradiation 97% of patients on ondansetron had complete control of emesis compared to only 46% of those given metoclopramide (p=0.001), during the same period 73% of those taking the 5HT3-antagonist had no nausea compared to only 41% taking metoclopramide (p=0.001) (Priestman et al, 1990). In view of these differences the trial was terminated at this point but during the period of the analysis randomisation had continued and a further 24 patients entered on study. A final analysis was therefore carried out to include these individuals. Of the 121 subjects entered 105 were ultimately evaluable and the results are shown in Tables 1 & 2. As can be seen the benefit of ondansetron remained highly significant, there was 100% either complete or major control of emesis on day 1, whereas 28% of those on metoclopramide failed to be controlled or achieved only minor control.

Table 1. Control of emesis in first 24 hours after single exposure radiotherapy

Emetic control	*Complete*	*Major*	*Minor*	*Failure*
Ondansetron	45 (92%)	4 (8%)	0	0
Metoclopramide	26 (46%)	14 (25%)	7 (12%)	9 (16%)
Nausea	*None*	*Mild*	*Moderate*	*Severe*
Ondansetron	33 (67%)	10 (21%)	4 (8%)	1 (2%)
Metoclopramide	22 (39%)	12 (21%)	10 (18%)	12 (21%)

Days 2 to 5 were also analysed. Naturally over this period the emetic effect of the radiation was diminishing and the smaller differences between the two drugs did not reach statistical significance. However emesis continued to be almost completely controlled by ondansetron, as shown in Table 2. Nausea, on the other hand, did persist in 10 to 20% of cases through days 2 to 5 and was not fully conrolled by either drug (Collis et al, 1991).

Table 2. Control of emesis during days 1 to 5 after single exposure radiotherapy

Day	*1*	*2*	*3*	*4*	*5*
Ondansetron	100/88*	98/82	100/75	98/79	98/74
Metoclopramide	71/60	86/76	93/76	91/84	96/83

* all figures are percentages, the first relates to emetic control (complete or major) the second to nausea (none or mild)

Although single exposure treatments are widely used for palliation in Britain most courses of radiotherapy elsewhere, and curative treatments in the UK, rely on fractionated courses of radiation usually extending over several weeks. The second comparative trial looked at patients undergoing fractionated irradiation to the upper abdomen who were to receive five or more daily treatments with fractions sizes of 1.8 Gy or more. They were randomised to receive ondansetron 8g tds or prochlorperazine 10mg tds from one hour before their first treatment, as emesis prohpylaxis. The methods of assessment and grading of responses were similar to those in the previous study. This trial is now complete and a final analysis is currently in preparation. Interim results have, however, been published (Priestman et al, 1992). These were based on 183 evaluable patients. The initial assessment was based on a 'worst day' analysis and showed a significant benefit for ondansetron (p=0.022), the details are given in Table 3. A further analysis looked at the number of emesis-free days in both groups, the figures here were 71% for ondansetron and 56% for prochlorperazine (p=0.005). A more detailed final report is in preparation.

Table 3 'Worst day' comparison of ondansetron and prochlorperazine in fractionated radiotherapy

Emetic response	*Ondansetron*	*Prochlorperazine*
Complete	56 (58%)	30 (35%)
Major	11 (11%)	26 (30%)
Minor	8 (8%)	7 (8%)
Failure	21 (22%)	24 (27%)

In an open study patients receiving fractionated upper abdominal irradiation in daily doses of 1.8 to 4 Gy were given ondansetron, again at a dose 8mg tds orally. Emesis was completely controlled in 19 of 20 patients throughout their radiation course (Frazen et al, 1991).

A final study was also non-randomised and assessed the value of a second 5HT3 anatagonist, granisetron, in the prevention of emesis when lower hemi-body irradiation was given. In an open study 22 patients with bone secondaries were given granisetron intravenously at a dose of either 20μg/kg or 40μg/kg one hour prior to a single midline dose of 8 Gy. A complete response (no nausea or vomiting) was noted in 9 of 13 (69%) patients at the lower dose level and 6 of 9 (66%)at the higher level (Logue et al, 1991). The value of anti-emetic therapy in this study is difficult to guage as a previous series showed that only 33% of patients receiving single dose, lower half body irradiation would experience significant sickness (Danjoux et al, 1979).

Studies in total body irradiation (TBI)

Nausea and vomiting is almost universal after TBI and is equally prevelant whether treatment is given as a single dose or in a fractionated course with doses as low as 1.2 Gy daily, this is despite the use of conventional anti-emetics such as metoclopramide (Westbrook et al, 1987; Spitzer et al, 1990). Two non-randomised studies have made initial asessments of 5HT3 antagonists in this situation.

The first of these used ondansetron and included both children and adults undergoing conditioning for bone marrow transplantation. The conditioning included both chemotherapy (with cyclophosphamide) and TBI but separate assessments of emesis were made for the two components of the conditioning process. The radiation dose for children was 1.8 Gy twice daily for four days and they were given ondansetron 5 to 8mg/m^2 iv during conditioning. For adults the regimen was 6 Gy for two doses or 8 Gy as a single dose with ondanstron 8mg tds iv during conditioning. Among the children complete or major control of emesis was achieved in 9 of 11 (82%) during TBI whilst in the adults 74 had complete and 95% complete or major control (Hewitt et al, 1991).

The second study evaluated granisetron in thirty two consecutive patients receiving single fraction TBI at a dose of 7.5 Gy, previous experience had indicated that 95% of such patients would suffer severe emesis despite the use of conventional antiemetics. All patients were aged 14 years or more and were given granisetron 40μg/kg 30 to 60 minutes prior to irradiation with the option of two further doses over the next 24 hours if needed. 18 patients (56%) experienced total protection and a further 13 (41%) had major anti-emetic protection. The criteria for the latter were, however, rather different from the other studies cited here, but overall 70% of patients had no vomiting and nausea graded only as either none or mild. Only three patients required a second dose of granisetron (Hunter et al, 1991).

DRUG SAFETY

At the relatively low doses used for the relief of radiation-induced emesis side-effects with metoclopramide and prochlorperazine are few and minor. Happily the new generation of 5HT3 antagonists appear to be equally well tolerated, no major toxicities have been reported, occasional headache and constipation are the only consistent adverse events to have been documented and these occur in less than 10% of patients in most series (Priestman et al, 1990; Logue et al, 1991; Hunter et al, 1991).

CONCLUSIONS

Recent clinical trials indicate that the 5HT3 receptor antagonist, ondansetron, has shown a clear superiority over agents such as prochlorperazine and metoclopramide in the prevention and control of radiation induced emesis, with the abolition of vomiting and retching in more than 90% of patients at high risk of developing sickness, and complete relief of nausea in approximately 80% of these patients.

Ondansetron was the first 5HT3 antagonist to become commercially available in Britain and has now been joined by granisetron (although the latter is, as yet, only available in an intravenous formulation). Further similar drugs are under development. Future clinical trials with these agents are likely to be directed towards comparisons betwen the drugs and the assessment of combination anti-emetic therapy, with agents such as dexamethasone, in order to identify the optimum regimen for the prevention or relief of emesis casue by radiotherapy.

REFERENCES

Collis C.H., Priestman T.J., Priestman S., Lucraft H., Roberts J.T., Adams M. & Upadhyaya B.K. (1991) The final assessment of a randomized double blind comaprative study of ondansetron vs metoclopramide in the prevention of nausea and vomiting following high dose upper abdominal irradiation. *Clin. Oncol.* 3, 241-242.

Danjoux C.E., Rider W.D. & Fitzpatrick P.J. (1979) The acute radiation syndrome - a memorial to William Michael Court-Brown. *Clin. Radiol.* 30, 581-584.

Frazen L., Israelsson G., Lomberg H., Modig H. & Henriksson R (1991) Ondansetron prevents emesis induced by fractionated radiotherapy. *Eur. J. Cancer Clin. Oncol.* Supplement 2, S295 (abstract)

Harding R.K. (1988) Prodromal effects of radiation: pathways models and protection by antiemetics. *Pharmac. Ther.* 39, 335-345.

Hewitt M., Croockewit S., Abram W.P., Upadhyaya B.K. & Lane-Allman E.(1991) Ondansetron prophylaxis against emesis produced by total body irradiation and chemotherapy conditioning for bone marrow transplantation. *Eur. J. Cancer Clin Oncol.* Supplement 2, S294 (abstract).

Hunter A.E., Prentice H.G., Pothecary K., Coumar A., Collis C., Upward J., Murdoch R., Gandhi L., Hamon M., Butler M & Wells J. (1991) Granisetron a selective 5HT3 receptor antagonist, for the prevention of radiation induced emesis during total body irradiation. *Bone Marrow Transplant.* 7, 439-441.

Logue J.P., Magee B., Hunter R.D. & Murdoch R.D. (1991) The antiemetic effect of granisetron in lower hemibody radiotherapy. *Clin. Oncol.* 3, 247-249.

Lucraft H.H. & Palmer M.K. (1982) Randomised clinical trial of levonantradol and chlropromazine in the prevention of radiotherapy induced vomiting. *Clin.Radiol.* 33, 621-622.

Priestman T.& Priestman S. (1984) An initial evaluation of nabilone in the control of radiotherapy-induced nausea and vomiting. *Clin. Radiol.* 35, 265-266.

Priestman S., Priestman T. & Canney P. (1987) A double-blind randomised cross-over comparison of nabilone and metoclopramide in the control of radiation-induced nausea. *Clin. Radiol.* 38, 543-544.

Priestman T.J., Roberts J.T., Lucraft H., Collis C.H., Adams M., Upadhyaya B.K. & Priestman S. (1990) Results of a randomized double blind comparative study of ondansetron and metoclopramide in the prevention of nausea and vomiting following high dose abdominal irradiation. *Clin. Oncol.* 2, 71-75.

Priestman T.J., Roberts J.T., Lucraft H. & Upadhyaya B.K. (1992) Randomized double-blind trial of ondansetron (OND) and prochlorperazine (PCP) in the prevention of radiotherapy (RT) induced emesis. *Proc. Am. Soc. Clin. Oncol.* 13, in press (abstract).

Sokol G.H., Greenberg H.M., McCarthy S., Sledjeski L & Lyman G. (1986) Radiation induced nausea (RIN): the comparative efficacy of oral metoclopramide (M) versus prochlorperazine (P) and placebo. A double blind randomized study. *Proc. Amer. Soc. Clin. Oncol.* 5, 248 (abstract).

Spitzer T.R., Deeg H.J., Torrisi J., Cottler-Fox M.,Cahill R., Pickle L. & Dubois A. (1990) Total body irradiation (TBI) induced emesis is universal after small-dose fractions (120cGy) and is not cumulative dose related. *Proc. Amer. Soc. Clin. Oncol.* 9, 50 (abstract).

Ungerleider J.T., Andrysiak T.A., Fairbanks L.A., Tesler A.S. & Parker R.G. (1984) Tetrahydrocannabinol vs prochlorperazine. The effects of two antiemetics on patients undergoing radiotherapy. *Radiology* 150, 598-599.

Westbrook C., Glaholm J. & Barrett A. (1987) Vomiting associated with whole body irradation. *Clin. Radiol.* 38, 263-266.

Mechanisms and Control of Emesis. Eds A.L. Bianchi, L. Grélot, A.D. Miller, G.L. King. Colloque INSERM/ John Libbey Eurotext Ltd. © 1992, Vol. 223, pp. 167-168

Prevalence and severity of patient reported nausea from four studies of consecutive chemotherapy patients

Gary R. Morrow, Mary Jo Barry, Wei Jiang and Jacque Lindke

University of Rochester Cancer Center, 601 Elmwood Avenue, Box 704, Rochester, NY 14642, USA

The success of chemotherapy treatment often depends on the physician's ability to both administer an entire treatment regimen and manage the patient's treatment related side effects. Nausea and vomiting are among the most common side effects reported. The systematic investigation of their development, expression and control is important for a variety of reasons. Nausea/vomiting[1,2]:

- Make cancer patients' lives miserable and severely disrupt their daily functioning.
- Can promote further treatment complications like anorexia, dehydration, metabolic imbalance, and psychological problems such as depression.
- Pose significant challenges to both the successful completion and scientific interpretation of randomized clinical trials of cancer treatments.

The Figure on the next page summarizes the severity of nausea reported by four sequential series of consecutive chemotherapy patients (N=2,499) studied over 12 years from 1978 to 1990. All patients had histologically confirmed cancer and were receiving treatment at one of the five hospitals affiliated with the University of Rochester Cancer Center.

From 62% to 70% of the patients in the four samples experienced nausea/vomiting at their fourth treatment despite normal clinical care, including the use of antiemetic drugs. Comparability is seen across the four time periods. Overall, approximately one in three of the patients described their nausea as "moderate", and approximately one in three described nausea as "severe", "very severe", or "intolerable". These data are not idiosyncratic to our cancer center, but consistently mirror findings in the literature[3].

It may seem puzzling that these prevalence rates and patient reported severity remain high despite the recent development and use of antiemetic drugs. As control of side effects has gotten better over time, patients have been given more potent doses of chemotherapy drugs on increasingly aggressive regimens[4]. For example, while earlier studies of chemotherapy for breast cancer used one or at most two drugs, several recent treatment protocols use up to nine drugs in a rotating regimen.

We compared the dosage per treatment of eleven chemotherapy drugs being given in consecutive cancer patients studied in 1991 (n=329) with drug dosages used 10 years previously (n=1620), and found a 10% to 20% dosage increase for several common chemotherapy drugs such as 5-FU, cytoxan and methotrexate along with an increase from 2.6 to 3.0 in average number of chemotherapy drugs given and an increase in rated emetic potential of treatment regimen.

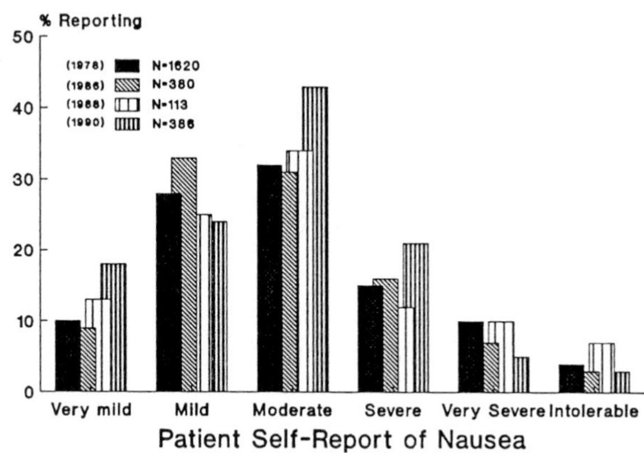

This dose escalation pattern is likely to continue. Colony stimulating factors seem to reverse chemotherapy induced neutropenia; erythropoietin has shown effectiveness in altering chemotherapy induced anemia. Since neutropenia and anemia are two common dose limiting factors in chemotherapy treatment, drugs that correct these side effects will allow significantly more aggressive treatments to be given.

We believe that the next significant advance in side effect control will result from improvements in methodology and a better understanding of the mechanisms involved[5].

REFERENCES

1. Martin, M.: Myth and realities of antiemetic treatment. Br J Cancer. (In press).
2. Kucharczyk, J., Stewart, D.J., Miller, A.D. (1991): Nausea and vomiting: Recent research in clinical advances. Boston:CRC Press.
3. Lindley, C.M., Bernard, S., Fields, S.M. (1989): Incidence and duration of chemotherapy-induced nausea and vomiting in the outpatient oncology population. J Clin Oncol 7: 1142-1149.
4. Morrow, G.R., Black, P.M., Dudgeon, D.J. (1991): Advances in data assessment: Application to the etiology of nausea reported during chemotherapy, concerns about significance testing and opportunity in clinical trials. Cancer 67: 780-787.
5. Morrow, G.R. (1984): The assessment of nausea and vomiting: Past problems, current issues, and suggestions for future research. Cancer 53: 2267-2278.

Supported in part by RCDA K04-CA-01038, and by research grants NR01905 from the National Center for Nursing Research, DHHS and PBR42D from the American Cancer Society.

Mechanisms and Control of Emesis. Eds A.L. Bianchi, L. Grélot, A.D. Miller, G.L. King. Colloque INSERM/ John Libbey Eurotext Ltd. © 1992, Vol. 223, pp. 169-170

Pre-chemotherapy total autonomic activity assessed via heart rate spectral analysis as a predictor of chemotherapy induced self-reported nausea

Gary R. Morrow, Mary Jo Barry, Wei Jiang, * Cynthia Angel and * Brent DuBeshter

*University of Rochester Cancer Center, 601 Elmwood Avenue, Box 704, Rochester, NY 14642, * University of Rochester Medical Center, 601 Elmwood Avenue, Box 668, Rochester, NY 14642, USA*

The adequate management of nausea/vomiting and other side effects caused by chemotherapy treatment is critical to total patient care since completing a planned course of chemotherapy treatment on time, with no dose reductions, maximizes patient survival. Side effects caused by cancer chemotherapy can increase patient reluctance to continue treatment, reduce the likelihood that patients will complete the full treatment regimen, and require reduced drug dosages[1].

Increased knowledge of the mechanisms of side effect development may lead to better prediction and control of chemotherapy-induced nausea and vomiting symptoms. Particularly, changes in autonomic activity have been associated with nausea/vomiting in a variety of research. Our research program in this area examines chemotherapy induced changes in several measures of autonomic activity and their relationship with the patient's self-report of chemotherapy induced nausea/vomiting. The specific aim of the current study was to determine if general autonomic activity measured through heart rate variability assessed prior to the administration of chemotherapy drugs predicts subsequent nausea/vomiting.

Heart rate was monitored through three 3M Red Dot monitoring electrodes (2257-25) placed on the chest at approximately the sixth intercostal space. EKG was recorded through a Healthdyne monitor (model 16000; Healthdyne, Ga) that stored the data in an Oxford Medilog MR14 (Holter monitor) on a standard 120-minute cassette tape. Software programs were developed using the ASYST programming language.

General autonomic activity was assessed through Fourier mathematical analysis of millisecond variations in the heart's successive R-R intervals. Fourier analysis of R-R rate enables the separation of different frequencies involved in autonomic activity; specifically, the areas under curves representing frequencies from 0.0 to 0.5 Hz. represent the level of autonomic activity. The validity and reliability of this technique has been established in both human and animal studies[2,3].

Following pilot studies on two outpatient and five inpatient subjects, 20 patients with ovarian cancer being treated with cisplatin or carboplatin were evaluated. Total autonomic activity was assessed by spectral analysis of heart rate frequencies between 0.0 and 0.5 Hz. in patients lying quietly prior to the administration of chemotherapy or antiemetics. Total autonomic activity was compared between patients reporting low levels of posttreatment nausea (n=11) and high levels (n=9); high autonomic activity was defined as greater than 4.0 $BPM^2 \times 10^3$ and low activity as below that level. A median split of patient reported nausea on a 7 point scale defined high vs. low posttreatment nausea. Chi-square analysis showed significantly more pre-treatment autonomic activity in patients experiencing high levels of nausea two to 12 hours later ($x^2=7.2$, $p<.05$). Separating patients experiencing no nausea from those experiencing low nausea indicated a possible linear relationship between autonomic activity and nausea. This was confirmed through multiple regression analysis using continuous values for nausea and autonomic activity; a substantial linear relationship was found between total autonomic activity and subsequent nausea and vomiting ($R^2=0.69$; $p<.05$).

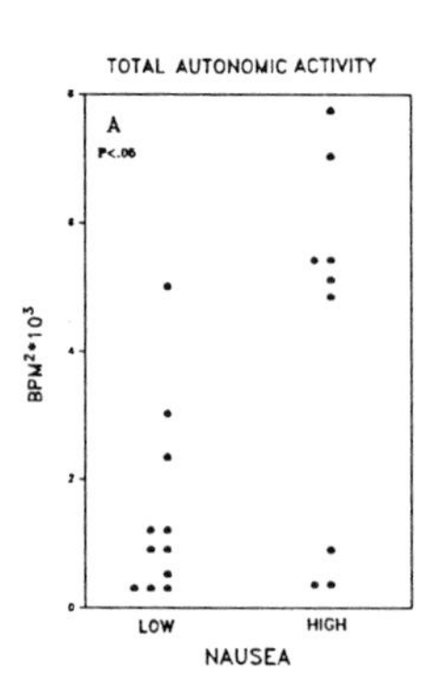

None of the following differentiated between high vs. low nausea patients[4] (all p's$>.10$): i) Expectation of experiencing nausea, vomiting or anxiety; ii) Patient report of anxiety, depression or fatigue on the Profile of Mood States (POMS); iii) Rated tension either in the morning or the afternoon of the day of chemotherapy treatment; iv) Coping style as measured by the Blunter/Monitor dimension of the Miller Behavioral Inventory; v) Type of chemotherapy, i.e. cisplatin vs. carboplatin; and vi) Age.

Further development of this technique may provide an independent and objective endpoint measurement associated with nausea/vomiting and lead to improved methodology to study individual differences in the patient report of subjective nausea. Clinically, this research could help improve control of nausea/vomiting through both pharmacologic and behavioral interventions by making it possible to individually tailor interventions to specific patients. The ability to predict the probable severity of individual patients' nausea/vomiting would also assist clinical decision-making regarding appropriate antiemetic regimens and whether or not to consider hospitalization for more intensive nausea/vomiting control.

REFERENCES

1. Morrow, G.R. (1987): Management of nausea in the cancer patient. In Medical Care of the Cancer Patient, eds S. Rosenthal, J.R. Carrigan and B.D. Smith, pp. 381-388. Philidelphia PA: W.B. Saunders.
2. Axelrod, S. et al. (1985): Hemodynamic regulation: Investigation by spectral analysis. Am J Physiol 249: H867-H875.
3. Saul, J.P. et al. (1991): Transfer function analysis of the circulation: Unique insights into cardiovascular regulation. Am J Physiol 261: H1231-H1245.
4. Morrow, G.R. (in press): Behavioral factors influencing the development and expression of chemotherapy induced side effects. Br J Cancer. (In press).

Supported in part by RCDA K04-CA-01038, and by research grants NR01905 National Center for Nursing Research, RR00044 Clinical Research Center, DHHS and PBR43 from the American Cancer Society.

Mechanisms and Control of Emesis. Eds A.L. Bianchi, L. Grélot, A.D. Miller, G.L. King. Colloque INSERM/ John Libbey Eurotext Ltd. © 1992, Vol. 223, pp. 171-172

The effects of X-irradiation on the sensitivity of guinea-pig isolated ileum to 5-hydroxytryptamine and acetylcholine-mediated responses

O. Gisanrin, S. Headford and H. Marr

SmithKline Beecham Pharmaceuticals, Coldharbour Road, The Pinnacles, Harlow, Essex CM19 5AD, UK

The involvement of 5-hydroxytryptamine (5-HT) in the emetic response resulting from X-irradiation or chemotherapy is well established (Andrews et al, 1988). Many investigators (Penttilla et al, 1975; Matsuoko et al, 1962) have reported a decrease in the intestinal content of this amine in rodents following X-irradiation. In the guinea-pig isolated ileum, Schworer et al, 1990, have shown that the cytotoxic drug cisplatin may induce sensitization of 5-HT_3 receptors within the gut. It was therefore of interest to us to establish the effects of whole body X-irradiation on the sensitivity of 5-hydroxytryptamine (5-HT) and acetylcholine (ACh) mediated responses in the guinea-pig isolated ileum or colon.

Tissues were taken either from X-irradiated animals (total dose = 50 Gy over 10.4 mins) killed 25 mins from the onset of X-irradiation or from non-irradiated (control) animals. Longitudinal muscle strips were prepared from each tissue and maintained in Krebs solution containing 2 μM methysergide. The tissues were allowed to equilibrate for 30 mins before concentration response curves to either 5-HT or ACh over the concentration range of 3×10^{-15} to 3×10^{-4}M in the ileum, or 3×10^{-11} to 3×10^{-4}M in the colon were constructed. In addition, the effects of X-irradiation on colonic gut motility were investigated, using isolated lengths of colon containing faecal pellets taken from control or X-irradiated animals. In these experiments the colon was removed and allowed to equilibrate in Krebs solution for 30 mins at room temperature, after which time it was maintained at 37°C and the number of faecal pellets extruded over one hour was recorded.

A large increase ($p<0.01$) in the amplitude of the ileal responses to 5-HT, compared to control, over the concentration range of 3×10^{-13} to 3×10^{-12}M and ACh 3×10^{-14} to 3×10^{-13}M was seen following X-irradiation. In the colon, a small non-significant increase in amplitude in the response to ACh (3×10^{-11} to 3×10^{-8}M) was seen with no change in the responses to 5-HT following X-irradiation.

The cumulative total of faecal pellets extruded from the irradiated colon was significantly ($p \leq 0.05$) increased 30 mins from the start of the observation period, with no change seen within the remaining 30 mins of the observation period.

These data demonstrate that following whole body X-irradiation in the guinea-pig, there is a marked increase in the sensitivity of the ileum to low concentrations of 5-HT and ACh. Negligible effects on the sensitivity of colonic longitudinal muscle to these agonists was seen, although an increase in the cumulative number of faecal pellets extruded from the colon was observed. These results indicate that the radiosensitivity of the gut is non-uniform.

These rapidly occurring changes in colonic motility and sensitivity of the isolated ileum bear a temporal relationship to the development of motility patterns seen *in vivo* prior to and during emesis evoked by X-irradiation in species which vomit. Under such conditions, normal gut reflexes may become sensitized and produce aberrant patterns of motility which in turn contribute to the sensation of nausea and reinforcement of the emetic reflex.

These studies will be extended to include an animal species with the vomiting reflex.

References

Andrews PLR and Wood KL (1988) J Physiol, 395: 1-16.

Matsuoka O et al (1962) J Rad Res, 3: 104-108.

Pentilla A et al (1975) Strahlentherapie 149: 426-437.

Schworer H et al (1991), Naunyn Schmiedeberg's Arch Pharmacol 344: 143-149.

Mechanisms and Control of Emesis. Eds A.L. Bianchi, L. Grélot, A.D. Miller, G.L. King. Colloque INSERM/ John Libbey Eurotext Ltd. © 1992, Vol. 223, pp. 173-174

Tolerability and pharmacokinetics of single doses of DAU 6215 CL in healthy volunteers

Christian J. Schilling, *Maria G. Marini, *Aldo Vidi, Joachim P. Leonard, *Carlo A. Rizzi, *Sergio Daniotti and *Arturo Donetti

*Human Pharmacology Centre, Boehringer Ingelheim Deutschland GmbH, D-6507 Ingelheim/Rhein Germany, * Research and Medical Department, Boeringer Ingelheim Italia, Via Serio 15, 20139 Milano, Italy*

The azabicycloalkyl benzimidazolone derivative DAU 6215 CL is a new antagonist at serotonin 5-HT_3 receptors (Turconi *et al.*, 1991a), which was proved to be effective as an anti-emetic in a variety of animal models of vomiting induced by oncolytic drugs (Sagrada *et al.*, 1991). Preclinical investigations also showed a therapeutic potential in central nervous system (CNS) diseases (Turconi *et al.*, 1991b). The first clinical studies with DAU 6215 CL, hereunder presented, were aimed to evaluate the tolerability and the pharmacokinetic profile of the compound in healthy volunteers.

In two separate studies, the drug was administered in single rising i.v. doses (0.1, 0.3, 0.7, 1.4, 2.8, 5.6 and 11.2 mg), as a slow infusion and p.o. doses (0.5, 1.5, 5, 15, 30, and 60 mg) to groups of 8 healthy volunteers (6 verum, 2 placebo) for each dose level.

Vital function (blood pressure, heart rate and respiratory rate), ECG as well as laboratory parameters (including liver enzymes and selected hormon parameters) were not affected by any of the dose tested both after i.v and p.o. administration. No relevant substance-induced changes on pharmacopsychological tests (tracking, tapping, concentration test, mood scales) were observed. The pupillary parameters were not affected by any of the i.v. doses. A slight increase in the pupil diameter was observed after administration of oral doses of 60 mg.

Only mild adverse events which could not be clearly attributed to the compound were reported by volunteers receiving i.v. doses. Gastrointestinal symptoms (constipation, hard stools) occurred in some volunteers after administration of p.o. dose of 15 mg and higher. Four of the 6 volunteers receiving 60 mg of DAU 6215 CL reported a dryness of the mouth.

The pharmacokinetics of i.v. DAU 6215 CL, calculated on the basis of plasma and urinary levels of the drug, were linear in the dose range tested. A linear proportion of the area under the plasma curves (AUC) was observed after administration of p.o. doses up to 30 mg. The AUC value was not linearly proportional to the p.o. 60 mg dose. However, no change of the elimination rate occurred at this dose level. The terminal half-life time was 10.6 $\pm$ 2.4 h for i.v. DAU 6215 CL and 12.4 $\pm$ 2.7 for p.o. DAU 6215 CL. A high volume of distribution (5.7 $\pm$ 0.9 l/kg for i.v. doses, 7.6 $\pm$ 1.7 l/kg for p.o. doses) was related to the low drug plasma levels. Total clearance values ranged from 403 to 740 ml/min for i.v. doses and from 530 to 991 ml/min for p.o doses. The somewhat higher total clearance value after oral administration might be due to the first pass effect; the oral bioavailability, calculated by comparison of the AUCs of the two studies was approximately 68%.

The unchanged fraction of the dose excreted in the urine did not vary according to the different routes of administration (range: 42.5-70%, from the i.v. doses; 44-81%, from the p.o.doses).

These results show that DAU 6215 CL is well tolerated after administration of single i.v. (up to 11.2 mg) as well as p.o. (up to 60 mg). This dose range covered the predicted therapeutic doses resulting from animal models (Turconi ***et al.***, 1991b; Sagrada ***et al.***, 1991).

Some differences in the pharmacokinetic profile of DAU 6215 CL emerged when compared to that of other 5-HT_3 receptor antagonists. Ondansetron and granisetron were shown to be almost totally cleared *via* the metabolic system (Cassidy J ***et al.***, 1988; Colthup ***et al.***, 1989), while DAU 6215 CL is eliminated by both renal and hepatic routes. In addition, DAU 6215 CL and granisetron seem to undergo a slower elimination rate than ondansetron (Cassidy J ***et al.***, 1988; Colthup ***et al.***, 1989; present results).

The clinical impact of these first observations in humans, which indicates a good tolerability and pharmacokinetic profile of DAU 6215 CL in healthy volunteers, will be evaluated in studies on patients.

References

Cassidy, J., Raina, V., Lewis, L., Adams, L., Shoukop, M., Rapeport, W.G., Zussmann, B.D., Rankin, E.M. and Kaye S.B. (1988). Pharmacokinetics and antiemetic efficacy of BRL 43694, a new selective 5-HT_3 antagonist. *Br. J. Cancer.* 58, 651-653

Colthup, P.V. and Palmer, J.L. (1989): The determination in plasma and pharmacokinetics of ondansetron. *Eur. J. Cancer Clin. Oncol.*, 25,1(S), 571-574

Sagrada, A., Turconi, M., Bonali, P., Schiantarelli, P., Micheletti, R., Montagna, E., Nicola, M., Algate, D.R., Rimoldi, E.M. and Donetti, A. (1991): Antiemetic activity of the new 5-HT_3 antagonist DAU 6215 in animal models of cancer chemotherapy and radiation. *Cancer Chemother. Pharmacol.* 28, 470-474.

Turconi, M., Donetti, A., Schiavone, A., Sagrada, A., Montagna, E., Nicola, M., Cesana, R., Rizzi, C.A. and Micheletti R. (1991): Pharmacological properties of a novel class of 5-HT_3 receptor antagonists. *Eur. J. Pharmacol.* 203, 203-211.

Turconi, M., Schiantarelli, P., Borsini, F., Rizzi, C.A., Ladinsky, H. and Donetti, A. (1991): Azabicycloalkyl benzimidazolones: interactions with serotoninergic 5-HT_3 and 5-HT_4 receptors and potential therapeutic implications. *Drugs of the Future* 16, 1011-1026.

III. Motion sickness: mechanisms and treatments

III. Le mal des transports: mécanismes et traitements

Mechanisms and Control of Emesis. Eds A.L. Bianchi, L. Grélot, A.D. Miller, G.L. King. Colloque INSERM/ John Libbey Eurotext Ltd. © 1992, Vol. 223, pp. 177-184

Signs and symptoms of motion sickness and its basic nature

K.E. Money

Defence and Civil Institute of Environmental Medicine, P.O. Box 2000, North York, Ontario, M3M 3B9 Canada and Payload Specialist, Canadian Space Agency, Ottawa, Canada

ABSTRACT:

The cardinal signs and symptoms of motion sickness are malaise, pallor, (and/or flushing), cold sweating, abdominal discomfort, changes in gastric motility, and changes in levels of circulating hormones. Cardiovascular, respiratory, and other signs have also been reported, as have a variety of other sensations, feelings and performance changes.

It is reasonable to think that motion sickness is basically the activation, by motion, of a poison-response mechanism.

Signes et symptômes du mal des transports: éléments de base.

Résumé: *Les signes cardinaux et les symptômes du mal des transports sont malaise, pâleur, (et/ ou bouffées), sueurs froides, inconfort abdominal, changements de la motricité gastrique et des hormones circulantes. Des signes cardiovasculaires, respiratoires et autres ont aussi été signalés, ainsi que diverses autres sensations, affectant impressions et performance.*

On peut penser que le mal des transports est à la base une activation par le mouvement d'un mécanisme de type réponse à un empoisonnement.

BASIC NATURE

In essence, motion sickness is the activation, by motion, of poison-response mechanism. This is obvious: motion gives rise to vomiting.

In certain motion environments, something that must be called "peculiar" happens. Motion sickness occurs. Motion sickness will be described here, and the description of motion sickness will be based on the assumption that only one peculiar thing happens: a poison response is provoked by motion. Common sense suggests that two or three peculiar things do not independently occur at the same time.

There are two currently-popular theories of why this peculiar thing happens, why motion gives rise to a poison response. The older of these two theories, the conflict theory, holds that in motion sickness environments the poison response occurs because of a conflict. In a motion sickness environment, the pattern of sensory inputs concerning orientation and motion (vestibular, visual, and proprioceptor inputs) is in conflict with the pattern of inputs anticipated on the basis of previous experience (6,17). The conflict somehow gives rise to vomiting. The theory (unmodified) does not explain why such a conflict is utterly unable (8,9,14,15) to provoke vomiting in individuals who are lacking the vestibular apparatus of the inner ear. The theory also does not explain why such a conflict should produce vomiting instead of deep breathing, discharge from the nose, or orgasm. The theory would apply equally well if the conflict produced one of these things instead of vomiting.

The more modern theory, that of Treisman (25), incorporates the conflict theory and does explain why vomiting should occur. Treisman's theory holds that the conflicting sensory inputs are interpreted centrally as neurophysiological dysfunction caused by poisoning. Treisman postulated that the brain stem mechanisms of orientation and motion normally perform an additional function as well as maintenance of bodily equilibrium, stabilility of gaze, etc: the additional function is to detect and respond to certain poisons. In motion sickness situations the conflict in sensory inputs simulates poisoning in those neural mechanisms.

There is convincing evidence of the basic validity of Treisman's theory. It seems clear that the brain stem mechanisms of orientation and motion do in fact function also to detect and respond to certain poisons. The experiment showing this (13,14) found that, in experimental animals, surgical removal of the vestibular apparatus of the inner ear rendered the animals defective in the emetic response to certain poisons injected intramuscularly. This is positive evidence that the vestibular system is involved in poison response. The surgery encroached only on the ear and, of course, it also rendered the animals completely nonsusceptible to motion sickness. The vestibular system is involved in poison response in circumstances of motion sickness and also in circumstances of poisoning with certain toxic chemicals.

Motion sickness is a poison response provoked by motion. It is a poison response provoked by motion acting (directly or indirectly) on the vestibular system.

SIGNS AND SYMPTOMS

The signs and symptoms of motion sickness can be considered the manifestations of the poison response. Although Treisman confined his theory of motion sickness to nausea and vomiting (25), it is clear that, whenever vomiting is provoked by motion, other bodily responses are also provoked, and sometimes these other responses occur and vomiting does not occur. Sometimes pallor, cold sweating, and malaise occur in a motion environment and vomiting does not. Motion sickness is a poison response provoked by motion, not just vomiting.

Motion sickness is possibly the purest and simplest poison response available for study, because it can be produced for study without the complicating presence of a poison. It is produced by a motion stimulus that masquerades as a poison. It is interesting to think that a person known to be poisoned (for example, by apomorphine) would think that the poison is a terrible one because of the horrible nausea, pallor, cold sweating, vomiting, etc; but the reality might be that the dose of apomorphine had no adverse effect on the body, except that it triggered one of the body's poison-response mechanisms; then the body inflicted all those miseries on itself. A poison that causes facial pallor might not do so by a direct influence on the blood vessels of the skin, or even by a direct influence on the autonomic nervous system; it could do so by activating one of the body's poison-response mechanisms, and that mechanism could then act on the hypothalamic centers controlling the autonomic nervous sytem to produce the facial pallor. In motion sickness it seems that when the poison-response mechanism is activated the body then inflicts on itself a variety of signs and symptoms, to be described below.

Motion sickness signs and symptoms are often thought of as, first, nausea and vomiting, and second, all the "other" ones. However, as indicated above, it will be assumed here that only one peculiar thing happens in motion sickness environments: a poison response is provoked. There is no reason to think that anything else is happening, and <u>all</u> the signs and symptoms will be considered to be part of the poison response. The signs and symptoms of motion sickness will therefore be classified as, first, those associated with emptying the stomach, and second, those associated with counteracting or surviving the part of the poison detected (incorrectly) in the bloodstream.

There is a considerable number and variety of signs and symptoms that differ in different individuals (1,2,3,4,6,12,17). However, some signs and symptoms appear to occur in all, or almost all, cases of motion sickness in humans, and only these signs and symptoms will be listed here.

SIGNS AND SYMPTOMS ASSOCIATED WITH EMPTYING THE STOMACH

- Abdominal awareness
- Abdominal discomfort
- Nausea
- Motility of the stomach
- Vomiting

SIGNS AND SYMPTOMS ASSOCIATED WITH COUNTERACTING OR SURVIVING THE POISON IN THE BLOOD

- Malaise
- Sleepiness
- Headache
- Pallor (and/or flushing)
- Cold sweating
- Cardiovascular changes
- Endocrinological changes

Abdominal awareness, abdominal discomfort, and nausea are possibly parts of a gradient of a single symptom that would have the effect of preventing the further consumption of a toxic food. They would also tend to have the effect of preventing the consumption of that food again on future occasions (25). They are possibly the conscious reflection of unusual activity in the central emetic mechanisms (6,12).

Motility and tonus of the stomach decrease with motion sickness in most human subjects (7,12). Gastric (and intestinal) motility has been observed in motion sickness in humans by listening to the gut sounds with stethescopes and microphones (24); the sounds diminish, usually to silence, with motion sickness in spaceflight. X-ray studies of the gut before and after exposure to nauseogenic motion (16) also reveal decrease motility with nausea in most subjects. Balloons have been placed in the stomachs of humans subjected to motion sickness (3,7,26); overall, decreases of tonus and motility predominate, but some prominent exceptions are reported (3). In one subject with a gastric fistula, direct visualization of the stomach during nausea was possible, and this subject together with three normal subjects with gastric balloons was exposed to vestibular and other nauseogenic stimuli; "nausea occurred only during gastric relaxation and hypomotility" (26).

The electrical activity of the gut has also been studied during motion sickness (6,19,20) using electrodes attached to the skin over the stomach. The electrical activity recorded in this way is called the electrogastrogram or EGG. The EGG changes with motion sickness; the change is typically a decreased magnitude of the EGG voltage (6,20) and an increase in the basic electrical rhythm from the normal 3 cycles per minute to 5-7 cycles per minute (19,20). This increase of the basic electrical rhythm of the EGG, although it is called tachygastria, is in fact associated with gastric stasis, decreased gastric motility (20,23), so that the increased EGG frequency is consistent with the decreased gastric motility observed with microphones, balloons, and x-rays. The decreased amplitude of the EGG is also associated with decreased motility.

The EGG is an index of interest in studies of motion sickness; it is an index of something underlying motility. There is no simple relationship between recorded EGG values and, for example, recordings (in dogs) from force tranducers fixed to the gastric serosa (18). The basic electrical rhythm of the EGG reflects "pacesetter potentials of the stomach, but not gastric contractions" (20). However, when gastric contractions do occur they are time-locked to the EGG. At the higher basic EGG rhythms, contractions tend not to occur at all. Also, "the amplitude of the EGG increases when a contraction occurs" (20). In motion sickness, both the increased frequency of the basic electrical rhythm of the EGG and the decreased EGG amplitude indicate decreased gastric motility.

It is possible that the decrease in gastric motility would have survival value in someone who had ingested a poison: it would tend to keep the poison in the stomach, where absorption might be slower and where vomiting could remove it.

Vomiting removes the poison (that is not there) from the stomach. The physiology of vomiting has been recently reviewed (6).

It is not clear how (or whether) malaise, sleepiness, and headache would improve the chances of surviving poisoning, but they would tend to encourage the poisoned individual to lie down.

The pallor, the cold sweating, the cardiovascular changes, and the endocrinological changes of motion sickness can all be seen as parts of a general stress response that includes an overall activation of the sympathetic nervous system (SNS). The stress response (it is assumed) enhances the chances of surviving poisoning, and it occurs in the absence of any stress on the body, for the same reason that vomiting occurs without any poison in the stomach: a poison-response mechanism has been activated. It should be noted that most motion sickness environments do not stress the body; babies sleep in these environments. Only if the poison response is provoked does the stress response appear (in the absence of stress).

It is unlikely that pharmaceuticals selected to counteract the autonomic signs of motion sickness would be satisfactory, because no one suffering from motion sickness cares about the autonomic signs; only pharamaceuticals that counteract the nausea and vomiting are relevant to the sufferer's desires.

Pallor is a result of vasoconstriction in the skin, probably in response to an increase in the SNS activity to the blood vessels of the skin (6), and it is a sign of motion sickness that is almost invariably (3) seen before vomiting. It has been found recently, however, that in some individuals there is flushing as part of the skin's reaction in motion sickness (11). Sweating (eccrine sweating) similarly results from an increase in activity in the SNS supply to the sweat glands, although the postganglionic SNS supply to the sweat glands is cholinergic (6). The cardiovascular changes of motion sickness are also consistent with an overall activation of the SNS: the pulse rate increases slightly (2,3) and the blood flow to skeletal muscle increases (21).

The endocrinological changes with motion sickness also resemble a stress response. Recent studies have found that humans in motion sickness have increased circulating levels of AVP, ACTH, EPI, NE, GH, and PRL (5,6,10,22). AVP means antidiuretic hormone, ACTH means adrenocorticotrophic hormone, EPI means epinephrin, NE means noradrenalin, GH means growth hormone, and PRL means prolactin.

Although this particular collection of autonomic and endocrinological responses is typical of a stress response, it is not clear exactly how it would improve the chances of surviving a poison. Perhaps this would be clear if it were known what poison the body thinks it has ingested in motion sickness; or perhaps the response is appropriate for several, or even most, poisons.

To the extent that motion sickness is nausea and vomiting, the "other" signs and symptoms are peculiar epiphenomena, but if it is assumed that only one peculiar thing happens in motion sickness (a poison response is provoked by unnatural motion), then all the signs and symptoms must be part of that poison response. If the autonomic effects were peculiar epiphenomena, it would be difficult to understand how their manipulation by cortical control, using autogenic feedback, could influence the nausea and vomiting: it would be like pushing on a string. However, if the autonomic effects are part of apoison response it is immediately understandable that a cortical input to the autonomic effectors could take a route (for example) through the poison-response mechanism and affect also other parts of the poison response, such as nausea and vomiting. Autogenic feedback training does, of course, influence nausea and vomiting, but how it does so is perhaps easier to understand if it is assumed that all signs and symptoms of motion sickness are part of a poison response.

If cortical input to the autonomic effectors of motion sickness can exert a desired influence on the nausea and vomiting, then perhaps (with training) a cortical influence on the sleepiness and malaise might be beneficial also; the cortex might convince itself (by way of the poison-response mechanism) that it feels fine, that it is in excellent health, and that it is wide awake; in doing so it might attenuate the nausea and vomiting.

CONCLUSION

The signs and symptoms of motion sickness indicate that motion sickness is a poison response. This, together with the central role of the vestibular system, suggests that motion sickness can be defined as a poison response provoked by motion acting (directly or indirectly) on the vestibular system.

There is positive evidence that the vestibular system is also involved in the poison response to lobeline, levodopa, and nicotine. The involvement of the vestibular system in the poison response to emetic poisons is convincing evidence for the basic validity of Treisman's theory of motion sickness: in motion sickness situations the conflict in sensory inputs simulates poisoning in the vestibular system and thus triggers the poison response.

ACKNOWLEDGEMENT

This paper was published first as part of an in-house lecture series: Motion Sicknes: Significance in Aerospace Operations and Prophylaxis, AGARD Letcure Series 175, pp 1-1 to 1-4, September 1991.

REFERENCES

1. Cowings, P.S. Autogenic-feedback training: a treatment for motion and space sickness. Chapt 17, pp 353-372, in: Motion and Space Sickness, edited by G.H. Crampton, CRC Press, Boca Raton, Florida, 451 pages, 1990.

2. Cowings P.S., Suter S., Toscano W.B., Kamiya J., and Naifeh K. General autonomic components of motion sickness. Psychophysiol. 23: 542-551, 1986.

3. Crampton G.H. Studies of motion sickness: XVII. Physiological changes accompanying sickness in man. J. Appl. Physiol. 7: 501-507, 1955.

4. Crampton G.H., editor. Motion and Space Sickness. CRC Press, Boca Raton, Florida, 451 pages, 1990.

5. Eversman T., Gottsman M., Uhlich E., Ulbrecht G., von Werder K., and Scriba P.C. Increased secretion of growth hormone, prolactin, antidiuretic hormone, and cortisol induced by the stress of motion sickness. Aviat. Space Environ. Med. 49: 53-57, 1978.

6. Harm D.L. Physiology of motion sickness symptoms. Chapt 10, pp 153-177, in: Motion and Space Sickness, edited by G.H. Crampton, CRC Press, Boca Raton, Florida, 451 pages, 1990.

7. Hemingway A. Review. Study of research on the problem of airsickness in the Army Air Forces. Project 381, Research Report No. 1, The Research Laboratory, The Army Air Forces School of Aviation Medicine, Randolph Field, Texas, pp 1-35, 20 April 1945.

8. James W. The sense of dizzyness in deaf mutes. Am. J. Otol. 4: 239-254, 1882.

9. Kellogg R.S., Kennedy R.S., and Graybiel A. Motion sickness symptomatology of labyrinthine defective and normal subjects during zero gravity maneuvers. Aerospace Med. 36: 315-318, 1965.

10. Kohl R.L. Endocrinology of space/motion sickness. Chapt 6, pp 65-86 in: Motion and Space Sickness, edited by G.H. Crampton, CRC Press, Boca Raton, Florida, 451 pages, 1990.

11. Oman C.M. and Cook W.J. Dynamics of skin pallor in motion sickness as measured using an infrared reflective technique. Abstract. 54th Annual Aerospace Medical Association Meeting, Houston, Tx, May 1983. -as quoted in ref 6, above.

12. Money K.E. Motion Sickness. Physiol. Rev. 50: 1-39, 1970.

13. Money K.E. Motion Sickness and evolution. Chapt 1, pp 1-7, in: Motion and Space Sickness, edited by G.H. Crampton, CRC Press, Boca Raton, Florida, 451 pages, 1990.

14. Money K.E. and Cheung B.S. Another function of the inner ear: facilitation of the emetic response to poisons. Aviat. Space Environ. Med. 54: 208-211, 1983.

15. Money K.E. and Friedberg J. The role of the semicircular canals in causation of motion sickness in the dog. Can. J. Physiol. Pharmacol. 42: 793-801, 1964.

16. McDonough F.E. and Schneider M. The effect of motion on the roentgenographic appearance of the stomach and small bowel. Gastroenterology 2: 32-45, 1944.

17. Reason J.T. and Brand J.J. Motion Sickness. Academic Press, London, New York, 310 pages, 1975.

18. Smout A.J.P.M. Van der Schee E.J., and Gasthuis J.L. What is measured in electrogastrography? Digestive Diseases and Sciences 25: 179-187, 1980.

19. Stern R.M., Koch K.L., Leibowitz H.W., Linblad I.M., Shupert C.L., and Stewart W.R. Tachygastria and motion sickness. Aviat. Space Environ. Med. 56: 1074-1077, 1985.

20. Stern R.M., Koch K.L., Stewart W.R., and Vasey M.W. Electrogastrography: current issues in validation and methodology. Psychophysiol. 24: 55-64, 1987.

21. Sunahara F.A., Farewell J., Mintz L., and Johnson W.H. Pharmacological interventions for motion sickness: cardiovascular effects. Aviat. Space Environ. Med. 58 (9, Suppl): A270-A276, 1987.

22. Taylor N.B.G., Hunter J., and Johnson W.H. Antidiuresis as a measurement of laboratory induced motion sickness. Can J. Biochem. Physiol. 35: 1017-1027, 1957.

23. Telander R.L., Morgan K.G., Kreulin D.L., Schmalz P.F., Kelly K.A., and Szursewski J.H. Human gastric atony with tachygastria and gastric retention. Gastroenterology 75: 497-501, 1978.

24. Thornton, W.E., Linder B.J., Moore T.P., and Pool S.L. Gastrointestinal motility in space sickness. Aviat. Space Environ. Med 58. (9, Suppl): A16-A21, 1987.

25. Treisman M. Motion sickness: an evolutionary hypothesis. Science 197: 493-495, 29 July 1977.

26. Wolf S. The relation of gastric function to nausea in man. J. Clin. Invest. 22: 877-882, 1943.

Mechanisms and Control of Emesis. Eds A.L. Bianchi, L. Grélot, A.D. Miller, G.L. King. Colloque INSERM/
John Libbey Eurotext Ltd. © 1992, Vol. 223, pp. 185-194

Space sickness symptom severity correlates with average head acceleration

Charles M. Oman and Ilya Shubentsov

Man Vehicle Laboratory, Department of Aeronautics and Astronautics, Center for Space Research, Massachusetts Institute of Technology, Cambridge, MA 02139, USA

SUMMARY

Astronauts have identified head movements as an important stimulus for space sickness. Do some crew members make head movements more frequently and/or vigorously than others ? Many try to limit their head movements during their first several days in orbit, to prevent or reduce sickness Do those who do so avoid severe symptoms ? Four Shuttle/Spacelab crew members recorded their symptoms and wore head accelerometers for extended periods. For each subject, 3 axis RMS head angular acceleration was estimated, and an overall Head Motion Index (HMI) was computed over successive 15 min intervals. All 4 subjects experienced space sickness, but their symptoms differed in severity: One who had a consistently low HMI pattern during the mission had only mild symptoms. The other 3 had multiple emesis episodes. The two most severe cases experienced prolonged discomfort. When symptoms abated, their HMI significantly ($p < 0.05$) increased. The third subject reported less discomfort, and maintained a lower HMI until near the end of the mission. Rank order pre- and post-symptomatic HMI correlated exactly with 3 concordant measures of sickness severity.

Sévérité du symptôme "mal de l'espace" et sa relation avec l'accélération de la tête.

Résumé: *D'après les astronautes, les mouvements de la tête se sont révélés être un stimulus important pour le mal de l'espace. Est-ce que certains membres d'équipage font des mouvements de tête plus fréquents et/ou plus vigoureux que d'autres ? Beaucoup essaient de limiter leurs mouvements de tête durant les premiers jours en orbite, pour prévenir ou réduire le mal de l'espace. Est-ce que ceux-là évitent des symptômes sévères ? Quatre membres d'équipage de la Navette Spatiale et de Spacelab ont consigné leurs symptômes et ont porté des accéléromètres fixés sur la tête pendant des périodes prolongées. Pour chaque sujet, l'accélération angulaire moyenne de la tête sur chacun des trois axes a été estimée, et un index global caractérisant le mouvement de la tête (*Head Motion Index *ou HMI) a été calculé sur des intervalles de temps successifs de 15 min. Les quatre sujets ont tous subi le mal de l'espace, mais l'intensité de leurs symptômes était différente : l'un, dont le HMI est resté bas de façon persistante pendant la mission, n'a présenté que des symptômes légers. Les trois autres ont subi des périodes de vomissements multiples. Les deux cas les plus sévères ont éprouvé un malaise prolongé. Lorsque leurs symptômes ont disparu, leur HMI s'est élevé de façon significative ($p < 0.05$). Le troisième sujet a rapporté avoir subi des malaises de moindre intensité, et son HMI est demeuré plus bas jusque vers la fin de la mission. Le rangement par ordre d'intensité des HMI pré- et post-symptômatiques était exactement corrélé avec trois mesures concordantes caractéristiques de la sévérité du malaise.*

BACKGROUND

Approximately two thirds of the crew members on the US Space Shuttle have experienced symptoms of space sickness (Davis et al., 1988; Davis and Beck, 1990). When characterized as a nausea and vomiting syndrome, the symptoms and signs of space sickness cannot readily be distinguished from those associated with other forms of chronic motion sickness, superimposed upon headache, nasal congestion, and other symptoms of 0-g fluid shift (Thornton et al., 1987; Oman et al., 1990). Fluid shift produced on earth by head down tilt does not elicit nausea or vomiting. However it remains possible that elevation of the viscera or biochemical changes represent a predisposing factor. Head movements - by some accounts particularly in pitch and roll - have been consistently identified as a provocative stimulus (Homick and Miller, 1975; Matsnev et al., 1983; Oman et al., 1986). Nauseous astronauts consistently report that the stimulus-response relationship is unambiguous, and drastically limit their head movements . Visual and tactile stimuli also are important (Oman et al., 1986): Visual orientation and inversion illusions, which cause a subjective change or uncertainty in perceived orientation, are known to exacerbate sickness in symptomatic crew members. Conversely, wedging or strapping the body firmly to a fixed surface has been reported palliative. Symptoms usually abate after 2-3 days, but occasionally reappear upon return to earth. These facts are consistent with the "sensory conflict" etiologic theory for motion sickness, which predicts that sickness should occur in weightlessness due to the unfamiliarity of otolith and proprioceptive cues during active movement, and sensory cue mismatch during illusory motion. However, the conflict theory is not very prognostic, and the conflict signals and emetic linkage postulated by the theory have not yet been identified. A variety ground and parabolic flight methods have been proposed to predict susceptibility to space sickness (Oman et al., 1986; Lackner et al., 1987; Mittelstaedt, 1988; Diamond et al., 1990). Unfortunately, all validation attempts have involved prediction of sickness incidence or severity as observed under normal mission operations, and to date none has been prospectively successful. Similarly, the efficacy of anti-motion sickness drugs has been difficult to evaluate. However, if head movements are the dominant stimulus causing space sickness, and if astronaut head movements are uncontrolled and differ substantially between crew members, then usefully reliable prediction may not be possible, and drug efficacy will be difficult to assess. Since the majority of crew members experience some degree of symptoms, we suspected that sickness incidence and severity may be largely determined by a crew member's ability to maintain head movement self discipline in the face of mission timeline demands, particularly prior to the onset of symptoms, and perhaps by the person's habitual head movement "style". The purpose of the present study was to determine whether crew members were able to consistently limit their head movements under operational conditions. Is there any correlation between head movement and symptom severity ?

METHODS

Our subjects were four science crew members on NASA/ESA Space Shuttle missions Spacelab-1 (December, 1983) and D-1 (November, 1985), denoted with a letter code: B, C, I, and J. All four were pilots, but none had previously flown in space. They were trained on reporting of the symptoms and signs of space sickness and fluid shift, the anticipated relationship of these to head movements, and the effect of visual and tactile cues on spatial orientation and sickness intensity. During their missions, subjects used pocket voice recorders and symptom checklists to record detailed observations on symptoms. To obtain frequent reports for correlation with head movement data, subjects were asked to make "brief" reports, consisting of Mission Elapsed Time (MET) and a numerical magnitude estimate of "overall discomfort". Instructions to subjects were: "Pick a sensation magnitude of overall discomfort in the middle of the 'moderate' range, halfway to vomiting. Call this standard 10. Estimate the magnitude of overall subjective discomfort with respect to it. If no discomfort sensation, say 'absent'. If just noticeable, say 'threshold'." This method (Bock and Oman, 1982) was designed to produce a ratio scale (Stevens, 1957). It has been useful in assessing the dynamics of the stimulus/response relationship in other forms of motion sickness (Oman, 1982), and has been employed for symptom assessment on 4 Spacelab missions.

In order to document the relationship between head movements and symptom recording, our subjects wore an Acceleration Recording Unit (ARU) shown in Fig. 1. This consisted of an head mounted accelerometer package, connected via a flexible cable to a digital cassette tape recorder (NASA CDTR Model II, SRI International, Inc.) worn on a waist belt along with a separate lithium battery power module. The accelerometer package itself contained three angular (Schaevitz ASM-300; 150 rad/s squared range) and three linear (SL-1: Kulite GY-125-120; D-1: Setra 141a) accelerometers mounted within a rectangular metal case. The accelerometers were mounted so that their sensitive axes were orthogonal, and parallel to the sides of the case. This package (total mass 0.34 kg on SL-1; 0.58 kg on D-1) was held firmly in place on the back of the head by an adjustable cloth head band (SL-1) or aviator's "Snoopy" cap (D-1). Wearing the head band or cap contributed to occasional headache in most subjects. The yaw and Z accelerometer axes normally were titled some 20-30 degrees from the principal anatomical sagittal head axis, and the roll and X accelerometer axes were correspondingly pitched up above the head frontal axes. The digital tape recorder sampled each of the 6 accelerometer signals in the frequency range below 30 Hz at a 100 Hz rate with 10 bit resolution. Once per minute, time of day replaced one sample of data on all 6 recorder tracks. Data was stored on replaceable tape cassettes, which were normally changed every 8 h.

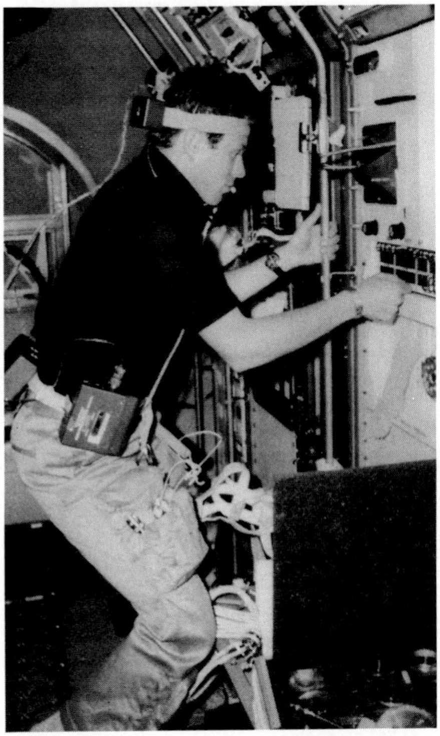

Subjects were asked to don the ARU as soon as possible after reaching orbit, and to wear it as much as possible during their waking hours on their shift, particularly during the first days of the mission. However, this was not always possible for operational reasons. Our 4 subjects wore the ARU during 4-11 recording sessions, totaling 88, 49, 26, and 12 hours duration, respectively. Subjects B and C took anti-motion sickness drugs in orbit, as detailed in (Oman et al., 1986). Subjects I and J did not use anti-motion sickness medication.

Fig.1 SL-1 crew member wearing ARU

For post flight data analysis, magnitude estimates of overall discomfort vs. MET were obtained from crew member voice tapes, notes, and post flight debriefing transcripts. Acceleration data was transferred to a (VAX 11/780) computer via a special purpose playback unit, which simultaneously checked each data word for errors introduced by the record/playback process. On average 10% of the data were found to be in error, and on sections of individual tapes, the rate was occasionally much higher, with runs of consecutive errors sometimes lasting several minutes, due to various technical problems associated with the CDTR recorder, playback unit, and tape quality. Also, subsequent to our analysis of SL-1 data, occasional data errors were discovered which had not been properly detected by the playback unit. Special purpose software was developed which detected and removed these errors in the data sets from both missions (Shubentsov, 1989). The remaining time series data available from each subject contained randomly distributed gaps of varying duration. This precluded the analysis originally planned (including integration to head velocity, and measurement of the time interval between head movements). Also, insufficient resolution on the SL-1 linear accelerometers prevented comparative analysis of the linear acceleration channels across the two missions. Re analysis of the SL-1 data showed that the previously undetected CDTR errors had artifactually increased the baseline values of head acceleration which we reported after SL-1. Fortunately, the errors were found to be unrelated to head movement, so the conclusions reached (Oman et al., 1986) do not require revision.

As an alternative, we elected to assess temporal changes in the statistical distribution of head angular acceleration amplitude, and correlate this with reported symptoms. The amplitude histogram for each of the three angular channels was computed using only the valid data over successive 15 minute time intervals (McCoy, 1985). Each 15 minute interval was termed a "data block". The 15 minute duration was chosen because it was an order of magnitude longer than the largest typical CDTR data gap, but short enough so that some of the intrinsic variations in daily crew activity pattern could be assessed as they performed different experiments. Also, we believed that tape recorded verbal symptom reports would usually reflect discomfort sensation over several preceding minutes. Finally, if space sickness is similar to other forms of motion sickness, one of the dominant characteristic time constants of the emetic linkage should be several minutes long (Oman, 1990).

One characteristic of the amplitude histogram which we thought should be a representative measure of the head movment stimulus was the second moment (standard deviation) of the distribution. The latter is also an estimator for the root-mean-square (RMS) head angular acceleration over the block. A preliminary analysis showed that RMS angular accelerations were consistently highest about the yaw axis, and smallest about the roll axis. RMS linear accelerations were highly correlated with RMS angular in pitch and yaw, probably because the linear accelerometers were several inches from the center of rotation.

To assess trends in each crew member's overall activity (regardless of axis), a composite angular Head Motion Index (HMI) was defined for each block. The RMS acceleration on each axis was weighted by the number of valid data points on that axis in that data block. Formally, if $\mathbf{A_{ij}}$ is the RMS angular acceleration about the **i**th axis for the **j**th data block, then a head motion index, $\mathbf{HMI_j}$ was defined as:

$$\mathbf{HMI_j} \equiv \sqrt{\frac{\sum_{i=1}^{3} n_{ij} A_{ij}^2}{N_j}} \qquad 1)$$

where $\mathbf{n_{ij}}$ is the number of valid data points for the **i**th axis in the **j**th block ($\leq 9 \times 10^4$ samples/axis/block) and

$$N_j = \sum_{i=1}^{3} n_{ij} \qquad 2)$$

where $\mathbf{N_j}$ is the total number of valid data points on all 3 axes in the 15 minute block ($\leq 2.7 \times 10^4$ samples/block).

As a measure of each crew member's activity over an entire recording session (i.e. a series of successive 15 minute data blocks), a mean Head Motion Index, "HMI bar" was also defined:

$$\overline{\mathbf{HMI}}_k \equiv \sqrt{\frac{\sum_{j=1}^{k} N_j \, \mathrm{HMI}_j^2}{N_k}} \qquad 3)$$

Where $\mathbf{N_k}$, the total number of valid points in a recording session of **k** blocks (always $\leq$ 10.8×10^4 samples/session hour) is:

$$N_k = \sum_{j=1}^{k} N_j \qquad 4)$$

We chose these particular **HMI** definitions (Eqns. 1-4) because it would be inappropriate to simply average the RMS accelerations $\mathbf{A_{ij}}$ across time or axes. The resulting mean would depend on the grouping in time of the original data, and would be different from the mean computed from the entire original dataset. By squaring and weighting the block activity indices $\mathbf{HMI}_j$, the same $\overline{\mathbf{HMI}}$ is obtained as would be computed directly from the entire original dataset. It is important also to note that **HMI** and $\overline{\mathbf{HMI}}$ are ad-hoc practical measures of average head acceleration, which correlate with other metrics of head movement (e.g., RMS velocity or displacement). Since most crew member movements are created by muscular force, and the average moment of inertia of the head and body are likely approximately constant over time, one can infer that **HMI** and $\overline{\mathbf{HMI}}$ also reflect the time average muscular effort ("vigor") associated with movement. The frequency with which head movements are made will also directly effect the time average statistics. **HMI** and $\overline{\mathbf{HMI}}$ thus should reflect combined effects of head movement vigor and frequency during the block and session, respectively.

Occasionally the subjects participated in life science experiments ("dome", "hop and drop" and "neck collar") which artificially constrained their head movements. Since this study focused on the effects of symptoms on spontaneously made head movements, data blocks associated with these experiments were identified and excluded from this analysis.

RESULTS:

All four subjects experienced symptoms of space motion sickness. Their experiences were different, and distinguishable in terms of sickness severity. As detailed in Table 2 below, subjects were ranked in terms of three different measures of sickness severity: average overall discomfort report, duration of frank sickness, and number of vomiting episodes. The rank ordered results of all three measures were consistent. Subjects B and I had more severe symptoms, ranking first and second, respectively. Head movement statistics for and corresponding overall discomfort reports are shown in Fig. 2 for these two subjects. **HMI** data within the same session are plotted with common symbols, and $\overline{\mathbf{HMI}}$ for that session is overlaid with an open square. Both subjects experienced continuing malaise for the

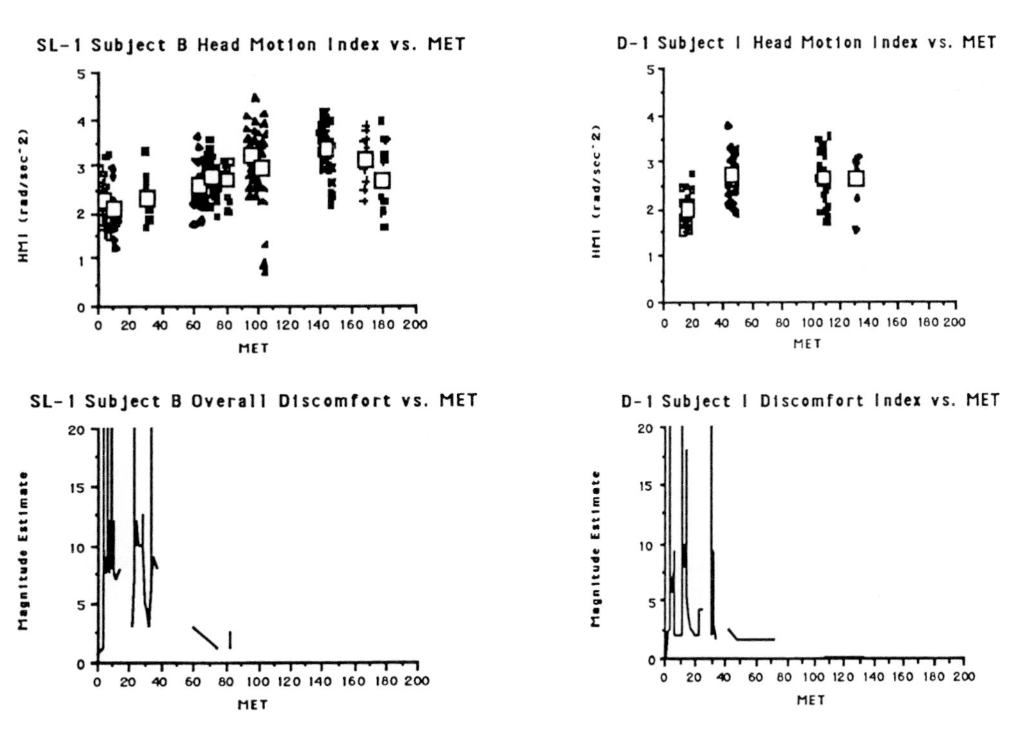

Fig. 2. HMI and Overall Discomfort vs. Mission Elapsed Time for Subjects B and I.

first two days of the mission. Subject B reported that he did not restrict his head movements during the first two hours of the mission, but shortly thereafter became symptomatic, and attempted to keep his head movements to a minimum for the first 40-50 hours of the mission while continuing to work as best he could. He vomited repeatedly. The causal relationship between head movements and increase in overall discomfort was readily apparent to him. B's overall discomfort reports were consistently in the 8-10 range for most of his first two work shifts. His detailed narrative is available (Oman et al., 1990). Subject I also became symptomatic early in the mission, and thereafter attempted to limit his head movements. As shown in Figure 2, **HMI and $\overline{\text{HMI}}$** was reduced for both subjects while symptomatic. When discomfort was high, **HMI** was generally trended around 2 rad/sec^2. Later in the mission, **HMI** gradually increased, eventually by 50 - 100%, and showed somewhat greater variability, as one might expect as subjects conducted activities requiring different degrees of physical activity, but were no longer constraining their head movements.

In contrast, Subject C and J had less severe symptoms, ranking third and fourth, respectively in terms of average discomfort report, duration of frank sickness, and number of vomiting episodes (Table 2). Their head movement statistics and overall discomfort scores are shown in Fig. 3. Subject C experienced no symptoms until the end of his brief first shift, when he vomited suddenly, with only a few moments warning. Early in his next shift, he vomited again, also with little warning. For the rest of his second shift, he experienced slight discomfort. Occasional mild discomfort persisted into his third shift when exacerbated by rapid head movements. He reported that he generally avoided rapid head movements through the first four and a half days of the mission. This is corroborated by the head acceleration data shown in Fig. 3 Subject J reported early mission fatigue and reduced appetite, but no nausea and only a brief moment of epigastric awareness (during a run on the "space sled"). He reported deliberate head movement restriction only on the second day.

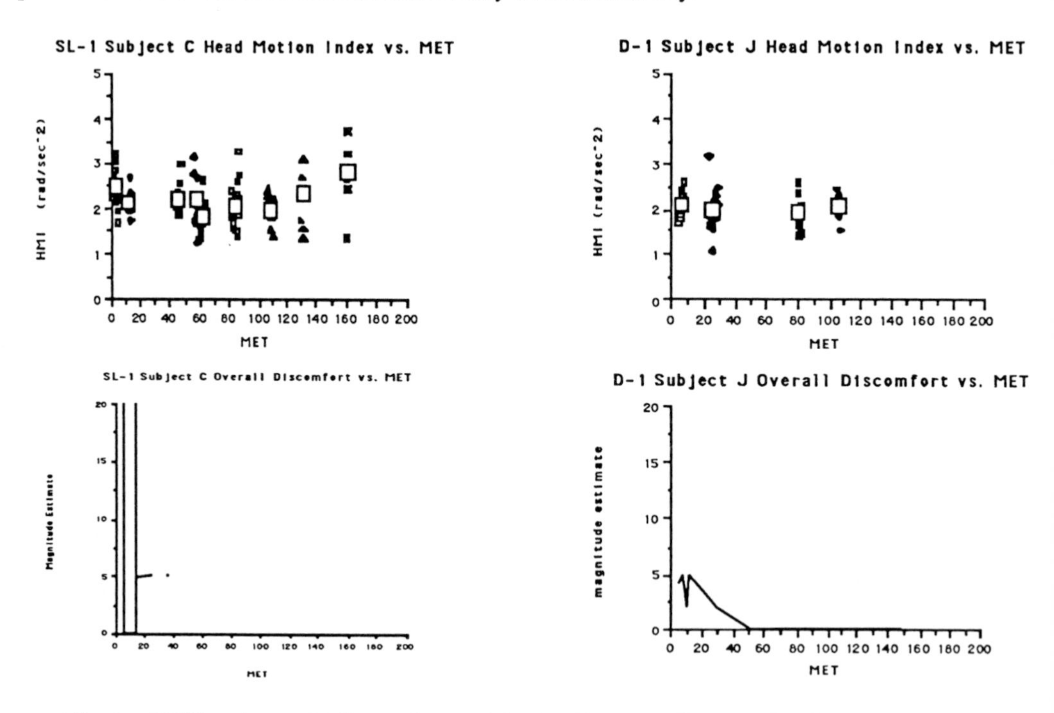

Fig. 3. HMI and overall discomfort vs. Mission Elapsed Time for Subjects C and J.

The $\overline{\text{HMI}}$ data for the two more symptomatic subjects B and I suggested that they reduced the vigor and/or frequency of their head movements during the portion of the mission when they were symptomatic, and then increased again when symptoms subsided ("post-symptomatic" period). The post-symtomatic trend in subject C's data was less clear. Subject J showed consistently lower $\overline{\text{HMI}}$

scores than the other three subjects, suggesting that either deliberately or by habit, he was moving less vigorously or making fewer head movements than the others.

Were the trends in $\overline{\mathbf{HMI}}$ noted for subjects B and I statistically significant ? To investigate, we calculated the difference between $\overline{\mathbf{HMI}}$ for symptomatic and post -symptomatic sessions for each subject. We defined a parameter $\mathbf{t^2}$ as the square of the difference in $\overline{\mathbf{HMI}}$ between two groups of sessions, **a** and **b**, divided by a pooled estimate of the variance in $\overline{\mathbf{HMI}}$:

$$t^2 \equiv \frac{\left(\overline{HMI_a} - \overline{HMI_b}\right)^2}{S_p^2} \qquad 5)$$

Where

$$S_p^2 = \left[\frac{1}{N_a} + \frac{1}{N_b}\right] \left[\frac{(N_a - 1)\, S_a^2 + (N_b - 1)\, S_b^2}{(N_a - 1) + (N_b - 1)}\right] \qquad 6)$$

The variance of **HMI** in each of the two groups S_a^2 and S_b^2 was estimated from:

$$S_k^2 = \frac{\sum_{j=1}^{k} D_j\, HMI_j^2 - N_k \overline{HMI}_k^2}{N_k - 1} \qquad 7)$$

where **k**= **a**, **b**, and:

$$D_j = \frac{\sum_{j=1}^{k} n_{ij} - 1}{3} \qquad 8)$$

$\mathbf{D_j}$ is an estimate of the number of independent points (degrees of freedom) in the **j**th data block, estimated conservatively because the data on the 3 accelerometer axes was assumed to be correlated.

Since **HMI** in asymptomatic sessions was noted to be more variable, S_a^2 and S_b^2 were not assumed to be equal (as would be required to justify use of the $\mathbf{t^2}$ distribution for hypothesis testing). Where two groups may have different variances, the probability, **p**, of a difference between groups as large as $\mathbf{t^2}$ is given by Chebyshev's inequality (Kendall and Stuart, 1977):

$$p \leq \frac{1}{t^2} \qquad 9)$$

Comparing Subject B's **HMI** data during 3 early mission symptomatic (group "a") sessions with 5 post-symptomatic (group "b") late mission sessions, indeed $\mathbf{t^2}$ was 87.6, so Subject B's increased **HMI** while symptomatic was significant at the $\mathbf{p} < 0.011$ level. Similarly, as shown in Table 1, Subject I's **HMI** data while symptomatic was significantly lower than that obtained in 3 sessions later in the mission. Applying the same Chebyshev $\mathbf{t^2}$ criterion to the **HMI** data from the other two less symptomatic subjects (C and J), significant trends were not found.

The **HMI** data available from all 4 subjects collectively showed, (contrary to our original expectations) that $\overline{\mathbf{HMI}}$ did not correlate with overall discomfort level when subjects were symptomatic. All four limited their head movements during this time so that their $\overline{\mathbf{HMI}}$ remained below 2.2 rad/sec^2. Was this deliberate caution, because they were experiencing symptoms (or feared they might), or was the style of head movement each naturally adopted in weightlessness prior to experiencing symptoms a factor ? Are individuals who habitually move their heads slowly and frequently less likely to experience intense symptoms ? Subjects B, C, and J donned the ARU shortly after reaching orbit. As shown in Fig. 2, during the pre-symptomatic period (before overall discomfort reached, say, 5), the 15 minute block **HMI** data for Subjects B and C have relatively high values, as compared to Subject J's data and also to their own. Although they may have been trying to limit their head movements somewhat during the pre-symptomatic period, in a relative sense, B and C were not particularly successful. Plausibly this early mission activity triggered or at least contributed to the subsequent appearance of symptoms, which in turn caused these subjects to further restrict their head movements. It is interesting that subjects ranked B, C, and then J in terms of $\overline{\textbf{HMI}}$ magnitude during the pre symptomatic" period. As shown in Table 2, this also corresponded to their rank order in terms of subsequent sickness severity. Unfortunately, no pre-symptomatic **HMI** data is available for Subject I, who donned the ARU well after becoming sick.

Session	12-20 hr	43-50 hr	104-113 hr	130 -133 hr
12-20 hr	-	35.5	26.6	22.5
43-50 hr		-	0.28	0.25
104-113 hr			-	0.01
130 -133 hr				-

Table 1. Subject I session HMI comparisons. Values of t^2 by session. Shaded comparisons are significant at the $p < 0.05$ level.

Post symptomatic ARU $\overline{\textbf{HMI}}$ data was available from all 4 subjects, which provides additional indirect information concerning the head movement characteristics of the individual subjects. $\overline{\textbf{HMI}}$ was calculated over the final three sessions for each subject, and alternatively for the final two, and the subjects were ranked from least to most in terms of $\overline{\textbf{HMI}}$. As shown in Table 2, rank order post symptomatic $\overline{\textbf{HMI}}$ correlated exactly with pre symptomatic $\overline{\textbf{HMI}}$, and also with all 3 measures of inflight sickness severity. The relationship between post symptomatic $\overline{\textbf{HMI}}$ and sickness severity rank measures is statistically significant (Spearman rho = 1.0; $p < 0.05$).

Subject Code	Presymptomatic $\overline{\textbf{HMI}}$	Postsymptomatic $\overline{\textbf{HMI}}$ (last 3 sessions)	Postsymptomatic $\overline{\textbf{HMI}}$ (last 2 sessions)	Number of Vomiting Episodes (#)	Average Overall Discomfort	Duration of Frank Sickness (hrs)
B	1	1	1	1 (6)	1	1 (35 hr)
I	-	2	2	2 (3)	2	2 (33 hr)
C	2	3	3	3 (2)	3	3 (14 hr)
J	3	4	4	4 (0)	4	4 (-)

Table 2. Subjects ranked by measures of pre and post symptomatic head movements and sickness severity. Rank 1 = highest.

DISCUSSION AND CONCLUSIONS

Although several different types of stimuli may contribute to space sickness, the statistical absence of sickness in the confining Mercury and Gemini spacecraft indicates that head and body movements probably represent the dominant factor. Our statistical analysis of head acceleration data supports the hypothesis that space sickness severity correlates with the average vigor and/or frequency of head movement. Both our (limited) head movement data obtained prior to the development of significant symptoms and our (more extensive) data obtained after symptom remission are consistent with this view. However, correlation does not itself prove causality. Evidence that head movements actually cause space sickness comes from the firsthand observations by astronauts that head movements are provocative, and not from the correlations demonstrated here in a relatively small number of subjects.

This study suffered from a number of limitations. As previously noted, there were numerous gaps in our angular acceleration data caused by CDTR record/playback errors, which limited the types of analysis possible. The definitions we chose for **HMI** and $\overline{\textbf{HMI}}$ were dictated by practical and statistical considerations, and certainly influenced the character of our results. Superior metrics of the provocative character of 0-g head movements possibly exist. Our subjects were not naive to our hypotheses, and some took drugs in an effort to limit their symptoms. Although our subjects were cooperative, some did not always report symptoms as frequently and consistently as we ideally would have liked. All our subjects had "visual reorientation episodes" and subjects B and I had "inversion illusions". Both phenomena probably also contributed to sickness. Most importantly, this study involved only passive monitoring under operational conditions. The experiment activities assigned to of each of our subjects by mission timeliners was different to some degree. Was this important ? Subjects B and C flew on SL-1, and had generally similar assignments. C and J were on D-1, and also had similar jobs, but largely different than those on SL-1. We believe it unlikely that the differences seen in ranked **HMI** were the result of consistent differences in job assignments throughout the entire mission. Reviewing the mission timelines, which contained many heterogeneous activities, we see no strong support for this idea. Rather, it seems more parsimonious that the **HMI** differences seen reflect the individual crew member's physical style of head and body movement while working.

Our data show that when experiencing symptoms, all crew members reduced **HMI** to 2 rad/sec^2 or less whenever possible. All 4 subjects told us they tried to restrict their head movements during the entire early portion of the mission. However, Subjects B and C's higher early mission, pre symptomatic **HMI** data illustrate that some crew members have difficulty maintaining volitional head movement restraint when they are not actually experiencing symptoms - perhaps because of the press of work or enthusiasm for weightlessness . Subject J's data are particularly interesting, because his **HMI** had a lower mean and was less variable than the other 3 subjects. This difference was very apparent during the pre symptomatic period. Was he simply more disciplined in maintaining head movement restriction, or was his intrinsic style of head movement consistently slower and less frequent ? We cannot be certain. His notes indicate that he abandoned deliberate head movement restriction after the first two days. In debriefing, he said that throughout the flight he tried to remain physically relaxed, and not to be overly concerned about his spatial orientation. He believed this helped him avoid symptoms. Since J's early and mid-mission HMI data were similar, it suggests that his general approach to moving about and orienting in weightlessness may have been the important determinant.

We will have the opportunity to obtain additional HMI data using the same ARU equipment on two more subjects on Spacelab SLS-2, currently planned for launch in 1993. In addition to flight HMI data, we plan to obtain control data on head movement style in 1-G simulations conducted on the same subjects, to further investigate the issue of head movement style. A foam neck collar will be flown and worn by our subjects during a scheduled period late in the mission, to see whether such restraints are quantitatively effective in reducing **HMI**.

ACKNOWLEDGMENTS

Supported by NASA Contracts NAS9-15343 and 17371. Preliminary publications of this work have appeared (Shubentsov, 1989; Oman and Shubentsov, 1990). We thank R.K. McCoy, who originally developed our accelerometer analysis software, Dr. A. Natapoff, who contributed to the statistical analysis, Dr. W. F. Mayer and his MIT Lab for Space Experiments team who built our flight hardware; F. Amlee and D. Harris of NASA Johnson Space Center. Special thanks to our subjects.

REFERENCES

Bock, O. L.& Oman, C. M. (1982): Dynamics of subjective discomfort in motion sickness as measured with a magnitude estimation method. *Aviation, Space, and Environmental Medicine* 53: 733-737.

Davis, J.& Beck, B. (1990): Update on the incidence of space motion sickness since STS-26 (abstract). *Aviation, Space, and Environmental Medicine* 61(5): p.483.

Davis, J. R., et al. (1988): Space motion sickness during 24 flights of the Space Shuttle. *Aviation, Space, and Environmental Medicine* 59: 1185-1189.

Diamond, S. G., et al. (1990): Instability of ocular torsion in zero gravity:possible implications for space motion sickness. *Aviation, Space, and Environmental Medicine* 61(10): 899-905.

Homick, J. L.& Miller, E. F. (1975): Apollo flight crew vestibular assessment. *Biomedical results of Apollo*. US Government Printing Office. pp. 323-340.

Kendall, M. G.& Stuart, A. (1977): The Advanced Theory of Statistics. *The Advanced Theory of Statistics*. New York, Macmillan. pp. 90-91.

Lackner, J. R., et al. (1987): Asymmetric otolith function and increased susceptibility to motion sickness during exposure to variations in gravitoinertial acceleration level. *Aviation, Space, and Environmental Medicine,* 58: 652-657.

Matsnev, E. I., et al. (1983): Space motion sickness: phenomenology, countermeasures, and mechanisms. *Aviation, Space, and Environmental Medicine,* 54: 312-317.

McCoy, R. K. (1985): The study of human head movement on Spacelab 1, Massachusetts Institute of Technology, SM Thesis, Dept. of Aeron. & Astron.

Mittelstaedt, H. (1988): Determinants of space perception in space flight. *Advances in Oto-Rhino-Laryngology* , 42: 18-23.

Oman, C. M. (1982): A heuristic mathematical model for the dynamics of sensory conflict and motion sickness. *Acta Otolaryngologica (Stockholm)* , Suppl 392.

Oman, C. M. (1990): Motion sickness: a synthesis and evaluation of the sensory conflict theory. *Canadian Journal of Physiology and Pharmacology* 68: 294-303.

Author (1990): Symptoms and signs of space motion sickness on Spacelab-1. In: *Motion and Space Sickness*, ed. Oman, C. M., et al., pp. 217-246. Boca Raton, FL. CRC Press.

Oman, C. M., et al. (1986): MIT/Canadian vestibular experiments on Spacelab-1: 4. Space motion sickness: symtoms, stimuli, and predictability. *Experimental Brain Research* 64(2): 316-334.

Oman, C. M.& Shubentsov, I. (1990): *Space motion sickness intensity correlates with average head angular acceleration (Abstract).* Annual Scientific Meeting of the Aerospace Medical Association, New Orleans, LA

Shubentsov, I. (1989): Relationship between astronaut head motion and space motion sickness on Spacelabs 1 and D1, Massachusetts Institute of Technology, SM Thesis

Stevens, S. S. (1957): On the psychophysical law. *Psychcological Reviews* 64: 153-184.

Thornton, W. E., et al. (1987): Clinical characterization and etiology of space motion sickness. *Aviation, Space, and Environmental Medicine* 58(9): A1-A8.

Mechanisms and Control of Emesis. Eds A.L. Bianchi, L. Grélot, A.D. Miller, G.L. King. Colloque INSERM/ John Libbey Eurotext Ltd. © 1992, Vol. 223, pp. 195-201

Prevention of motion sickness by 5-HT_{1A} agonists in cats

James B. Lucot

Department of Pharmacology, Wright State University, Dayton, OH 45435, USA

SUMMARY

A device that elicits motion sickness in cats was built and the parameters for screening and testing of susceptible subjects were determined. Four 5-HT_{1A} agonists from three chemical families were found to suppress motion sickness. Comparison of their dose-response curves are discussed in terms of the literature and the pharmacology of this receptor. These considerations lead to the suggestions that the antiemetic dose range is much higher than the antianxiety dose range and that postsynaptic rather than presynaptic 5-HT_{1A} receptors are involved.

Prévention du mal des transports par les agonistes 5-HT_{1A} chez le chat.

Résumé: *Nous avons construit un dispositif capable d'engendrer le mal des transports chez le chat, et déterminé ses paramètres de fonctionnement permettant de sélectionner puis de tester des sujets sensibles. Nous avons trouvé quatre agonistes 5HT_{1A} provenant de 3 familles de composés chimiques capables de supprimer le mal des transports. La comparaison de leurs courbes de dose-réponse a été discutée en relation avec les données de la littérature sur la pharmacologie de ce récepteur. Ces observations nous ont conduit à suggérer que les doses anti-émétiques sont beaucoup plus fortes que celles des doses anxiolytiques, ce qui est l'indication d'une action sur des récepteurs post-synaptiques plutôt que pré-synaptiques.*

INTRODUCTION

Much of the work from this laboratory has focused on the characterization of the broad spectrum antiemetic effect of drugs which stimulate 5-HT_{1A} receptors in cats. This paper focuses on summarizing the results from studies with provocative motion as the emetic stimulus. Dose-response curves will be compared and antiemetic dose ranges correlated with other effects of these drugs to suggest the relevant dose range in human subjects. Finally, the arguments for post- vs pre-synaptic sites of action will be reviewed.

CHARACTERIZATION OF THE MOTION STIMULUS

A motorized motion testing device modelled after a Ferris wheel was used to produce motion sickness. The cats rode alone in two clear plastic boxes suspended from the ends of a 0.89 m beam that rotated about a horizontal axle. The boxes were counterrotated by a chain and sprocket system to keep the boxes vertical. A parametric study determined that the most provocative motion was achieved at a rotation rate of 0.28 Hz (17 RPM), a value similar to that reported for other species (Daunton, 1990; Guignard and McCauley, 1990). A standard test was then defined as 30 min of motion at 0.28 Hz followed by one min of observation at rest. The latency to the first retch fits the two parameter Weibull distribution in cats as it does in human subjects (Park and Crampton, 1988). Susceptibility was determined in female cats by testing them at two week intervals for five tests. Only those responding on at least two tests were considered adequately susceptible for inclusion in motion studies. Roughly half of the population tested responded on none of the screening tests, while roughly 10 percent responded at each level of susceptibility, i.e. 10 percent vomited on one of five tests, etc. Thus, only 40 percent of screened cats are adequately susceptible to this stimulus (Crampton and Lucot, 1985).

A separate study determined that tests performed at two week intervals resulted in no habituation to the motion stimulus. Five weekly tests resulted in significant habituation and five daily tests resulted in even more rapid habituation. In both cases, the susceptibility of the group recovered when tested two weeks later. Further analysis revealed that the rate of habituation was not related to the susceptibility of the subjects (Crampton and Lucot, 1991).

5-HT$_{1A}$ AGONISTS

Four agonists produce a dose-dependent inhibition of motion sickness (Fig. 1). Several interesting points may be made from this figure. First, the dose-response curve for 8-OH-DPAT (DPAT) is very steep. Second, flesinoxan is slightly more potent than DPAT, whereas in several other in vivo measures it is roughly an order of magnitude less potent (Dreteler et al., 1990; Ramage and Wilkinson, 1989). Resolution of the potency anomaly may lie in current studies investigating the heterogeneity of 5-HT$_{1A}$ receptors. Third, BMY 7378 exhibits agonist effects in this model when a 5 min pretreatment time is used. While originally described as an antagonist (Yocca et al., 1987), this drug exerts agonist effects on some measures as a result of either large receptor reserve (Meller et al., 1990) or of heterogeneity of 5-HT$_{1A}$ receptors (Zemlin et al., 1990). Fourth, buspirone and its structural analogue, BMY 7378, have rather low potencies and shallow dose-response curves.

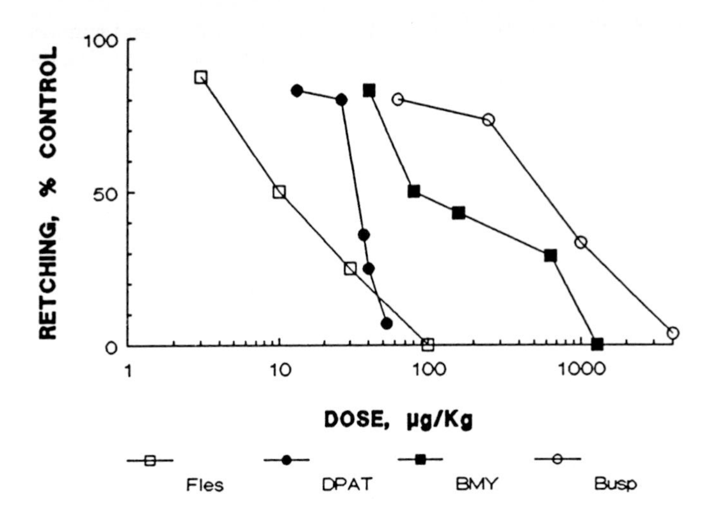

Fig. 1. Dose-response curves for four $5\text{-}HT_{1A}$ agonists in the suppression of motion sickness. All doses (including DPAT) are in terms of the salt. References for relevant published data are in the text.

Another interesting point is the absence of nonspecific behavioral effects of all these agonists over this dose range with the notable exception of buspirone. The doses of 1000 and 4000 µg/kg produced prominent, long lasting behavior changes in the cat manifested as defensiveness upon approach that is characterized by flattened ears, backing into a defensive position, growling, scratching and strong resistance to handling (Lucot and Crampton, 1987). When viewed from outside the room, these treated cats moved about their home cages with no evident behavior changes. The defensiveness is not uniquely produced by the buspirone structure, as it is seen also following the doses of 210 and 845 µg/kg of DPAT and 300 µg/kg of flesinoxan (Lucot and Crampton, 1989). Thus, the defensive behavior exhibits a dose-dependency for these three agonists that is different from that for the suppression of motion sickness. While there is no clear explanation for this, one possibility lies in the suggested heterogeneity of $5\text{-}HT_{1A}$ receptors. These receptors act through several signal transduction systems which are linked to the receptor by different G proteins. The identity of the G protein may alter the response to some drug-receptor complexes such that one drug may have differing efficacies at different sites (Shenker et al., 1987; Zemlin et al., 1990).

ANTIEMETIC DOSE RANGE COMPARED WITH OTHER MEASURES

It is necessary to relate the doses that produce antiemetic effects to other measures so that relevant doses for other species may be suggested. This is particularly important for studies with human subjects because of the difficulty of determining full dose-response curves in clinical trials. A useful measure is an antianxiety effect, which is the current clinical indication for buspirone. However, antianxiety doses for these drugs have not been established in the cat. The comparison becomes possible by adding another measure, suppression of firing of the dorsal raphe nucleus, and another species, the rat.

Buspirone. The threshold dose for producing a significant effect on the Vogel conflict procedure in the rat is 1 mg/kg orally (Taylor et al., 1985), which is the same as the ED_{50} for suppression of firing in the dorsal raphe nucleus (Tunicliff, 1991). These two effects occur at the same dose given by the same route of administration. In the cat, the ED_{50} for suppression of firing in the dorsal raphe nucleus is 360 μg/kg when given subcutaneously (Trulson and Trulson, 1986). From Figure 1, this dose produces only about 40 percent inhibition of motion sickness. A 90 percent inhibition of motion sickness (at 4000 μg/kg) occurs at a dose 11-fold higher than the ED_{50} for the suppression of firing in the dorsal raphe nucleus. Applying this relationship to the antianxiety dose range of 20-30 mg/day orally in humans (Physician's Desk Reference, 1991), a substantial inhibition of motion sickness would occur in the dose range of 220 to 330 mg given orally. However, buspirone would also interact with dopamine receptors at these doses (Riblet et al., 1989; Taylor, 1988). This estimation may be conservative, given that buspirone administered into the dorsal raphe nucleus is 5 to 25 fold more potent at producing antianxiety effects in rats than at changing the functioning of 5-HT neurons, as measured by the ratio of the neurotransmitter to its metabolite (Higgins et al., 1988).

DPAT. A similar line of reasoning may be applied to the data available on the relevant effects of DPAT. The route of administration must also be considered, because the subcutaneous route of administration yields potencies 17-fold greater than the intraperitoneal route (Fuller and Snoddy, 1987). Using this correction factor for route of administration, the threshold dose for antianxiety effects in the rat (Engel et al., 1984; Sanger and Joly, 1990) occurs at only one half the ED_{50} for changing 5-HT function in projection fields of the dorsal raphe nucleus (Meller et al., 1990). In the cat, the ED_{50} for suppression of firing in the dorsal raphe nucleus is 10-15 μg/kg given subcutaneously (Tada et al., 1991; Wilkinson et al., 1991), from which it may be inferred that the antianxiety range is roughly 5 to 8 μg/kg. From Fig. 1, these doses produce less than 20 percent inhibition of motion sickness. A greater than 90 percent inhibition of motion sickness occurs at doses 6.6- to 10-fold higher than doses presumed to have antianxiety effects. As with buspirone, this estimate is conservative, as injection of DPAT into the dorsal raphe nucleus is 25-fold more potent at producing antianxiety effects in rats than at changing the 5-HT to 5-HIAA ratio (Higgins et al., 1988).

The doses which produce antiemetic effects appear to be higher than are necessary to produce antianxiety effects. However, simply using huge doses does not insure an adequate test, as a very high dose of DPAT can elicit emesis in dogs (Di Francesco et al., 1988), while a lesser amount of $5\text{-}HT_{1A}$ stimulation with the nonselective agonist, LSD, inhibits emesis elicited by three of six chemical stimuli in this species (Dhawan and Gupta, 1961). Therefore, careful selection of an appropriate range of doses in important when evaluating this mechanism in other species.

POST- VS PRE-SYNAPTIC SITES OF ACTION

It is of both theoretical and practical importance to determine if the $5\text{-}HT_{1A}$ sites are located presynaptically, where the effects would result from reduced 5-HT neurotransmission, or postsynaptically. This determination is relevant to the maximum antiemetic efficacy obtainable, to dose ranges relevant to clinical use and to ascertaining the anatomical location of these receptors.

The section above makes it clear that antiemetic effects occur at doses higher that those which produce 50 percent inhibition of firing in the dorsal raphe nucleus. The major 5-HT cell groups differ in their sensitivity to suppression by DPAT. For this reason, the slope of the dose-response curve and the sensitivity of other raphe nuclei must now be considered. In the cat, the nucleus raphe pallidus and nucleus raphe obscurus are slightly more sensitive to suppression produced by DPAT than is the dorsal raphe nucleus (King et al., 1991). The raphe centralis superior (equivalent to the medial raphe nucleus of the rat; Fornal, pers. comm.) is roughly 3-fold less sensitive to suppression produced by DPAT than is the dorsal raphe nucleus (Tada et al., 1991). Thus, the least sensitive group of 5-HT neurons appears to be located in the raphe centralis superior.

The dose of 50 µg/kg of DPAT given subcutaneously produces complete suppression of the dorsal raphe nucleus in the cat (Wilkinson et al., 1991). By extension, the dose of 150 µg/kg should completely suppress firing in all major 5-HT cell groups, including the nucleus centralis superior. If DPAT suppresses emesis by stimulating presynaptic receptors, the dose of 150 µg/kg should elicit the maximum antiemetic effect obtainable. In contrast to this prediction, increasing the dose of DPAT from 210 to 845 µg/kg produces an appreciably greater inhibition of emesis elicited by more powerful emetic stimuli such as xylazine and RU 24969 (Lucot and Crampton, 1989; Lucot, 1990a). Therefore, it is highly unlikely that presynaptic sites of action account for the range of antiemetic effects produced by $5\text{-}HT_{1A}$ agonists.

Another test of the hypothesis that the antiemetic effects result from stimulation of presynaptic receptors was performed by attempting to mimic the presynaptic action by blocking all $5\text{-}HT_1$ and $5\text{-}HT_2$ receptors with the antagonist, metergoline, and by depleting the nerve terminals of 5-HT by repeated administration of the synthesis inhibitor, PCPA (Lucot, 1990b). If the suppression of emesis results from stimulation of presynaptic receptors, then each of these manipulations should also decrease emesis. In contrast, metergoline produced a weak but significant increase in motion sickness and PCPA produced a trend toward increased motion sickness.

From the above two lines of reasoning, it is clear that postsynaptic $5\text{-}HT_{1A}$ receptors are involved in the antiemetic effects of the agonists. Other indirect lines of reasoning that support this conclusion have been presented elsewhere (Lucot, 1990).

CONCLUSIONS

Much work on the mechanism underlying the antiemetic effect of 5-HT_{1A} agonists remains to be done. Appropriate doses in other species need to be tested against a variety of emetic stimuli. Some notable work in this regard has been performed by Dr. Matsuki in Suncus murinus. The possible heterogeneity of 5-HT_{1A} receptors remains to be characterized and related to the antiemetic effect. The results of these experiments may yield both clinical benefit and greater understanding of the neural mechanisms underlying vomiting.

REFERENCES

Crampton, G.H. & Lucot, J.B. (1985): A stimulator for laboratory studies of motion sickness in cats. *Aviat. Space Environ. Med.* 56, 462-465.

Crampton, G.H. & Lucot, J.B. (1991): Habituation to motion sickness in the cat. *Aviat. Space Environ. Med.* 62, 212-215.

Daunton, N.G. (1990) Animal models in motion sickness research. In *Motion and Space Sickness*, ed. G.H. Crampton, pp 87-104. Boca Raton, CRC Press, Inc.

Dhawan, B.N. & Gupta, G.P. (1961): Antiemetic activity of D-lysergic acid diethylamine. *J. Pharmacol. Exp. Ther.* 133, 137-139.

Di Francesco, G.F., Petty, M.A. & Fozard, J.R. (1988): Antihypertensive effects of 8-hydroxy-2-(di-n-propylamino)tetralin (8-OH-DPAT) in conscious dogs. *Eur. J. Pharmacol.* 147, 287-290.

Dreteler, G.H., Wouters, W. & Saxena, P.R. (1990): Comparison of the cardiovascular effects of the 5-HT_{1A} receptor agonist flesinoxan with that of 8-OH-DPAT in the rat. *Eur. J. Pharmacol.* 180, 339-349.

Engel, J.A., Hjorth, S., Svensson, K., Carlsson, A. & Liljequist, S. (1984): Anticonflict effect of the putative serotonin receptor agonist 8-hydroxy-2-(DI-n-propylamine)tetralin (8-OH-DPAT). *Eur. J. Pharmacol.* 105, 365-368.

Fuller, R.W. & Snoddy, H.D. (1987): Influence of route of administration on potency of the selective 5-HT-1A agonist, 8-hydroxy-2-(DI-n-propylanimo)tetralin, in rats. *Res. Comm. Chem. Path. Pharmacol.* 58, 409-412.

Guignard, J.C. & McCauley, M.E. (1990): The accelerative stimulus for motion sickness. In *Motion and Space Sickness*, ed. G.H. Crampton, pp 123-152. Boca Raton, CRC Press, Inc.

Higgins, G.A., Bradbur, A.J., Jones, B.J. & Oakley, N.R. (1988): Behavioral and biochemical consequences following activation of 5-HT_1-like and GABA receptors in the dorsal raphe nucleus of the rat. *Neuropharmacology* 27, 992-1001.

King, K.A., McCall, R.B. & McCall, J.M. (1991): Inhibition of 5-HT unit firing and sympathetic discharge by 8-OH-DPAT in the baroreceptor denervated cat. *Soc. Neurosci. Abstr.* 17, 341, 141.11.

Lucot, J.B. (1990a): RU 24969-induced emesis in the cat: 5-HT_1 sites other than 5-HT_{1A}, 5-HT_{1B} or 5-HT_{1C} implicated. *Eur. J. Pharmacol.* 180, 193-199.

Lucot, J.B. (1990b): Effects of serotonin antagonists on motion sickness and its suppression by 8-OH-DPAT in cats. *Pharmacol. Biochem. Behav.* 37, 283-287.

Lucot, J.B. & Crampton, G.H. (1987): Buspirone blocks motion sickness and xylazine-induced emesis in the cat. *Aviat. Space Environ. Med.* 58, 989-991.
Lucot, J.B. & Crampton, G.H. (1989): 8-OH-DPAT suppresses vomiting in the cat elicited by motion, cisplatin or xylazine. *Pharmacol. Biochem. Behav.* 33, 627-631.
Meller, E., Goldstein, M. & Bohmaker, K. (1990): Receptor reserve for 5-hydroxytryptamine$_{1A}$-mediated inhibition of serotonin synthesis: Possible relationship to anxiolytic properties of 5-hydroxytryptamine $_{1A}$ receptors. *Mol. Pharmacol.* 37, 231-237.
Park, W.J. & Crampton, G.H. (1988): Statistical analysis of censored motion sickness latency data using the two-parameter Weibull distribution. *Int. J. Biomed. Computing* 22, 295-301.
Physician's Desk Reference (1991): Medical Economics Co., Inc.
Ramage, A.G. & Wilkinson, S.J. (1989): Evidence that different regional sympathetic outflows vary in their sensitivity to the sympathoinhibitory actions of putative 5-HT$_{1A}$ and alpha$_2$-adrenoceptor agonists in anaesthetized cats. *Br. J. Pharmacol.* 98, 1157-1164.
Riblet, L.A., Taylor, D.P., Eison, M.S. & Stanton, H.C. (1982): Pharmacology and neurochemistry of buspirone. *J. Clin. Psychiat.* 43, 11-16.
Sanger, D.J. & Joly, D. (1989-1990): Performance of a passive avoidance response is disrupted by compounds acting at 5-HT$_{1A}$ receptors. *Behav. Pharmacol.* 1, 235-240.
Shenker, A., Maayani, S., Weinstein, H. & Green, J. (1987): Pharmacological characterization of two 5-hydroxytryptamine receptors coupled to adenylate cyclase in guinea pig hippocampal membranes. *Mol. Pharmacol.* 31, 357-367.
Tada, K., Fornal, C.A., Marrosu, F., Metzler, C.W. & Jacobs, B.L. (1991): Single-unit responses of n. raphe dorsalis and centralis superior neurons to 5-HT$_{1A}$ drugs in behaving cats. *Soc. Neurosci. Abstr.* 17, 1437, 569.14.
Taylor, D.P. (1988): Buspirone, a new approach to the treatment of anxiety. *FASEB J.* 2, 2445-2452.
Taylor, D.P., Eison, M.S., Riblet, L.A. & Vandermaelen, C.P (1985): Pharmacological and clinical effects of buspirone. *Pharmacol. Biochem. Behav.* 23, 687-694.
Trulson, M.E. & Trulson, T.J. (1986): Buspirone decreases the activity of serotonin-containing neurons in the dorsal raphe in freely-moving cats. *Neuropharmacology* 25, 1263-1266.
Tunnicliff, G. (1991): Molecular basis of buspirone's anxiolytic action. *Pharmacol. Toxicol.* 69, 149-156.
Wilkinson, L.O., Auerbach, S.B. & Jacobs, B.L. (1991): *J. Neurosci.* 11, 2732-2741.
Yocca, F.D., Hyslop, D.K., Smith, D.W. & Maayani, S. (1987): BMY 7378, a buspirone analog with high affinity, selectivity and low intrinsic activity at the 5-HT$_{1A}$ receptor in rat and guinea pig hippocampal membranes. *Eur. J. Pharmacol.* 137, 293-294.
Zemlin, F.P., Zieleniewski-Murphy, A., Murphy, R.M. & Behbehani, M.M. (1990): BMY 7378: Partial agonist at spinal cord 5-HT$_{1A}$ receptors. *Neurochem. Int.* 16, 515-522.

Mechanisms and Control of Emesis. Eds A.L. Bianchi, L. Grélot, A.D. Miller, G.L. King. Colloque INSERM/ John Libbey Eurotext Ltd. © 1992, Vol. 223, pp. 203-212

Prevention and treatment of motion sickness in man

J.R. Rollin Stott

RAF Institute of Aviation Medicine, Farnborough, Hampshire, GU14 6SZ, UK

SUMMARY

The treatment of motion sickness is considered under three headings. First, the sensory conflict theory of motion sickness forms a basis for rational measures to reduce the intensity of the stimulus or to minimise its nauseogenic effect. Secondly, drugs may be used both prophylactically and in the treatment of established motion-induced vomiting, though side-effects may limit their value. Drugs that are effective in nausea and vomiting from other causes are however not necessarily effective in motion sickness. Thirdly, repeated or continued exposure to an initially nauseogenic stimulus produces a state of increased tolerance. This adaptive response often constitutes a spontaneous cure but may also be exploited in treatment programmes for individuals in whom motion sickness is an occupational problem.

Prévention et traitement du mal des transports chez l'homme.
Résumé: *Le traitement du mal des transports est considéré sous trois aspects. Tout d'abord, la théorie du conflit sensoriel dans le mal des transports forme une base pour une évaluation rationnelle en vue de réduire l'intensité du stimulus ou de minimiser ses effets nauséeux. Deuxièmement, des drogues peuvent être utilisées aussi bien à titre préventif que pour le traitement du mal des transports déjà établi , bien que leur usage soit limité par leurs effets secondaires. Des drogues qui sont efficaces contre la nausée et le vomissement ayant pour origine d'autres causes ne sont cependant pas nécessairement efficaces contre le mal des transports. Troisièmement, l'exposition répétée ou continue à un stimulus auparavant émétique produit un état de tolérance augmentée. Cette réponse adaptative constitue souvent une guérison spontanée mais peut aussi être exploitée dans les programmes de traitement des individus chez lesquels le mal des transports est un problème professionnel.*

THE REDUCTION OF SENSORY CONFLICT

Sensory conflict can occur between visual and vestibular sensors of motion when vestibular-sensed motion cannot be related to a space-stable visual scene, between the canal and otolith components of the vestibular system when rotation of the head out of the horizontal plane is not associated with a corresponding change in the otolith-sensed direction of gravity, and between the utricular and saccular components of the otolithic system when changing stimuli on the two components do not summate to the expected 1 G.

Visual-vestibular conflict An essential function of the vestibular system is to generate compensatory eye movements that stabilise the retinal image of an earth-fixed visual target in the presence of motion of the head. In circumstances in which the visual world shares the same motion as that of the head, this reflex is inappropriate and there is consequent sensory conflict.

The navigator who is map-reading while the aircraft is manoeuvring experiences angular motion sensed by the semi-circular canals, but because his field of view is confined to objects within the cockpit, he lacks any visual evidence of rotation. Similar visual-vestibular conflict occurs below decks in a ship in rough weather and susceptible individuals will experience less conflict if on deck with a view of the horizon. A similar problem affects the occupants of enclosed military vehicles such as tanks and armoured personnel carriers when travelling over rough terrain.

Car sickness is more common in children than in adults possibly because of the limited view of the outside world obtained by a small child confined to the rear seat of a car, in particular, a view of the road ahead that would provide him with the visual accord when the vehicle corners or changes speed.

Reading in a moving vehicle is well known to precipitate motion sickness in susceptible individuals. In this situation the detailed scanning eye movements coupled with the need to suppress vestibular induced eye movements may be an intensifying factor (Guedry et al, 1982).

Canal-otolith conflict The expected sensory linkage between canal and otolith is easily broken in a cornering vehicle whether the turn is flat, as in a car on an uncambered corner, or banked as when cornering on a motorcycle or flying a co-ordinated turn in an aircraft. Curvilinear motion is associated with a centripetal acceleration that acts radially from the centre of curvature. In a flat turn the otoliths sense the resultant acceleration formed by the addition of the gravity vector to the radial acceleration associated with the curved path of the vehicle. This resultant inertial force is directed downwards and outwards, but its outward swing from the vertical as the vehicle enters the corner is unaccompanied by any corresponding rotation signal in roll from the semicircular canals. This conflict can be minimised by a reduction of speed when cornering. The amplitude of the radial acceleration for a given radius of curvature is proportional to the square of the vehicle forward velocity. Hence a small reduction in velocity will give a disproportionately large reduction in radial acceleration and consequent sensory conflict.

In a co-ordinated turn the aircraft is rolled by an amount which maintains the resultant vector directed at right angles to the aircraft floor. The resulting sensory conflict involves a perception of roll that is unaccompanied by any relative change in the direction of acceleration sensed by the otoliths. Commercial airline pilots minimise this conflict by limiting the rate of roll to levels approaching the $2^{\cdot}deg.s^{-1}$ threshold of perception, and by limiting the angle of bank to 30deg so that there is only a small increase, to 1.15G_z, in the intensity of what is perceived as gravity by the passengers.

Intra-otolithic conflict Neuromuscular activity is carried out against the background of a gravitational environment that is constant in intensity and direction. Variations in the otolith-sensed intensity of gravity, apart from those relatively high frequency fluctuations produced by walking or running, evoke a sensory conflict. In a ship at sea in rough weather the principal oscillatory motions of the vessel are vertical translation, and pitch and roll rotations (Lawther & Griffin 1986). The pitch motion of the vessel, which occurs about a transverse axis roughly mid-way along the length of the ship, results in vertical oscillatory motion at the bow and stern which for a vessel 100m in length may be a factor of four or five times greater than amidships. The frequency spectrum of vertical acceleration in passenger ferries shows a peak in the range 0.15 - 0.3 Hz which coicides with the peak of nauseogenicity of this type of stimulus in man (McCauley et al.,1976). Seasickness in passenger ferries has been shown to correlate most strongly with the amplitude of low frequency vertical oscillatory motion of the ship (Lawther & Griffin, 1988). Consequently, to minimise the nauseogenic consequences of this type of motion, one of the most effective strategies a susceptible passenger can adopt is to station himself over the axis of pitch motion of the vessel.

Vertical oscillatory motion is encountered in aircraft when flying in turbulence and may lead to airsickness. In commercial flying this is nowadays infrequent since passenger aircraft fly at altitudes well above the turbulence of the weather. It may occur if the aircraft encounters clear air turbulence at altitude or storm cloud activity on the approach but such problems can often be avoided by re-routing. By contrast, in military flying the vertical oscillatory motion induced by turbulence is a feature of low-level flying which can in certain weather conditions be very severe.

In cars frequent braking and acceleration generate what is in effect a low frequency horizontal oscillatory stimulus and this can also be nauseogenic for susceptible vehicle occupants.

The influence of head movements In conditions of sustained rotation, as, for example, in certain aerobatic manoeuvres or on fairground amusements, head movement in any plane other than that of the rotation will induce a cross-coupled vestibular signal that is both disorientating and nauseogenic. Head movements are also provocative of motion sickness in abnormal G environments. In the zero gravity environment of space astronauts find that head movements particularly in pitch and roll are provocative of nausea and that, in addition to keeping head movement to a minimum, symptoms are relieved by the tactile cues of wedging the body into a corner of the spacecraft or using some system of body restraint (Oman et al, 1986). A similar nauseogenic effect of head movements has been shown in the 0 - 2 G environment of parabolic flight ((Lackner & Graybiel, 1986). While voluntary restriction of head movement reduces the incidence of motion sickness, an additional beneficial effect has been shown from the use of a cervical collar to immobilise the head (Lackner et al., 1991).

It would seem to follow that head movements made in the alternating hyper- and hypo-gravity environment produced by low frequency vertical oscillation would be an additional factor in the provocation of motion sickness. This, however, has not been clearly established. A study of motion sickness induced by vertical oscillatory motion found no potentiating effect from the addition of head movements or whole body pitch and roll movements (McCauley et al, 1976). Initial trials in paratroops of the use of restraints to minimise head movement found significant benefit, but only in conditions of "normal turbulence". In conditions described as "rough" or "violent" no significant differences in the incidence of airsickness were found (Johnson & Mayne, 1953). A similar study (Keist et al, 1956) failed to show any benefit from head restraint, whereas hyoscine 0.65mg taken 1 hour before flight reduced the incidence of vomiting from 31% to 7.5%.

The influence of body posture Several comparative studies to investigate the effect of different body orientation in relation to the direction of low frequency oscillation have been carried out in aircraft undergoing roller-coaster type manoeuvres (von Baumgarten et al, 1980), in an ambulance car while alternately braking and accelerating (Vogel et al 1982), and in laboratory based horizontal and vertical motion devices (Golding & Kerguelen, 1992). In addition, in the treatment of seasickness it is well known that seasick mariners are better if made to lie down. The principle that emerges from these experimental and clinical observations is that an oscillatory stimulus is best tolerated in a posture which requires a minimum of postural regulatory activity in order to maintain it.

Effect of being in control of the vehicle It is well known that the driver of a car or coach is spared the motion sickness that may, as a consequence of his energetic driving, afflict his passengers. Several factors may contribute to the relative immunity of the driver, but probably the most important is his ability to anticipate the effects of his actions in accelerating, braking and cornering. In consequence, the driver will lean into the corner while his passenger tends to be thrown outwards, and likewise, the driver will brace himself in preparation for braking whereas his passenger is initially thrown forwards. An unexpected change in the force environment generates proprioceptive signals that are suddenly at variance with those expected as a consequence of the existing postural regulatory efferent activity. It may be that this constitutes a neural mismatch signal that contributes to other discordant motion signals in the provocation of motion sickness.

A similar benefit from being in control is enjoyed by the pilot of an aircraft as compared with his navigator, though this may be less evident in early training while he is still becoming accustomed to the sensory consequences of his control actions. Likewise seasick crew members on sailing boats may derive some benefit from taking the helm.

A further benefit of being in control may derive from the mental distraction that it provides. There is experimental evidence to suggest that motion sickness symptoms are reduced by mental activity that decreases the subject's awareness of the provocative motion (Correia & Guedry, 1966).

THE USE OF ANTI-MOTION SICKNESS DRUGS

Many of the drugs that are used to treat nausea and vomiting from other causes are ineffective in motion sickness. Thus metoclopramide, widely used for vomiting due to gastrointestinal disorders, migraine, anaesthetic agents and cytotoxic drugs is almost certainly ineffective in motion-induced nausea and vomiting (Kohl 1987), although an earlier study (Von Baumgarten 1980) had indicated some benefit. Likewise prochlorperazine, also used in the treatment of nausea and vomiting, has been shown to have negligible benefit in motion sickness (Wood & Graybiel 1968). A recently introduced drug, odansetron, is a $5HT_3$ receptor antagonist which is highly effective in the treatment of nausea and vomiting induced by radiation and chemotherapy, but has no effect on laboratory-induced motion sickness (Stott et al 1989).

The successful use of prophylactic drugs relies upon a knowledge of their time to peak therapeutic activity, their side effects, and duration of action. It is also useful to know something of the variability of response between individuals to a standard dose. However, the protection afforded by drugs in motion sickness is far from complete. A survey of over 20,000 passengers aboard ferries (Lawther & Griffin 1988) found that 26% had taken medication. Of these, 11.4% vomited during the voyage compared with only 5.6% of those who took no medication.

Table 1. Anti-motion Sickness Drugs

Drug	Route	Dose	Onset	Duration (hr)
Hyoscine	oral	.3-.6mg	30 min	4
	patch	.2mg+.02mg/hr	6-8 hr	72
	injection	.2mg	15 min	4
Cinnarizine	oral	30 mg	4 hr	8
Promethazine	oral	25 mg	2-4 hr	24
	injection	50 mg	15 min	18
Dimenhydrinate	oral	50-100mg	2 hr	8
Cyclizine	oral	50 mg	2 hr	12

Table 1 lists the currently used drugs, their dose, and time course of action. Despite its longevity, hyoscine probably remains the most potent single anti-motion sickness drug. It is rapidly absorbed following oral administration and reaches a peak concentration in the blood after 30 min to 1 h. Its relatively short half life of about 2.5 h implies that its duration of action is no longer than about 4 h. It is therefore most suitable for short exposures to relatively intense provocative motion stimuli. Side effects from hyoscine are frequent, in particular light headedness, drowsiness and dry mouth. The drug is not recommended for children in whom the therapeutic margin is probably narrower and who are therefore more at risk of serious toxic central effects of restlessness, hallucinations and psychosis. For similar reasons hyoscine is not well tolerated in the elderly. Additionally it should not be used in patients with glaucoma and only used with caution in patients with urinary retention from bladder neck obstruction. Hyoscine has also been shown to impair vigilance and short-term memory (Brazell et al. 1989), possibly a desirable feature in motion sick travellers but not in the training environment.

A more sustained effect from hyoscine is obtained using a dermal patch (Scopoderm TTS, Transderm-Scop) which delivers a loading dose of 200 micrograms hyoscine and 20 micrograms per hour for up to 72 hours when applied to the post-auricular skin. An effective drug concentration is not reached until 6-8 hours after application of the patch. Drug excretion continues for up to 48 hours after removal of the patch probably indicating that the skin beneath the patch continues to provide a reservoir of active drug (Schmitt & Shaw 1981). The principal use of this presentation of hyoscine must therefore be in exposures to a motion stimulus lasting more than 24 hours, as for example on longer sea voyages. Even more than with oral hyoscine, the dermal patch is unsuitable for use in children on account of the risk of overdose (Gibbons et al 1984).

Cinnarizine an antihistamine which also has calcium antagonist properties has in recent years been widely used in the prophylaxis of seasickness (Hargreaves 1980). Adequate drug levels can be maintained with an 8 hourly dosage scheme and the drug is said to be relatively free of the side effect of drowsiness. However, after a single dose, drowsiness tends to occur after about 5 hours rather than at 2 hours when peak plasma level is reached, and there is evidence to suggest that its anti-motion sickness effects are similarly delayed (Pingree & Pethybridge, 1989). Consequently, cinnarizine in a dose of 30mg should be taken at least 4 hours before exposure to provocative motion.

The 24 hour duration of action of promethazine may be of advantage in some circumstances, and would allow for a single daily dosage preferably at night so that the peak sedative effect occurs during sleep. Promethazine belongs to the phenothiazine group of ugs, and, in addition to H_1 receptor antagonism, this group possesses considerable anticholinergic activity, so that marked sedation and dry mouth are frequent side effects. This drug can also be given intramuscularly in a dose of 50 mg to treat established motion-induced vomiting.

Other antihistamines such as dimenhydrinate and cyclizine are effective in the prophylaxis of motion sickness. They vary in their duration of action, but all have undesirable sedative side effects.

The central sympathomimetic drug dexamphatamine has been shown to have an anti-motion sickness effect when used alone and to act synergistically when combined with hyoscine, promethazine, or dimenhydrinate (Wood 1990). It also antagonises the soporific and performance decrementing effects of hyoscine. The combination of hyoscine 0.4mg and dexamphetamine 5mg (Scop/dex) is the primary medication used by US astronauts to combat space sickness and is probably the most effective drug combination available. However, because of its habituating properties and its potential for abuse, dexamphetamine is a controlled drug. In consequence, its general use in motion sickness prophylaxis cannot be justified. A similar alerting effect without the associated risks can be obtained with ephedrine 15-30mg.

Recently introduced antihistamine drugs claim benefit over earlier drugs in having less sedating properties. This is ascribed to an inability of the drug to cross the blood-brain barrier. As a general principle drugs that lack any activity within the central nervous system are likely to be ineffective in motion sickness. In support of this principle the H_1 antagonist astemizole is without benefit in motion sickness (Kohl et al. 1987). However, terfenadine, also said to have no central nervous system penetration, has been shown to possess anti-motion properties following a single dose of 200mg (Kohl et al. 1991). (This dose exceeds the manufacturers recommended maximum of 120mg). Whether at this higher dose some drug does cross the blood-brain barrier is not yet clear.

A recent study on the prophylactic use of phenytoin (Chelen et al. 1990) found a tenfold increase in tolerance to cross-coupled stimulation when given in a dosage (1-1.4 grams over 24 hours) that produces anti-epileptic blood levels.

ADAPTATION / HABITUATION TO PROVOCATIVE STIMULI

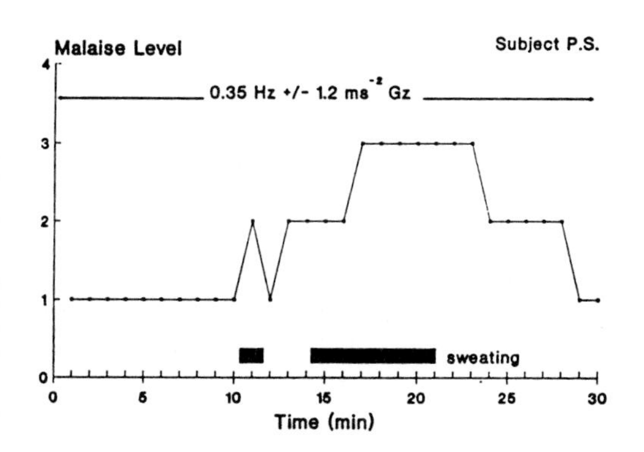

Figure 1. Short term adaptive response to a 30 min exposure to low frequency vertical oscillation. The changes in the subject's level of malaise are reflected in episodes of forehead sweating.

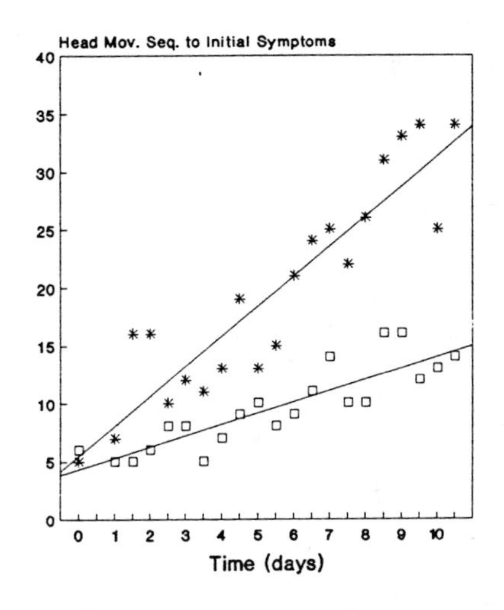

Figure 2. Habituation of two subjects to twice daily sessions of cross-coupled stimuli

A further important factor in reducing motion sickness susceptibility is the increase in tolerance to a nauseogenic stimulus that occurs over a period of several days or even weeks of repeated exposure. The neurophysiologist would use the term habituation for this phenomenon, and would reserve the term adaptation to refer to changes in the magnitude of the response during the course of the application of the stimulus. Both types of adaptive response can be seen with motion sickness. Exposed to an appropriate level of stimulus over say 30 minutes an individual may show an initial loss of well-being followed by partial or complete recovery indicative of a short term adaptation within the period of the test (Fig 1).

Similarly subjects exposed twice daily to cross-coupled stimulation over a 10 day period are able to tolerate increasing levels of stimulus, though the rate at which tolerance is acquired varies between individuals (Fig 2).

The phenomenon of adaptation is well known among mariners in whom seasickness symptoms abate during the first few days at sea accompanied by an improvement in locomotor co-ordination aboard ship, a phenomenon colloquially known as 'getting one's sea legs'. Adaptation is also a feature of aircrew training. The familiarisation sortie may give rise to airsickness in 15% of trainee aircrew but tolerance builds up with continued flying, though airsickness may recur with the introduction of new manoeuvres such as steep turns, spinning and aerobatics (Tucker et al, 1965). In space flight the malaise and nausea that may initially be provoked by head movements in the zero gravity environment gradually diminishes, typically over a period of 2 to 4 days.

A distinction can be made between those environments that produce a consistently reorganised relationship between the various sensory inputs of motion such as the microgravity environment of space, the continued wearing of image reversing spectacles, and to a lesser degree the motion environment of a ship, and those environments to which exposure is brief and intermittent, such as flight involving aerobatics. In the former group of environments it is hypothesised that new sensory inter-relationships are established that to some extent replace or overlie those that previously existed. As a consequence the return to the normal terrestrial environment is associated with a temporary degree of mal-adaptation and even mild motion sickness symptoms, termed mal de débarquement. In contrast, adaptation to aerobatic flight may be qualitively different and involve an extension of the repertoire of patterns of sensory input that the brain accepts as legitimate.

Adaptation treatment for motion sickness The use of adaptation as a therapeutic procedure is most appropriate to those situations in which, following treatment, there is sufficient continuity of exposure to the stimulus to maintain the state of adaptation and also in which the economic or personal consequences of continued motion sickness make a time-consuming treatment programme worthwhile. Though spaceflight fits these criteria it is impossible as yet to predict who will suffer spacesickness and uncertain as to whether tolerance acquired to any earth-bound stimulus would transfer to the microgravity environment in space. It is perhaps in the treatment of airsickness in military aircrew that adaptation treatment has proved to be of most value. Various schemes have been described (reviewed in Stott,1990). All involve adaptation to ground-based motion stimuli that are nauseogenic. Some use biofeedback and relaxation techniques. They vary in the extent to which remedial flying is incorporated into the programme. Detailed comparison of results is complicated by differing criteria of success, but it is possible to reduce by 80 to 90% the number of trainee aircrew who would otherwise be eliminated from training on account of persistent airsickness.

REFERENCES

Brazell C, Preston GC, Ward C, Lines CR & Traub M.(1989): The scopolamine model of dementia: chronic transdermal administration. J. Psychopharmacol. 3, 76-82.

Chelen W, Kabrisky M, Hatsell C, Morales R, Fix E & Scott M.(1990): Use of phenytoin in the prevention of motion sickness. Aviat. Space Environ. Med. 61, 1022-5.

Correia MJ & Guedry FE.(1966): Modification of vestibular responses as a function of rate of rotation about an earth horizontal axis. Acta Otolaryngol. 62, 292-308.

Gibbons PA, Nicolson SC, Betts EK, Rosenberry KR & Jobes DR.(1984): Scopolamine does not prevent post-operative emesis after pediatric surgery. Anaesthesiol. 61, A 435.

Golding JF & Kerguelen M.(1992): A comparison of the nauseogenic potential of low frequency vertical versus horizontal linear oscillation. Aviat. Space Environ. Med. (in press).

Guedry FE, Benson AJ & Moore HJ.(1982): Influence of a visual display and frequency of whole body angular oscillation on the incidence of motion sickness. Aviat. Space Environ. Med. 53, 264-269.

Hargreaves J.(1980): A double-blind placebo controlled study of cinnarizine in the prophylaxis of seasickness. Practitioner 244, 547-50.

Johnson WH & Mayne JW.(1953): Stimulus required to produce motion sickness. Restriction of head movement as a preventive of airsickness - field studies on airborne troops. J. Aviat. Med. 24, 400-411.

Keist BF, Shelley WT, Byers JM & Chinn HI.(1956): Effect of head immobilisation on incidence of airsickness. J. Appl. Physiol. 8, 369-370.

Kohl RL.(1987): Failure of metoclopramide to control emesis or nausea due to stressful angular or linear acceleration. Aviat. Space Environ. Med. 58, 125-31.

Kohl RL, Homick JL, Cintron N & Calkins DS.(1987): Lack of effects of astemizole on vestibular ocular reflex, motion sickness and cognitive performance in man. Aviat. Space Environ. Med. 58, 1171-4.

Kohl RL, Calkins DS & Robinson RE.(1991): Control of nausea and autonomic dysfunction with terfenadine, a peripherally acting antihistamine. Aviat. Space Environ. Med. 62, 392-6.

Lackner JR & Graybiel A.(1986): Head movements in non-terrestrial force environments elicit motion sickness: Implications for the etiology of space motion sickness. Aviat. Space Environ. Med. 57, 443-448.

Lackner JR, Graybiel A & DiZio PA. (1991): Altered sensorimotor control of the body as an aetiological factor in space motion sickness. Aviat. Space Environ. Med. 62, 765-71.

Lawther A & Griffin MJ.(1986): The motion of a ship at sea and the consequent motion sickness among passengers. Ergonomics 29, 535-552.

Lawther A & Griffin MJ.(1988): A survey of the occurrence of motion sickness amongst passengers at sea. Aviat. Space Environ. Med. 59, 399-406.

McCauley ME, Jackson WR, Wylie CD, O'Handlon JF & Mackie RR.(1976): Motion sickness incidence: exploratory studies of habituation, pitch and roll, and the refinement of a mathematical model. Human factors Research Inc. Santa Barbara Research Park Goleta Ca. Technical Report. 1733-2.

Oman CM, Lichtenberg BK, Money KE & McCoy RK.(1986): MIT/Canadian vestibular experiments on the Spacelab-1 mission: 4. Space motion sickness: symptoms, stimuli and predictability. Exp. Brain Res. 64, 316-334.

Pingree BJW & Pethybridge RJ.(1989): A double-blind placebo controlled comparison of hyoscine with early administered cinnarizine in increasing tolerance to a nauseogenic cross-coupled stimulus. Pharmaceut. Med. 4, 29-42.

Schmitt MN & Shaw JE.(1981): Comparison of transdermal and intravenous administration of scopolamine. Clin. Pharmacol. Ther. 29, 282.

Stott JRR, Barnes GR, Wright RJ & Ruddock CJS.(1989): The effect on motion sickness ond oculomotor function of GR38032F, a 5-HT_3 receptor antagonist with anti-emetic properties. Br. J. Clin. Pharmac. 27, 147-57.

Stott JRR.(1990): Adaptation to nauseogenic motion stimuli and its application in the treatment of airsickness. In: Motion and Space Sickness. Ed. Crampton GH. Ch.18, 373-90. Boca Raton: CRC Press.

Tucker GJ, Hand DJ, Godbey AL & Reinhardt RF.(1965): Airsickness in student aviators. Pensacola Fla. Naval School of Aviation Medicine. NSAM-939.

Vogel H, Kohlhaas R & von Baumgarten RJ.(1982): Dependence of motion sickness in automobiles on the direction of linear acceleration. Eur. J. Appl. Physiol. 48, 399-405.

Von Baumbarten RJ, Baldrighi G, Vogel H & Thümler R.(1980): Physiological responses to hyper-and hypo-gravity during rollercoaster flight. Aviat. Space Environ. Med. 51, 145-154.

Von Baumgarten RJ, Thümler R & Vogel H.(1980): Experimentelle Untersuchungen über die Wirksamkeit von Metoclopramid bei Kinetose. Therapiewoche 30, 5974-81.

Wood CD & Graybiel A.(1968): Evaluation of sixteen anti-motion sickness drugs under controlled laboratory conditions. Aerospace Med. 39, 1341-4.

Wood CD.(1990): Pharmacological countermeasures against motion sickness. In: Motion & Space Sickness. Ed. Crampton GH, Ch.16, 343-51. Boca Raton: CRC Press.

Mechanisms and Control of Emesis. Eds A.L. Bianchi, L. Grélot, A.D. Miller, G.L. King. Colloque INSERM/
John Libbey Eurotext Ltd. © 1992, Vol. 223, pp. 213-214

The effect on adaptive rate of varying the malaise level to be attained on repeated exposures to a nauseogenic cross-coupled motion challenge

J.F. Golding and J.R.R. Stott

Royal Air Force Institute of Aviation Medicine, Farnborough, Hants, GU14 6SZ, UK

INTRODUCTION. Desensitisation treatment for airsickness at the RAF Institute Aviation Medicine (IAM) involves a ground-phase of treatment followed by an airborne-phase (Bagshaw and Stott, 1985; Stott, 1991). In the ground-phase tolerance is developed to cross-coupled motion and to low frequency vertical oscillation. This study focuses on the cross-coupled component of the ground-phase desensitisation programme. It is known that incremental exposure to motion provides faster rates of adaptation than abrupt exposure (Graybiel et al, 1969; Hu et al, 1991). However, a complementary strategy to grading the intensity of the stimuli (as used at present in the IAM programme) is to vary the malaise endpoint to be achieved for any particular motion sickness desensitisation session. The aim of the present study was to determine whether the adaptive rate over sessions would be affected by varying the malaise level to be achieved, from moderate nausea, to mild symptoms without nausea.

METHOD. A baseline week of standard clinical vestibular and motion challenge assessments was followed by 20 motion challenges at two per day over a further two week period at the start of the desensitisation programme. Motion was stopped at a malaise level of mild symptoms during one week and at moderate nausea during the other week, on a cross-over design randomised between subjects. The last challenge of each week was to a level of moderate nausea for all subjects and served as a probe stimulus. Subjects were seated in the centre of an enclosed box which was spun around the subject's vertical axis. A staircase profile of rotational velocity was employed that incremented from 2 to 90 deg s^{-1} in steps of 2 deg s^{-1} every half minute. Subjects performed head movements of approximately 45 deg to the left, right, back and forward in a random order determined by tape-recorded instructions. Eight head movements were completed every 30 s, at the end of which subjects rated their malaise level on a 1-4 sickness scale (1 = O.K.; 2 = mild symptoms, no nausea; 3 = mild nausea with or without other symptoms; 4 = moderate nausea with or without other symptoms). The motion challenge was stopped at sickness ratings of either 2 or 4 which were taken as the experimenter-determined endpoints. Forehead skin conductance was recorded as an additional indicator of motion sickness (Golding, 1992).

RESULTS. The results are reported for the ten aircrew seen to date. Good reliability of the motion challenge was indicated by significant correlations (r= 0.7 to 0.9) between baseline measures, whether scored in terms of number of sets, or motion dose, to sickness rating levels 2,3 or 4. Correlations between baseline and sessions in the subsequent two weeks, decreased as a function of time elapsed between each of the measures under scrutiny. ANOVA for repeated measures was performed on the baseline assessment and the subsequent desensitisation sessions. Differences between the two order groups were not significant. Number of trials to reach various malaise levels (rating=2,3, or 4) increased significantly over sessions but the order group x time (sessions) interaction failed significance. In a minority of subjects the usual linkage between electrodermal activity and malaise ratings broke down in later sessions as desensitisation progressed, suggesting that the constellation of symptoms forming motion sickness either adapt at varying rates or 'uncouple' from each other.

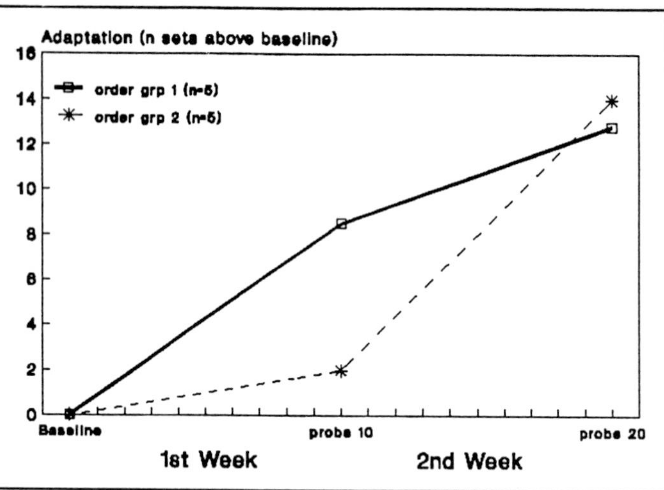

Mean adaptation shown for 'probe' motion challenges to endpoint of moderate nausea in the last session of each week. Order group 1: desensitisation sessions to moderate nausea in the 1st week and to mild symptoms in 2nd week; Order group 2: vice-versa.

CONCLUSIONS. Significant habituation to the cross-coupled challenge occurred over successive sessions, reflecting the desensitisation process. There was a tendency in the means suggesting that the attainment of higher malaise levels during desensitisation sessions promoted faster rates of habituation but effects failed statistical significance. This may have been due to the relatively small n per treatment order group analysed to date, combined with large individual variability. The effects of varying malaise level may become more apparent when a target n=16 is reached.

REFERENCES.

Bagshaw M, Stott JRR. (1985) The desensitisation of chronically motion sick aircrew in the Royal Air Force. Aviat. Space Environ. Med., 56: 144-51.

Golding JF. (1992) Phasic skin conductance activity and motion sickness. Aviat. Space Environ. Med., 63: 165-71.

Graybiel A, Deane FR, Colehour JK. (1969) Prevention of overt motion sickness by incremental exposure to otherwise highly stressful Coriolis accelerations. Aerospace Medicine, 40: 142-8.

Hu S, Stern RM, Koch KL. (1991) Effects of pre-exposures to a rotating optokinetic drum on adaptation to motion sickness. Aviat. Space Environ. Med., 62: 53-6.

Stott JRR. (1991) Prevention and treatment of motion sickness: non-pharmacological therapy. In Motion sickness: significance in aerospace operations and prophylaxis. AGARD-LS-175, ed A.J. Benson, pp. 9-1 to 9-9, Neuilly sur Seine: Advisory Group for Aerospace Research and Development.

IV. New antiemetic drugs

IV. Nouveaux agents anti-émétiques

Mechanisms and Control of Emesis. Eds A.L. Bianchi, L. Grélot, A.D. Miller, G.L. King. Colloque INSERM/ John Libbey Eurotext Ltd. © 1992, Vol. 223, pp. 217-226

Possible potentiation of the emetic response to oral S(-) zacopride by various receptor ligands in the ferret

Gregory L. King and John K. Weatherspoon

Department of Physiology, Armed Forced Radiobiology Research Institute, Bethesda, Maryland, 20889-5145, USA

SUMMARY

Three classes of receptor ligands (the D2 receptor agonist (+) apomorphine, the cholinergic-nicotinic receptor agonists (-) nicotine and (+)-nicotine-(+)-di-p-toluoyltartrate ((+)-NDPT), and the nonspecific opioid receptor antagonist (-) naloxone) were evaluated for their ability to potentiate the emetic response to two different doses (0.003 and 0.30 mg/kg) of p.o. S(-) zacopride. These S(-) zacopride doses evoked responses from 4/6 and 7/10 ferrets, respectively. Prior treatment (s.c.) with nonemetic doses (n = 2-4) of (+) apomorphine (0.01 mg/kg), (-) nicotine (0.30 mg/kg), or (-) naloxone (3.0 mg/kg) appeared to potentiate the emetic response to the higher dose of S(-) zacopride by initiating an earlier onset ($P < 0.05$) of the response. (-) Naloxone also increased the overall duration of the emetic episodes to the higher dose of S(-) zacopride. These preliminary results suggest that ligands acting at D2, nicotinic, and opioid receptors can enhance the emetic response to S(-) zacopride. However, it is unclear from these studies whether that enhancement is mediated centrally or peripherally.

Potentialisation possible de la réponse émétique à la prise orale de S(-) Zacopride par divers ligands chez le furet.

Résumé: *Trois classes de ligands (l'apomorphine: agoniste (±) des récepteurs D2, la nicotine (-) et le (+) nicotine-di-p-toluoyltartrate ((+) -NDPT): agonistes des récepteurs cholinergiques-nicotiniques, et le (-) naloxone: antagoniste non-spécifique des récepteurs opioides) ont été évaluées pour leur capacité à potentialiser la réponse émétique à 2 doses différentes (0,003 et 0,30 mg/Kg) de S(-) zacopride per os. Ces doses de S(-) zacopride ont induit des réponses chez respectivement 4/6 et 7/10 furets. Le traitement initial (s.c.) avec des doses non émétiques (n = 2-4) de (±) apomorphine (0,01 mg/Kg), de (-) nicotine (0,30 mg/Kg), ou de (-) naloxone (3,0 mg/Kg) est apparu comme potentialisant la réponse émétique à la plus forte dose de S(-) zacopride en provoquant un déclenchement plus précoce (P < 0,05) de la réponse. (-) Naloxone a aussi augmenté la durée totale des épisodes émétiques à la plus forte dose de S(-) zacopride. Ces résultats préliminaires suggèrent que les ligands agissant au niveau des récepteurs D2, nicotiniques et opioides peuvent augmenter la réponse émétique au (-) S zacopride. Cependant, ces études ne peuvent préciser si le niveau d'action de cette augmentation est central ou périphérique.*

INTRODUCTION

The substituted benzamide zacopride (4-amino-N-[1-azabicyclo(2.2.2)oct-3-yl]-5-chloro-2-methoxybenzamide[E])-2-buteniodiate) is a serotonin (5-hydroxytryptamine; 5-HT) subtype-three ($5\text{-}HT_3$) receptor antagonist and antiemetic that also evokes emesis at therapeutic (*i.e.*, antiemetic) doses in the ferret (King, 1990b; Sancilio **et al.**, 1990). The emetic response to zacopride occurs regardless of whether zacopride is given i.v., i.p., i.m., or p.o., and also predominantly to the S(-) but not the R(+) enantiomer (King, 1990b; King & Landauer, 1990; Sancilio **et al.**, 1990, 1991; Middlefell & Price, 1991; Bhandari & Andrews, 1991). Although emesis to p.o. administration is abolished by prior abdominal vagotomy (King, 1990b), the response after all administration routes is mitigated by several classes of receptor ligands (King, 1990b; Sancilio **et al.**, 1990, 1991; Middlefell & Price, 1991; Bhandari & Andrews, 1991).

The previous studies used prior treatment with specific receptor ligands to *palliate* the emetic response. In contrast, the present study was designed to determine whether prior treatment with specific receptor ligands could *potentiate* the emetic response to p.o. S(-) zacopride. Results from such studies should further our understanding about the pharmacology of the emetic response to S(-) zacopride and perhaps emesis in general.

For our studies, three individual classes of receptor ligands were chosen. The first two classes, receptor agonists, were chosen based on our previous findings that either the dopaminergic subtype-two (D_2) receptor antagonist domperidone or the cholinergic-muscarinic receptor antagonist and racemate glycopyrrolate ameliorates the emetic response to p.o. S(-) zacopride (King, 1990b). Thus one compound selected was the racemic mixture of the D_2 receptor agonist ($\pm$) apomorphine. Two other compounds selected were the stereoisomers of the cholinergic-nicotinic receptor agonists, (-) nicotine and (+)-nicotine-(+)-di-p-toluoyltartrate ((+)-NDPT). These latter compounds were chosen because quaternary ammonium analogs of atropine (*e.g.*, glycopyrrolate; King, 1990b) exhibit nicotinic receptor antagonist properties (Brown, 1990). The third class of ligand chosen to challenge p.o. S(-) zacopride was the nonspecific opioid-receptor antagonist (-) naloxone, which has been previously shown to potentiate emesis to other emetic agents (Scherkl **et al.**, 1990; Barnes **et al.**, 1991).

METHODS

Subjects: All subjects were male, castrated, and descented ferrets (Fitch) from Marshall Farms (North Rose, NY). Ferrets were housed in the AAALAC-accredited animal facility at AFRRI and provided with water and ferret chow *ad libitum*.

Procedure: Five to 10 animals were injected s.c. with a challenging agent (($\pm$) apomorphine [0.01 mg/kg], (-) nicotine tartrate [0.30

mg/kg], (+)-NDPT [0.30 mg/kg], or (-) naloxone [0.30 or 3.0 mg/kg] before administering p.o. S(-) zacopride (0.003 or 0.30 mg/kg]. (±) Apomorphine and (-) naloxone were given 20 min before S(-) zacopride; (-) nicotine and (+)-NDPT, 5 min before. Following administration of p.o. S(-) zacopride, the ferrets were placed in a large, well-ventilated Plexiglas® box, and behaviors were observed and recorded on a personal computer for 1-1.5 hr, as previously described (King & Landauer, 1990). The doses of challenging agents were chosen from preliminary results (2-4 animals) showing that these doses, when tested alone, did not evoke retching or emesis over a 45-60 min observation period. A single group of control animals was given p.o. 0.003 (n = 6) or 0.30 mg/kg (n = 10) S(-) zacopride and used to compare their responses with those groups receiving a drug challenge. Each ferret was tested only once with p.o. S(-) zacopride because we had previously observed that ferrets quickly develop an aversion after a single (emetic) dose. That is, after given an emetic dose of zacopride, the animals struggled to avoid subsequent administration at later times. In addition, each ferret was given a challenging agent only once to avoid tachyphylaxis to that agent.

Drugs: (±) Apomorphine and (-) naloxone were purchased from Sigma (St. Louis, MO), and (-) nicotine and (+)-NDPT from RBI (Natick, MA). All compounds were made fresh in NaCl as vehicle and given in a final volume of less than 1 ml. S(-) zacopride (Wyeth-Ayerst, Princeton, NJ) was made fresh in 5% dextrose/water as vehicle and given in 1-3 ml volume.

Data Analysis: The latencies and durations of recorded behaviors of the various groups were compared and analyzed with nonparametric tests (Kruskall-Wallis Rank Sum test and Dunn's test), and the incidence and total number of behavioral events with parametric tests (ANOVA and Newman-Keul's multiple range test). When only two groups were compared, the Student's t-test or Mann-Whitney test was used, as appropriate. Comparison of the percentages of responding animals was made by analysis of proportions by a contingency table. Significance was accepted at $P < 0.05$.

RESULTS

Preliminary testing for emesis in response to the doses of challenging agents showed that, for these agents alone, the following proportion of animals showed an emetic response. For (±) apomorphine, 0/3 animals responded to a 0.01 mg/kg dose, whereas 3/4 retched or vomited to a 0.05 mg/kg dose. For (-) nicotine, 0/3 and 0/4 responded to respective doses of 0.10 and 0.30 mg/kg. In response to (+)-NDPT, 0/3 responded to a dose of 0.30 mg/kg. For (-) naloxone, 0/2 and 0/4 responded to respective doses of 0.30 and 3.0 mg/kg.

Table 1 shows that a nonemetic (0.01 mg/kg) dose of (±) apomorphine appeared to potentiate the emesis to a high dose (0.30 mg/kg) of p.o. S(-) zacopride. This potentiation by (±) apomorphine of the high-dose response to S(-) zacopride was expressed as an earlier onset of the response when compared with controls. (±) Apomorphine also seemed to reduce the latency of onset for the response to the lower zacopride dose but this was not significant.

Table 1. (±) APOMORPHINE[a] PRETREATMENT EFFECTS ON EMETIC RESPONSE TO P.O. S(-) ZACOPRIDE

Drug dose (mg/kg)	Responders	Latency: 1st retch (min)[b]	Episode duration (min)	Number of retches
0.003 S(-) Zaco	4/6	24.4 ± 6.3	7.2 ± 3.0	36.2 ± 7.7
+ 0.01 Apo	6/6	11.7 ± 4.2	10.6 ± 5.0	48.0 ± 15.8
0.30 S(-) Zaco	7/10	7.6 ± 1.9[c]	4.2 ± 1.1	29.2 ± 6.9
+ 0.01 Apo	5/5	1.0 ± 0.4[c]	2.8 ± 1.0	24.0 ± 7.5

[a]Given s.c. 20 min before S(-) zacopride. [b]All values are mean ± SEM. [c]$P < 0.05$ between groups.

Table 2 shows that only the greater dose of (-) nicotine (0.30 mg/kg) appeared to potentiate the emetic response to the high dose of p.o. S(-) zacopride. Again this potentiation was expressed as an earlier onset of the response. Note, however, that (-) nicotine and (+)-NDPT seemed to both reduce the latency to the first retch and increase the episode duration of the response to the lower dose of S(-) zacopride.

As seen in Table 3, the greater dose (3.0 mg/kg) of (-) naloxone seemed to clearly potentiate the emesis to the greater dose of p.o. S(-) zacopride. In contrast to pretreatment with either (±) apomorphine or the nicotinic receptor agonists (-) nicotine, however, not only did the responses to the higher dose of S(-) zacopride occur with a shorter latency, but the overall duration of the episodes was greater. In addition, although not significant, (-) naloxone appeared to evoke a greater number of retching events.

Table 2. (-) NICOTINE[a] OR (+)-NDPT[a] PRETREATMENT EFFECTS ON EMETIC RESPONSE TO P.O. S(-) ZACOPRIDE

Drug dose (mg/kg)	Responders	Latency: 1st retch (min)[b]	Episode duration (min)	Number of retches
0.003 S(-) Zaco	4/6	24.4 ± 6.3	7.2 ± 3.0	36.2 ± 7.7
+ 0.30 (-) Nico	4/6	18.7 ± 5.6	12.8 ± 4.4	35.7 ± 8.9
+ 0.30 (+)-NDPT	6/6	10.5 ± 2.3	21.6 ± 6.9	49.0 ± 7.6
0.30 S(-) Zaco	7/10	7.6 ± 1.9[c]	4.2 ± 1.1	29.2 ± 6.9
+ 0.30 (-) Nico	7/8	0.8 ± 0.1[c]	3.5 ± 0.7	30.4 ± 13.1
+ 0.30 (+)-NDPT	7/8	2.6 ± 1.7	4.4 ± 1.8	31.0 ± 8.3

[a]Given s.c. 5 min before S(-) zacopride. [b]All values are mean ± SEM. [c]$P < 0.05$ between groups.

Table 3. (-) NALOXONE[a] PRETREATMENT EFFECTS ON EMETIC RESPONSE TO P.O. S(-) ZACOPRIDE

Drug dose (mg/kg)	Responders	Latency: 1st retch (min)[b]	Episode duration (min)	Number of Retches
0.003 S(-) Zaco	4/6	24.4 ± 6.3	7.2 ± 3.0	36.2 ± 7.7
+ 0.3 Nal	2/6	22.6 ± 8.6	0.8 ± 0.3	20.5 ± 3.5
+ 3.0 "	6/6	28.2 ± 8.3	11.6 ± 8.1	45.3 ± 11.1
0.30 S(-) Zaco	7/10	7.6 ± 1.9[c]	4.2 ± 1.1	29.2 ± 6.9
+ 0.3 Nal	8/10	3.6 ± 2.2	3.0 ± 1.3[d]	37.1 ± 15.1
+ 3.0 "	9/10	0.8 ± 0.3[c]	21.1 ± 7.2[d]	61.7 ± 19.2

[a]Given s.c. 20 min before S(-) zacopride. [b]All values are mean ± SEM. [c,d]$P < 0.05$ between groups.

DISCUSSION

The principal finding of these preliminary studies was that three different classes of receptor ligands appeared to potentiate the emetic response to a moderately high dose of S(-) zacopride. This potentiation was expressed primarily as a significant reduction in the latency to the first retching response. (-) Naloxone, however, also significantly increased the episode duration. Furthermore, in some cases, the latencies and durations to the lower dose of S(-) zacopride appeared to also be modified by these compounds. The reduced latencies to emesis reported here do not conclusively demonstrate an effect of these compounds. However, surgical procedures such as vagotomies ameliorate emetic responses by altering the latencies (Andrews **et al.**, 1990; King and Landauer, 1990). This suggests that we have perturbed the system by pharmacological methods, but that further studies are warranted that use other doses of these compounds, as well as S(-) zacopride.

Two of the classes of ligands used here are receptor agonists and none bind at the 5-HT_3 receptor. These data thus suggest that activation of these receptor sites can modulate the emetic response to p.o. S(-) zacopride. The D_2 receptor agonist (±) apomorphine appeared to potentiate the emetic response, which further corroborates an earlier finding by this laboratory (King, 1990b) that a D_2 receptor antagonist ameliorates the emetic response. Our earlier finding of involvement of a cholinergic receptor in the emetic response was partially corroborated by the apparent potentiation of the emetic response with the nicotinic receptor agonist (-) nicotine. Although quaternary atropine derivatives such as glycopyrrolate also act at the nicotinic receptor (Brown, 1990), Alaranta **et al.** (1990) found that the ganglionic-blocking property of glycopyrrolate was 16x less potent than hexamethonium, one half as potent as tetraethylammonium, and 2x as potent as decamethonium. These latter data suggest that our previous results with glycopyrrolate are most likely due to muscarinic receptor antagonism. Finally, our finding that the opioid receptor antagonist (-) naloxone also potentiated the emetic response further corroborates the general role of the opioids in emetic events

Table 4. RECEPTOR LIGANDS THAT ALTER EMETIC RESPONSE TO S(-) OR RS($\pm$) ZACOPRIDE

Receptor ligand	Response to challenge		
	No effect	Attenuate	Potentiate
Serotonergic			
$5\text{-}HT_{1P}$			
antagonist	N-acetyl-5-HTP-DP[a*]	-	-
$5\text{-}HT_3$			
agonist	-	$2\text{-}CH_3\text{-}5HT$[b**]	-
antagonist	Granisetron[c]	Granisetron[b]	-
	R(+) Zacopride[d]	R(+) Zacopride[e,f]	-
	ICS 205-930[c]	Ondansetron[e]	-
$5\text{-}HT_4$			
agonist	-	-	-
antagonist	-	ICS 205-930[a,c]	-
	-	S(-) Zacopride[d,e,f]	-
Dopaminergic			
D_2			
agonist	-	-	($\pm$) Apomorphine?
antagonist	-	Domperidone[b]	-
	-	Haloperidol[a]	-
	-	Prochlorperazine[a]	-
Cholinergic			
Muscarinic			
antagonist	Atropine[e]	Glycopyrrolate[b]	-
Nicotinic			
agonist	(+)-NDTP?[***]	-	-
	-	-	(-) Nicotine?
Opioid			
antagonist			
δ, k, μ, σ	-	-	(-) Naloxone?

*N-acetyl-5-hydroxytryptophyl-5-tryptophan amide. **2-methyl-serotonin. ***(+)-nicotine-(+)-di-p-toluoyltartrate.
[a]Sancilio, **et al.**, 1990; [b]King, 1990; [c]Bhandari and Andrews, 1991; [d]King, in preparation; [e]Middlefell and Price, 1991; [f]Sancilio, **et al.**, 1991.

(Costello & Borison, 1977). These latter results also suggest that more specific opioid receptor antagonists should be evaluated for their ability to modulate the emesis to p.o. S(-) zacopride.

From the present results it is unclear whether these compounds acted centrally or peripherally to potentiate the emesis to p.o. S(-) zacopride. Although we were careful to give nonemetic pretreatment doses of these agents, all three (apomorphine, nicotine, and naloxone) can evoke emesis when given either peripherally at higher doses or centrally (Kamerling **et al**, 1982; Spealman, 1983; Beleslin & Krstic, 1987; Gupta **et al.**, 1989; Jovanivic-Micic **et al.**, 1989; Torii **et al.**, 1991; see review, King, 1990a). Our previous work (King, 1990b) used receptor antagonists that did not cross the blood-brain barrier, but the compounds used in the experiments reported here do not share that property. For example, within 5-10 min after injection, the brain concentrations of both (-) nicotine and (-) naloxone considerably exceed those of the serum (Applegren **et al.**, 1962; Tsujimoto **et al.**, 1975; Tepper **et al.**, 1979; Berkowitz **et al.**, 1975; Ngai **et al.**, 1976). Even after s.c. administration, higher brain concentrations are seen for both (-) nicotine and (+)-NDPT (Martin **et al.**, 1983). Thus the site of potentiating action of these three compounds could be central in nature. Such central action by these compounds could be at the *area postrema* (chemoreceptor trigger zone), as ablations of this region can abolish the emesis to centrally administered apomorphine and nicotine, but not (-) naloxone (see King, 1990a). Other behavioral responses to nicotine imply a generalized central excitation that may be possible to detect from measures of locomotor activity. We have not yet analyzed the vertical locomotor activity of the ferrets in this study. Nevertheless, this behavioral measure has detected sedative-like effects of RS(±) and S(-) zacopride (*e.g.*, reduced vertical locomotor activity) (King & Landauer, 1990; King, in preparation).

(±) Apomorphine, (-) nicotine, and (+)-NDPT could be acting peripherally at the *area postrema* to potentiate the emetic response to p.o. S(-) zacopride. Depending on the species (see King, 1990a), *area postrema* ablations will fully or partially abolish the emetic response to peripherally administered apomorphine and nicotine. (Such studies have not been done with (-) naloxone). A predominantly peripheral action of apomorphine is supported by the work of Burkman **et al.** (1974) who found that, after an i.v. bolus of apomorphine, its plasma content remained approximately 23x greater than that of the brain for up to 50 min.

Dopaminergic, nicotinic-cholinergic, and opioid receptor binding sites are also found within the ganglia of the enteric nervous system (Costa **et al.**, 1987). Thus the three compounds could also be acting at or near the vagal afferent endings that respond to the actions of p.o. S(-) zacopride (King, 1990b). Applegren **et al.** (1962) found both immediate nicotine binding in the gastric mucosa after an i.v. bolus and preliminary evidence for binding at sympathetic ganglionic sites. With respect to nicotine, however, its immediate binding after a bolus injection is greater in the adrenal cortex than in the brain (Tsujimoto **et al.**, 1975; Tepper **et al.**, 1979). This suggests the possibility that nicotine may release catecholamines from the adrenal cortex, which in turn could modulate the emesis to S(-) zacopride.

Table 4 summarizes those receptor ligands that have been shown to modify the emetic response to S(-) or RS(±) zacopride. That several receptor agonists or antagonists can affect the response suggests that there are multiple receptor sites that can modulate the response. In those studies in which atropine or a quaternary derivative were used, the results are contradictory. It also remains unclear as to which 5-HT receptor the S(-) enantiomer binds to elicit the emetic response. For example, it has been suggested that the emetic response could be mediated by binding at either the 5-HT_3 or 5-HT_4 receptor. This question is further confounded by a lack of agreement as to whether the reported pharmacological (*i.e.*, 5-HT_{1P} and 5-HT_4 receptor antagonist) properties of N-acetyl-5-HTP-DP are similar (Wade **et al.**,

1991; Andrade & Chaput, 1991). As further example, the 5-HT_3 receptor antagonist Granisetron mitigated zacopride-induced emesis during the first 30 min of a 1 hr observation period (King, 1990a), but had no effect when the observation period was extended to 2 hr (Bhandari & Andrews, 1991). Likewise, some, but not others, have found that the R(+) enantiomer of zacopride mitigated the emetic response.

Some of the results obtained from these *in vivo* studies also raise questions about the appropriate experimental design for such studies. For example, the reported antiemetic properties of the R(+) enantiomer for S(-) zacopride would confound those studies in which the RS($\pm$) racemate is used as the emetic stimulus. Likewise, the antiemetic properties of the S(-) enantiomer for its own emetic response would confound those studies in which a cumulative dosing regimen is used to test for its emetic properties. Because the experimental designs and the routes of administration used have varied considerably among all these studies, resolving the question at which receptor the S(-) enantiomer is acting to evoke the emetic response will require further study.

In summary, we have presented preliminary data suggesting that three different classes of receptor ligands (a D_2 receptor agonist, nicotinic receptor agonists, and an opioid receptor antagonist) appeared to potentiate the emetic response to p.o. S(-) zacopride. Some of these results confirm our previous findings showing that activation of non-5-HT_3 receptor sites can modulate the emetic response to p.o. S(-) zacopride. This provides further insight into the complex interactions of neurotransmitters in evoking emesis.

REFERENCES

Alaranta, S., Kling, E., Patsi, T., & Sjostrand, N.O. (1990): Inhibition of nicotine-induced relaxation of the bovine retractor penis muscle by compounds known to have ganglion-blocking properties. *Br. J. Pharmacol.* 101, 472-476.

Andrade, R., & Chaput, Y. (1991): 5-Hydroxytryptamine$_4$-like receptors mediate the slow excitatory response to serotonin in the rat hippocampus. *J. Pharmacol. Exp. Ther.* 257, 930-937.

Andrews, P.R.L., Davis, C.J., Bingham, S., Davidson, H.I.M., Hawthorn, J., & Maskell, L. (1990): The abdominal visceral innervation and the emetic reflex: Pathways, pharmacology, and plasticity. *Can. J. Physiol. Pharmacol.* 68, 325-345.

Applegren, L.-E., Hansson, E., & Schmiterlow, C.G. (1962): The accumulation and metabolism of C^{14}-labelled nicotine in the brain of mice and cats. *Acta Physiol. Scand.* 56, 249-257.

Barnes, N.M., Bunce, K.T., Naylor, R.J., & Rudd, J.A. (1991): The actions of fentanyl to inhibit drug-induced emesis. *Neuropharmacology*, 30, 1073-1083.

Beleslin, D.B. & Krstic, S.K. (1987): Further studies on nicotine-induced emesis: nicotinic mediation in area postrema. *Physiol. Behav.* 39, 681-686.

Berkowitz, B.A., Ngai, S.H., Hempstead, J., & Spector, S. (1975): Disposition of naloxone: Use of a new radioimmunoassay. *J. Pharmacol. Exp. Ther.* 195, 499-504.

Bhandari, P., & Andrews, P.L.R. (1991): Preliminary evidence for

the involvement of the putative 5-HT_4 receptor in zacopride- and copper sulphate-induced vomiting in the ferret. *Eur. J. Pharmacol.* 204, 273-280.
Brown, J.H. (1990): Atropine, scopolamine, and related antimuscarinic drugs. In *The Pharmacological Basis of Therapeutics*, ed. A.G. Gilman, T.W. Rall, A.S. Nies & P. Taylor, pp. 150-165. New York: Pergamon Press.
Burkman, A.M., Notari, R.E., & Van Tyle, W.K. (1974): Structural effects in drug distribution: Comparative pharmacokinetics of apomorphine analogues. *J. Pharm. Pharmac.* 26, 493-507.
Costa, M., Furness, J.B., & Llewellyn-Smith, I.J. (1987): Histochemistry of the enteric nervous system. In *Physiology of the Gastrointestinal Tract*, ed. L.R. Johnson, pp. 1-40. New York: Raven Press.
Costello, D.J., & Borison, H.L. (1977): Naloxone antagonizes narcotic self-blockade of emesis in the cat. *J. Pharmacol. Exp. Ther.* 203, 222-230.
Gupta, Y.K., Bhandari, P., Chugh, A., Seth, S.D., Dixit, K.S., & Bhargava, K.P. (1989): Role of endogenous opioids and histamine in morphine induced emesis. *Indian J. Exp. Biol.* 27, 52-54.
Jovanivic-Micic, D., Strbac, M., Krstic, S.K., Japundzic, N., Samardzic, R., & Beleslin, D.B. (1989): Ablation of the area postrema and emesis. *Metab. Brain Dis.* 4, 55-60.
Kamerling, S.G., Wettstein, J.G., Sloan, J.W., Su, T.P., & Martin, W.R. (1982): Interaction between nicotine and endogenous opioid mechanisms in the unanesthetized dog. *Pharmacol. Biochem. Behav.* 17, 733-740.
King, G.L.: The antiemetic and other properties of R(+)-zacopride in the ferret. (in preparation).
King, G.L. (1990a): Animals models in the study of vomiting. *Can. J. Physiol. Pharmacol.* 68, 260-268.
King, G.L. (1990b): Emesis and defecations induced by the 5-hydroxytryptamine (5-HT_3) receptor antagonist zacopride in the ferret. *J. Pharmacol. Exp. Ther.* 253, 1034-1041.
King, G.L., & Landauer, M.R. (1990): Effects of zacopride and BMY25801 (batanopride) on radiation-induced emesis and locomotor behavior in the ferret. *J. Pharmacol. Exp. Ther.* 253, 1026-1033.
Martin, B.R., Tripathi, H.L., Aceto, M.D., & May, E.L. (1983): Relationship of the biodisposition of the stereoisomers of nicotine in the central nervous system to their pharmacological actions. *J. Pharmacol. Exp. Ther.* 226, 157-163.
Middlefell, V.C., & Price, T.L. (1991): 5-HT_3 receptor agonism may be responsible for the emetic effects of zacopride in the ferret. *Br. J. Pharmacol.* 103, 1011-1012.
Ngai, S.H., Berkowitz, B.A., & Yang, J.C. (1976): Pharmacokinetics of naloxone in rats and man. *Anesthesiology* 44, 398-401.
Sancilio, L.F., Pinkus, L.M., Jackson, C.B., & Munson, H.R., Jr. (1990): Emetic activity of zacopride in ferrets and its antagonism by pharmacological agents. *Eur. J. Pharmacol.* 181, 303-306.
Sancilio, L.F., Pinkus, L.M., Jackson, C.B., & Munson, Jr., H.R. (1991): Studies on the emetic and antiemetic properties of zacopride and its enantiomers. *Eur. J. Pharmacol.* 192, 365-369.
Scherkl, R., Hashem, A., & Frey, H.H. (1990); Apomorphine-induced emesis in the dog -- routes of administration, efficacy and

synergism by naloxone. *J. Vet. Pharmacol. Ther.* 13, 154-158.
Spealman, R.D. (1983): Maintenance of behavior by postponement of scheduled injections of nicotine in squirrel monkeys. *J. Pharmacol. Exp. Ther.* 227, 154-159.
Tepper, J.M., Wilson, J.R., & Schlesinger, K. (1979): Relations between nicotine-induced convulsive behavior and blood and brain levels of nicotine as a function of sex and age in two inbred strains of mice. *Pharmacol. Biochem. Behav.* 10, 349-353.
Torii, Y., Saito, H., & Matsuki, N. (1991): Selective blockade of cytotoxic drug-induced emesis by 5-HT_3 receptor antagonists in *Suncus murinus. Jpn. J. Pharmacol.* 55, 107-113.
Tsujimoto, A., Nakashima, T., Tanino, S., Dohi, T., & Kurogochi, Y. (1975): Tissue distribution of [^{3}H]nicotine in dogs and rhesus monkeys. *Toxicol. Appl. Pharmacol.* 32, 21-31.
Wade, P.R., Mawe, G.M., Branchek, T.A., & Gershon, M.D. (1991): Use of stereoisomers of zacopride to analyze actions of 5-hydroxytryptamine on enteric neurons. *Am. J. Physiol.* 260, G80-G90.

ACKNOWLEDGMENTS

This research was supported by the Armed Forces Radiobiology Research Institute, Defense Nuclear Agency, under work unit 00107. The authors wish to thank Mr. T. Lively for writing the software used to record the behavioral events. This research was conducted according to the principles described in the Guide for the Care and Use of Laboratory Animals prepared by the Institute of Laboratory Animal Research, National Research Council.

Mechanisms and Control of Emesis. Eds A.L. Bianchi, L. Grélot, A.D. Miller, G.L. King. Colloque INSERM/ John Libbey Eurotext Ltd. © 1992, Vol. 223, pp. 227-233

Pharmacokinetic properties in experimental animals and volunteers of DAU 6215, a 5-HT$_3$ receptor antagonist indicated for emesis induced by anticancer therapy

Pierino Schiantarelli, Maria G. Marini *, Aldo Vidi, Giuliano Bensi *, Carlo A. Rizzi and Arturo Donetti

*Research and Development Division and * Medical Division of Boehringer Ingelheim Italia, Via Serio 15, 20139 Milano, Italy*

SUMMARY

Some pharmacokinetic properties of DAU 6215, a novel 5-HT3 receptor antagonist, have been assessed in experimental animals (rats, dogs and monkeys) and in healthy volunteers. Animal studies, performed using both 14C-radiolabelled and cold DAU 6215, showed dose-dependency, excellent oral absorption, rather short terminal half-life (ranging from 1 to 2.7 h in the various experimental conditions), major metabolic clearance and important, species-dependent, first-pass metabolism. In addition, DAU 6215 was shown to be able to efficiently cross the blood-brain barrier in dogs. The results in volunteers, obtained during phase I clinical studies after intravenous and oral administration, showed dose- linearity, relatively long elimination half-life (ranging from 8.7 h to 14.4 h), minor metabolic clearance and very high absolute bioavailability. The pharmacokinetic profile emerging from these preliminary clinical trials represents a favourable feature for the clinical potential of the drug in emesis associated with cancer chemotherapy and radiotherapy.

Propriétés pharmacocinétiques étudiées chez l'animal expérimental et des volontaires du DAU 6215, un antagoniste 5-HT3 indiqué pour le vomissement induit par la thérapie anticancéreuse.

Résumé: *Certaines propriétés pharmacocinétiques du DAU 6215, un nouvel antagoniste des récepteurs 5-HT3, ont été évaluées chez l'animal expérimental (rats, chiens et singes) et chez*

des volontaires sains. Les études animales, réalisées à la fois au moyen de DAU 6215 marqué au carbone 14 et de DAU 6215 "froid", ont montré une dose dépendance, une excellente absorption orale, une demie vie assez courte (s'échelonnant de 1 à 2,7 h. dans les diverses conditions expérimentales), une épuration métabolique majeure et une importante dépendance interspécifique du métabolisme primaire. De plus, nous avons montré que le DAU 6215 est capable de traverser efficacement la barrière hémato-encéphalique chez le chien. Les résultats obtenus chez des volontaires en études cliniques de phase I après administrations intraveineuse et orale, ont montré une relation dose-réponse linéaire, une demie vie d'élimination relativement longue (s'échelonnant de 8,7 à 14,4 h.), une faible épuration métabolique et une très haute bio-disponibilité absolue. Le profil pharmacocinétique émergeant de ces essais cliniques préliminaires représente un facteur favorable pour le potentiel clinique de cette drogue dans le traitement des nausées et vomissements associés aux chimiothérapies et radiothérapies anticancéreuses

INTRODUCTION

Emesis induced by anticancer therapy is a clinically relevant side effect mediated by the activation of serotonin 5-HT_3 receptors. Antagonists at these receptors, like ondansetron and granisetron, have proved to be effective in controlling nausea and vomiting caused by oncolytic agents both in experimental animals and in patients (Milne and Heel 1991; Plosker ang Goa, 1991).

DAU 6215 (N-(endo-8-methyl-8-azabicyclo[3.2.1]oct-3-yl)-2,3-dihydro-2-oxo-1H-benzimidazol-1-carboxamide HCl) is a potent and selective 5-HT_3 receptor antagonist belonging to the chemical class of the azabicycloalkyl benzimidazolones (Turconi ***et al.***, 1990). Its pharmacological profile has been previously reported (Turconi ***et al.***, 1991). DAU 6215 exhibited substantially similar affinity as ondansetron and tropisetron for 5-HT_3 receptors, both in receptor binding (rat cerebral cortex, pK_i = 8.42) and in functional "in vitro" bioassays (antagonism of 5HT-induced contractions in guinea-pig ileum, pA_2 = 7.50; antagonism of 5-HT-induced tachycardia in rabbit heart, pA_2 = 10.45). Like the other 5-HT_3 receptor antagonists, DAU 6215 antagonized (ID_{50} = 0.3 μg/kg i.v.) the transient bradycardia and hypotension (the Bezold-Jarisch reflex) induced by stimulation of the 5-HT_3 receptors on afferent nerve terminals of rat heart.

The preclinical properties of DAU 6215 as an antiemetic have been reported in several animal models related to nausea and vomiting induced by various anticancer agents (Sagrada ***et al.***, 1991). DAU 6215 is endowed with potent, dose-dependent and fully-effective antiemetic activity, both parenterally and orally, against cytotoxic treatment-evoked emesis in dogs and ferrets and against X-radiation-induced emesis in ferrets. DAU 6215 was more potent than ondansetron in antagonizing cisplatin-induced emesis in dogs (the ID_{50s} for DAU 6215 were 25 µg/kg i.v. and 6 µg/kg p.o.) and doxorubicin-induced emesis in ferrets (complete protection with 100 µg/kg DAU 6215 both p.o. and i.v.). DAU 6215 antagonized the radiation-induced emesis in ferrets with similar potency (full protection with 300 µg/kg p.o. and i.v.) to ondansetron, but longer lastingly.

Considering the generally extended time-course of nausea-emesis phenomenon associated with cancer chemotherapy, the pharmacokinetic profile of an antiemetic drug can be a decisive factor in conditioning the effectiveness in clinical practice in relation with the therapeutic dosage regimen. Subject of the present study is an assessment of the pharmacokinetic properties of DAU 6215 in three animal species (rat, dog and cynomolgus monkey) using both cold and ^{14}C-radiolabelled DAU 6215. Results are compared with the main pharmacokinetic variables of the unchanged compound evaluated in healthy volunteers during early clinical studies.

RESULTS

The pharmacokinetic properties of DAU 6215 in experimental animals have been assessed using both liquid scintigraphic determination and HPLC-UV assay; the urinary metabolic pattern in the three animal species has been obtained by autoradiography of TLC-chromatographed urinary samples. Determinations of parent compound in plasma and urine of human volunteers have been performed by HPLC-mass spectrometry.

Animal pharmacokinetics of total radioactivity.

The main parameters relative to animal pharmacokinetics of total radioactivity are expressed in table 1. DAU 6215 was well absorbed by the gastrointestinal tract in all the three animal species, as demonstrated by the ratios between the areas under the curves (AUCs) of plasma concentration-time obtained after oral and intravenous administration (ratios = 0.81, 0.95 and 0.85 in rats, dogs and monkeys, respectively). The terminal half-life of radioactivity was appreciably longer in the rat (14 h after i.v. route) than in dogs (5.5 h) and monkeys (4.7 h). The elimination of radioactivity in 96 h was similar by the fecal and urinary routes in the three species, and following both i.v. and p.o. administration. Total elimination amounted to 88% of the dose in rats and about 80% in dogs and monkeys.

The urinary metabolic pattern has been determined from the pooled urines collected over a 24-h period after a dose of 1 mg/kg (table 2). For the three species, elimination of the unchanged parent compound was considerably higher after i.v. than p.o. route, indicating first-pass metabolism; the elimination following i.v. route was about 4-fold greater than after oral route in the rat, about 3-times greater in the dog and 2-times higher in the monkey, suggesting that the first-pass metabolism is species-dependent. The metabolic pattern appeared to be qualitatively similar for the three animal species,

TABLE 1: PHARMACOKINETICS OF ^{14}C-DAU 6215 (1 mg eq/kg) IN EXPERIMENTAL ANIMALS (means ± SEM)

SPECIES	ROUTE OF ADMINISTR.	C MAX (μg eq/ml)	ORAL ABSORPTION $\frac{\text{AUC p.o}}{\text{AUC i.v.}} \times 100$	TERMINAL HALF-LIFE (h)	URINARY ELIMINATION IN 96 HRS (% of the dose)	FECAL ELIMINATION IN 96 HRS (% of the dose)
RAT	i.v.			~14	47.1 ± 1.9	40.4 ± 1.5
(NO = 5)	p.o.	~98	81	~19	35.3 ± 2.9	52.7 ± 4.7
DOG	i.v.			5.5 ± 0.1	40.3 ± 3.1	42.5 ± 1.2
(NO = 4)	p.o.	326 ± 15	95	5.3 ± 1.7	39.0 ± 2.6	39.3 ± 1.6
MONKEY	i.v.			4.7 ± 0.5	52.4 ± 2.1	29.5 ± 2.7
(NO = 4)	p.o.	277 ± 54	85	4.0 ± 0.5	45.4 ± 3.1	31.8 ± 2.4

nine to ten metabolites being present. However, the relative proportion of the various metabolites differed appreciably from species to species. Metabolite M9, which was present in rat urine in major proportion, corresponded to the hydroxylated derivative at the benzene ring. In a separate study in the rat, no appreciable differences were found in the urinary metabolic pattern up to a dose as high as 10 mg/kg oral ^{14}C-DAU 6215 (data not shown). This suggests that no metabolic saturation occurred up to this dose.

Plasma protein binding of total radioactivity was negligible.

TABLE 2: METABOLIC PATTERNS IN URINE (0-24 h) OF RATS, DOGS AND MONKEYS AFTER 1 mg eq/kg ^{14}C-DAU 6215 (% of total radioactivity)

SPECIES	ROUTE OF ADMIN.	M1	M2	M3	M4	M5	M6	M7	M8	M9	M10	^{14}C-DAU 6215
RAT	i.v.	13.3	2.7	1.7	2.7	1.5	6.4	2.1	1.7	34.9	-	33.0
	p.o.	22.4	2.1	2.1	3.1	2.3	11.6	3.1	2.5	42.9	-	8.6
DOG	i.v.	17.9	12.1	4.0	4.4	2.8	5.0	7.0	15.2	8.5	0.9	22.2
	p.o.	17.2	17.8	5.0	7.1	5.0	3.2	10.0	16.0	9.9	1.3	7.6
MONKEY	i.v.	15.4	9.9	1.9	2.8	2.1	9.5	1.6	14.6	6.6	0.7	34.8
	p.o.	16.7	10.4	2.6	5.2	4.2	10.2	1.9	22.0	7.7	0.5	18.6

Animal pharmacokinetics of unchanged DAU 6215

Pharmacokinetics of the unchanged compound in the three animal species suggested a biexponential trend, consistent with a two-compartment model. Terminal half-lives of DAU 6215 (0.9 h, 1.4 h and 2.6 h for rats, dogs and monkeys, respectively) (table 3) were appreciably shorter than the corresponding terminal half-lives of radioactivity (table 1). These results are consistent with the high metabolism of DAU 6215 in the experimental animals. Metabolic clearance represented the main route of elimination; this is indicated by the low amount of excreted unchanged compound in urines of the three animal species (range 3.5-18 % after i.v. and 1.8-8.5% after p.o. administration).

Absolute bioavailability was 20% in rats, 34% in dogs and 48% in monkeys, confirming a species-dependent first-pass metabolism, which is major in rats.

The apparent distribution volumes were high in all the animal species, ranging from 7.5 l/kg in rats to 6.1 l/kg in monkeys, this finding being consistent with the rather high lipophilicity of DAU 6215 (log P = 2.2). This may account at least in part for the capability of the compound to efficiently cross the blood-brain barrier: in the dog, the ratios between the concentration of DAU 6215 in the cerebrospinal fluid and plasma, measured 20 and 40 min after administration of 5 mg/kg i.v., were shown to be 0.45 and 0.58, respectively (table 4).

Toxicokinetics studies carried out during the 28-days toxicity tests in rats and dogs, both intravenously and orally, showed dose-dependency, no sex influence and lack of accumulation and autoinduction phenomena up to dose levels exceeding by three logarithmic units the pharmacologically-active doses (data not shown).

Human pharmacokinetics.

Two phase I clinical studies have been completed with DAU 6215 administered to healthy volunteers intravenously (dose-range 0.5-10 mg) and orally (dose-range 0.5-60 mg) as single doses. The pharmacokinetic results (table 3) showed a linear proportion between doses and AUCs (up to 30 mg for the oral administration). Differently from the experimental animals, a rather long elimination half-life was found, the mean values ranging from 8.7 to 12.4 h after intravenous route and from 11.3 to 14.4 h after oral route. In addition, absolute bioavailability was considerably higher (64% to 72%) than in the experimental animals, indicating a considerably lower first-pass metabolism. The urinary elimination of unchanged compound was much greater (nearly 60% of the doses, both intravenously and orally).

TABLE 3: PHARMACOKINETICS OF UNCHANGED DAU 6215 IN EXPERIMENTAL ANIMALS AND IN VOLUNTEERS (Means ± SEM)

SPECIES	DOSE	ROUTE OF ADMIN.	C MAX (ng/ml)	AUC (ng.h/ml)	ABSOLUTE BIOAVAILABILITY (%)	TERMINAL HALF LIFE (h)	DISTRIB. VOLUME (l/kg)	URINARY EXCRETION (% of dose)
	1mg/kg	i.v.						~16
	5mg/kg	i.v.		548 ± 24		~0.9	7.5	
RAT	1mg/kg	p.o.						~3.0
(NO = 5)	5mg/kg	p.o.	104 ± 17	108 ± 5	20	~2.7		
	1mg/kg	i.v.				1.3 ± 0.1		3.5 ± 1.2
	5mg/kg	i.v.		1270 ± 115		1.4 ± 0.1	7.3	
DOG	1mg/kg	p.o.	55 ± 4		34	~1		1.8 ± 0.3
(NO = 4)	5mg/kg	p.o.	150	438 ± 11		1.6 ± 0.3		
MONKEY	1mg/kg	i.v.		536 ± 101		2.6 ± 0.3	6.1	~18
(NO = 4)	1mg/kg	p.o.	55 ± 7	259 ± 50	48	1.8 ± 0.1		~8.5
	0.62 mg	i.v.		26 ± 1.6		12.4 ± 0.7	5.6 ± 0.6	53 ± 0.8
	1.25 mg	i.v.		49 ± 2.5		11.1 ± 0.7	5.8 ± 0.2	55 ± 2.5
MAN	2.5 mg	i.v.		87 ± 4.1		10.4 ± 1.4	5.3 ± 0.3	63 ± 1.6
(HEALTHY	5.0 mg	i.v.		173 ± 10.2		10.5 ± 1.0	5.6 ± 0.3	63 ± 2.0
VOLUNTEER)	10.0 mg	i.v.		283 ± 9.8		8.7 ± 0.6	6.3 ± 0.3	60 ± 2.0
(NO = 6)								
	5 mg	p.o.	11.8 ± 0.8	107 ± 5.6		11.4 ± 1.9		59 ± 4.9
	15 mg	p.o.	28.6 ± 0.8	297 ± 12	64 ÷ 72	14.4 ± 0.5		62 ± 3.3
	30 mg	p.o.	56.4 ± 1.5	671 ± 23		12.4 ± 0.5		73 ± 0.4
	60 mg	p.o.	122 ± 3.7	1730 ± 76		11.3 ± 0.4		49 ± 0.8

TABLE 4: CEREBROSPINAL AND PLASMA CONCENTRATIONS OF UNMODIFIED DAU 6215 IN BEAGLE DOGS 20 AND 40 MIN AFTER I.V. ADMINISTRATION OF DAU 6215 5 MG/KG.

DOG NO.	DAU 6215 CONCENTRATION (ng/ml)					
	20 min			40 min		
	CSF	Plasma	Ratio CSF/PL	CSF	Plasma	Ratio CSF/PL
1	320	548	0.58	248	350	0.71
2	266	858	0.31	272	602	0.45
3	297	655	0.45	238	400	0.60
Mean	294	687	0.45	252	450	0.58
SEM	19	111	0.09	12	94	0.09

CONCLUSIONS

DAU 6215 shows, in the three animal species considered, a pharmacokinetic profile characterized by a very good oral absorption, dose-dependency, short terminal half-life, major metabolic clearance and pronounced, species-dependent, first-pass metabolism. The compound has a relatively high distribution volume, and crosses efficiently the blood-brain barrier.

The results from the preliminary clinical trials in healthy volunteers show that the pharmacokinetic properties of DAU 6215 in humans are substantially more favourable than in rats, dogs and monkeys: slow plasma decay, minor metabolic clearance, very high bioavailability.

A relatively long duration of antiemetic activity would be expected from the half-life value of DAU 6215, which is markedly longer than those reported for other 5-HT_3 antagonists in healthy volunteers: 3 h for ondansetron (Milne and Heel, 1991) and 3.1-5.9 h for granisetron (Plosker and Goa, 1991).

In conclusion, the overall pharmacokinetic profile of DAU 6215 represents a favourable feature for the clinical potential of the drug. Early results from the phase II studies are, in fact, encouraging.

REFERENCES

Milne, R.J. and Heel, R.C. (1991): Ondansetron - therapeutic use as an antiemetic. Drugs 41: 574-595.

Plosker, G.L. and Goa, K.L. (1991): Granisetron - A review of its pharmacological properties and therapeutic use as an antiemetic. Drugs 42: 805-824.

Sagrada, A., Turconi, M., Bonali, P., Schiantarelli, P., Micheletti, R., Montagna, E., Nicola, M., Algate, D.R., Rimoldi, E.M. and Donetti, A. (1991): Antiemetic activity of the new 5-HT_3 antagonist DAU 6215 in animal models of cancer chemotherapy and radiation. Cancer Chemother. Pharmacol. 28: 470-474.

Turconi, M., Nicola, M., Gil Quintero, M., Maiocchi, L., Micheletti, R., Giraldo, E., Donetti, A. (1990): Synthesis of a new class of 2,3-dihydro-2-oxo-1H-benzimidazolone-1-carboxylicacid derivatieves as highly potent 5-HT_3 receptor antagonists. J. med. Chem. 33: 2101-8.

Turconi, M., Schiantarelli, P., Borsini, F., Rizzi, C.A., Ladinsky, H. and Donetti, A. (1991): Azabicycloalkyl benzimidazolones: Interaction with serotonergic 5-HT_3 and 5-HT_4 receptors and potential therapeutic implications. Drugs Fut. 16: 1011-1026.

Mechanisms and Control of Emesis. Eds A.L. Bianchi, L. Grélot, A.D. Miller, G.L. King. Colloque INSERM/ John Libbey Eurotext Ltd. © 1992, Vol. 223, pp. 235-236

Single-dose ondansetron for the prevention of acute cisplatin-induced emesis: analysis of efficacy and prognostic factors

P.J. Hesketh, P. Plagge and J.C. Bryson

Boston University Medical Center, Boston, MA, USA; Glaxo Inc. Research Institute, Research Triangle Park, NC, USA

Ondansetron (OND) is a selective 5-HT_3 antagonist which has demonstrated significant activity as an antiemetic in patients receiving cisplatin (DDP). This multicenter study was designed to compare the efficacy and safety of two single dose regimens (32 mg and 8 mg) with the approved three dose regimen (0.15 mg/kg q 4 hrs x 3) in the prevention of acute cisplatin-induced emesis.

Chemotherapy naive patients receiving high dose (HD$\geq$ 100 mg/m^2) DDP or medium dose (MD 50-70mg/m^2) DDP were eligible for inclusion. A stratified (DDP dose), randomized, double-blind, parallel group study design was employed. Patients were randomized to receive intravenous OND 0.15 mg/kg x 3 doses, q 4 hrs, or a single 8 mg or 32 mg dose followed by two saline doses, beginning 30 minutes prior to DDP administration.

Six hundred and ninety-nine patients received DDP, and 618 were evaluated for antiemetic efficacy, 317 patients on the HD DDP arm and 301 on the MD DDP arm. Parameters recorded for the 24 hrs after DDP administration were emetic episodes (EE), nausea assessments (100 mm visual analogue scales) and adverse events. Patient groups were well matched by age, gender, and history of alcohol use. Antiemetic response was as follows: (Complete response (CR) = no EE; Failure (F) = > 5 EE, rescued or withdrawn for any reason). Results are displayed in Table 1.

TABLE 1

Cisplatin dose	Response	Ondansetron dose 8mg x 1	0.15mg/kg x 3	32mg x1
$\geq$100mg/m^2	CR	40/115 (35%)	41/100 (41%)	49/102 (48%)
	F	39/115 (34%)	36/100 (36%)	20/102 (20%)
50-70mg/m^2	CR	54/107 (50%)	62/101 (61%)	68/93 (73%)
	F	25/107 (23%)	22/101 (22%)	8/93 (9%)

The 32 mg dose was superior to the 8 mg dose for: total number of emetic episodes (HD DDP p=0.015 and MD DDP p < 0.001), complete response (HD DDP 48% vs 35%, p=0.048; MD DDP 73% vs 50%, p=0.001), and failure rate (HD DDP 20% vs 34%, p=0.018; MD DDP 9% vs 23%, p=0.005). The 32 mg single dose was also superior to the 0.15 mg/kg x 3 dose regimen for number of emetic episodes (MD DDP p=0.033) and failure rate (HD DDP 20% vs 36%, p=0.009 and MD DDP 9% vs 22%, p=0.011).

OND was well tolerated. The most common adverse events were headache (20%), fever (9%), and diarrhea (8%). An approximate tenfold increase in the incidence of clinically significant transaminase elevations was observed in the high vs medium dose cisplatin stratum (AST 6.5% vs 0.7%, ALT 5.0% vs 0.3%).

An analysis of treatment and patient factors potentially predictive of antiemetic outcome was carried out. Factors assessed included cisplatin stratum, OND regimen, gender, ethanol consumption history, and patient age. Results are displayed in Table 2.

TABLE 2

Factor	P-Value Complete/Major Response (0-2EE)	Extent of Nausea
Cisplatin stratum	<0.001	<0.001
Ondansetron regimen	<0.001	0.005
Alcohol consumption	<0.001	<0.001
Gender	<0.001	<0.001
Age	0.138	0.011

With respect to rate of antiemetic response (0 - 2 EE), with the exception of patient age, all were independently significant. Antiemetic control was superior with the medium dose DDP stratum; in males, and in patients with a history of heavy ethanol consumption. In patients receiving HD DDP, age was a significant factor, with younger patients faring worse than older patients (p=0.012).

When these factors were analyzed with respect to extent of nausea, similar results were noted with cisplatin stratum, OND regimen, history of alcohol consumption, gender and age all found to be significant.

In conclusion, a single 32 mg iv dose of OND is superior to a single 8 mg iv dose and at least as effective as the standard regimen of 0.15 mg/kg x 3 doses in the prevention of acute cisplatin-induced emesis. In addition, cisplatin dose, ondansetron regimen, patient age, gender and history of ethanol consumption are all significant predictive factors for antiemetic therapeutic outcome.

Mechanisms and Control of Emesis. Eds A.L. Bianchi, L. Grélot, A.D. Miller, G.L. King. Colloque INSERM/ John Libbey Eurotext Ltd. © 1992, Vol. 223, pp. 237-238

Prokinetic and antiemetic properties of BIMU 1, a $5HT_4$ receptor agonist and $5HT_3$ receptor antagonist

Carlo A. Rizzi, Herbert Ladinsky, Angelo Sagrada, Pierino Schiantarelli, Antonio Schiavone and Arturo Donetti

Research Department, Boehringer Ingelheim Italia, Via Serio 15, 20139 Milano, Italy

BIMU 1 (endo-N-(8-methyl-8-azabicyclo[3.2.1.]oct-3-yl)-2,3-dihydro-3-ethyl-2-oxo-1H-benzimidazole-1-carboxamide hydrochloride) is an azabicycloalkyl benzimidazolone derivative which belongs to a class of potent serotonin $5HT_3$ receptor antagonists (Turconi ***et al.***, 1991a). The profile of interactions at this serotonin receptor has been previously reported (Turconi ***et al.***, 1991a,b). The affinity of BIMU 1 for $5HT_3$ receptors, evaluated in binding and functional assays, is comparable to that of other $5HT_3$ receptor antagonists like ondansetron or DAU 6215, another benzimidazolone derivative (Turconi ***et al.***, 1991b).

In spite of their structural similarity, BIMU 1 and DAU 6215 exhibit a different activity at the newly discovered serotonin receptor, $5HT_4$. BIMU 1 is a potent agonist in all models related to $5HT_4$ receptor-mediated actions both in the central nervous system (Dumuis ***et al.***, 1991) and in the periphery (Turconi ***et al.***, 1991b; Baxter & Clarke, 1992). This latter activity may account for the gastrointestinal prokinetic properties of the compound (Rizzi ***et al.***, 1992). On the contrary, DAU 6215 displays negligible activity at $5HT_4$ receptors (Dumuis ***et al.***, 1991; Baxter & Clarke, 1992). while ondansetron is ineffective either as an agonist or an antagonist (Dumuis ***et al.***, 1991; Rizzi ***et al.***, 1992). In summary the overall picture of receptor interactions shows that BIMU 1 is a potent $5HT_3$ receptor antagonist and $5HT_4$ receptor agonist. No appreciable affinity was found for other serotoninergic, muscarinic, adrenergic or dopaminergic receptors.

In the present work, the *in vivo* properties of BIMU 1 were investigated in experiments related to chemotherapy-induced emesis and gastrointestinal prokinetic activity, since such clinical aspects are at present regarded as the main therapeutic fields for $5HT_3$ receptor antagonists and $5HT_4$ receptor agonists, respectively.

The antiemetic properties of BIMU 1 were studied in two separate models. In the dog, BIMU 1 (1-30 μg/kg i.v.) dose-dependently protected against emesis induced by cisplatin. The antiemetic potency of BIMU 1 was greater than that previously reported by us for equipotent $5HT_3$ receptor antagonists (Sagrada ***et al.***, 1991): the estimated ID_{50} of BIMU 1 (the dose reducing by 50% the number of emetic episodes of control animals) was 4.3 μg/kg (95% confidential limits: 2.9-6.6), compared to 25 μg/kg (16-40) and 46 μg/kg (25-87) of DAU 6215 and ondansetron, respectively.

In the ferret, doxorubicin induced vomiting was dose-dependently inhibited by BIMU 1 at 3-100 μg/kg i.v.. At 30 μg/kg, three out of four ferrets did not show vomits or retches over the 4 h post-dosing observation, while 100 μg/kg was a full protective dose in all animals tested. This picture of anti-emetic activity was superimposeable to that previously described for DAU 6215 in the same model, while a lower potency was reported for ondansetron (Sagrada ***et al.***, 1991).

The gastrointestinal prokinetic potential of BIMU 1 was evaluated in mechanical models of gut motility and in a functional test of gastric emptying. In the anaesthesized cat, BIMU 1 dose-dependently (0.1-1 mg/kg i.v.) increased the tone of the lower oesophageal sphincter. In the conscious dog, the compound increased the spontaneous motility of a denervated stomach pouch (Heidenhain pouch) at 0.03-0.1 mg/kg i.v. and at 0.1-1 mg/kg p.o.) and that of a colonic Thiry fistula at 30 μg/kg/min i.v. infusion rate. In all the aforementioned activities ondansetron was ineffective, thus ruling out an involvement of $5HT_3$ receptor blockade in this response.

In a functional test, BIMU 1 (0.1-1 mg/kg i.v.) enhanced gastric emptying of a liquid meal (a solution containing phenol red as a marker) in the conscious dog. The amount of liquid collected from the stomach after 10 min from the instillation of the solution through a gastric fistula was reduced by 47.7 $\pm$ 16.7%, 69.8 $\pm$ 5.9%, and 71.8 $\pm$ 7.5% after the administration of 0.1, 0.3 and 1 mg/kg BIMU 1, respectively. In the same model, ondansetron (1 mg/kg i.v.) was ineffective.

The present results indicate that BIMU 1 is a potent $5HT_3$ receptor antagonist and $5HT_4$ receptor agonist with a potentially wide spectrum of activity in the gastrointestinal field. The dual interaction at serotonin receptors may therefore represent the feature of a new generation of anti-emetic drugs with gastrointestinal prokinetic properties, which, at variance with substituted benzamides like metoclopramide, are devoid of anti-dopaminergic activity.

References

Baxter, G.S. and Clarke, D.E. (1992): Benzimidazolone derivatives act as $5\text{-}HT_4$ receptor ligands in rat oesophagus. *Eur. J. Pharmacol.* 212, 225-229.

Dumuis, A., Sebben, M., Monferini, E., Nicola, M., Turconi, M., Ladinsky, H. and Bockaert, J. (1991): Azabicycloalkyl benzimidazolone derivatives as a novel class of potent agonists at the $5\text{-}HT_4$ receptor positively coupled to adenylate cyclase in brain. *Naunyn-Schmiedeberg's Arch. Pharmacol.* 343, 245-251.

Rizzi, C.A., Coccini, T., Onori, L., Manzo, L. and Tonini, M. (1992): Benzimidazolone derivatives: a new class of $5\text{-hydroxytryptamine}_4$ receptor agonists with prokinetic and acetylcholine releasing properties in the guinea pig ileum. *J. Pharmacol. Exp. Ther.* 261, May issue.

Sagrada, A., Turconi, M., Bonali, P., Schiantarelli, P., Micheletti, R., Montagna, E., Nicola, M., Algate, D.R., Rimoldi, E.M. and Donetti, A. (1991): Antiemetic activity of the new $5\text{-}HT_3$ antagonist DAU 6215 in animal models of cancer chemotherapy and radiation. *Cancer Chemother. Pharmacol.* 28, 470-474.

Turconi, M., Donetti, A., Schiavone, A., Sagrada, A., Montagna, E., Nicola, M., Cesana, R., Rizzi, C.A. and Micheletti R. (1991a): Pharmacological properties of a novel class of $5\text{-}HT_3$ receptor antagonists. *Eur. J. Pharmacol.* 203, 203-211.

Turconi, M., Schiantarelli, P., Borsini, F., Rizzi, C.A., Ladinsky, H. and Donetti, A. (1991b): Azabicycloalkyl benzimidazolones: interactions with serotoninergic $5\text{-}HT_3$ and $5\text{-}HT_4$ receptors and potential therapeutic implications. *Drugs of the Future* 16, 1011-1026.

Mechanisms and Control of Emesis. Eds A.L. Bianchi, L. Grélot, A.D. Miller, G.L. King. Colloque INSERM/
John Libbey Eurotext Ltd. © 1992, Vol. 223, pp. 239-240

Resinferatoxin: a broad spectrum antiemetic in the ferret

P. Bhandari and P.L.R. Andrews

Department of Physiology, St. George's Hospital Medical School, Cranmer Terrace, London, SW17 ORE, UK

Resinferatoxin (RTX) is an ultrapotent analog of capsaicin, extracted from the bark of trees of the genus Euphorbia (Szallasi & Blumberg 1989). In adult rats, when given subcutaneously, it has been shown to produce chronic desensitisation to the algesic effects of capsaicin and is therefore assumed to be toxic to C-fibre nociceptive afferents In the ferret the abdominal vagal afferents, the majority of which are C-fibres, have been implicated in the emetic response to intra-gastric copper sulphate and total body radiation but not to the centrally acting opiate receptor agonist loperamide (Andrews et al. 1990; Bhandari, Bingham & Andrews 1992). These studies have used surgical lesioning of the abdominal vagus and hence both the afferents and the efferents are sectioned making interpretation of the effects of the lesion complex. In a pilot study we attempted to circumvent this problem by using neonatal capsaicin treatment but unfortunately a conventional dose of 50 mg/kg sc was ineffective and a dose of 100 mg/kg sc, that was effective against radiation-induced emesis when the animals were tested in the adult state, had an unacceptable mortality rate. In view of these difficulties it was decided to investigate whether RTX could be used to produce visceral afferent blockade and hence anti-emesis.

Adult ferrets were given RTX (L.C. Services Corporation, USA), dissolved in 10% ethanol + 10% Tween 80 + 80% normal saline, subcutaneously in a dose of 100 µg/kg 3 - 4 hours before exposure to one of the following emetic stimuli: radiation (X-ray, 200 rads, 250 kV, 15 mA), intra-gastric copper sulphate (30ml, 40 mg%), or loperamide (0.5 mg/kg sc). RTX showed no indications of being algesic when given by the sc route and in the three hours prior to emetic administration they appeared to behave normally, explored their surroundings and would accept food.

The emetic response to radiation was decreased by RTX as indicated by a reduction in the mean (± sem) number of retches (78.6 ± 14.5) and vomits (10.1 ± 1.3) in the control group to 0.5 ± 0.5 retches and 0.25 ± 0.25 vomits in the RTX group ($p < 0.001$). Similarly the responses to copper sulphate (control retches = 15.9 ± 4.0, control vomits = 7.1 ± 1.7; retches after RTX = 0, vomits after RTX = 0; $p<0.01$) and loperamide (control retches = 75.6 ± 14.0, control vomits = 8.3 ± 1.6; retches after RTX = 5.7 ± 3.1, vomits after RTX = 0.4 ± 0.3; $p<0.01$) were also significantly reduced. In animals either given RTX several days prior to emetic testing or where possible (copper sulphate and loperamide) retested several days after the initial test with RTX it was found that the responses had returned to within control values by 3-8 days.

As in the rat (Szallasi & Blumberg 1989) there was a rapid decrease in core temperature (38.48 ± 0.28 °C to 36.38 ± 0.34 °C, n=6, p=0.002) within about 30 min of RTX administration although the animals did not exhibit any signs of hypothermia e.g. shivering. The reduction was sustained throughout the 3 hour monitoring period, the minimum being 35.9°C at 120 min, although the magnitude of decrease was variable with a maximum fall of 4.8° one animal. In a series of experiments on urethane anaesthetized ferrets there was no effect of RTX on the von Bezold-Jarisch reflex.

The results demonstrate that RTX has broad spectrum anti-emetic effects in the ferret. The observation that RTX was effective against emesis induced via activation of visceral afferents as well as the area postrema was unexpected and suggests an action at some convergence point between visceral afferents and the area postrema in the brainstem. The way in which RTX has this effect is not clear but in other systems RTX has been shown to induce activation of C-fibre afferents leading to transmitter depletion, produce prolonged neuronal depolarisation and increase Ca^{++} uptake in neurones (Winter et al. 1990; Szallasi & Blumberg 1989). The most likely mechanism for the anti-emetic action appears to be via a modulation of neurotransmission within the brainstem, possibly the nucleus tractus solitarius.

References

Andrews, P.L.R., Davis, C.J., Bingham, S., Davidson, H.I.M., Hawthorn, J., and Maskell, L. (1990): The abdominal visceral innervation and the emetic reflex: pathways, pharmacology, and plasticity. *Can. J. Phys. Pharmacol.* 68, 325-345.

Bhandari, P., Bingham, S., Andrews, P.L.R. (1992): The neuropharmacology of loperamide-induced emesis in the ferret: the role of the area postrema, vagus, opiate and $5\text{-}HT_3$ receptors. *Neuropharmacology* (in press)

Szallasi, A., Blumberg, P.M. (1989): Resinferatoxin, a phorbol-related diterpene, acts as an ultrapotent analog of capsaicin, the irritant constituent in red pepper. *Neuroscience*, 30, 515-520.

Winter, J., Dray, A., Wood, J.N., Yeats, J.C., and Bevan, S. (1990): Cellular mechanism of action of resinferatoxin: a potent sensory neuron excitotoxin. *Brain Res.* 520, 131-140.

Mechanisms and Control of Emesis. Eds A.L. Bianchi, L. Grélot, A.D. Miller, G.L. King. Colloque INSERM/
John Libbey Eurotext Ltd. © 1992, Vol. 223, pp. 241-242

Phenylephrine-induced emesis: alpha-1 adrenoceptors or alpha-2 adrenoceptor subtypes

Danica Jovanović-Mićić, Ranka Samardžić, Nina Japundžić
and Dušan B. Beleslin

Department of Pharmacology, Medical Faculty , P.O. Box 662, 11 000 Belgrade, Serbia, Yugoslavia

Phenylephrine-induced emesis has been described (Beleslin **et al.**, 1990), but the mechanism and site of the emesis has not yet been studied. Therefore, the aim of the present experiments was to characterize the pharmacological profile of emesis evoked by phenylephrine, after its intracerebroventricular (ICV) injections in cats, according to its sensitivity to prazosin and yohimbine. In addition, the site of emetic action of the drug was assessed by the ablation of the area postrema.

In an aseptic operation under pentobarbital sodium (35-40 mg/kg ip) anaesthesia, an infusion cannula was implanted into the left lateral cerebral ventricle of cats of either sex (2-4 kg), so that ICV injections of drugs could be made without anaesthesia. In one group of the cats, the area postrema was destroyed electrolytically as described in detail in our previous report (Beleslin & Štrbac, 1987). Only the expulsion of the gastric content was taken as a positive emetic response.

Table 1

The effect of yohimbine and prazosin on phenylephrine-induced emesis in cats

DRUG	DOSES in mg	NUMBER OF CATS VOMITED/TESTED
Phenylephrine	0.3	6/6
Ablation of the area postrema + Phenylephrine	0.3	0/6
Yohimbine + Phenylephrine	0.0001	5/6
	0.0003	2/6
	0.001	3/6
	0.003	2/6
	0.01	1/6
	0.1	0/6
Prazosin + Phenylephrine	0.00003	0/6
	0.0001	0/6
	0.0003	1/6
	0.001	1/6
	0.1	0/6
Controls 0.9 % NaCl	0.1-0.3 ml	0/6

Yohimbine and prazosin were injected ICV 20 minutes before emetic challenge of phenylephrine. Cats with ablated area postrema were tested 2 weeks after ablation of the area postrema.

The percentage of cats showing emesis after ICV phenylephrine (0.03-2.0 mg) was dose-dependent ($r = 0.91$; $p < 0.05$; ED_{50} * 0.196 + 0.07 mg). The emesis occurred in bouts of one to three at irregular time intervals. The vomiting lasted up to 10 minutes. In cats with lesion of the area postrema, 0.3 mg of phenylephrine injected ICV failed to evoke emesis (Table 1). In the next series of experiments the alpha-2 adrenoceptor antagonist, yohimbine (0.0001-0.1 mg) and the alpha-1 adrenoceptor antagonist, prazosin (0.00003-0.1 mg) were injected ICV 20 minutes before the emetic challenge of 0.3 mg of phenylephrine. As shown in Table 1 the inhibitory effect of yohimbine was dose-dependent ($r = 0.86$; $p < 0.05$). All doses of prazosin depressed or abolished the phenylephrine-induced emesis (Table 1).

The results of this study revealed that phenylephrine, injected ICV produced shortlasting and dose-dependent emesis in unanaesthetized cats. Phenylephrine did not evoke emetic response in cats with ablated area postrema. It is apparent, therefore, that the locus of the emetic action of phenylephrine is the area postrema.

As shown in these experiments, both the predominantly alpha-1 blocking drug, prazosin, as well as the predominantly alpha-2 blocking agent, yohimbine, depressed or abolished the phenylephrine-induced emesis in cats. Based on minimal inhibitory effects of prazosin and yohimbine, prazosin was at least thousand times more potent then yohimbine in producing its antiemetic effect. The simplest explanation, therefore, is that phenylephrine acted via alpha-1 adrenoceptors in the area postrema. However, Bylund (1985) proposed that it is possible to differentiate alpha-2 adrenoceptors on the basis of their affinity to prazosin: alpha-2-A subtype with low affinity and alpha-2-B with high affinity for prazosin. Since both yohimbine and prazosin inhibited the phenylephrine-induced emesis the possibility exists that phenylephrine acted at one of the subtypes of alpha-2 adrenoceptors in the area postrema.

This work was supported by a grant of the Scientific Fund of Serbia.

REFERENCES

Beleslin, D.B. & Štrbac, M. (1987): Noradrenaline-induced emesis: alpha-2 adrenoceptor mediation in the area postrema. *Neuropharmacology* 26, 1157-1165.

Beleslin, D.B., Jovanović-Mićić, D., Samardžić, R. & Malobabić, Z.S. (1990): Studies on behavioural effects of phenylephrine in cats. *Iugoslav. Physiol. Pharmacol. Acta* 26, 17-21.

Bylund, D.B. (1985): Heterogeneity of alpha-2 adrenergic receptors. *Pharmacol. Biochem. Behav.* 22, 833-843.

Mechanisms and Control of Emesis. Eds A.L. Bianchi, L. Grélot, A.D. Miller, G.L. King. Colloque INSERM/ John Libbey Eurotext Ltd. © 1992, Vol. 223, pp. 243-244

Suppression of clonidine-induced emesis by cyclophosphamide

Dušan B. Beleslin, Snežana Bošnjak, Danica Jovanović-Mićić, Ranka Samardžić and * Slobodan B. Nikolić

*Department of Pharmacology, Medical Faculty, P.O. Box 662 and * Institute of Oncology and Radiology, 11 000 Belgrade, Serbia, Yugoslavia*

All the previous studies have shown that the anticancer chemotherapy-induced emesis may be related to the area postrema as well as to the central and peripheral 5-HT_3 receptor subtype. However, there is evidence that cyclophosphamide injected intracerebroventricularly (icv) produce vomiting unpredictably in cats and that the anticancer chemotherapy agent may have an inhibitory effect on emesis (Fetting ***et al.***, 1982). Therefore, the aim of the present experiments was to investigate the effect of icv cyclophosphamide on emesis induced by clonidine similarly injected in unanaesthetized cats.

Cats of either sex, weighing 2-4 kg, were anaesthetized by pentobarbital sodium (35-40 mg/kg, ip). For icv injections of drugs, a Collison cannula was implanted into the left lateral cerebral ventricle, as described in detail previously (Beleslin & Štrbac,1987). The solutions of drugs were injected manually from a 1.0 ml syringe, in a volume of 0.1 ml over a period of 15-20 s and washed in 0.1 ml of saline. The area postrema was destroyed electrolytically. Copper sulphate was administered intragastrically in a volume of 50 ml as 2.5% aqueous solution. Only the expulsion of gastric contents was taken as a positive emetic response.

In these experiments cyclophosphamide injected icv was used to prevent emesis evoked either by icv clonidine or by intragastric copper sulphate. As shown in Table 1 cyclophosphamide 2 hours after its icv administration, suppressed the clonidine-, but not the copper sulphate-induced emesis. In addition, the ablation of the area postrema failed to change significantly the clonidine-induced emesis.

Contrary to previous studies, the major finding of the present experiments is that the icv anticancer drug, cyclophosphamide suppressed the icv clonidine-induced emesis, but not the emesis evoked by intragastric copper sulphate. Further, as shown in these experiments icv clonidine-induced emesis was virtually not changed in cats with ablated area postrema. It is apparent, therefore, that icv clonidine produced emesis through emetogenic sites in the brain outside the area postrema. Since intragastric copper sulphate induces emesis via the emetic centre of the lateral reticular formation of the brainstem (Wang & Borison, 1951), the finding of the present study that icv cyclophosphamide did not significantly change the emetic response to intragastric copper sulphate shows that the emetic centre of the brainstem cannot be the central locus of antiemetic action of cyclophosphamide.

Table 1

The effect of cyclophosphamide on clonidine- and copper sulphate emesis in cats

TREATMENT	DOSES	ROUTE	NUMBER OF CATS VOMITED/TESTED
Cyclophosphamide	1.0 mg	icv	1/6
Clonidine	0.1 mg	icv	5/6
Clonidine + ablation of the area postrema	0.1 mg	icv	4/6
Cyclophosphamide + Clonidine	1.0 mg 0.1 mg	icv icv	1/6*
Copper sulphate	1.75 mg	intragastrically	6/6
Cyclophosphamide + Copper sulphate	1.0 mg 1.75 mg	icv intragastrically	6/6
Controls (saline)	0.1-0.3 ml	icv	0/4

Cyclophosphamide was injected icv 2 hours before emetic challenge of clonidine and copper sulphate. Cats with ablated area postrema were tested 2 weeks after ablation of the area postrema. *$p < 0.05$ when compared with clonidine group (Student t-test).

In conclusion the present experiments provided evidence that icv clonidine-induced emesis, but not the emesis evoked by intragastric copper sulphate is sensitive to the inhibitory action of icv cyclophosphamide. In addition, the ablation of the area postrema virtually had no effect on the clonidine-induced emesis. It is apparent, therefore, that cyclophosphamide suppressed the clonidine-induced emesis through emetogenic site/s in the brain outside the area postrema and the vomiting centre of the lateral reticular formation of the brainstem.

This work was supported by a grant of the Scientific Fund of Serbia.

REFERENCES

Beleslin, D.B. & Štrbac, M. (1987): Noradrenaline - induced emesis: alpha-2 adrenoceptor mediation in the area postrema. *Neuropharmacology* 26, 1157-1165.

Fetting, J.H., McCarthy, L.E., Borison, H.L. & Colvin, M. (1982): Vomiting induced by cyclophosphamide and phosphoramide mustard in cats. *Cancer Treat. Rep.* 66, 1625-1629.

Wang, S.C. & Borison, H.L. (1951): Copper sulphate emesis: a study of afferent pathways from the gastrointestinal tract. *Am. J. Physiol.* 164, 520-526.

Mechanisms and Control of Emesis. Eds A.L. Bianchi, L. Grélot, A.D. Miller, G.L. King. Colloque INSERM/ John Libbey Eurotext Ltd. © 1992, Vol. 223, pp. 245-246

Novel $5HT_3$ receptor antagonists. Quinoxaline derivatives with antiemetic activity in ferrets

J. Del Río [(1)], B. Lasheras [(2)], A. Berjón [(1)], G. Romero [(1)], J.C. Del Castillo [(3)], J. Roca [(3)] and A. Monge [(2)]

Schools of Medicine [(1)] and Pharmacy [(2)], University of Navarra, Pamplona, Spain and Research Department, Vita Laboratories [(3)], Barcelona, Spain

Antagonism of serotonin $5HT_3$ receptors appears to be an effective approach for the control of nausea and vomiting induced by radiation or by cytostatic drugs used in the treatment of cancer. Since the already developed $5HT_3$ antagonists are not entirely free of side effects and do not either represent the ultimate answer in the problem of cancer chemotherapy-induced emesis, it still seems of interest to investigate new potential antiemetic compounds acting

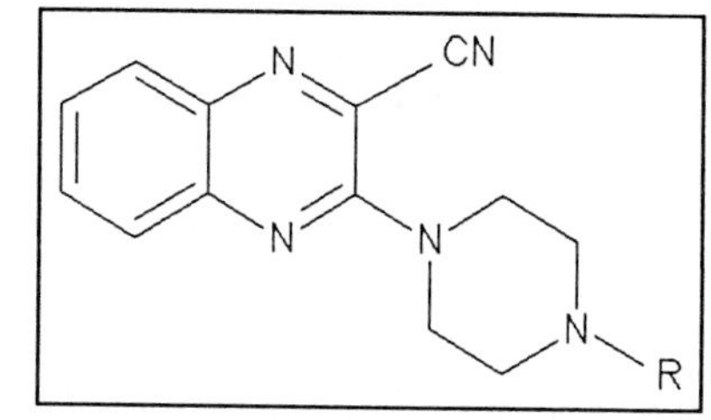

N CN N N N R

Fig. 1. General chemical structure

through serotonergic mechanisms. In the present study, some preliminary results obtained with new quinoxaline derivatives (fig. 1) endowed with antiemetic and gastroprokinetic activity are reported.

METHODS

Binding to several neurotransmitter receptors. Binding of [3H]BRL-43694 to $5HT_3$ receptors from rat cerebral cortex homogenates was performed according to the method of Nelson and Thomas (1989). Binding to [3H]5HT-labelled $5HT_1$ receptors as well as binding to serotonin $5HT_{1A}$ and $5HT_2$ and dopamine D_2 receptors from rat brain was also performed using [3H]8-OH-DPAT, [3H]ketanserin and [3H]spiperone respectively as radioligands, using previously described procedures.

Antagonism to 2-methyl-5HT in the isolated guinea pig ileum. The longitudinal muscle/myenteric plexus preparation was used for calculating the pA_2 values of the new compounds. In some instances, the field-stimulated preparation was also used.

Von Bezold-Jarisch reflex. The antagonism to the bradycardic effect of 5HT in anaesthetized rats was evaluated as described by Fozard (1984).

Gastroprokinetic activity in rats. Gastric emptying was studied as previously reported (Costall et al., 1987).

Antiemetic activity in ferrets. Emesis was induced in ferrets by 2-methyl-5HT , 20 mg/kg p.o. (Sancilio et al., 1991) or by cisplatin, 9 mg/kg i.p. (Miner and Sanger, 1986). Test compounds were i.p. or orally given at varying times before the emetic stimuli and the latency to vomiting as well as the number of emetic episodes was recorded for a 5 hr period.

RESULTS and DISCUSSION

Several of the quinoxaline derivatives were able to displace binding to rat brain $5HT_3$ receptors at concentrations from 10 nM to 100 nM, the IC_{50}'s being in the range of ondansetron or slightly higher. For example, the IC_{50}'s for VC60d5 ($R=CH_2$-$CH=CH_2$) and ondansetron were 16 and 13 nM respectively. A much lower affinity affinity was found with the other neurotransmitter receptors studied.

When these compounds were studied on the longitudinal muscle of the guinea pig ileum stimulated by the $5HT_3$ agonist 2-methyl-5HT, a rather potent antagonistic effect was obtained in some cases. VC60d5 was approximately 2-3 orders of magnitude more potent than zacopride or ondansetron; pA_2's were 10.1, 8.0 and 6.9 respectively. The correlation between the $5HT_3$ receptor binding studies and the data from the guinea pig ileum was consequently rather poor. Interestingly, some of these compounds, in particular VC50d2 ($R=CH_3$), showed an intrinsic agonist activity in the range of 5 to 50 μM. It was conceivable that this moderate agonist activity was due to an agonist effect on $5HT_4$ receptors. However, when the preparation was incubated with the $5HT_4$ agonist 5-methoxytryptamine in order to desensitize the corresponding $5HT_4$ receptors, the enhancement of the field-stimulated neurogenic contractions produced by either VC50d2 or VC60d5 was not at all prevented. Consequently, it seems that this effect can be ascribed to a partial agonist action on ileum $5HT_3$ receptors.

The bradycardia induced in the anaesthetized rat by 5HT was also blocked by several of the tested compounds. However, these quinoxaline derivatives were much weaker than ondansetron; ED_{50}'s for VC50d2, VC60d3 ($R=C_2H_5$) and ondansetron were 27, 15 and 0.5 μg/kg respectively. As already suggested in previous studies with other $5HT_3$ antagonists (see review in Hoyer, 1990), the correlation between the three test systems was again not very adequate.

Like with ondansetron or zacopride, a significant gastroprokinetic effect in rats was found after low doses (0.1-1 mg/kg p.o.) of some of the new $5HT_3$ antagonists such as VC50d2 or VC60d3. According to the experiments in the guinea pig ileum, it is probable that this is not either a $5HT_4$ receptor-mediated effect.

The antiemetic profile of some of these quinoxaline derivatives was finally investigated in the present study. Vomiting produced by 2-methyl-5HT was prevented by low doses, 0.5-1 mg/kg, of either VC50d2 or VC60d3 given i.p. or p.o. The more severe emetic episodes induced by cisplatin were also blocked by the same doses of these drugs. It should be noted, however, that, like in the case of zacopride (King, 1990), some retches were occasionally produced by these new compounds. Retches were always short-lasting and not dose-related. This is probably a consequence of the partial $5HT_3$ agonist activity suggested by the experiments in isolated preparations.

These quinoxaline derivatives represent a new class of $5HT_3$ antagonists with antiemetic and gastroprokinetic activity. The present results tend also to suggest the probable heterogeneity of $5HT_3$ receptors in different tissues from different species.

REFERENCES

Costall, B., Gunning, S.J., Naylor, R.J. & Tyers, M.B. (1987). Brit.J.Pharmacol. 91, 263-264.
Fozard, J.R. (1984). Neuropharmacology 23, 1473-1486.
Hoyer, D. (1990). Neuropsychopharmacology 3, 371-383.
King, G.L. (1990). J. Pharmacol. exp. Ther. 253, 1034-1041.
Miner, W.D. & Sanger, G.J. (1986). Brit. J. Pharmacol. 88, 497-499.
Nelson, D.R. & Thomas D.R. (1989). Biochem. Pharmacol. 38, 1693-1695.
Sancilio, L.F., Pinkus, L.M., Jackson, C.B. & Munson Jr., H.R. (1991). Eur. J. Pharmacol. 192, 365-369.

Mechanisms and Control of Emesis. Eds A.L. Bianchi, L. Grélot, A.D. Miller, G.L. King. Colloque INSERM/
John Libbey Eurotext Ltd. © 1992, Vol. 223, pp. 247-248

Mechanisms of cisplatin- and serotonin $(5\text{-HT})_3$ receptor agonist-induced emesis in ferrets: effects of YM060 and section of vagus and greater splanchnic nerves

Takeshi Kamato, Hiroyuki Ito, Yukinori Nagakura, Akito Nishida, Hidenobu Yuki, Mayumi Yamano and Keiji Miyata

Medicinal Research Laboratories I, Central Research Laboratories, Yamanouchi Pharmaceutical Co. Ltd., 21 Miyukigaoka, Tsukuba, Ibaraki 305, Japan

It is well known that serotonin $(5\text{-HT})_3$ receptor antagonists effectively inhibit cytotoxic drug-induced emesis in man and animals. However, the mechanisms by which cytotoxic drugs cause emesis are not yet clear. In ferrets, cisplatin increases the concentration of 5-HT in the small intestine (Stables et al., 1987) and the section of abdominal visceral afferent nerves abolishes cisplatin-induced emesis (Hawthorn et al., 1988). These reports suggested that cisplatin's site of action is peripheral and that 5-HT is involved peripherally in the relay of emetic stimuli. On the other hand, central 5-HT_3 receptor involvement in this emesis is also suggested by the finding that 5-HT_3 receptor antagonists injected into the area postrema inhibited cisplatin-induced emesis (Higgins et al., 1989). This idea is supported by studies showing that the dorsal vagal complex including the area postrema is rich in 5-HT_3 receptor ligand binding sites (Barnes et al., 1990). Although both peripheral and central 5-HT_3 receptors may be involved in cisplatin-induced emesis, the role of each 5-HT_3 receptor remains unclear. In the present study, we demonstrated the emetic activity of m-chlorophenylbiguanide (mCPBG), a potent and selective 5-HT_3 receptor agonist. We then examined the effects of YM060 and the combination of vagotomy and greater splanchnicectomy (VGX/GSNX) on cisplatin- and mCPBG-induced emesis to investigate the 5-HT_3 receptor sites responsible for initiating emesis.

Table 1 shows that YM060, a potent and selective 5-HT_3 receptor antagonist (Miyata et al., 1991a, b) administered intravenously or intra-4th cerebroventricularly (i.c.v.) inhibited established cisplatin (10 mg/kg i.v.)-induced emesis. This emesis was also abolished by VGX/GSNX. Intraperitoneal mCPBG (1 to 10 mg/kg) produced emesis in a dose-dependent manner, and the emesis induced by mCPBG 10 mg/kg i.p. was abolished by YM060 (3 µg/kg i.v. or 0.1 µg i.c.v.) and by VGX/GSNX (Table 2). These results suggest that cisplatin acts peripherally, probably in the gastrointestinal tract, and stimulates abdominal visceral afferent nerves through an increase of 5-HT level, and that mCPBG stimulates abdominal afferent nerves via 5-HT_3 receptors to cause emesis. These findings indicate that peripheral 5-HT_3 receptors are important in initiating cisplatin and mCPBG-induced emesis in ferrets, although both peripheral and central 5-HT_3 receptors are involved in the emesis.

Table 1. Effects of YM060 and abdominal visceral nerve transection (VGX/GSNX) on cisplatin-induced emesis.

Treatment	No. of ferrets emesis/tested	No. of emetic episodes [a]
Control	5/5	18.4 ± 1.9 [b]
YM060		
0.1 μg/kg i.v.	0/3	0 ± 0 [b]
0.1 μg i.c.v.	1/3	0.7 ± 0.7 [b]
Control	5/5	24.4 ± 2.7 [c]
Sham operation	3/3	16.7 ± 4.7 [c]
VGX/GSNX	0/3	0 ± 0

[a] Each value represents the mean ± S.E.M.
[b] Number of emetic episodes after saline or YM060. Saline or YM060 was administered 70 min after cisplatin.
[c] Total number of emetic episodes during the observation period of 6 h after cisplatin.

Table 2. Effects of YM060 and VGX/GSNX on mCPBG-induced emesis.

Treatment	No. of ferrets emesis/tested	No. of emetic episodes [a]
Control	3/3	5.0 ± 1.0
YM060		
3 μg/kg i.v.	0/4	0 ± 0
0.1 μg i.c.v.	0/3	0 ± 0
Sham operation	3/3	4.3 ± 0.9
VGX/GSNX	0/4	0 ± 0

[a] Each value represents the mean ± S.E.M.

REFERENCES

Barnes, J.M., Barnes, N.M., Costall, B., Naylor, R.J. and Rudd, J.A. (1990): Topographical distribution of 5-HT_3 receptor recognition sites in the ferret brain stem. Naunyn Schmiedeberg's Arch. Pharmacol. 342, 17-21.

Hawthorn, J., Ostler, K.J. and Andrews, P.L.R. (1988): The role of the abdominal visceral innervation and 5-hydroxytryptamine M receptors in vomiting induced by the cytotoxic drugs cyclophosphamide and cis-platin in the ferret. Quat. J. Exp. Physiol. 73. 7 21.

Higgins, G.A., Kilpatrick, G.J., Bunce, K.T., Jones, B.J. and Tyers, M.B. (1989): 5-HT_3 receptor antagonists injected into area postrema inhibit cisplatin-induced emesis in the ferret. Br. J. Pharmacol. 97, 247-255.

Miyata, K., Kamato, T., Nishida, A., Ito, H., Katsuyama, Y., Iwai, A., Yuki, H., Yamano, M., Tsutsumi, R., Ohta, M., Takeda, M. and Honda, K. (1991a): Pharmacologic profile of (R)-5-[(1-methyl-3-indolyl)carbonyl]-4,5,6,7-tetrahydro-1H-benzimidazole hydrochloride (YM060), a potent and selective 5-$hydroxytryptamine_3$ receptor antagonist, and its enantiomer in the isolated tissue. J. Pharm. Exp. Ther. 259, 15-21.

Miyata, K., Kamato, T., Yamano, M., Nishida, A., Ito, H., Katsuyama, Y., Yuki, H., Tsutsumi, R., Ohta, M., Takeda, M. and Honda, K. (1991): Serotonin $(5\text{-HT})_3$ receptor blocking activities of YM060, a novel 4,5,6,7-tetrahydro-benzimidazole derivatives, and its enentiomer in anesthetized rats. J. Pharm. Exp. Ther. 259, 815-819.

Stables, R., Andrews, P.L.R., Bailey, H.E., Costall, B., Gunning, S.J., Hawthorn, J., Naylor, R.J. and Tyers, M.B. (1987): Antiemetic properties of the $5HT_3$ receptor antagonist, GR38032F. Cancer Treat. Rev. 14, 333-336.

Mechanisms and Control of Emesis. Eds A.L. Bianchi, L. Grélot, A.D. Miller, G.L. King. Colloque INSERM/ John Libbey Eurotext Ltd. © 1992, Vol. 223, pp. 249-250

Blockade of 5-hydroxytryptamine$_3$ receptors modifies vagally driven and basal antral motility in the anaesthetised ferret

S. Bingham and P.D. King

SmithKline Beecham Pharmaceuticals, Coldharbour Road, The Pinnacles, Harlow, Essex CM19 5AD, UK

5-HT$_3$ receptor antagonists block a number of vagal reflexes activated by 5-HT, including emesis and the Bezold-Jarisch reflex. In the gastrointestinal tract, both 5-HT and the vagus are important in the control of motility and it is possible that, as in other systems, there are interactions between the two which are mediated by 5-HT$_3$ receptors. The aim of the present study was to investigate the effect of the 5-HT$_3$ receptor antagonists granisetron (GRAN), ondansetron (OND) and tropisetron (TROP) on the vagally mediated gastric corpo-antral reflex. Experiments were performed in urethane anaesthetised ferrets (1.5 g kg^{-1} i.p.). The stomach was divided into corpus and antrum and pressure monitored in the distended antrum (1 ml 154 mM NaCl) during inflation of the corpus (7 ml 154 mM NaCl min^{-1}. Total 21 ml). The increase in antral contraction amplitude (CA) during inflation was compared before and 30 min after administration of the 5-HT$_3$ receptor antagonists and the mean change (±SEM) calculated. Basal antral CA was measured 5 min before and after their administration and the mean change (± SEM) also calculated. The results are summarised below.

CHANGE IN CA (cm H_2O)

mgkg^{-1}		0.05	0.1	0.5	2.0	3.0
REFLEX	GRAN	-0.4±0.4	-2.6±0.8** (n=8)	-3.5±1.7 (n=8)	-3.6±1.7 (n=8)	-
	TROP		+0.3±0.5 (n=6)			-3.7±1.5* (n=6)
	OND	-0.8±0.4	+1.9±1.5 (n=5)	+2.3±1.3 (n=8)	+0.5±0.9 (n=6)	-
BASAL	GRAN	+0.3±0.2	-1.9±0.6 (n=7)	-1.5±0.5* (n=10)	-5.5±2.1* (n=8)	-
	TROP		+0.7±0.5 (n=8)	-	-	-4.0±2.3 (n=8)
	OND	+0.7±0.7	-0.7±1.5 (n=5)	+0.6±0.5 (n=8)	+1.4±0.5* * (n=15)	-

**$p \leq 0.01$, *$p \leq 0.05$ Student's paired 't' test

Granisetron, at a dose of 0.5 $mgkg^{-1}$, (which completely blocks emesis in the ferret (Andrews et al, 1991)), had no effect on the corpo-antral reflex, but significantly decreased basal CA. This effect on basal CA became more pronounced as the dose was increased. Tropisetron, which is known to be active at both $5\text{-}HT_3$ and $5\text{-}HT_4$ receptors had no effect on either the reflex or basal CA at a $5\text{-}HT_3$ receptor blocking dose of 0.1 mgkg i.v. but significantly decreased the reflex at a dose of 3 mg/kg i.v. It is uncertain whether this is due to an effect at $5\text{-}HT_3$ or $5\text{-}HT_4$ receptors. Ondansetron, which may be less selective for the $5\text{-}HT_3$ receptor than granisetron (ibid.) had a non-significant stimulant effect on the corpo-antral reflex and basal motility at the lower doses but significantly increased basal CA at 2 mg/kg i.v.

This study demonstrates a marked difference in the ability of the $5\text{-}HT_3$ receptor antagonists granisetron, ondansetron and tropisetron to influence both the corpo-antral reflex and basal motility which may be related to differences in potency and/or selectivity between the compounds. During emesis a number of vagally mediated reflex changes in motility occur which may be associated with nausea. As all three compounds are anti-emetic agents, differences in their capacity to modify such reflexes may lead to differences in clinical efficacy.

References

1. Andrews, P.L.R. ***et al*** (1991): Are all 5-hydroxytryptamine$_3$ receptors the same? *6th European Congress of Clinical Oncology & Cancer Nursing*, Florence, Italy, October 1991.

2. Andrews, P.L.R. & Scatchard, T. (1980): The gastric motility patterns induced by direct and reflex excitation of the vagus nerves in the anaesthetised ferret. *J. Physiol.* 302, 363-378.

Mechanisms and Control of Emesis. Eds A.L. Bianchi, L. Grélot, A.D. Miller, G.L. King. Colloque INSERM/ John Libbey Eurotext Ltd. © 1992, Vol. 223, pp. 251-252

Agonist evidence for the involvement of $5HT_3$ receptors in emesis in the ferret

M. Ravenscroft, U. Wells, P. Bhandari and P.L.R. Andrews

Department of Physiology, St. George's Hospital Medical School, Cranmer Terrace, London, SW17 ORE, UK

Prior to the publication in 1986 by Miner and Sanger that a $5HT_3$ receptor antagonist (then known as 5HT-M) blocked the emesis induced by cisplatinum in the ferret there was virtually no evidence implicating 5HT in the emetic mechanism. For example 5HT given icv was rarely emetic (Feldberg & Sherwood 1954), and the emetic effects of 5HTP were ascribed to catecholamine release (Cahen 1964). The identification of the anti-emetic effects of a range of $5HT_3$ receptor antagonists against the emesis induced by cytotoxic drugs and radiation (see review by Andrews et al. 1990) has prompted studies of the role of 5HT in emesis. To date the bulk of the direct evidence is from anti-emetic studies of the spectrum of action of the antagonists, neurochemical and autoradiographic ligand binding studies (e.g. Leslie et al. 1990, Andrews et al. 1990). Although some agonist evidence has been published, these studies have neither compared different routes of administration and different agonists, nor the effect of a selective $5HT_3$ antagonist and visceral nerve lesion in the same species (Torii et al. 1991, Sancilio et al. 1991, Miller & Nonaka 1992). This abstract reports some of the results from such a study in the ferret.

In conscious adult ferrets a range of $5HT_3$ receptor agonists were given at a dose of 5 mg/kg either intraperitoneally or into the stomach by intubation. The animals were observed for general behaviourial changes, retching and vomiting for at least one hour. The agonists used were 2-methyl-5HT (2me5HT), l-phenyl-biguanide (PBG) and chloro-phenyl-biguanide (CPBG). The effect of the $5HT_3$ receptor antagonist granisetron (1 mg/kg sc) and combined abdominal vagotomy (VX) and greater splanchnic nerve section (GSNX) were tested for their effect on the emetic response to intragastric CPBG as this produced the most reliable and maximum emetic response.

All three agonists irrespective of route of administration induced retching with a relatively short latency (mean ± sem). For example, CPBG given ip had a latency of 11.9 ± 6.7 min (n=4/6) and when given ig had a latency of 7.4 ± 3.3 min (n=4/6). For CPBG the response incidence for retching and vomiting was the same for both ip and ig routes but for PBG and 2me5HT the ig route more reliably induced both retching and vomiting than when given ip (ip vomiting incidence: PBG = 1/6, 2me5HT = 2/6; ig vomiting incidence: PBG = 6/6, 2me5HT = 5/5; $p = 0.0078$ for PBG & 0.0486 for 2me5HT by Fisher's Exact test). For both routes CPBG was the most emetic as assessed by retching (ip = 30.25 ± 8.0, ig = 18.75 ± 8.0, n=6) although because of the variability these values were not significantly different from either PBG or 2me5HT. The emetic response to ig CPBG was abolished by pre-treatment with granisetron and by VX+GSNX when the animals were tested 7-10 days post-lesion. These treatments also markedly reduced the "flopping down" behaviour induced by CPBG and by the other agonists.

Emesis has rarely been induced by 5HT given intravenously. As the jugular vein is often used for such injections we wondered if the reason for this was because of the activation of vagal afferents in the cardiopulmonary region that suppressed the emetic reflex. This was tested by injecting PBG (50 μg/kg) into the jugular vein of chronically cannulated ferrets (n=2) after they had been given loperamide (0.5 mg/kg sc) or exposed to radiation (2Gy whole body). In these animals in which emesis had been established, vomiting was blocked transiently (6 - 8 min) by the bolus injection of PBG.

This study demonstrates that selective $5HT_3$ receptor agonists can induce emesis in the ferret by a pathway involving the abdominal visceral innervation although the relative contribution of the vagus and splanchnic nerves has yet to be assessed as does the precise site of action. It is proposed that the difficulty in inducing emesis by iv injection of the $5HT_3$ receptor agonists is due to activation of cardiopulmonary vagal afferents that have been shown to modulate other somatic reflexes such as cough and postural control.

References

Andrews, P.L.R., Davis, C.J., Bingham, S., Davidson, H.I.M., Hawthorn, J., and Maskell, L. (1990): The abdominal visceral innervation and the emetic reflex: pathways, pharmacology, and plasticity. *Can. J. Phys. Pharmacol.* 68, 325-345.

Cahen, R.L. (1964): On the mechanism of emesis induced by 5-hydroxytryptamine. *Proc. Soc. Exp. Biol. Med.* 116, 402-404.

Feldberg, W. and Sherwood, S.L. (1954): Injections of drugs into the lateral ventricle of the cat. *J. Physiol.* 123, 148-167.

Leslie, R.A., Reynolds, D.J.M., Andrews, P.L.R., Grahame-Smith, D.G., Davis, C.J., and Harvey, J.M. (1990): Evidence for presynaptic $5\text{-hydroxytryptamine}_3$ recognition sites on vagal afferent terminals in the brainstem of the ferret. *Neurosci.* 3, 667-673.

Miller, A.D., and Nonaka, S. (1992): Mechanisms of vomiting induced by serotonin-3 receptor agonists in the cat: effect of vagotomy, splanchnicectomy or area postrema lesion. *J. Pharmacol. Expt. Ther.* 260, 509-517.

Miner, W.D. and Sanger, G.J. (1986): Inhibition of cisplatin-induced vomiting by selective 5-hydroxytryptamine M-receptor antagonism. *Br. J. Pharmacol.* 88, 4987-499.

Sancilio, L.F., Pinkus, L.M., Jackson, C.B., and Munson, Jr., H.R. (1991): Studies on the emetic and antiemetic properties of zacopride and its enantiomers. *Eur. J. Pharmacol.* 192, 365-369.

Torii, Y., Saito, H., and Matsuki, N. (1991): 5-Hydroxytryptamine is emetogenic in the house musk shrew, *Suncus murinus*. *Naunyn-Schmiedeberg's Arch. Pharmacol.* 344, 564-567.

Kenneth R. Brizzee lecture

Conférence Kenneth R. Brizzee

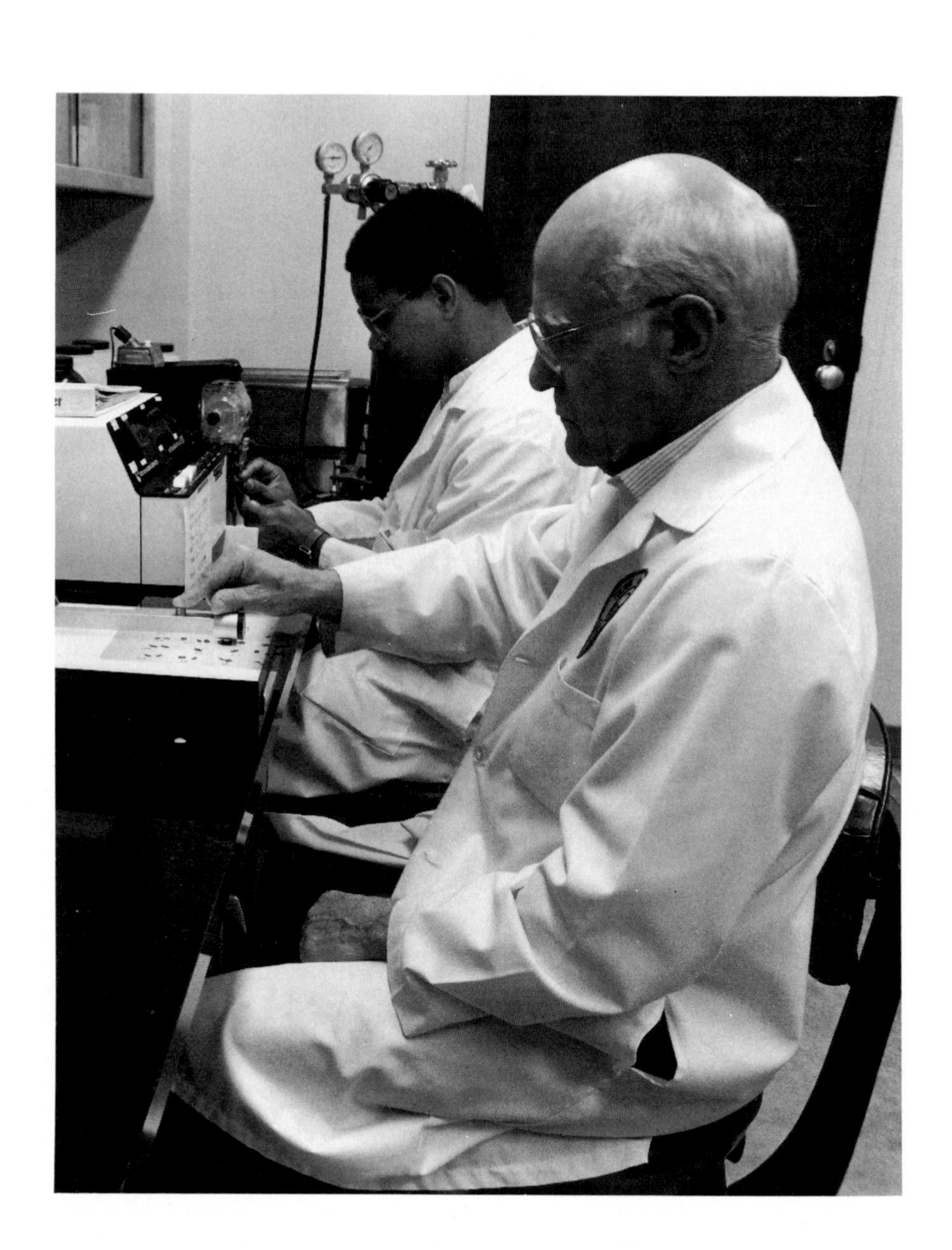

Mechanisms and Control of Emesis. Eds A.L. Bianchi, L. Grélot, A.D. Miller, G.L. King. Colloque INSERM/
John Libbey Eurotext Ltd. © 1992, Vol. 223, pp. 255-257

In memorial
Kenneth Raymond Brizzee (1916-1990)

R.A. Fox

School of Social Sciences, Department of Psychology, San José State University, San José, CA 95192-0120, USA

Dr. Kenneth Brizzee, a quiet and caring gentleman, and a distinguished scientist and scholar, died of cancer on June 11, 1990. Ken had a reverence for, and life-long commitment to learning and research, a great respect for people, and a love of the outdoors, particularly for the American West. He is survived by his wife of 45 years, Elizabeth Jane, three children, Barbara Lynne, David L., and William D., and three grandchildren.

Professor Brizzee earned B.S (1939) and M.S. (1941) degrees in Zoology at the University of Utah. During World War II he served as a naval aviator in the Pacific Theater, and then returned to school to earn the Ph.D. in Anatomy at St. Louis University (1949). After completing the Ph.D. he joined the faculty of the College of Medicine at the University of Utah where he remained until 1961. He was at the College of Medicine at the University of Nebraska (1961 to 1964) where he was Professor of Anatomy and a Research Professor in Obstetrics and Gynecology while earning the M.D. degree (1963). He then returned to the College of Medicine at the University of Utah where he remained until 1968 when he joined the Delta Regional Primate center and became an Adjunct Professor of Anatomy at Tulane University. He served briefly as Chair of the School of Dental Medicine and Professor of Anatomy at Southern Illinois University (1971-1972) before returning to the Delta Regional Primate Center where he was Head of Neurobiology from 1978 until 1990. During this period he was Professor, and later Professor Emeritus (1988), in the Tulane University School of Medicine.

Dr. Brizzee was an active member of several professional societies including the AAAS, the American Academy of Neurology, the American Association of Anatomy, the American Association of Neuropathology, the Gerontology Society (elected fellow in 1970), the Radiation Research Society, and the Society for Neuroscience. In 1980 he was elected president of the American Aging Association.

Dr. Brizzee's scholarly career had an early start with the publication of three papers by the time he completed the Ph.D. This tradition of writing continued throughout his career with the publication of more than 100 papers in journals, several chapters in books, and the co-editorship of two books.

In the area of research on the emetic system, his study of brain anatomy, particularly that of the area postrema, produced several papers that defined much of our early (Borison & Brizzee, 1951; Brizzee & Neal, 1954; Brizzee, Neal, & Williams, 1955), and present (Brizzee & Mehler, 1986) understanding of neural mechanisms important to the emetic reflex. He also explicated temporal aspects of the mechanical actions of emesis by conducting important cineradiographic studies of gut actions occurring before and during vomiting (Smith & Brizzee, 1961). His expertise and early reputation in this area contributed to his participation in the first application of area postrema lesions in man for the relief of intractable vomiting (Lindstrom & Brizzee, 1962). His study of the mechanisms of motion-induced emesis produced several papers that contribute importantly to our current understanding of the mechanisms underlying the maladies of motion and space sickness (e.g., Ordy & Brizzee, 1980; Brizzee, Ordy, & Mehler, 1980; Fox, Corcoran, & Brizzee, 1990). This work depended heavily on his excellent skills as a quantitative morphologist and surgeon.

Dr. Brizzee conducted important investigations of the neurobiology of aging, particularly with studies of the relationship of lipofuscin to the aging process. His morphometric skills led to the development of methods for quantitative evaluation of cell populations (Brizzee, Sherwood, & Timiras, 1968) and lipofuscin accumulation in the brain (Brizzee & Johnson, 1970; Brizzee & Cancilla, 1972; Brizzee, Ordy, & Kaack, 1974). These techniques were used to investigate the correlation of lipofuscin with age-related changes in learning, memory, and motor functions (e.g., Ordy, Brizzee, Kaack, & Hansche, 1978). In 1978 he received the annual research award of the American Aging Association for this work.

In addition to serious commitment to research, Professor Brizzee was a dedicated teacher. He addressed all forms of teaching seriously with a genuine concern for learning. His continuing excellence in teaching was acknowledged with student-selected awards at the University of Utah College of Medicine (the Golden Apple award in 1966 for "excellent presentation of material and sincere interest in the student") and at the Tulane University School of Medicine (the Owl Club award in 1989 for the outstanding course in that year). He was an outstanding role model with great concern for students.

But to his many friends, Ken Brizzee was much more than a dedicated scientist, scholar, and teacher. His vigor and enthusiasm for activity and life were amazing to those who knew him well. My introduction to his strength and vigor occurred the first time I assisted him in surgery. Here was a man 24 years my senior who stood for hours conducting delicate surgery through a microscope and evidenced no apparent fatigue while I was exhausted. He had a steady hand, intense concentration, and amazing strength. His youthful vigor is further evident in his beginning to play tennis at age 68 and the rediscovery of skiing at 72. He impressed his grandchildren by jumping rope and doing chin-ups with ease in his 70's.

As a young man, while working in New Jersey, Ken discovered jazz music in Harlem and developed a love of music that he maintained throughout his life. He was an accomplished clarinetist who played professionally in both Utah and California as a young man. With maturity in his professional life he resumed serious playing in the 1980's, taking lessons and participating in a semi-professional Dixieland band in New Orleans. He also loved classical music and played clarinet concertos with amazing proficiency.

Ken Brizzee was a quiet, modest, unassuming, reserved and respectful gentleman who has the unqualified respect of many people. He touched the lives of many people in many capacities: friend, teacher, scientist, pilot, and musician among others. Although he was loved dearly and is missed by all who knew him, the grace and dignity he bestowed on those around him is treasured. Many recall their interactions with him with high regard and are pleased to have known him.

REFERENCES

Borison, H. L. & Brizzee, K. R. (1951): Morphology of emetic chemoreceptive trigger zone in cat medulla oblongata. *Proceedings of Society Exp. Biol. Med.* 77, 38-42.

Brizzee, K. R. & Cancilla, P. A. (1972): Differential accumulation of lipofuscin pigment in cerebral cortex of rat. *Gerontologia* 18, 1-13.

Brizzee, K. R. & Johnson, R. A. (1970): Depth distribution of lipofuscin pigment in cerebral cortex of rat. *Acta Neuropathologica* 16, 205-219.

Brizzee, K. R. & Mehler, W. R. (1986): The central nervous connections involved in the vomiting reflex. In *Nausea and vomiting: Mechanisms and treatments,* ed. C. J. Davis, G. V. Lake-Bakaar & D. G. Grahame-Smith, pp. 31-55. New York: Springer Verlag.

Brizzee, K. R., Neal, L. M. (1954): A re-evaluation of the cellular morphology of the area postrema in view of recent evidence for a chemoreceptor function. *J. Comp. Neuro.* 100, 41-62.

Brizzee, K. R., Neal, L. M., & Williams, P. M. (1955): The chemoreceptive trigger zone for emesis in the monkey. *Am. J. Physiol.* 180, 659-662.

Brizzee, K. R., Ordy, J. M., & Kaack, B. (1974): Early appearance and regional differences in intraneuronal and extraneuronal lipofuscin accumulation with age in the brain of a nonhuman primate. *J. Gerontology* 29, 366-381.

Brizzee, K. R., Ordy, J. M., & Mehler, W. R. (1980): Effect of ablation of area postrema on frequency and latency of motion sickness-induced emesis in the squirrel monkey. *Physiol. Behav.* 24, 849-853.

Brizzee, K. R., Sherwood, N., & Timiras, P. S. (1968): A comparison of cell populations at various depth levels in cerebral cortex of young adult and aged Long-Evans rats. *J. Gerontology* 23, 389-397.

Fox, R. A., Corcoran, M. L., & Brizzee, K. R. (1990): Conditioned taste aversion and motion sickness in cats and squirrel monkeys. *Can. J. Physiol. Pharmacol.* 68, 269-278.

Lindstrom, P. A. and Brizzee, K. R. (1962): Relief of intractable vomiting from surgical lesions in the area postrema. *J. Neurosurg.* 19, 228.

Ordy, J. M. & Brizzee, K. R. (1980): Motion sickness in the squirrel monkey. *Aviat. Space Environ. Med.* 51, 215-223.

Ordy, J. M., Brizzee, K. R., Kaack, B, & Hansche, J. (1978): Age differences in short-term memory and cell loss in the cortex of the rat. *Gerontology* 24, 276-285.

Smith, C. C. and Brizzee, K. R. (1961): Cineradiographic analysis of vomiting in the cat. *Gastroenterology* 40, 654.

[1]This paper was prepared by Robert A. Fox, Department of Psychology, San José State University. The author is grateful for comments and information that were provided by many individuals. The assistance of Ken's family, especially Barbara and William Brizzee, was invaluable. Thanks also go out to Drs Bernice Kaack, George Crampton, and Bill Mehler. The author assumes full responsibility, of course, for any errors that occur.

Mechanisms and Control of Emesis. Eds A.L. Bianchi, L. Grélot, A.D. Miller, G.L. King. Colloque INSERM/
John Libbey Eurotext Ltd. © 1992, Vol. 223, pp. 259-272

5-HT$_3$ - 5-HT$_4$ receptors

John R. Fozard

Preclinical Research, Sandoz Pharma Ltd., CH-4002 Basel, Switzerland

SUMMARY

The 5-HT$_3$ receptor is unique among 5-HT receptors in forming directly a ligand-gated ion channel and hence not being a member of the G-protein receptor "superfamily". Fast neuronal depolarization associated with an increase in cation conductance is the initial cellular response to activation of 5-HT$_3$ receptors. Many powerful and selective ligands for these sites are available which have allowed definition of their widespread functional significance and revealed evidence of 5-HT$_3$ receptor heterogeneity with an inter-species basis. Nausea and vomiting associated with cancer treatments is currently an important clinical target for 5-HT$_3$ receptor antagonists and further novel treatments for a variety of gastrointestinal and psychiatric disorders are likely to emerge. The 5-HT$_4$ receptor is linked positively to adenylate cyclase in central neurones, cardiac myocytes and oesophageal smooth muscle. Novel ligands for this site, which include benzamide and benzimidazoline derivatives, have helped reveal the widespread distribution of 5-HT$_4$ receptors. The 5-HT$_4$ receptor of the enteric nervous system may mediate the gastrokinetic effects of the benzamide derivatives; however, the physiological and/or patho-physiological significance of the 5-HT$_4$ receptors in other parts of the gastrointestinal tract, the heart and the brain remains to be elucidated.

5-HT$_3$ - 5-HT$_4$ récepteurs

Parmi les récepteurs à la sérotonine (5-HT), le récepteur 5-HT$_3$ est unique puisqu'il forme un canal ionique et, de ce fait, ne fait pas partie de la "superfamille" des récepteurs couplés aux protéines G. L'effet cellulaire initial de l'activation des récepteurs 5-HT$_3$ se traduit par une dépolarisation neuronale rapide associée à une augmentation de conductance cationique. Il existe une variété de ligands puissants et sélectifs pour ces récepteurs qui ont permis la caractérisation de leurs multiples effets fonctionnels et suggéré l'hétérogénéité des récepteurs 5-HT$_3$ particulièment en termes d'espèces. Actuellement, les épisodes nauséeux et le vomissement associés au traitement anticancéreux par chimiothérapie représentent une indication clinique majeure pour les antagonistes de type 5-HT$_3$; d'autre part, on peut s'attendre à de nouveaux traitements par ce type de substances d'une variété de syndromes d'origine gastro-intestinale et psychiatrique. Le récepteur 5-HT$_4$ est couplé positivement à l'adénylate cyclase dans des neurones centraux, les myocytes cardiaques et les cellules du muscle lisse de l'oesophage. De nouveaux *ligands pour ce récepteur, qui comprennent des dérivés de benzamides et des benzimidazolines, ont permis la mise en évidence de la distribution très variée des récepteurs 5-HT$_4$. On pense que ce récepteur, localisé dans le système nerveux entérique, est impliqué dans la médiation des effets gastrocinétiques produits par les dérivés des benzamides. Cependant, la signification physiologique et/ou pathophysiologique des récepteurs 5-HT$_4$ présents dans le coeur, le cerveau et d'autres régions du tractus digestif, n'est pas encore élucidée.*

INTRODUCTION

With hindsight it is clear that 5-HT$_3$ and 5-HT$_4$ receptors were mediating many of the earliest pharmacological effects of 5-hydroxytryptamine (5-HT; serotonin) to be defined (Fozard, 1984; Clarke et al., 1989). However, it is only recently, and largely as a consequence of the advent of selective agonists and antagonists that this has been recognized and the overall significance of 5-HT$_3$ and 5-HT$_4$ receptors to physiology and pathophysiology has begun to emerge. The nominal aim of this review is to present the most important recent developments in this context; in practice, constraints of space allow only the most general points to be made and the reader is referred to more detailed reviews for supplementary information (Hoyer, 1990, 1991; Peters et al., 1991; Fozard, 1992a, b, c; Bockaert et al., 1992).

5-HT$_3$ RECEPTORS

Nature and definition of 5-HT$_3$ receptors; 5-HT$_3$ receptor subtypes

The 5-HT$_3$ receptor is unique, not just amongst 5-HT receptors, but also amongst mono- and diamine neurotransmitter receptors, in not being coupled via a G protein to its effector system. Rather it forms a ligand-gated ion channel (Derkach et al., 1989) analogous to the nicotine. GABA$_A$ and glycine receptors (Strange, 1988). Recently, Maricq et al. (1991) isolated a complementary DNA clone encoding a 5-HT$_3$ receptor from NCB-20 cells. The predicted protein shows many of the features of the other members of the ligand gated ion channel family and, when expressed in Xenopus oocytes, manifests pharmacological and electrophysiological properties broadly similar to those of the native receptor.

The 5-HT$_3$ may be defined pharmacologically according to a slightly revised version of the scheme for the classification of functional 5-HT$_3$ receptors proposed by Bradley et al. (1986); thus, it should be resistant to blockade by antagonists at 5-HT$_1$-like, 5-HT$_2$ and 5-HT$_4$ receptors, be responsive to phenylbiguanide (or m-chlorophenylbiguanide) - but see below in the context of 5-HT$_3$ receptor subtyes - and 2-methyl-5-HT and be blocked selectively by low concentrations of MDL 72222, tropisetron, granisetron or ondansetron. A further important discriminatory feature is that 5-methoxytryptamine, which has affinity approaching that of 5-HT at all other 5-HT receptor subtypes, lacks affinity at the 5-HT$_3$ receptor.

Evidence is accumulating for the existence of 5-HT$_3$ receptor subtypes and for species differences being the basis of the receptor heterogeneity. The evidence includes the following:

- the blocking potency of selective 5-HT_3 receptor antagonists on guinea-pig tissues (ileum, colon, vagus nerve, superior cervical ganglion, nodose ganglion) is consistently and substantially (≥ 1-2 log units) less than that on rabbit (heart, vagus nerve) or rat (vagus nerve, superior cervical ganglion) tissues (data summarized and analysed in Fozard (1992a, b).

- phenylbiguanide (and/or m-chlorophenylbiguanide) interact(s) highly selectively as an antagonist with the 5-HT_3 receptors present on rabbit and rat autonomic and afferent fibres (see Fozard, 1990) and displaces the selective radioligand, ^{3}H-GR 67330, from the 5-HT_3 receptors in rat and rabbit ileum and rat brain (Kilpatrick et al., 1991). However, neither compound appears to have affinity for the 5-HT_3 receptors in guinea-pig tissues (for extensive discussion and data sources see Fozard, 1990; Kilpatrick and Tyers, 1992a).

- (+)-tubocurarine has low nanomolar affinity for, and is appreciably (≥ 100-fold) more potent as an antagonist of, 5-HT_3 receptors in mouse tissues (superior cervical ganglion, NG 108-15 and NIE-115 cells, hippocampal cells in culture, cloned site from NCB-20 cells) than those from rabbit (nodose ganglion) and rat (superior cervical ganglion), (see Fozard, 1992b). Conversely, cocaine appears to be substantially more potent as an antagonist at the 5-HT_3 receptors in rabbit and rat tissues than in mouse tissues (Malone et al., 1991). (+)-Tubocurarine is essentially inactive at the 5-HT_3 receptors in a variety of guinea-pig tissues (see Peters et al., 1991; Fozard, 1992b for further discussion).

- marked differences exist in the 5-HT_3 receptor single channel conductance values in different tissues. For instance, the values from several cells derived from murine neuronal tissue are substantially lower (0.3 - 4 pS) than those recorded from either guinea-pig submucous plexus neurones (9 and 15 pS) or rabbit nodose ganglion cells (17 pS) (reviewed in Fozard, 1992b; Peters et al., 1991).

The above is entirely consistent with the existence of 5-HT_3 receptor subtypes and for species differences being the basis of the heterogeneity. No convincing evidence is yet available for the existence of subtypes within a particular species.

Location of 5-HT_3 receptors

5-HT_3 receptors are located exclusively on neurones and are present in both the peripheral and central nervous systems. In the periphery they are located on pre- and postsynaptic elements of both branches of the autonomic nervous system and on afferent and enteric neurones (Fozard, 1984; Wallis, 1989). In the central nervous system 5-HT_3 receptors have a widespread distribution with particularly high concentrations being associated with the area postrema, hippocampus, and several regions involved in the perception and processing of pain (dorsal vagal complex, spinal trigeminal nucleus and the substantia gelatinosa at all levels of the spinal cord) (Laporte et al., 1992).

Cellular responses to 5-HT_3 receptor activation

The cellular events which may be induced following 5-HT_3 receptor activation are represented schematically in Fig. 1.

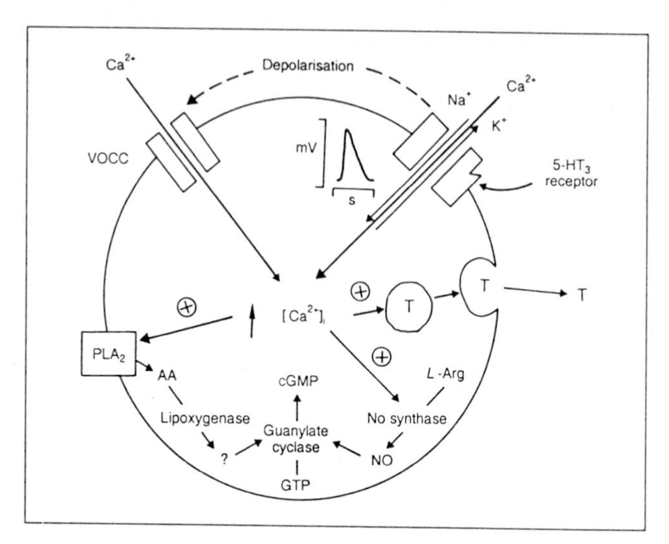

Fig. 1: Diagrammatic representation of the cellular events following stimulation of neuronal 5-HT_3 receptors. Information culled from the literature and in particular Fozard (1984), Yang (1990) and Reiser (1991). Taken with permission from Fozard, 1992a.

Activation of 5-HT_3 receptors triggers rapid depolarization associated with an increase in conductance to Na^+, K^+ and Ca^{2+} (n.b. the size of the arrows in Fig. 1 does not indicate a quantitative comparison of ion permeabilities). Ca^{2+} may also enter the cell through voltage operated calcium channels (VOCC). The subsequent rise in cytosolic Ca^{2+} ($[Ca^{2+}]_i$) triggers exocytotic transmitter (T) release from neurones and, in NG 108-15 cells, a rise in cGMP in part a consequence of activation of phospholipase A_2 (PLA_2) and formation of lipoxygenase products of arachidonic acid (AA) and in part the result of an increase in nitric oxide (NO) formation from L-arginine (L-Arg).

Selective ligands for 5-HT_3 receptors

Both selective agonists and antagonists are currently available for 5-HT_3 receptors. Of the agonists, 2-methyl-5-HT, phenylbiguanide and m-chlorophenylbiguanide are the most interesting. However, as discussed in detail previously (Fozard, 1990) both 2-methyl-5-HT (not fully selective) and the arylbiguanides (partial agonist properties; no affinity for guinea-pig 5-HT_3 receptors - see above) are less than ideal tools for probing 5-HT_3 receptor function. By contrast, there is now almost a glut of potent and very highly selective 5-HT_3 receptor antagonists. A recent review (Glennon and Dukat, 1992) lists over 60 such compounds emanating from 21 pharmaceutical companies; disappointingly, none appears to bring tangible advantages over the first generation of 5-HT_3 receptor antagonists, MDL 72222, tropisetron, granisetron and ondansetron. Radiolabelled ligands derived from many of these antagonists (for details, see Fozard, 1990; Hoyer, 1991) have been of particular value in identifying and quantifying the actions and interactions of ligands at 5-HT_3 receptors and for the autoradiographic mapping of these sites in the central and peripheral nervous systems (Laporte et al., 1992).

Pharmacological and clinical significance of 5-HT_3 receptors

Predictably, based on their wide distribution, 5-HT_3 receptor activation produces many and varied pharmacological effects. Certain of these have led to new approaches to therapy using selective antagonists and these are emphasized below.

Reflex effects account for the major cardiovascular and respiratory changes induced by administration of 5-HT_3 receptor agonists (Fozard, 1984; McQueen and Mir, 1989; Saxena and Villal6n, 1991). However, the 5-HT_3 receptors involved have not been implicated in pathophysiology and no therapeutic principle has emerged based on their activation or inhibition. This is not the case for the gastrointestinal tract where 5-HT_3 receptor activation modulates both secretion (Furman and Waton, 1989) and motility (Costall and Naylor, 1990) in animal models. With respect to secretion, 5-HT_3 receptor antagonists reduce hypersecretion induced by cholera toxin in rats (Beubler and Horina, 1990) and suppress the watery diarrhoea associated with carcinoid syndrome in man (Anderson et al., 1987). With respect to gastro-intestinal motility, 5-HT_3 receptor antagonists generally facilitate motor activity although this may be dependent on the degree of basal tone (Costall and Naylor, 1990); in healthy man, colonic transport is slowed selectively (Gore et al., 1990). The role of 5-HT_3 receptors in the nausea and vomiting associated with cancer chemo- and radiotherapy, is now established and several 5-HT_3 receptor antagonists are marketed for this indication. Cytotoxic drugs and x-radiation appear to disrupt 5-HT containing cells in the gastro-intestinal tract thereby releasing 5-HT which elicits the vomiting reflex by stimulation of 5-HT_3 receptors on the vagal afferent fibres (Andrews et al., 1988). The clinical aspects of the use of 5-HT_3 receptor antagonists in emesis are dealt with in detail elsewhere in this volume.

Pain and flare due to activation of local axon reflexes are a prominent response in man to stimulation of 5-HT_3 receptors on cutaneous primary afferent nerve endings (see Fozard, 1992c). In animal models, inflammatory pain can be alleviated by 5-HT_3 receptor antagonists (see Hamon et al., 1990; Fozard, 1992c) and, consistent with this, clinical benefit has been reported with certain 5-HT_3 receptor antagonists against the pain of migraine (Loisy et al., 1985; Couturier et al., 1991) and aspects of the visceral discomfort of irritable bowel syndrome (Prior and Reid, 1990).

The unequivocal demonstration of 5-HT_3 receptors in mammalian brain (Kilpatrick et al., 1987) came only after certain pharmacological effects of 5-HT_3 receptor antagonists had been observed which could only have reflected activity at a central site of action (see Costall et al., 1990). Thus, positive effects in animal models of anxiety (Costall et al., 1990), psychosis (Costall and Naylor, 1991) and cognitive dysfunction (Barnes et al., 1990) have been demonstrated as well as suppression of the biochemical and behavioural consequences of the administration of drugs of abuse (Costall et al., 1990). Plausible biochemical substrates for these functional effects have also been identified (see Fozard, 1992a; Kilpatrick and Tyers, 1992b). Recent clinical findings (Symposium, 1991) encourage the belief that at least some of the predictions from such studies will translate into useful therapies for psychiatric disease.

$5\text{-}HT_4$ RECEPTORS

Nature and definition of $5\text{-}HT_4$ receptors; $5\text{-}HT_4$ receptor subtypes

The $5\text{-}HT_4$ receptor was first named by Dumuis et al. (1988) following their identification of a novel 5-HT receptor linked positively to adenylate cyclase in neonatal mouse collicular neurones. Although its structure is not yet known and the designation $5\text{-}HT_4$ has not yet been officially recognised by the nomenclature committee of the Serotonin Club, its status as a novel 5-HT receptor is not in question and a pharmacological definition can be attempted. Adopting the approach of Bradley et al. (1986), the $5\text{-}HT_4$ receptor can be tentatively characterised as a site resistant to blockade by antagonists at $5\text{-}HT_1$-like, $5\text{-}HT_2$ and $5\text{-}HT_3$ receptors, where substituted benzamide (e.g. zacopride, renzapride, cisapride) and benzimidazolone (e.g. BIMU 1, BIMU 8) derivatives show agonist activity (see Baxter and Clarke, 1992; Dumuis et al., 1992) and where tropisetron, SDZ 205-557 (Buchheit et al., 1991) and DAU 6285 (Dumuis et al., 1992) act as surmountable antagonists (for further discussion see below and Bockaert et al., 1992). The evidence to date indicates that the $5\text{-}HT_4$ receptor is a member of the G-protein coupled receptor superfamily and that activation of adenylate cyclase is the principal second messenger response to its stimulation (see below). Despite occasional pharmacological discrepancies (for discussion see Baxter et al., 1991; Kaumann et al., 1991) the bulk of the evidence to date does not support $5\text{-}HT_4$ receptor heterogeneity.

Location of $5\text{-}HT_4$ receptors

It is becoming increasingly clear that $5\text{-}HT_4$ receptors have a wide general distribution both within and across species. In the brain, $5\text{-}HT_4$ receptors have been demonstrated on neurones of mouse colliculus (Dumuis et al., 1988) and rat (Andrade and Chaput, 1991) and guinea-pig (Bockaert et al., 1990) hippocampus. In the periphery, these sites are present on myenteric neurones of guinea-pig ileum (Craig and Clarke, 1990) and ascending colon (Elswood et al., 1991), the smooth muscle of rat ocsophagus (Baxter et al., 1991) and myocardial cells from pig (see Saxena and Villalón, 1991) and man (Kaumann et al., 1990; 1991; Ouadid et al., 1992).

Cellular responses to $5\text{-}HT_4$ receptor activation

Evidence from a number of tissues indicates that $5\text{-}HT_4$ receptors are coupled positively to adenylate cyclase resulting in a rise in cAMP and activation of cAMP-dependent protein kinase A (Kaumann et al., 1990; Ford et al., 1992; Ouadid et al., 1992). Depending on the cellular location of the sites such changes could be the basis of closure of K^+ channels leading to depolarisation, opening of VOCC and induction of transmitter release from both central (Andrade and Chaput, 1991; Fagni et al., 1992) and myenteric (Kilbinger and Wolf, 1992) neurones, increased calcium current amplitude and inotropism in cardiac myocytes (Kaumann et al., 1991; Ouadid et al., 1992), steroid secretion from frog adrenocortical cells (Idres et al., 1991) and smooth muscle relaxation (Ford et al., 1992).

Selective ligands for $5\text{-}HT_4$ receptors

Although there are now several ligands available with appreciable affinity for $5\text{-}HT_4$ receptors all have disadvantages in the context of their use as pharmacological tools. The principal features of the most important of these agents are summarised in Table 1.

Table 1: Principle features of 5-HT_4 receptor ligands

Ligand	Structure	Comment	References
Tropisetron	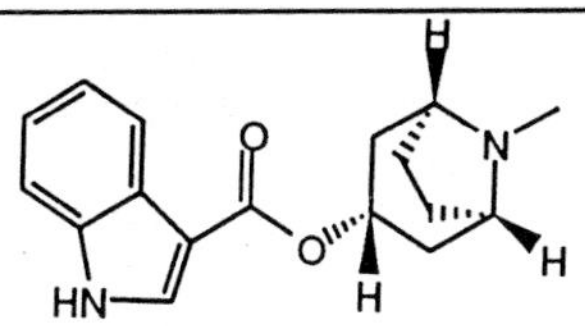	Surmountable antagonist at 5-HT_4 receptors but > 1000-fold greater affinity for 5-HT_3 receptors	Craig and Clarke (1990) Dumuis et al. (1988)
SDZ 205-557	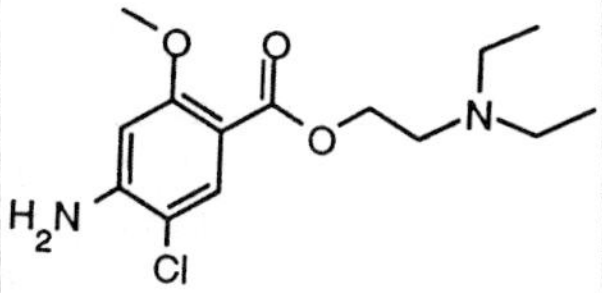	Some selectivity for 5-HT_4 receptors over guinea-pig 5-HT_3 receptors. However non-competitive antagonist of benzamide ligands in quiescent ileum	Buchheit et al. (1992) Ford et al. (1992)
DAU 6285	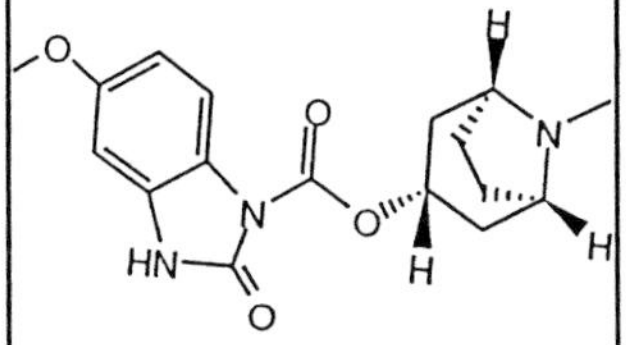	Surmountable antagonist at 5-HT_4 receptors but only marginally selective vis-à-vis 5-HT_3 sites	Dumuis et al. (1992)
Renzapride Zacopride Cisapride Metoclopramide	see Dumuis et al. (1989)	Partial agonists at 5-HT_4 receptors in most preparations but appreciably more potent as 5-HT_3 receptor antagonists	Dumuis et al. (1989) Craig and Clarke (1990)
BIMU 1 BIMU 8	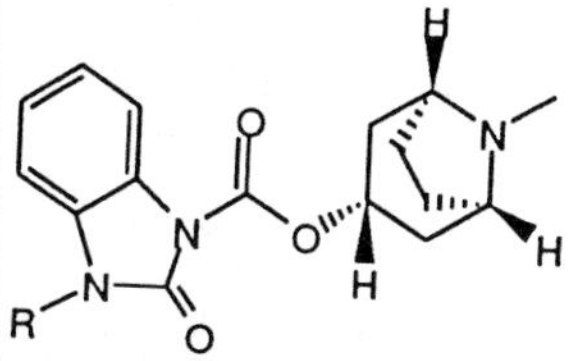 BIMU 1 R = $-CH_2CH_3$ BIMU 8 R = $-CH(CH_3)_2$	Close to full agonists at 5-HT_4 receptors but appreciably more potent as 5-HT_3 receptor antagonists	Dumuis et al. (1991) Baxter and Clarke (1992)

None of these agents has the potency and/or selectivity to be used as a radioligand and the 5-HT_4 receptor remains the only major 5-HT receptor subtype for which no radioligand exists.

Pharmacological and clinical significance of 5-HT_4 receptors

Each of the major organ systems in which 5-HT_4 receptors are found has yielded pharmacological effects which point to the potential physiological and/or pathophysiological relevance of

Table 2: Summary of the major properties of 5-HT$_3$ and 5-HT$_4$ receptors[a)]

	5-HT$_3$	5-HT$_4$
Structure known	yes	no
G-protein linked	no	yes
Transduction mechanism	cation channel	↑cAMP ↑PKA
Subtypes	yes - species based	not known
Localisation: periphery	enteric neurones autonomic neurones } many species sensory neurones	myenteric neurones (guinea pig) smooth muscle (rat) cardiac myocytes (pig, human) adrenocortial cells (frog)
Localisation: CNS	area postrema hippocampus dorsal vagal complex } many species spinal trigeminal nucleus dorsal horn of spinal cord	collicus (mouse) hippocampus (rat, guinea-pig)
Cellular functions	neuronal depolarisation (↑Na^+, K^+ conductance) transmitter release	neuronal depolarization (↓K^+ conductance) transmitter release smooth muscle relaxation cardiac inotropy cardiac chronotropy steroid release
Discriminatory agonists	2-methyl-5-HT phenylbiguanide (m-chlorophenylbiguanide)	5-methoxytryptamine[b)] cisapride renzapride zacopride BIMU 1 BIMU 8
Discriminatory antagonists	MDL 722222 ondansetron granisetron	tropisetron SDZ 205-557 DAU 6285
Disease relevance	emesis anxiety psychosis impaired cognition drug abuse	gastrointestinal stasis

a) see text for further details and reference sources

b) has affinity approaching that of 5-HT at all other 5-HT receptor subtypes but lacks affinity at 5-HT$_3$ receptors (Fozard, 1990) these sites and the possible therapeutic utility of 5-HT_4 receptor ligands. In the gastro-intestinal tract, for example, activation of the 5-HT_4 receptor facilitates the peristaltic reflex elicited in vitro in guinea-pig ileum (Buchheit and Buhl, 1991; Craig and Clarke, 1991). The observation provides a plausible explanation for the gastro-intestinal prokinetic properties of substituted benzamides such as metoclopramide and cisapride and provokes speculation as to the value of 5-HT_4 receptor antagonists in syndromes characterised by bowel hyperkinesia. In the heart, 5-HT_4 receptor activation is unlikely to be a useful therapeutic strategy since positive inotropic effects would be unlikely to occur without tachycardia (Saxena and Villalón, 1991). Moreover, the mechanistic basis of the effects on the heart, augmentation of cAMP, may actually predispose to arrhythmias in which case 5-HT_4 receptor antagonists would find application as antiarrhythmic therapies (patent application, 1991). Although both in vitro (Dumuis et al., 1988; Bockaert et al., 1990; Andrade and Chaput, 1991) and in vivo (Boddeke and Kalkman, 1990) evidence exists for the presence of functional 5-HT_4 receptors in the brain, the wider significance of these sites to central function remains unknown. The emergence of improved tools with which to probe 5-HT_4 receptor function (Table 2) should, if historical precedence is a guide, ensure progress towards a deeper understanding of the biological significance of this important site.

CONCLUSION

As the comparative summary of the major properties of the 5-HT_3 and 5-HT_4 receptors (Table 2) makes clear, these sites are of fundamental importance both to normal physiology and to a number of disease states involving most, if not all, of the major body systems. Potent and selective ligands are available and some have found clinical application. However, improvements are still possible and it can be confidently predicted that further novel therapeutic agents will emerge as the potency and/or selectivity of ligands for the 5-HT_3 and 5-HT_4 receptors is further refined.

REFERENCES

Anderson, J.V., Coupe M.O., Morris, J.A., Hodgson, H.J.F. & Bloom S.R. (1987): Remission of symptoms in carcinoid syndrome with a new 5-hydroxytryptamine M receptor antagonist. *Br. Med. J.* 294, 1129.

Andrade, R. & Chaput, Y. (1991): 5-Hydroxytryptamine$_4$-like receptors mediate the slow excitatory response to serotonin in the rat hippocampus. *J. Pharmacol. Exp. Ther.* 257, 930-937.

Andrews, P.L.R., Rapeport, W.G. & Sanger, G.J. (1988): Neuropharmacology of emesis induced by anticancer therapy. *Trends Pharmacol. Sci.* 9, 334-341.

Barnes, J.M., Costall, B., Coughlan, J., Domeney, A.M., Gerrard, P.A., Kelly, M.E., Naylor, R.J., Onaivi, E.S., Tomkins, D.M. & Tyers, M.B. (1990): The effects of ondansetron, a 5-HT_3 receptor antagonist, on cognition in rodents and primates. *Pharmacol. Biochem. Behav.* 35, 955-962.

Baxter, G.S. & Clarke, D.E. (1992): Benzimidazolone derivatives act as 5-HT_4 receptor ligands in rat oesophagus. *Eur. J. Pharmacol.* 212, 225-229.

Baxter, G.S., Craig, D.A. & Clarke, D.E. (1991): 5-Hydroxytryptamine$_4$ receptors mediate relaxation of rat oesophageal tunica muscularis mucosa. *Naunyn Schmiedeberg's Arch. Pharmacol.* 343, 439-446.

Beubler, E. & Horina, G. (1990): 5-HT_2 and 5-HT_3 receptor subtypes mediate cholera toxin-induced intestinal fluid secretion in the rat. *Gastroenterology* 99, 83-89.

Bockaert, J., Sebben, M. & Dumuis, A. (1990): Pharmacological characterization of 5-HT_4 receptors positively coupled to adenylate cyclase in adult guinea pig hippocampal membranes: Effect of substituted benzamide derivatives. *Mol. Pharmacol.* 37, 408-411.

Bockaert, J., Fozard, J.R., Dumuis, A. & Clarke, D.E. (1992): The 5-HT_4 receptor: a place in the sun. *Trends Pharmacol.* 13, 141.

Boddeke, H.W.G.M. & Kalkman, H.O. (1990): Zacopride and BRL 24924 induce an increase in EEG-energy in rats. *Br. J. Pharmacol.* 101, 281-284.

Bradley, P.B., Engel, G., Feniuk, W. Fozard, J.R., Humphrey, P.P.A., Middlemiss, D.N., Mylecharane, E.J., Richardson, B.P. & Saxena, P.R. (1986): Proposals for the classification and nomenclature of functional receptors for 5-hydroxytryptamine. *Neuropharmacology*, 25, 563-576.

Buchheit, K.H. & Buhl, T. (1991): Prokinetic benzamides stimulate peristaltic activity in the isolated guinea-pig ileum by activation of 5-HT_4 receptors. *Eur. J. Pharmacol.* 205, 203-208.

Buchheit, K.H., Gamse, R. & Pfannkuche, H.J. (1992): SDZ 205-557, a selective, surmountable antagonist for 5-HT_4 receptors in the isolated guinea-pig ileum. *Naunyn-Schmiedebergs's Arch. Pharmacol.* 345, 387-393.

Clarke, D.E., Craig, D.A. & Fozard, J.R. (1989): The 5-HT_4 receptor: naughty, but nice. *Trends Pharmacol. Sci.* 10, 385-386.

Costall, B. & Naylor, R.J. (1990): 5-Hydroxytryptamine: new receptors and novel drugs for gastrointestinal motor disorders. *Scand. J. Gastroenterol.* 25, 769-787.

Costall, B. & Naylor, R.J. (1991): Influence of 5-HT_3 receptor antagonists on limbic cortical circuitry. In *Serotonin: Molecular Biology, Receptors and Functional Effects,* ed. J.R. Fozard & P.R. Saxena, pp. 430-438. Basel: Birkhäuser.

Costall, B., Naylor, R.J. & Tyers, M.B. (1990): The psychopharmacology of 5-HT_3 receptors. *Pharmacol. Ther.* 47, 181-202.

Couturier, E.G.M., Hering, R., Foster, C.A., Steiner, T.J. & Rose, F.C. (1991): First clinical study of the selective 5-HT_3 antagonist, granisetron (BRL 43694), in the acute treatment of migraine headache. *Headache* 31, 296-297.

Craig, D.A. & Clarke, D.E. (1990): Pharmacological characterization of a neuronal receptor for 5-hydroxytryptamine in guinea-pig ileum with properties similar to the 5-HT_4 receptor. *J. Pharmacol. Exp. Ther.* 252, 1378-1386.

Craig, D.A. & Clarke, D.E. (1991): Peristalsis evoked by 5-HT and renzapride: evidence for putative 5-HT_4 receptor activation. *Br. J. Pharmacol.* 102, 563-564.

Derkach, V., Surprenant, A. & North, R.A. (1989): 5-HT_3 receptors are membrane ion channels. *Nature*, 339, 706-709.

Dumuis, A., Bouhelal, R., Sebben, M., Cory, R. & Bockaert, J. (1988): A non classical 5-hydroxytryptamine receptor positively coupled with adenylate cyclase in the central nervous system. *Mol. Pharmacol.* 34, 880-887.

Dumuis, A., Sebben, M. & Bockaert, J. (1989): The gastrointestinal prokinetic benzamine derivatives are agonists at the non-classical 5-HT receptor (5-HT_4) positively coupled to adenylate cyclase in neurons. *Naunyn-Schmiedeberg's Arch. Pharmacol.* 340, 403-410.

Dumuis, A., Sebben, M., Monferini, E., Nicola, M., Ladinsky, H. & Bockaert, J. (1991): Azabicycloalkyl benzimidazolone derivatives as a novel class of potent agonists at the 5-HT_4 receptor positively coupled to adenylate cyclase in brain. *Naunyn-Schmiedeberg's Arch. Pharmacol.* 343, 245-251.

Dumuis, A., Gozlan, H., Sebben, M., Ansanay, H., Rizzi, C.A., Turconi, M., Monferini, E., Giraldo, E., Schiantarelli, P., Ladinsky, H. & Bockaert, J. (1992): Characterization of a novel 5-HT_4 receptor antagonist of the azabicycloalkyl benzimidazolone class: DAU 6285. *Naunyn-Schmiedeberg's Arch. Pharmacol.* 345, 264-269.

Elswood, C.J., Bunce, K.T. & Humphrey, P.P.A. (1991): Identification of putative 5-HT_4 receptors in guinea-pig ascending colon. *Eur. J. Pharmacol.* 196, 149-155.

Fagni, L., Dumuis, A., Sebben, M. & Bockaert, J. (1992): The serotonin$_4$ receptor subtype inhibits K^+ current in colliculi neurons via activation of a cAMP-dependent protein kinase. *Br. J. Pharmacol.* 105, 973-979.

Ford, A.P.D., Baxter, G.S., Eglen, R.M. & Clarke, D.E. (1992): 5-Hydroxytryptamine stimulates cyclic AMP formation in the tunica muscularis mucosae of the rat oesophagus via 5-HT_4 receptors. *Eur. J. Pharmacol.* 211, 117-120.

Fozard, J.R. (1984): Neuronal 5-HT receptor in the periphery. *Neuropharmacology* 23, 1473-1486.

Fozard, J.R. (1990): Agonists and antagonists of 5-HT_3 receptors. In *Cardiovascular Pharmacology of 5-Hydroxytryptamine*, ed. P.R. Saxena, D.I. Wallis, W. Wouters & P. Bevan, pp. 101-115. Dordrecht: Kluwer.

Fozard, J.R. (1992a): Pharmacological relevance of 5-HT_3 receptors. In *Serotonin Receptor Subtypes: Pharmacological Significance and Clinical Implications*, ed. S.Z. Langer, J. Mendlewicz & G. Racagni, pp. 44-55. Int. Acad. Biomed. Drug Res. Basel: Karger.

Fozard, J.R. (1992b): 5-HT_3 receptors in the context of the multiplicity of 5-HT receptors. In *Central and Peripheral 5-HT_3 Receptors*, ed. M. Hamon. London: Academic Press, in press.

Fozard, J.R. (1992c): Role of 5-HT_3 receptors in nociception. In *5-HT_3 receptor antagonists*, ed. B. Jones, F.D. King, G.J. Sanger, Boca Raton: CRC Inc., in press.

Furman, B.L. & Waton, N.G. (1989): 5-Hydroxytryptamine and peripheral secretory mechanisms. In *The Peripheral Actions of 5-Hydroxytryptamine,* ed. J.R. Fozard, pp. 274-300. Oxford: Oxford University Press.

Glennon, R.A. & Dukat, M. (1992): 5-HT receptor ligands - update 1992. *Current Drugs: Serotonin*, pp. 1-45.

Gore, S., Gilmore, I.T., Haigh, C.G., Brownless, S.M., Stockdale, H. & Morris, A.I. (1990): Colonic transit in man is slowed by ondansetron (GR 38032 F), a selective 5-hydroxytryptamine receptor (type 3) antagonist. *Aliment Pharmacol. Ther.* 4, 139-144.

Hamon, M., Collin, E., Chantrel, D., Daval, G., Verge, D., Bourgoin S. & Cesselin, F. (1990): Serotonin receptors and the modulation of pain. In *Serotonin and Pain*, ed. J.M. Besson, pp. 53-72. Amsterdam: Elsevier.

Hoyer, D. (1990): Serotonin 5-HT_3, 5-HT_4 and 5-HT-M receptors. *Neuropsychopharmacology*, 3, 371-383.

Hoyer, D. (1991): The 5-HT receptor family: ligands, distribution and receptor-effector coupling. In *5-HT_{1A} Agonists, 5-HT_3 Antagonists and Benzodiazepines: Their Comparative Behavioural Pharmacology*, ed. R.J. Rodgers, & S.J. Cooper, pp. 31-57. Chichester: Wiley.

Idres, S., Delarue, C., Lefebvre, H. & Vaudry, H. (1991): Benzamide derivatives provide evidence for the involvement of a 5-HT_4 receptor type in the mechanism of action of serotonin in frog adrenocortical cells. *Mol. Brain Res.* 10, 251-258.

Kaumann, A.J., Sanders, L., Brown, A.M., Murray, K.J. & Brown, M.J. (1990): A 5-hydroxytryptamine receptor in human atrium. *Br. J. Pharmacol.* 100, 879-885.

Kaumann, A.J., Sanders, L., Brown, A.M., Murray, K.J., Brown & M.J. (1991): A 5-HT_4-like receptor in human right atrium. *Naunyn-Schmiedeberg's Arch. Pharmacol.* 344, 150-159.

Kilbinger, H. & Wolf, D. (1992): Effects of 5-HT_4 receptor stimulation on basal and electrically evoked release of acetylcholine from guinea-pig myenteric plexus. *Naunyn-Schmiedeberg's Arch. Pharmacol.*, 345, 270-275.

Kilpatrick, G.J., Barnes, N.M., Cheng, C.H.K., Costall, B., Naylor, R.J. & Tyers, M.B. (1991):

The pharmacological characterization of $5\text{-}HT_3$ receptor binding sites in rabbit ileum: comparison with those in rat ileum and rat brain. *Neurochem. Int.* 19, 389-396.

Kilpatrick, G.J. & Tyers, M.B. (1992a): Inter-species variants of the $5\text{-}HT_3$ receptor. *Biochem. Soc. Trans.* 20, 118-121.

Kilpatrick, G.J. & Tyers, M.B. (1992b): The pharmacological properties and functional roles of central $5\text{-}HT_3$ receptors. In *Central and Peripheral $5\text{-}HT_3$ Receptors*, ed. M. Hamon, London: Academic Press, in press.

Laporte, A.M., Kidd, E.J., Verge, D., Gozlan, H. & Hamon, M. (1992): Autoradiographic mapping of central $5\text{-}HT_3$ receptors. In *Central and Peripheral $5\text{-}HT_3$ Receptors*, ed. M. Hamon, London: Academic Press, in press.

Loisy, C., Beorchia, S., Centonze, V., Fozard, J.R., Schechter, P. & Tell, G.P. (1985): Effects on migraine headache of MDL 72222, an antagonist at neuronal 5-HT receptors. Double-blind, placebo-controlled study. *Cephalalgia* 5, 79-82.

Malone, H.M., Peters, J.A. & Lambert, J.J. (1991): (+)-Tubocurarine and cocaine reveal species differences in the $5\text{-}HT_3$ receptors of rabbit, mouse and guinea-pig nodose ganglion neurones. *Br. J. Pharmacol.* 104, 68P.

Maricq, A.V., Peterson, A.S., Brake, A.J., Myers, R.M. & Julius, D. (1991): Primary structure and functional expression of the $5\text{-}HT_3$ receptor, a serotonin-gated ion channel. *Science* 154, 432-437.

McQueen, D.S. & Mir, A.K. (1989): 5-Hydroxytryptamine and cardiopulmonary and carotid body reflex mechanisms. In *The Peripheral Actions of 5-Hydroxytryptamine*, ed. J.R. Fozard, pp. 301-326. Oxford: Oxford University Press.

Ouadid, H., Seguin, J., Dumuis, A., Bockaert, J. & Nargeot, J. (1991): Serotonin increases calcium current in human atrial myocytes via the newly described $5\text{-hydroxytryptamine}_4$ receptors. *Mol. Pharmacol.* 41, 346-351.

Patent Application (1991): Use of $5\text{-}HT_4$ receptor antagonists in the treatment of arrhythmias and stroke. International Patent Classification, A61K 31/00, 31/46.

Peters, J.A. and Lambert, J.J. & Malone, H.M. (1991): Physiological and pharmacological aspects of $5\text{-}HT_3$ receptor function. In *Aspects of Synaptic Transmission: LTP, Galanin, Opioids, Autonomic and 5-HT*, ed. T.W. Stone, pp. 283-313. London: Taylor & Francis.

Prior, A. & Read, N.W. (1990): Reduction of rectal sensitivity and postprandial motility by granisetron, a $5\text{-}HT_3$ receptor antagonist, in patients with irritable bowel syndrome (IBS). *Gut* 31, A1174.

Reiser, G. (1991): Molecular mechanisms of action induced by $5\text{-}HT_3$ receptors in a neuronal cell line and by $5\text{-}HT_2$ receptors in a glial cell line. In *Serotonin: Molecular Biology,*

Receptors and Functional Effects, ed. J.R. Fozard & P.R. Saxena, pp. 69-83. Basel: Birkhäuser.

Saxena, P.R. & Villalón, C.M. (1991): 5-Hydroxytryptamine: A chameleon in the heart. *Trends Pharmacol. Sci.* 12, 223-227.

Strange, P.G. (1988): The structure and mechansisms of neurotransmitter receptors. Implications for the structure and function of the central nervous system. *Biochem. J.* 249, 309.

Symposium (1991): The role of ondansetron, a novel 5-HT_3 antagonist, in the treatment of psychiatric disorders. *Abstr. Satellite Symp. 5th World Congr. Biological Psychiatry*, Florence, June 9, 1991.

Wallis, D.I. (1989): Interaction of 5-hydroxytryptamine with autonomic and sensory neurones. In *The Peripheral Actions of 5-Hydroxytryptamine*, ed. J.R. Fozard, pp. 220-246. Oxford: Oxford University Press.

Yang, J. (1990): Ion permeation through 5-hydroxytryptamine-gated channels in neuroblastoma N 18 cells. *J. Gen. Physiol.* 96, 1177-1198.

V. New issues in vomiting

V. Nouvelles avancées dans l'étude du vomissement

Mechanisms and Control of Emesis. Eds A.L. Bianchi, L. Grélot, A.D. Miller, G.L. King. Colloque INSERM/ John Libbey Eurotext Ltd. © 1992, Vol. 223, pp. 275-284

Plasticity and modulation of the emetic reflex

P.L.R. Andrews, P. Bhandari and C.J. Davis

Department of Physiology, St. George's Hospital Medical School, Cranmer Terrace, London, SW17 ORE, UK

SUMMARY:

This paper reports a series of experiments in the ferret indicating that following abdominal vagotomy there may be some reorganisation of the emetic response. The possibility of the induction of an endogenous emetic agent by the gut, released by high dose radiation and acting on the area postrema is discussed. Evidence is also presented that the response to a range of emetic stimuli (e.g. radiation, loperamide) can be enhanced by naloxone and domperidone implicating opiate and dopamine receptors in the central modulation of the emetic response in the ferret.

Plasticité et modulation du réflexe émétique.

Résumé: *Cet article rend compte d'une série d'expériences réalisées sur le furet indiquant qu'à la suite d'une vagotomie abdominale il y a peut être une certaine réorganisation de la réponse émétique. Il y est discuté de la possibilité de l'induction d'un agent émétique endogène par l'intestin, libéré par l'irradiation à haute dose et agissant sur l'area postrema. Il est aussi présenté des preuves indiquant que la réponse à divers types de stimuli émétiques (par exemple l'irradiation, le lopéramide) peut être augmentée par le naloxone et le dompéridone ce qui implique les récepteurs opiacés et dopaminergiques dans la modulation centrale de la réponse émétique du furet.*

INTRODUCTION:

Over the past 100 years numerous lesioning studies have identified the major afferent systems that detect emetic stimuli and lead to activation of the brain stem nuclei coordinating the visceral and somatic motor outputs for emesis. The key inputs identified are the area postrema, the abdominal vagal afferents, the vestibular labyrinths and poorly defined "higher central nervous system inputs". In general these triggers for emesis have been regarded as acting in isolation with the effect of a discrete stimulus on one pathway not being affected by an input from another pathway. Although this view of "segregated inputs " is common there is evidence to suggest interaction. For example: i) head position in man influences the emetic response to apomorphine acting on the area postrema (Isaacs 1957); ii) in the ferret the emetic response to loperamide (μ and δ opiate receptor agonist) is modified by gastric distension (Andrews et al. 1990b); iii) vagal afferent activation modifies activity in the area postrema (Andrews et al. 1990a); and iv) the convergence of vagal afferents and outputs from the area postrema in the nucleus tractus solitarius provides further opportunities for interaction.

Viewing the various emetic detectors as completely separate has influenced interpretation of the lesion studies. If, for example, section of the abdominal visceral afferents was without effect on a particular emetic response this was usually interpreted as evidence that these nerves were not involved. Consideration was not given to the possibility that in the intact animal these afferents were involved but when they were removed one of the other emetic detectors triggered the response due to some degree of "plasticity" in the organisation.

This paper presents experimental evidence from studies in the ferret and from the literature that suggest the occurrence of "plasticity" in the emetic system. The possible mechanisms are reviewed with particular reference to the interpretation of the effects of abdominal vagotomy. Pharmacological studies of emesis have rightly focused on the identification of drugs that reduce or block the emetic response. However, identification of agents that enhance the emetic response or receptor antagonists that themselves induce emesis may give an insight into the mechanisms that modulate the sensitivity of the emetic reflex and which could be involved in the post-lesion responses.

TERMINOLOGY:

The term "plasticity" will be used to refer to a permanent change in a component of the emetic reflex that is probably associated with some form of structural change; "modulation" will be used to describe a transient or reversible modification of the emetic reflex that may be induced pharmacologically (or hormonally) or by activation of an afferent input to the coordinating system.

Statistics:

The results are expressed as mean ± SEM, and comparison between means of two groups has been done by t-tests assuming unequal variance (UNISTAT-III). A "p" value of ≤ 0.05 has been considered statistically significant. The notation "n=x/y" denotes number of animals responding (retching or vomiting) as x upon the number of animals tested as y.

EMESIS INDUCED BY RADIATION IN THE FERRET: AN EXAMPLE OF PLASTICITY?

Studies of the pathway by which radiation induces emesis in the ferret have revealed some evidence for "plasticity" in the emetic pathway that are reviewed here together with novel data. Two doses of radiation have been used both of which are above the ED100 of ≈125 rads for the ferret : 200 rads which we will designate as "low" dose and 800 rads as "high" dose. The use of two doses has been critical to the understanding of mechanisms particularly following nerve lesions. One interesting aspect of studying the effects of two doses has been to better define the role of 5-hydroxytryptamine3 (5HT3) receptors in the response to radiation. The construction of dose-response curves for 5-HT3 receptor antagonists using both 200 rads and 800 rads as the emetic stimuli reveal that a higher dose of the antagonists was required to influence the higher dose of radiation; for granisetron the dose required to reduce retching by 50% was 4.84 ± 1.6 μg/kg for 200 rads and 37.2 ± 6.8 μg/kg for 800 rads. This observation shows that at least in this context the two doses of radiation may be regarded as two different doses of an "agonist" causing activation of 5HT3 receptors to trigger emesis.

Exposure of adult ferrets to 800 rads total body X-radiation (250 kV, 15 mA, approx. 120-150 rads/min) induced a highly reproducible emetic response with a latency of 17.2 ± 0.7 min (n= 30/30). Under surgical anaesthesia the abdominal vagi (VX) were sectioned either alone or in combination with the greater splanchnic nerves (GSNX) and the animals allowed to recover for 7-10 days before exposure to radiation (see Andrews et al. 1990a for method). These lesions do not interfere with the ability of the animal to respond to loperamide, the response to which was abolished by area postrema ablation (Bhandari, Bingham and Andrews 1992). Following the abdominal nerve lesions the response to radiation was modified, with the latency being significantly increased by VX to 33.6 ± 3.8 min (n=6/6, p=0.008) and by VX+GSNX to 31.7 ± 2 (n=4/4, p=0.005). The number of retches and vomits decreased after the lesions and it was significant (p<0.05) for VX although there was no difference between VX and VX+GSNX. GSNX reduced the latency (15.5 ± 0.4 min; n= 4/4, p=0.045) and increased the number of retches and vomits (p >0.05). These initial studies were extended using groups of animals with combined VX and GSNX left for longer periods of 3 wks and 21 wks and these responded with latencies of 29.5 ± 1.6 min (n=4/4, p=0.002) and 36.0 ± 3.4 min (n=5/5, p=0.003) respectively.

Initially these results were interpreted as suggesting that the emetic response to "high" dose radiation had two components in the ferret: an "early" vagally dependent component and a "later" vagally independent component possibly involving the area postrema (Andrews and Hawthorn 1987). The observation that in intact animals the emetic response was markedly reduced by 5HT3 receptor antagonists prompted an examination of the 5HT3 receptor antagonist sensitivity of the post-vagotomy residual response. Using doses of granisetron and ondansetron that were highly effective (84 - 96 % decrease in vomiting) in intact animals (0.5-1.0 mg/kg sc) it was not possible to demonstrate significant reduction in the response in lesioned animals. In addition a very large dose of granisetron of 5 mg/kg sc was without effect. Atropine sulphate at a dose (1 mg/kg sc), that reduced the emetic response to radiation and cyclophosphamide in the ferret (Roylance et al. 1988), caused a non-significant reduction in the post-vagotomy emetic responses. In addition treatment with parachloro-phenylalanine (180 mg/kg, ip X 3 days) increased the latency (39.6 ± 4.1 min, n=3/3, p=0.003) and significantly (p≤0.003) reduced but did not abolish the response. This effect is consistent with the general suppressant effect that PCPA treatment has on emesis in the ferret (Barnes et al. 1988). The comparison of the effects of chronic vagotomy and 5HT3 receptor antagonists in intact and lesioned animals indicated that following the nerve lesion a mechanism had been induced that was not operational in the intact animal.

Because of a body of evidence linking 5HT3 receptors and vagal afferents in the emetic mechanism (Andrews et al. 1990 for ref.) it was suspected that in the intact animal the entire response to this "high" dose of radiation was vagally mediated. As it was not possible to use chronic nerve lesions we developed a technique for acute vagotomy. Under surgical anaesthesia the greater splanchnic nerves and the ventral abdominal vagus were sectioned, (previous chronic lesioning studies had shown that either vagus could support the entire emetic response). The dorsal vagus was mobilised and a noose placed loosely around. A fistula on the dorsal surface provided access to the nerve. Following recovery (7 days) the animals were exposed to radiation (200 rads or 800 rads) and the emetic response allowed to establish for at least 10 min at which point the dorsal vagus was sectioned. As soon as this was done emesis stopped, a response reminiscent of the virtually immediate cessation of emesis following intravenous injection of a 5HT3 receptor antagonist (Bermudez et al. 1988). The animal showed no signs of distress during this procedure and emesis did not return throughout the observation period of 4 hrs (i.e. 2 hrs longer than the response usually lasted). In animals where emesis had been induced by loperamide (n=4) emesis only stopped transiently (< 1 min).

Lesion studies in animals exposed to 200 rads revealed that the response was abolished in 5/7 animals when tested 7-10 days post-vagotomy. The response was markedly reduced in the remaining animals. The response to this dose of radiation was also abolished by area postrema ablation (Bhandari and Andrews 1990). Two animals tested 28 days post-vagotomy failed to respond to 200 rads and 45 days after lesion only 2/5 animals retched and one vomited with latencies > 60 min.

These studies show that in the intact ferret the emetic response to both "low" and "high" doses of radiation is mediated entirely by the abdominal vagus and is sensitive to 5HT3 receptor antagonism. When the vagus is sectioned a novel mechanism is either induced or unmasked; however, it is only expressed to its full extent when the animal is exposed to "high" doses of radiation as there is only a weak residual response with the "low" dose. The mechanism does not involve 5HT3 or muscarinic receptors (atropine study) although a component of the pathway may involve 5HT or catecholamines (PCPA study). Whilst we cannot say that the new response is permanent it is certainly persistent as it is still present 21 weeks after nerve lesion. The most likely mechanism involves the area postrema and this aspect is discussed below.

In addition to radiation induced emesis there is evidence in the literature indicating "plasticity" in the emetic responses to intragastric copper sulphate and sodium chloride, urethane, pharyngeal stimulation and apomorphine as well as conditioned taste aversion (see Andrews et al. 1990 for refs.).

MECHANISMS OF PLASTICITY:

The trigger for the changes in the emetic mechanism is predominantly section of both abdominal vagi. Studies sectioning either the dorsal or ventral abdominal vagus showed that in general either nerve can support a response not significantly different from control irrespective of whether 200 or 800 rads were used. Section of the greater splanchnic nerves in combination with vagotomy was without additional effect although greater splanchnic nerve section alone enhanced the emetic response to radiation and cisplatinum. This section outlines the effect that vagotomy may have on the emetic reflex and then discusses the expression of these changes.

1) What effect does vagotomy have?:

The abdominal vagus contains both afferent and efferent nerves with the afferents outnumbering the efferents by about 10:1. Thus the effects seen could be due to an effect on either system and a similar argument applies in the case of splanchnic nerve lesions. We have attempted to circumvent this problem using capsaicin. On day 3-5 of life ferrets were given capsaicin or vehicle under halothane anaesthesia. The dose used was 50 mg/kg sc which has been shown to be effective in the rat (Holzer 1991). When the animal reached a body weight of 700-1000 g they were tested for an emetic response to radiation (200 rads). Unexpectedly the response was present in both vehicle (retches = 38.5 ± 1.5, vomits = 8.5 ± 1.5, retch latency = 23.4 ± 3.1, n=2/2) and capsaicin groups (retches = 57.4 ± 7.6, vomits = 13.0 ± 1.4, retch latency = 16.5 ± 1.6, n=8/8) and the responses were not different from untreated control animals ($p=0.12$). Although this result could be interpreted as providing evidence against an involvement of the vagus in the response to radiation in the ferret, we were unable to find any evidence for C-fibre destruction as, for example, the von Bezold-Jarisch reflex was present. In addition as there is evidence of species differences in sensitivity to capsaicin (Holzer 1991) we undertook another study in which twice the dose of capsaicin was given and, although this dose was associated with a high mortality, in the 2 animals that survived the response to radiation was markedly reduced (retches = 5 ± 5, $p=0.001$; vomits = 1± 0.99, retch latency = 50 min, $p<0.001$, n=1/2) but the response to loperamide was unaffected. These studies whilst not conclusive provide support for the contention that it is activation of the vagal afferents that is responsible for the emetic response. It is clear from the results with the two doses of capsaicin that care must be taken in the interpretation of such studies. Although studying the effects of neonatal capsaicin treatment on the response to 800 rads would be of interest it may not necessarily be comparable to surgical vagotomy in the adult as the animal will have had the afferent lesion from early life. Therefore the type of plasticity induced may differ.

Returning to the mechanisms involved in the responses following vagotomy there are several possibilities that should be investigated (Fig. 1): i) Vagotomy induces changes in gut function particularly gastric motility (Andrews and Bingham 1990). Such effects may be of particular relevance to intra-gastric emetic agents where the motility changes may modify the rate at which an emetic is delivered to a detection site lower in the gut giving rise to a shift in the latency of emesis. It could be concluded that the vagus was directly involved in mediating the response whereas in fact the effect of the vagus on the response was secondary to its effects on motility. ii) The vagus has trophic

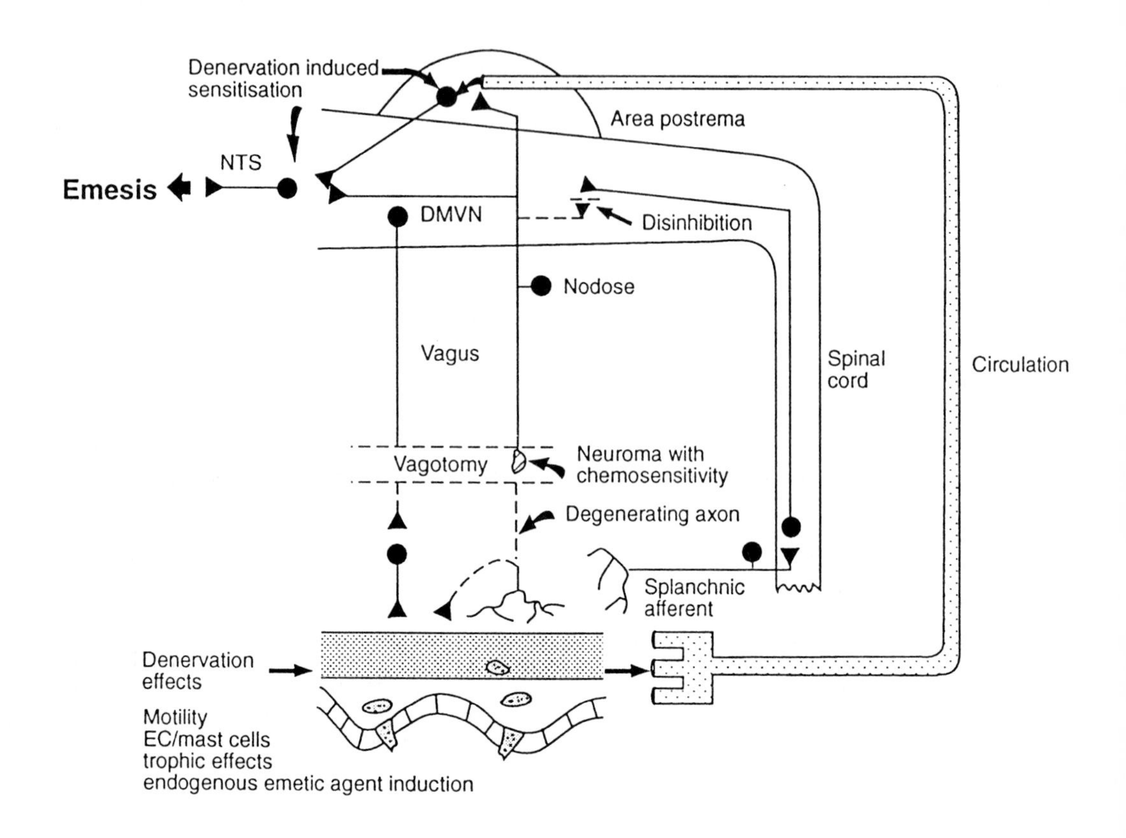

Fig. 1. Possible mechanisms involved in the responses following vagotomy.

effects on the gut, e.g. VX produces diffuse inflammation, villus atrophy, and biochemical changes (Bejar et al. 1968) within one week. The vagus can influence the release of 5HT from the enterochromaffin cells (Ahlman et al. 1978) and the release of a number of gut hormones (gastrin, somatostatin, pancreatic polypeptide, vasoactive intestinal peptide; Grundy 1988). However the effect of VX on the gut mucosal cells containing these hormones is poorly understood. The release of gut hormones provides a possible mechanism for the induction of emesis in VX animals and studies by Carpenter et al. (1984) have shown that many gut hormones can induce emesis by an action on the area postrema. iii) The interruption of the vagal afferents may have effects on the central components of the emetic reflex. Although this has not been formally investigated it appears that removal of the vagal afferent input to the nucleus tractus solitarius and the area postrema is likely to induce changes similar to those that have been observed in other afferent systems in adult animals. These include sprouting of adjacent afferents, opening of suppressed polysynaptic pathways, disinhibition, unmasking of ineffective synapses (Merrill and Wall 1978). Whilst abdominal nerve lesions do not block the response to centrally acting emetic agents little attempt has been made to determine whether the sensitivity of the central mechanisms is altered by such lesions. Such changes may begin immediately after denervation and sustain. Interactions between vagal and splanchnic afferents in the brain stem may go some way to explaining the complex relationships between the vagus and the splanchnic nerves in the induction of emesis. iv) Studies of cutaneous afferents have demonstrated that a neuroma may form that is not only mechanosensitive but may also be activated by catecholamines (Scadding 1987). If a neuroma was formed on the vagus or splanchnic nerve then this could provide a mechanism by which emesis could be induced particularly if the emetic was given intraperitoneally.

2) Expression of the novel mechanism:

From our studies it appears that the novel mechanism is only revealed to any extent by exposure to 800 rads as there is little if any residual response in VX animals exposed to 200 rads. If the mechanism is the induction by VX of the formation of an endogenous emetic peptide which then acts on the AP the difference between the two radiation doses suggests that some considerable degree of cellular damage is required to release the agent. Studies of the cellular mechanism by which radiation and cytotoxic drugs influence the release of peptides and 5HT from the gut mucosa are required in intact animals before we can understand how this may be modified following vagotomy and under pathological conditions. It is likely that the mechanism involves calcium mobilisation but how is this induced by radiation ?

MODULATION OF THE EMETIC REFLEX:

This section examines a different kind of modification to the emetic reflex from "plasticity", that of "modulation" by pharmacological agents. Instead of the usual pharmacological studies of agents that reduce or inhibit emesis, here we will consider agents that are not usually emetics in their own right but which enhance the response to another agent. The reason for drawing attention to this area is that not only it may give a different insight into ways in which emesis can be controlled but also some of the central neurochemical changes that may be involved in the "plasticity" of the reflex. This section includes data from our studies and the literature.

Effect of naloxone on the emetic response:

The opiate receptor antagonist naloxone acts on μ, δ, and k opiate receptors. Since the early studies of Costello and Borison (1977) there has been a growing body of evidence that it potentiates the emetic response to a range of stimuli.

1) Radiation. In the ferret naloxone hydrochloride when given subcutaneously at a dose of 1.0 mg/kg sc did not cause emesis; however, this dose when given 30 min before exposure to 200 rads, it enhanced both retching ($p < 0.02$) and vomiting ($p=0.002$) and reduced the latency ($p<0.0001$). Naloxonazine reported to be a more selective antagonist for $\mu 1$ receptors did not significantly increase retches although vomiting increased ($p=0.0001$) and latency decreased.

2) Loperamide. The emetic response to loperamide in the ferret lasts about one hour. Administration of naloxone (1 mg/kg sc) 5 min before loperamide delayed the appearance of the response from 9.2 ± 0.9 min to 98.3 ± 8.9 min (n=6/6, $p<0.001$) but when the response reappears retching but not vomiting is enhanced although not significantly (control= 69.6 ± 11.3 retches, naloxone= 120 ± 28.5 retches; Bhandari et al. 1992).

3) Motion. In the cat naloxone enhanced the susceptibility to motion (Crampton and Daunton 1983) and a similar phenomenon has been reported in man including a decrease in emetic latency (Allen et al. 1986). In addition in man naloxone (5 or 10 mg im) increased the duration of the malaise with some subjects experiencing nausea and some incapacitation 3 days after exposure. In a different study a lower dose of naloxone (0.4 mg iv) made subjects more resistant to nausea (Yasnetsov et al. 1986).

4) Apomorphine. In the dog naloxone (2 mg/kg iv) increased the number of vomits induced by both apomorphine and copper sulphate (Lang and Marvig 1989). In addition subthreshold doses of apomorphine (30 μg/kg iv) induced emesis in animals pretreated with naloxone.

5) Chemotherapy. In paediatric chemotherapy patients intravenous naloxone (10 and 40 μg/kg/hr for 12 hr) produced a dose related increase in nausea, vomiting and aversion score although naloxone itself was not emetic (Kobrinsky et al. 1988).

Facilitatory effect of domperidone on the emetic response:

The dopamine D2 receptor antagonist is a prokinetic agent which has restricted penetration into the central nervous system. Its anti-emetic activity was identified using apomorphine (a dopamine receptor agonist)-induced emesis and based on this it has been used as an anti-emetic in a range of indications, mostly where the emesis is mild to moderate (Reyntjens 1979). The mechanism of the anti-emetic action in many clinical indications has not been identified although the prokinetic effects have been implicated (Mc Ritchie et al. 1984). In the course of studies in the ferret using relatively high doses of domperidone (500 μg/kg sc 20 min before emetic administration) we noted that in contrast to the blockade of apomorphine-induced emesis the response to other stimuli was enhanced. This effect may be due to the dopamine (D2) receptor antagonist action of domperidone; it also has an antagonist effect on $\alpha 1$ adrenoreceptors, which although not significant at clinical doses may be involved at the doses used here. Further studies are required to examine the dose-response nature of the effects outlined below.

1) Radiation. The latency to retch and the number of vomits were not significantly different from control but the number of retches increased from 75 ± 7.7 to 153 ± 23 (n=4/4, p=0.03) and all animals in the group had an emetic response.

2) Diacetoxyscirpinol. The tricothecine mycotoxin, diacetoxyscirpinol (DAS, Anguidine) induced a short latency (22.0 ± 3.8 min) emetic response when given intraperitoneally (1.5 mg/kg). In the presence of domperidone the latency decreased to 13.9 ± 2.9 min and the number of vomits increased significantly (p=0.01) from 6 ± 2 to 18 ± 5 as did retching (72 ± 29 to 160 ± 49, p=0.001). All 5 animals treated with domperidone responded to DAS.

3) Loperamide. There was a tendency for domperidone to reduce the latency of the response to loperamide (9.2 ± 0.9 min to 6.3 ± 0.7 min) and to increase the number of retches (69.6 ± 11.3 to 112.5 ± 31.1) although neither change was significant. There was however a significant increase in the number of vomits from 8.4 ± 1.2 to 19 ± 1.1 with p<0.01 (Bhandari et al. 1992).

CLINICAL IMPLICATIONS OF PLASTICITY AND MODULATION:

This paper has provided limited evidence that the emetic reflex is not necessarily "hard wired". Although VX is a rather gross lesion and radiation an aggressive emetic stimulus these studies have lead to the identification of a novel phenomenon. In addition the pharmacological studies have implicated opiate and unexpectedly dopamine receptors in modulating the sensitivity of the emetic response. The precise clinical correlates of these observations is not yet clear although they illustrate the possible mechanisms that may be involved in individual differences in emetic and hence anti-emetic sensitivity. For example is the failure of 5HT3 receptor antagonists to block emesis induced by cisplatin in all patients (cf. ferret results) an indication of modification of the emetic pathway in these patients?

ACKNOWLEDGEMENT:

We wish to thank the MOD (Procurement Executive) and SmithKline Beecham Pharmaceuticals for financial support.

REFERENCES:

Ahlman, H., Bhargava, H.N., Donahue, P.E., Newson, B., Das Gupta, T.K., and Nyhus, L.M. (1978): The vagal release of 5HT from enterochromaffin cells in the cat. Acta Physiol. Scand. 104, 262-270.

Allen, M.E., McKay, C., Eaves, D.E., and Hamilton, D. (1986): Naloxone enhances motion sickness: endorphins implicated. Aviat. Space Enviorn. Med. 57, 647-653.

Andrews P.L.R., Davis C.J., Bingham S., Davidson H.I.M., Hawthorn J. and Maskell L. (1990a): The abdominal visceral innervation and the emetic reflex: pathways, pharmacology, and plasticity. Can. J. Phys. Pharmacol. 68, 325-345.

Andrews, P.L.R., and Hawthorn, J. (1987): Evidence for an extra-abdominal site of action for the 5-HT3 receptor antagonist BRL24924 in the inhibition of radiation-evoked emesis in the ferret. Neuropharmacology 26, 1367-1370.

Andrews, P.L.R., Bhandari, P., Garland, S., Bingham, S., Davis, C.J., Hawthorn, J., Davidson, H.I.M., Roylance, R., and Lane, S. (1990b): Does retching have a function ?: An experimental study in the ferret. Pharmacodynamics and Therapeutics (Life Sciences Advances) 9, 135-152.

Andrews, P.L.R., and Bingham S. (1990): Adaptation of the mechanisms controlling gastric motility following chronic vagotomy in the ferret. Exp. Physiol. 75, 811-825.

Bejar, J., Broitman, A., and Zamchek, N. (1968): Effect of vagotomy upon the small intestine. Gut 9, 87-90.

Bhandari, P., and Andrews, P.L.R. (1990): Abolition of radiation-induced emesis by abdominal vagotomy and area postrema lesion in the ferret. Proceedings of Perugia International Cancer Conference III, June 14-16, 110.

Bhandari, P., Bingham, S., and Andrews, P.L.R. (1992): The neuropharmacology of loperamide-induced emesis in the ferret: the role of the area postrema, vagus, opiate and 5-HT3 receptors. Neuropharmacology (in press).

Carpenter, D.O., Briggs, D.B., and Strominger, A. (1984): Behavioral and electrophysiological studies of peptide-induced emesis in dogs. Fed. Prod. Fed. Am. Soc. Exp. Biol. 43, 16-18.

Costello, D.J., and Borison, H.L. (1977): Naloxone antagonizes narcotic self-blockade of emesis in the cat. J. Pharmacol. Expt. Ther. 203, 222-230.

Crampton, G.H., and Daunton, N.G. (1983): Systemic naloxone increases the incidence of motion sickness in the cat. Pharmacol. Biochem. Behav. 19, 827-829.

Grundy, D. (1988): Vagal control of gastrointestinal function. Balliere's Clinical Gastroenterology 2, 23-43.

Holzer, P. (1991): Capsaicin: cellular targets, mechanisms of action, and selectivity for thin sensory neurons. Pharmacol. Rev. 43, 143-201.

Isaacs, B. (1957): The influence of head and body position on the emetic action of apomorphine in man. Clin. Sci.16, 215-221.

Iasnetsov, V.V., Vakulina, O.P., Sabaev, V.V., Mokrousova, A.V., Karsanova, S.K., Il'ina, S.L., Medvedev, O.S., Shashkov, V.A., and Tigranyan, R.A. (1985): Participation of endogenous opioid peptides in the pathogenesis of motion sickness. Bull. Exp. Biol. Med. 100, 164-167.

Kobrinsky, N.L., Pruden P.B., Cheang, M.S., Levitt, M. Bishop, A.J., Tenebein, M. (1988): Increased nausea and vomiting induced by naloxone in patients receiving chemotherapy. Am. J. Ped. Hematology-Oncology 10(3), 206-208.

Lang. I.M., and Marvig, J. (1989): Functional localization of specific receptors mediating gastrointestinal motor correlates of vomiting. Am. J. Physiol. 256, P1, G92-G99.

McRitchie, B., McClelland, C.M., Cooper, S.M., Turner, D.H., and Sanger, G.J. (1984): Dopamine antagonists as anti-emetics and as stimulants of gastric motility. In Mechanisms of gastrointestinal motility & secretion, ed. A. Bennett & G. Vela, pp. 287-301. New York: Plenum Press.

Merrill, E.G., and Wall, P.D. (1978): Plasticity and connection in the adult system. In Neuronal Plasticity, ed. C.W. Cotman, pp. 97-109. New York: Raven Press.

Reyntjens, A. (1979): Domperidone as an anti-emetic; summary of research reports. Postgrad. Med.J. 55(S1), 50-54.

Scadding, J.W. (1987): Development of ongoing activity, mechanosensitivity and adrenaline sensitivity in severed peripheral nerve axons. Exp. Neurol. 73, 345-364.

Mechanisms and Control of Emesis. Eds A.L. Bianchi, L. Grélot, A.D. Miller, G.L. King. Colloque INSERM/
John Libbey Eurotext Ltd. © 1992, Vol. 223, pp. 285-295

Neuroinhibition in the regulation of emesis

Jacob Zabara

Department of Physiology, School of Medicine, Temple University, Philadelphia, PA, USA

Evidence is presented for a theory of emesis based on meuroinhibitory stabilization of a brainstem neural network by stimulation of vagal afferents. Emesis produced by gastro-intestinal afferents or chemoreceptor activation is inhibited by vagal afferents. Emesis produced by motion sickness is investigated in the present study in squirrel monkeys, and is apparently significantly reduced by stimulation of vagal afferents. Another example of the importance of the vagal afferent inhibitory system is the prevention of epileptic seizures.

Neuroinhibition dans la régulation du mécanisme émétique.

Résumé: *Nous présentons des arguments en faveur d'une théorie de la réponse émétique basée sur une stabilisation neuroinhibitrice du réseau de neurones du tronc cérébral par la mise en jeu des afférences vagales. Le vomissement produit par l'activation d'afférences gastro-intestinales ou de messages chémosensibles est inhibé par les afférences vagales. Le vomissement, produit par le mal des transports, étudié chez le singe écureuil est apparemment réduit de façon significative par la mise en jeu des afférences vagales. Un autre exemple de l'importance de ce système afférent inhibiteur réside dans la prévention de l'épilepsie.*

Emesis represents a temporary instability of a brain network, such as occurs in motion sickness. Ordinarily, the brain monitors the internal stability of the organism (homeostasis) from afferent signals, many of which come from vagal afferents. This can be designated as negative feedback or inhibition (Zabara, 1973). The instability in a neural network of the brain takes the form of a resonance-like oscillation, resulting in the rhythmic muscular movements underlying emesis. Stimulation of vagal afferents may produce inhibition (negative feedback) stabilizing the network and preventing emesis. Most vagal afferents terminate in the nucleus of the tractus solitarius from which other pathways project to release inhibitory neurotransmitters causing desynchronization. The following experiments were done to test this new hypothesis of emesis.

Vomiting was initiated in two different animal models by two different processes. In the first model, emesis is induced in the dog by electrical stimulation of abdominal afferents (Zabara et al., 1972). Stimulation applied to the dorsal or ventral branches of the vagus at the supradiaphragmatic level causes emesis at a threshold frequency of 4 to 8 Hz, but rarely above 60 Hz. Emesis was prevented by simultaneous stimulation of cervical vagal afferents at parameters of 1 to 125 Hz, 1 to 5 msec pulse duration, and 1 to 15V pulse amplitude. However, once emesis was initiated, cervical vagal stimulation has no effect. Thus, vagal afferent stimulation can prevent vomiting, but cannot interrupt it in this case. Vagal afferents from the lungs appeared to be particularly important in the inhibition of emesis.
The second model is based on the activation of the chemoreceptor in the area postrema of the cat. Xylazine is utilized for this emesis (Colby, et al., 1981, McCarthy and Borison, 1984). Xylazine induced emesis can be prevented during the period of electrical stimulation of afferents in the cervical vagus (Zabara, 1988). Xylazine emesis can still occur after the termination of vagal afferent stimulation, but with a much longer latency than before stimulation. The result was that the latency to emesis with Xylazine increased proportionally to the duration of vagal afferent stimulation to a limiting value. A complete absence of Xylazine emesis resulted from a series of stimulation trials of approximately three. Repeated stimulations of vagal afferents appear therefore to be cumulative in their inhibitory effectiveness, indicating modulation of the receptor sensitivity. Thus, vagal afferent activity can initially delay the onset of emesis, but with repeated periods of afferent impulsation, can completely prevent emesis.

Thus, it appears that chemical or neural induced emesis can be prevented by a vagal afferent mechanism. Data is now presented to demonstrate the effect of vagal afferents on motion sickness and emesis.

METHODS

A nerve cuff was used to provide electrical stimulation to the vagus nerve. The cuff, which consists of stainless steel wire electrodes embedded within silicone rubber or teflon, maintains interelectrode separation and contact of the electrodes with the cervical vagus nerve so that the geometry of current is relatively constant for repeated stimulation. Since the cuff consists of silicone rubber, teflon and stainless steel, it can be steam autoclaved without special precautions.

Implantation of the cuff is performed on monkeys anesthetized with sodium pentobarbital IV (35 mg/Kg). After an initial incision in the neck, the right or left vagus nerve is exposed between the branching points of the superior pharyngeal nerve and the recurrent nerve, and freed of surrounding tissue. The cuff is positioned parallel to the nerve with the opening facing up. The nerve is slipped into the cuff through the opening and the opening closed with sutures. To test the integrity of the cuff, the impedance of each contact is measured by an impedance meter.

A pair of adjacent contacts is used for bipolar stimulation. Square pulse stimulations are applied at 1-10 ma. amplitude, and 4-100 Hz frequency. Biphasic stimulus pulses from 0.3 msec. to 0.6 msec. duration are used to minimize electrode polarization.

Five squirrel monkeys, weighing from .62 to 1.0 Kg, were implanted with cuff electrodes. Wires from the electrodes were led under the skin to connect with a headholder which could receive connectors from a pulse generator. The electrodes were monitored for several months in situ to verify their integrity and stability. The monkeys were tested in repeated sessions lasting at least two months after full recovery from surgery to implant the electrodes. Stimulation was provided by a pulse generator connected to a dual channel photon coupled linear isolator supplying constant current which was linear to 10 ma. Videotape was used to record behavioral responses of the animal to stimulation.

Five conscious and unrestrained adult male and female squirrel monkeys (Samiri sciureus) of Bolivian origin were exposed to 30 rpm horizontal rotation in a transparent plastic test chamber for up to 2 hours/day for 6 to 10 days. Rotation was sustained for the session with multiple vomiting episodes permitted. The animals were fed as much fresh banana as they could consume immediately before rotation. The elapsed time from the beginning of rotation to each emetic response (vomiting latency) was measured. Latency and frequency of vomiting were measured in controls and during vagal stimulation while monkeys were rotated.

To obviate extraneous influences of the experimenter, the monkeys were rotated in a separate room, and observed by video camera. All behavioral observations were video taped. The electronic equipment for stimulation and recording were located in this adjacent room, and controlled from the experimenter's station.

Animals were housed in AALAC-approved central animal facilities. Handling and care were in accordance with specifications in "Guide for the Care and Use of Laboratory Animals, Publication NIH".

Four monkeys were involved in the study of motion sickness. Monkey #90 was exposed to 10 rotations with vagal stimulation; monkey #82 was exposed to 9 rotations with vagal stimulation; monkey #95 was exposed to 8 rotations with vagal stimulation; monkey #85 was exposed to 6 rotations with vagal stimulation. Both experimental and control rotations (no vagal stimulation) were up to 2 hours in duration. There were two control rotations for each animal. One factor ANOVA was used to determine standard deviation and standard error.

RESULTS

The frequency of emesis during vagal stimulation is given in Fig. 1. The standard error is also presented. Table #1 presents the mean emetic frequency, standard deviation and standard error for each animal. Fig. #2 presents the mean emetic frequency (with standard error and number of rotation periods) during vagal afferent stimulation in comparison to the control frequency (without vagal afferent stimulation) for each animal.

Each monkey had a substantial reduction in emetic response to rotation during vagal afferent stimulation, including an overall average reduction in all animals (Fig. 2). The percentage reduction in each animal was 81% (#85), 88% (#82), 72% (#70) and 83% (#95). The average percent reduction for all animals was 81%.

Fig. 3 presents the frequency of emesis for each monkey as a function of the sequence of rotational periods. Vagal afferent stimulation occurs during the rotations. There is an overall

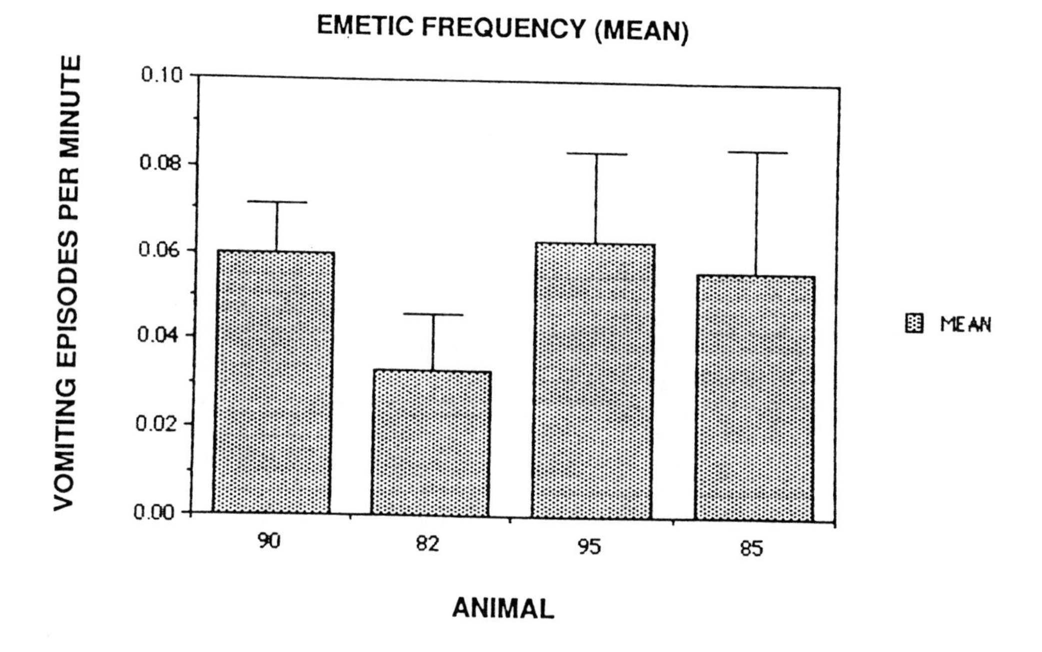

Fig. 1. Effect of vagal afferent stimulation on emetic frequency in each animal.

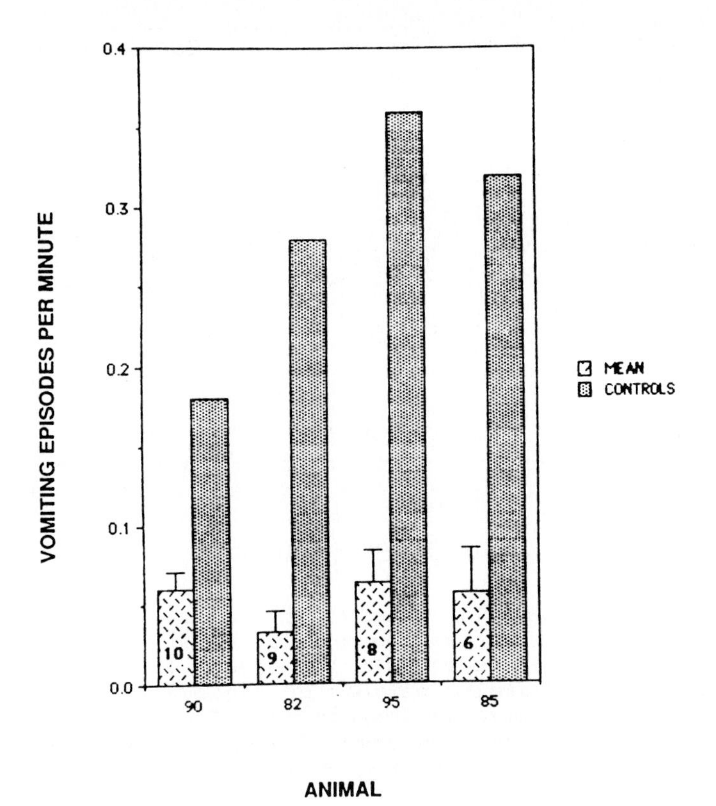

Fig. 2. Effect of vagal afferent stimulation on emetic frequency in comparison to control frequency in each animal. The experimental bars are light and the corresponding, adjacent controls are dark. The controls are the experimental monkeys observed under the same conditions of rotation except without vagal afferent stimulation.

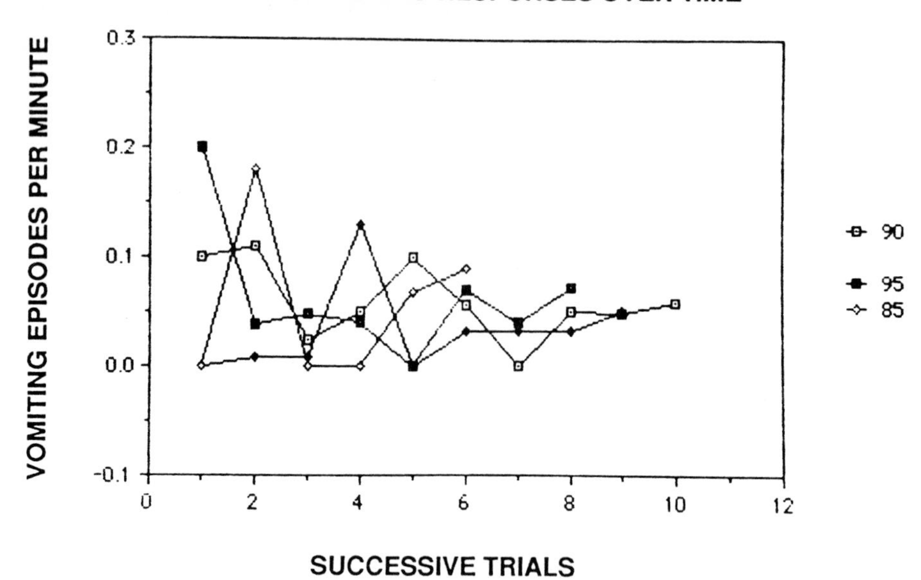

Fig. 3. The frequency of emesis for each monkey is presented as a function of the sequence of rotational periods. Vagal afferent stimulation occurs during the rotations. Thus, successive periods of vagal afferent stimulation appear to have an increasing effect. The abscissa represents the sequence of angular accelerations and the ordinate, the frequency of emesis in minutes.

One Factor ANOVA

ANIMAL	Count:	Mean:	Std. Dev.:	Std. Error:
90	10	.06	.035	.011
82	9	.033	.04	.013
95	8	.063	.059	.021
85	6	.056	.072	.029

2

Table 1. Analysis of variance is used to establish the mean and significance of the emetic frequency data in each animal.

decrease in emetic frequency in successive rotational periods. Thus, successive periods of vagal afferent stimulation appear to have an increasing or additive effect.

Physiological Response to Nerve Stimulation - A major response to electrical stimulation of the cervical vagus nerve was a series of forced exhalations. It consisted of a vigorous expulsion from the lungs often accompanied by a sound somewhat similar to sneezing. The head moved in synchrony with the exhalation as in a sneeze. In some trials, this forced exhalation occurred a few times during the stimulation, while in others it recurred repetitively at a relatively high frequency through part of the trial. Sometimes the forced exhalations continued a minute or two beyond the end of the stimulation periods. Infrequently (less than 5% of trials), retching or vomiting occurred as a consequence of cervical vagus stimulation. But the respiratory response was observed in over 90% of experimental trials and was utilized as an indication that the electrodes were functioning properly and the current was activating critical neurons in the nerve bundle. The experimental trial was discontinued if this response was not obtained. There appeared to be adaptation or habituation involved in the forced exhalation response in that after several weeks, the response became diminished. However, in spite of this habituation, the forced exhalation response remained the best monitor that the current was above threshold for the significant fiber groups in the cervical vagus which cause inhibition of emesis. Associated with these forced exhalations are sounds reminiscent of sneezing. And occasionally some mucous is expelled. However, there are no abdominal movements such as are present in retching or vomiting. These responses are obtained by stimulation before rotation is begun. Not only are the electrodes monitored for a stable impedance value, but the effectiveness of the current is monitored by observation of these physiological responses to stimulation. Presumably, the fiber group or groups eliciting the respiratory response belong to the respiratory afferents which respond to noxious substances in the bronchi, bronchioles or lungs and elicit a response similar to a sneeze (Zabara, 1988). Also, this fiber group may include slow stretch receptor neurons which can control the duration and magnitude of the expiratory response. Since, presumably the fiber groups causing inhibition of emesis are primarily respiratory afferents, the nerves causing the sneeze-like response to stimulation are probably involved in this inhibition.

Five categories of behavioral or reflex responses were observed during stimulation for the cervical vagus; pulling, scratching, sneezing with lateral head movements, chewing, and retching or vomiting. The current is steadily increased from 1 to 10 ma in each trial session to elicit the responses. There were 44 trial sessions on 5 animals for these observations.

Pulling refers to picking at the skin in the neck area usually localized to the same side at the electrode. Scratching refers to back and forth movements of the hind leg in the neck area. Sneezing with lateral head movements indicates rapid exhalations through the nose or mouth with accompanying sound.

Chewing refers to cyclic mandibular movements as in mastication. Retching or vomiting is observed as cyclic abdominal movements or material ejection from the mouth. Retching or vomiting resulted primarily from stimulation in a single animal and at a high level of current (10 ma). Pulling, scratching, sneezing and chewing could occur at a threshold of 1-2 ma. Retching or vomiting might be expected from stimulation of gastrointestinal afferents coursing through the cervical vagus (Zabara et al., 1972).

The latency to emesis does appear to be variable in these animals. Some animals might vomit earlier and then vomit less later, whereas other animals might vomit later, but continue to vomit at an appreciable rate. Therefore frequency of vomiting was judged to be the critical measurement. This also allowed different rotation periods to be compared. The frequency of emesis is simply the number of emetic events during the time of the rotation.

Some animals demonstrated pacing in the contrarotational direction in an attempt to attenuate labyrinthine stimulation. This usually did not prevent motion sickness, but may have delayed its induction. Other animals assumed a "Sleep-like" posture which also did not prevent motion sickness. Grooming activity was observed from time to time. This behavior did not appear to be different from control rotations without vagal stimulation. However, occasionally vagally stimulated animals would show "sneezing" behavior which was not observed in control rotations.

One animal (#82) demonstrated "conditioned vomiting" after two months of stimulation-rotation. After 1-1 1/2 minutes of being placed in the test chamber, the animal would retch and vomit several times. We attempted to "extinguish" the animal by ceasing either stimulation or rotation for a month, but were not successful. If the animal were vagally stimulated or eating a banana in the test chamber, the animal did not retch or vomit. The factors causing "conditioned vomiting" in this single animal remain unknown.

Inhibition of Motion Sickness - The primary observation resulting from electrical stimulation of the cervical vagus on motion sickness is that motion sickness can be reduced or prevented during the period of electrical stimulation.

In this study, vagal and vestibular afferent mechanisms interact through both excitatory and inhibitory neurotransmitters to produce a "tone" or "excitatory state" determining motion sickness. Neural changes such as enhanced neural tone (Zabara et. al., 1972) altered levels of stress hormones or proximity of the dorsal nucleus of the vagus to the vestibular nucleus add to this effect.

There are two primary observations resulting from vagal afferent stimulation during rotation to induce motion sickness. The first result is that inhibition of emesis can be accelerated during the period of increased vagal afferent input to the brainstem. Presumably, this is due to inhibitory neurotransmitters released by a vagal afferent system. The second result is that there is an accumulation of inhibitory neurotransmitters or receptor modulation as a result of continued vagal afferent stimulation throughout successive rotations. Thus the vagal afferent system causes the release of inhibitory transmitters or modulators to phase out inappropriate responses involving emesis.

DISCUSSION

Three animal models have now been investigated in relation to vagal afferent inhibition of emesis. The first model is stimulation of abdominal afferents in the dog to produce emesis. The second model is activation of the chemoreceptor in the area postrema of the cat to induce emesis. The third model is rotation of the monkey to produce motion sickness. Stimulation of afferents in the cervical vagus prevented, interrupted or reduced emesis in these animals. Respiratory vagal afferents appear to be an important fiber group in all three animal models causing the inhibition of emesis. Thus, it appears that no matter what the excitatory source or method of emetic induction, a vagal afferent mechanism can produce inhibition of emesis. The exact nature of this mechanism remains to be determined, but the afferent endings in the area postrema or nucleus of the solitary tract probably by their own release mechanisms or projective pathways give rise to the observed inhibitory effect. Other inhibitory effects of vagal afferents might be instructive in this regard.

Inhibitory effects of vagal stimulation on reflexes and behavior were apparently first reported in the 1930's (Schweitzer & Wright, 1937). Stimulation of vagal nerves arising in the lung were found to suppress skeletal muscle activity (Paintal, 1973). Puizillout and Foutz (1976) observed that complete atonia can be produced by vago-aortic stimulation which includes absence of the monosynaptic masseteric reflex. In addition, vago-aortic stimulation in the encephale isole cat preparation can trigger a complete sleep cycle, characterized by a progression of light to deep slow wave sleep, intermediary sleep, and paradoxical sleep. REM sleep episodes with muscular atonia and areflexia may immediately follow the onset of stimulation. Postural atonia occurs during the paradoxical sleep phase and depends upon tonic inhibition of both extensor and flexor motoneurons.

It is possible to obtain either synchronization or desynchronization of the electroencephalogram (EEG) consequent to vagal afferent stimulation (Chase and Nakamura, 1968), and apparently due to activation of different afferent fiber groups within the cervical vagus. Anatomically, vagal projections have been observed to the cerebellum (Hennemann & Rubia, 1978) and brainstem (Padel & Dell, 1965).

The extensive projections of vagal afferents in the brain, their significant effect on the EEG, and suppression of skeletal muscle activity or behavior indicate an important release of neurotransmitters by vagal afferent stimulation. However, behavior elicited by vagal stimulation is rather limited indicating that the effect of vagal afferent mechanisms on skeletal muscle activity is primarily by release of inhibitory neurotransmitters. This is supported by the observations of significant inhibitory effects on skeletal muscle and behavior.

The physical and mathematical analysis of brain networks (Zabara, 1976) led to the formulation of the importance of negative feedback (inhibition) from vagal afferents for stability and homeostasis. The results of this analysis were applied not only

to emesis, but also to epilepsy. Epilepsy can be considered as an instability in brain networks based on neural hypersynchronization. Over a hundred patients with complex partial seizures, refractory to existing therapy, have been implanted with a microcomputer based stimulator, the neurocybernetic prosthesis, connected to spiral electrodes surrounding the left cervical vagus nerve. Stimulation of the cervical vagus can be periodic or manual. In the manual mode, the patient turns on the device with a magnet when experiencing the aura preceding the seizure. In the periodic mode, the device is programmed through a wand held over the chest. Included in the program is a range of stimulation parameters of 130-1000 msec pulse width, 10-100 Hz frequency, 100-1000 uamp current, and a variable on-off period.

Clinical Application

Based on the efficacy of vagal stimulation in a study of canine seizures (Zabara, 1985a, 1985b, 1987) and the subsequent work of Lockard and colleagues (1990) in monkeys, clinical trials were initially undertaken in 15 patients who had had medically refractory complex and simple partial seizures (0.5 to 20 daily) for an average of 10 years and had failed to obtain seizure control with primary antiepileptic drugs in monotherapy and polypharmacy (Penry and Dean, 1990; Hammond et al., 1990; Wilder et al., 1991). Between November 1988 and September 1990, under investigational device exemption approval from the United States Food & Drug Administration, the patients underwent surgery to implant a microcomputer-based vagal stimulator, the Neurocybernetic Prosthesis, which controlled stimulation. Programmable functions included output current, signal frequency, signal pulse width, signal on-time, signal off-time, and magnet-activated stimulus parameters. Patients started stimulation during an aura or at seizure onset by activating their implanted stimulator with an external magnet. These clinical trials reflected both the interruption and carryover effects of vagal stimulation shown in the canine study (Zabara 1985a, 1985b, 1987). The clinical results so far are promising (Penry and Dean, 1990). Stimulation of the vagus nerve during an aura or at the onset of a complex partial seizure can shorten or block seizures (Hammond et al., 1990) and periodic stimulation can reduce or prevent seizures (Penry and Dean, 1990; Uthman et al., 1990). An extended trial of this therapy involving more than 100 patients with intractable complex and simple partial seizures is under way.

REFERENCES

Chase, M.H., and Y. Nakamura (1968). Cortical and Subcortical EEG Patterns of Response to Afferent Abdominal Vagal Stimulation: Neurographic correlates. Physiol Behav, 3:605-610.

Colby, E.D., McCarthy, L.E., and Borison, H.L. (1981): Emetic action of xylazine on the chemoreceptor trigger zone for vomiting in cats. J. Vet. Pharmacol. Therapy 4:93-96.
Hammond, E.J., Ramsay, E.R., Uthman, B.M., Reid, S.A., Wilder, B.J. (1990). Vagus nerve stimulation in humans: neurophysiological studies and electrophysiological monitoring. Epilepsia; 31:S51-S59.
Hennemann, H.E., and F.J. Rubia (1978). Vagal Representation in the Cerebellum of the Cat. Pflugers Arch, 375:119-123.
Lockard, J.S., Congdon, W.C., DuCharme, L.L. (1990). Feasibility and safety of vagal stimulation in monkey model. Epilepsia; 31:S20-S27.
McCarthy, L.E. and Borison, H.L. (1984): Cisplatin-induced vomiting eliminated by ablation of the area postrema in cats. Cancer Treatment Reports. 68:401-404.
Padel, Y.P., and P. Dell. (1965). Effets Bulbaires Et Reticulaires Des Stimulations Endormantes Du Tronc Vago-Aortique. J Physiol (Paris), 57:269-270.
Paintal, A.S. (1973). Vagal sensory receptors and their reflex effects. Physiol Rev, 53:159-227.
Penry, J.K., Dean, J.C. (1990). Prevention of intractable partial seizures by intermittent vagal stimulation in humans: preliminary results. Epilepsia; 31:S40-S44.
Puizillout, J.J., and A.S. Foutz. (1976). Vago-Aortic Nerves Stimulation and REM Sleep: Evidence for a REM-Triggering and a REM-Maintenance Factor. Brain Res, 111:181-184.
Schweitzer, A., and S. Wright. (1937). Effects on the knee jerk of stimulation and central end of the vagus and of various changes in the circulation and respiration. J. Physiol Lond. 88:459-475.
Uthman, B.M., Wilder, B.J., Hammond, E.J., Reid, S.A. (1990). Efficacy and safety of vagus nerve stimulation in patients with complex partial seizures. Epilepsia; 31:S44-S50.
Wilder, B.J., Uthman, B.M., Hammond, E.J., (1991). Vagal stimulation for control of complex partial seizures in medically refractory epileptic patients. PACE, 14:108-15.
Zabara, J., Chaffee, R.B., and Tansy, M.F. (1972): Neuroinhibition in the regulation of emesis. Space Life Sciences. 3:282-292.
Zabara, J. (1973): Autorhythmic structure of the brain: synaptic equivalence and connective feedback. Cybernetica 16:77-98.
Zabara, J. (1976): The Brain Clock: Density, Dimensionality and Transformation in Autorhythmic Structures. Cybernetica, 19:209-228.
Zabara, J. (1985a): Control of hypersynchronous discharge in epilepsy. Electroenceph Clin Neurophysiol:61-162.
Zabara, J. (1985b): Time course of seizure control to brief, repetitive stimuli. Epilepsia:26:518.
Zabara, J. (1987): Controlling seizures by changing GABA receptor sensitivity. Epilepsia; 28:604.
Zabara, J. Neurocybernetic Prothesis. U.S. Patent 4,702,254 - 1987; U.S. Patent 4,867,164 - 1989.
Zabara, J. (1988): Neuroinhibition of xylazine induced emesis. Pharmacology and Toxicology. 63:70-74.

Mechanisms and Control of Emesis. Eds A.L. Bianchi, L. Grélot, A.D. Miller, G.L. King. Colloque INSERM/
John Libbey Eurotext Ltd. © 1992, Vol. 223, pp. 297-306

Pregnancy sickness

Saffron A. Whitehead, Wendy A. Holden and P.L.R. Andrews

Department of Physiology, St. George's Hospital Medical School, Cranmer Terrace, London, SW17 ORE, UK

SUMMARY

While the first documentation of pregnancy sickness can be found in an ancient papyrus dated about 2000 B.C. we still cannot explain what causes this seemingly inappropriate symptom of early pregnancy. It is generally assumed that pregnancy hormones cause this sickness but there is no conclusive evidence to support this supposition. Thus we have set out to investigate other factors that may be associated with the occurrence of pregnancy sickness with a long term view of identifying the aetiology of the symptom. This report reviews some of our findings about the charactersitics of pregnancy sickness, the associations between pregnancy, taste changes and sickness and the possible effects of immune factors that may modulate the emetic response.

Nausée et grossesse.

Résumé: *Bien que le premier document faisant état de nausées associées à la grossesse peut être trouvé dans un papyrus ancien datant d'environ 2000 ans avant J.C., nous ne pouvons toujours pas expliquer quelles sont les causes de ce symptôme apparemment inaproprié du début de la grossesse. On admet généralement que les hormones de la grossesse sont à l'origine de cet état nauséeux mais il n'y a aucune preuve définitive qui confirme cette supposition. C'est ainsi que nous avons cherché à examiner d'autres facteurs qui peuvent être associés au déclenchement des nausées de la grossesse avec l'idée à plus longue échéance de l'identification de l'étiologie de ce symptôme. Ce rapport rend compte de certains de nos travaux à propos des caractéristiques des nausées de la grossesse, des relations entre la grossesse, les changements gustatifs et la nausée, et les effets possibles des facteurs immunitaires qui modulent la réponse émétique.*

INTRODUCTION

Based on simple observation one would have thought that the common symptom of nausea and vomiting during the first 2-3 months of pregnancy would be detrimental to the developing fetus. Fortunately there is no evidence that pregnancy sickness is associated with any adverse effect on fetal growth or the outcome of the pregnancy (Weigel & Weigel, 1989, Klebanoff et al., 1985). However, if one views nausea and vomiting as protective responses against the ingestion and/or absorption of toxins, then one might consider that the sickness could represent an adpative and advantageous response to pregnancy. It may help to protect the fetus against the maternal ingestion of toxins during the critical stage of fetal development.

While such a teleological approach could explain the apparent enigma of pregnancy sickness in humans, it should be noted that there is no evidence that pregnancy sickness occurs in animals even though distinct behavioural changes may occur soon after conception. Furthermore, it does not help to elucidate the aetiology of the symptom. In this respect many theories have been put forward but conclusive and consistent scientific evidence remains elusive. This may be because the development of the sickness is related to changes in response sensitivity as a result of pregnancy and that these changes are too subtle to be detected by simple one-off measurements of circulating hormones, metabolic products or gut function tests. At the same time, reviews of the available data often make no distinction between the common symptom of early pregnancy and the more severe hyperemesis gravidarum when vomiting continues into the later stages of pregnancy and treatment is required for the metabolic disturbances arising from the vomiting (Fairweather, 1986). Hyperemesis gravidarum only occurs in about 1:1,000 pregnancies.

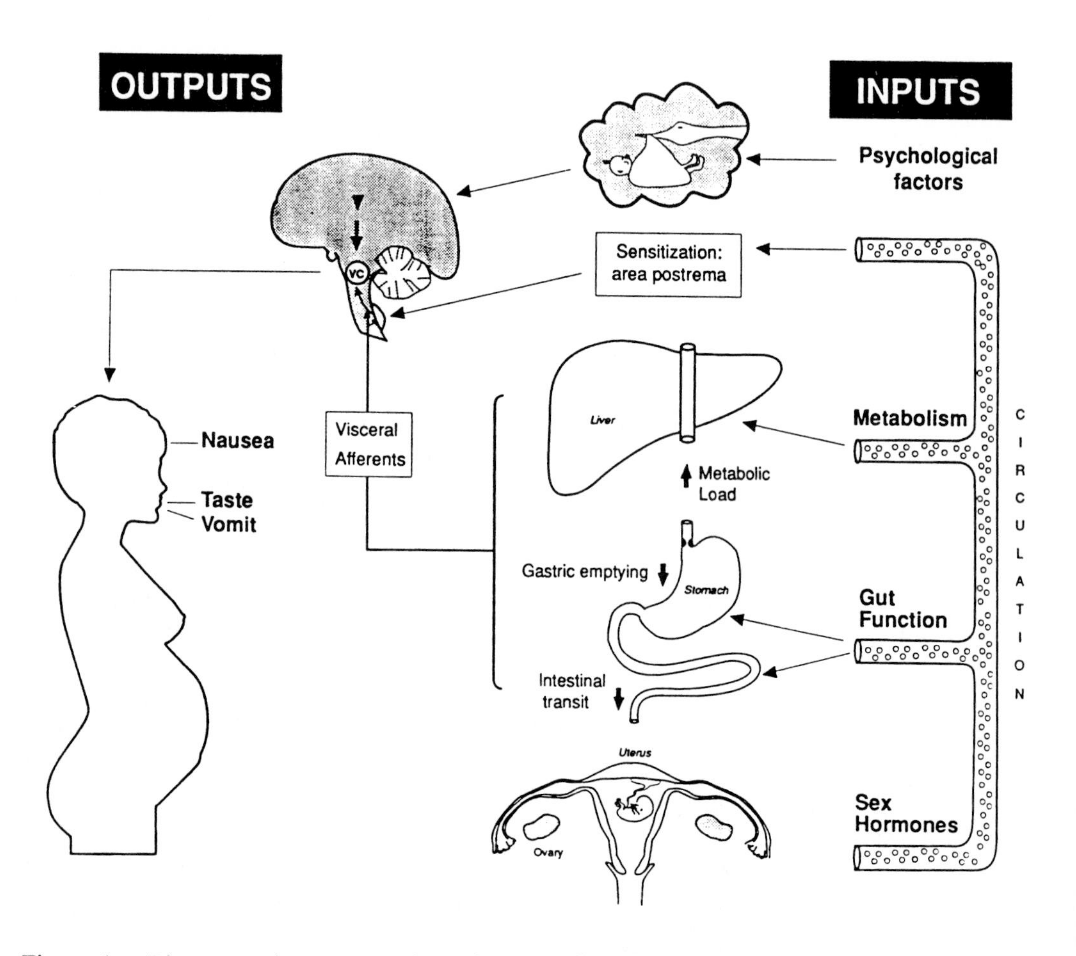

Figure 1. Diagrammatic representation of the possible factors which could induce pregnancy sickness. For explanation see text.

Hormones and pregnancy sickness

The most obvious and primary target for investigating the aetiology of pregnancy sickness is that of the hormonal changes that occur in the early stages of pregnancy. Human chorionic gonadotrophin (hCG) is a likely candidate because circulating levels of the hormone begin to rise within days after conception, peak at about 8-10 weeks of pregnancy and then fall to lower levels around 14-18 weeks when the sickness usually subsides. However, in different studies higher, lower or similar levels of hCG have been associated with emetic versus non-emetic pregnancies (Masson et al., 1985, Kucharczyk, 1991) and even molar pregnancies in which the hydatiform mole can secrete extrememly high concentrations of hCG have shown no correlation in the incidence or intensity of pregnancy sickness compared with normal pegnancies (Soules et al. 1980).

The other most likely hormonal candidates are the sex steroids, oestrogen and progesterone, which also begin to rise in early pregnancy. The noted side effect of nausea with the combined oral contraceptive pill, but not with the progesterone only pill, (see Jarnfelt Samsioe, 1987) suggests that oestrogen, in concert with other pregnancy hormones, may be responsible for the induction of the sickness. However, single measurements of circulating oestradiol or its metabolites and other hormones such as progesterone, thyroid hormones, cortisol, prolactin and testosterone remain stubbornly resistant to providing any positive basis for a simple hormonal explantation of the aetiology of pregnancy sickness (see Jarnfelt-Samsoie, 1987). Nevertheless, the fact that hormones are secreted in pulsatile pattern which is often superimposed on a daily secretory rhythm is often overlooked.

Metabolism and pregnancy sickness

The liver has been another target for speculation since steroid hormones are well known to alter hepatic function. They increase DNA, RNA and total protein synthesis as well as increasing the amounts of enzymes and plasma proteins synthesised in and released from the liver. Thus steroid-induced changes in liver function, coupled with pregnancy-associated changes in metabolism and an increased steroid load on the liver may result in an abnormal accumulation of substances in the circulation. These could be potentially toxic at high concentrations and so induce nausea and vomiting. Unfortunately no such metabolic products have, as yet, been identified. However, an increased metabolic load on the liver should not yet be discounted as a possible aetiologic factor in pregnancy sickness (see Andrews & Whitehead, 1990).

Gut function and pregnancy sickness

The third major physiological factor which could induce pregnancy sickness is that of gut function which is considerably disturbed in pregnancy. Such distrubances include delayed gastric emptying, reduced oesophageal sphincter pressure, decreased gall bladder motility and increased gut transit times and there is evidence that these may result from an inhibitory action of progesterone on the smooth muscle of the gut (Gill, Bowes & Kingma, 1985). Since gut stasis can be associated with nausea and vomiting, it follows that steroid effects on the gut could contribute to the genesis of pregnancy sickness. However, it is difficult to resolve the fact that pregnancy sickness usually declines after the first trimester while progesterone levels continue to rise and gut function becomes increasingly impaired during the later stages of pregnancy. This is indicated by the progressive increase in "heart-burn" during late pregnancy.

Apart from a direct action of hormones on the emetic response or hormonally-induced changes in liver and gut funtion, one cannot disregard psychosocial influences on the same system. Indeed, several studies have suggested that there is a strong psychsomatic input to the aetiology of pregnancy sickness (Wolkind & Zajicek, 1978). However, despite numerous studies over the last twenty years, we still have little insight as to why women do suffer from nausea and vomiting in the first trimester of pregnancy. In 1990 we proposed that pregnancy hormones may increase the sensitivity of the emetic response, possibly via an action on the chemoreceptor trigger zone (CTZ) in the area postrema (Andrews & Whitehead, 1990). The same area of the brain is also involved in the generation of conditioned taste aversions and this could explain why pregnancy is frequently associated with altered taste perceptions and the development of food cravings and aversions.

As a basis for more mechanistic studies we have initally undertaken a survey of 1,000 women attending the ante-natal clinic at St. George's Hospital during the early stages of their pregnancy (Whitehead et al., 1992). The purpose of this survey was to characterise the incidence, intensity and time-course of the symptoms and to establish whether these variables could be correlated with a variety of indicators of altered physiology. Continuing from these studies we have looked at the influence of steroid hormones on taste discrimination and investigated possible associations between pregnancy sickness, taste discrimination and the occurence of food cravings and aversions. Currently we are investigating whether polypeptide regulatory factors, in association with pregnancy hormones, may be a causative factor in pregnancy sickness. Of particular interest are the cytokines which have been implicated in the maternal immunologic recognition of the fetus and in the growth of the placenta (Clark, 1989, Banks et al., 1991,). While it is known that cytokines are primarily local modulatory factors released from macrophages, lymphocyctes and other immune cells, some do have significant effects on distant organs or tissues and so, in theory, could alter the sensitivity of the emetic response. The possible relationship between cytokines (notably the interleukins) and pregnancy sickness is based on the following observations. 1) Nausea and vomiting is a side effect of interleukin 2 (IL-2) immunotherapy (Mier et al., 1988). (2) IL-2 levels are elevted in pregnant women with peak levels being attained within the first month of pregnancy (Favier et al., 1990) 3) Fatigue, another symptom of early pregnancy, is a side effect of an infection and linked with raised levels of circulating interleukins (Krueger, 1990). 4) A favourable outcome of pregnancy has been positively associated with a higher incidence of vomiting in pregnancy (Weigel & Weigel, 1989).

THE CHARACTERSITICS OF PREGNANCY SICKNESS

1,000 pregnant women between the ages of 15-45 years (mean=27.9, 1SD=5.4 yrs) participated in this study and over 95% of the participants were between 11 and 28 weeks pregnant (mean=15.8, 1SD=3.8 weeks) when they completed a detailed questionnaire. The questionnaire was analysed with the SPSS computer programme; all percentages have been rounded up to the nearest whole figure and statistical tests were carried out with the Chi-square statsitic.

Nausea was reported by 85% of the participants and 52% actually vomited. An analysis of the onset of these symptoms showed that 34% of these women were already suffering from vomiting and/or nausea within four weeks of their last period, 73% within six weeks and 94% within 8 weeks. 45% reported that they suffered from pregnancy sickness before they knew they were pregnant or before their pregnancy was confirmed. As anticipated, symptoms of pregnancy sickness were found to decline sharply after the first trimester. Up to 12 weeks of pregnancy only 12% of women reported a reduction in both nausea and vomiting but by 16 weeks nausea was reduced in 60% and vomiting in 55% of women. These figures had increased to 81% and 75% respectively by 20 weeks of pregnancy.

An early onset of nausea and vomiting after conception was associated with an increased intensity of these symptoms, as indicated by their reported frequency (Fig. 2). This suggests that individual women have different emetic thresholds and sensitivities to the effects of hormones and/or other factors in pregnancy. This was supported by the association between the occurrence of pregnancy

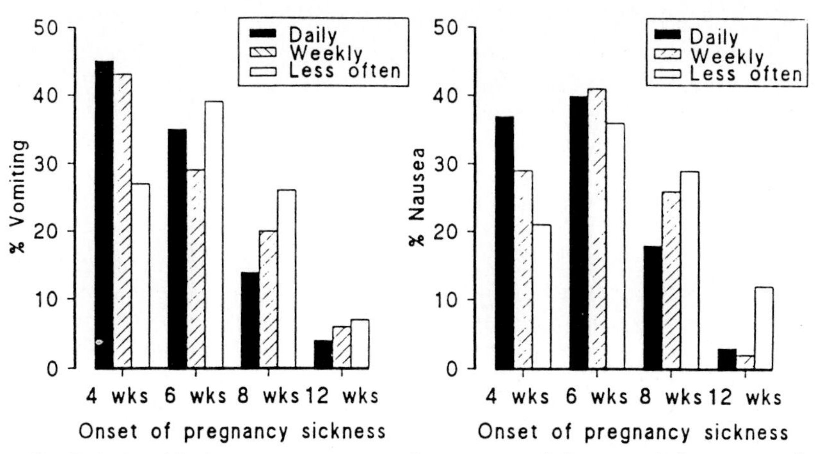

Figure 2. Relationship between the onset of pregnancy sickness and frequency of symptoms. The majority of women experienced daily symptoms of nausea and vomiting reported that the onset of their symptoms occurred within 4 or 6 weeks of their last menstruation.

sickness and sickness experienced as a side-effect of oral contraception. Of the 40% who regularly used oral contraception, 12% had experienced sickness as a side effect of the pill and these women were more likely to vomit in pregnancy ($p<0.02$) than those who had not experienced sickness as a side effect (Table 1). On the other hand prior exposure to hormones may help to desensitise the emetic response. There was a reduced frequency of vomiting associated with women who had used oral contraceptives prior to their pregnancy compared to women who had used other forms of contraception ($p<0.01$). Parallels were also observed with regard to travel sickness and migraine. There was a higher than expected incidence of vomiting ($p<0.05$) but not nausea, in pregnant women who reported sickness with motion (12%) or migraine (7.0%) (Table 1).

Pregnancy Sickness	Oral Contraceptive Sickness	Travel Sickness	Migraine
Vomiting	30 (70%)	77 (63%)	45 (65%)
No Vomiting	13 (30%)	46 (37%)	24 (35%)

Table 1. The number of women who reported sickness with oral contraceptives, travel or migraine tabulated against the incidence of vomiting in pregnancy. There was a higher than expected incidence of vomiting amongst these groups of women compared with women who had no sickness due to oral contraception ($p<0.02$), travel ($p<0.05$) or migraine ($p<0.05$).

A variety of other biological markers were also positively and significantly correlated with the occurrence of pregnancy sickness. These included an association between decreased bowel movements and the incidence of vomiting ($p<0.0001$), a reduced incidence and frequency of vomiting with increasing age ($p<0.0001$), an increased incidence of nausea amongst women who suffered from premenstrual tension ($p<0.005$) and a high positive correlation between nausea and vomiting with women who reported regular painful periods prior to pregnancy ($p<0.0001$ and

<0.005 respectively). Decreased bowel movements could imply a possible involvement of gut stasis in the development of pregnancy sickness. The other correlations suggest that women who tend to be more physically and emotionally influenced by fluctuating steroid hormone secretions through the menstrual cycle are more likely to suffer from pregnancy sickness. Interestingly, there was also an association between women in the clinic who experienced nausea and vomiting and their mothers having suffered from pregnancy sickness ($p<0.0001$). Over half of the women knew about their mothers' medical history of pregnancy sickness.

Parity was associated with an increased incidence of vomiting ($p<0.02$) but not nausea, although this was independent of the number or sex of previous children. Similarly, unplanned pregnancies (37% of the sample) were associated with a higher incidence of vomiting ($p<0.005$) although a lower incidence of nausea ($p<0.05$). While the correlation between an unplanned pregnancy and an increased incidence of vomiting may infer some sort of psychological input to the system, there was absolutely no correlation between the way a woman felt about being pregnant and the incidence of either nausea or vomiting. In a graded attitudinal-response, 33% reported being overjoyed and 49% happy.

It is clear from these studies that the onset of pregnancy sickness is related to the intensity of symptoms and that there is a relatively well defined period for the duration of sickness. This study also illustrated that the term "morning sickness" is a complete misnomer. Among those women who suffered from pregnancy sickness only 18% experienced nausea exclusively in the morning while the corresponding figure for vomiting was 31% (Fig. 3). Unfortunately the term morning sickness still persists and often no clear distinction is made between these temporary symtoms of early pregnancy and the continued vomiting of hyperemesis gravidarum. Whether or not hyperemesis gravidarum represents one extreme end of the spectrum of symptoms is not known.

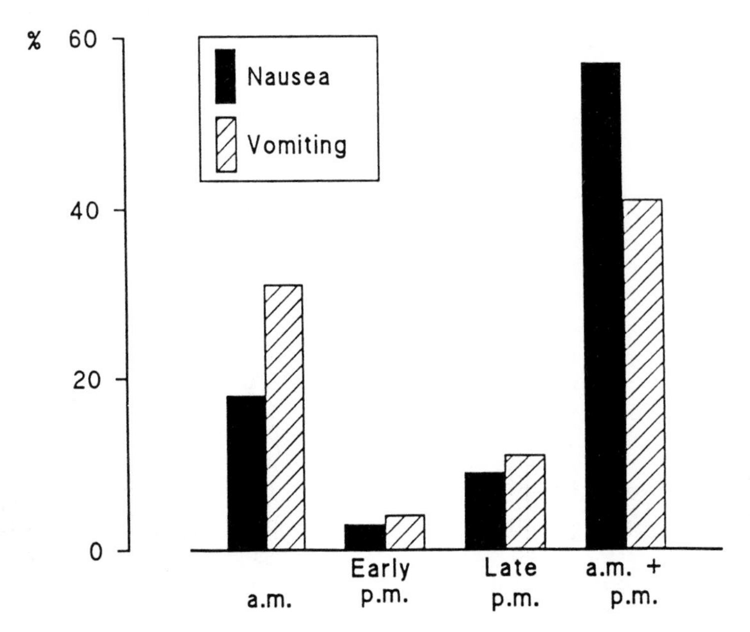

Figure 3. Percentage of women who experienced nausea or vomiting only in the morning (a.m.), afternoon (early p.m.) or evening (late p.m.) compared with the percentage of women whose symptoms would occur both in the morning and during other times of the day.

PREGNANCY-INDUCED CHANGES IN TASTE PERCEPTIONS

A half to two thirds of pregnant women experience changes in their taste and smell perceptions and these can lead to the development of cravings and aversions to particular types of food and drink (Taggert, 1961, Hook 1978). Specific dietary appetites may represent an adaptive need for a required nutritional substrate whereas the development of aversions may be part of that protective mechanism against the ingestion of harmful substances. However, these sensory changes are often documented through anecdotes or through surveys which are merely descriptive of the cravings and aversions experienced by pregnant women. Thus we wanted to establish how taste was altered in pregnancy and whether or not similar changes occurred in women taking oral contraceptives.

We have investigated taste thresholds and the ability to discriminate different concentrations of salt and sucrose solutions in 38 pregnant women (11 - 17 weeks pregnant) and compared the results with 48 non-pregnant age-matched controls amongst whom 15 were taking combined oral contraception. Taste solutions were made with distilled water and reagent grade sodium chloride and sucrose; the concentrations used were 200, 75, 50, 25, 10 and 5 mM. Women were presented with five salt or sucrose solutions in increasing order of concentration from 5 to 75 mM. They were asked to taste the solutions in order and the concentration at which they could identify the particular taste was taken as the taste threshold. However, there was no significant difference (Mann-Whitney U-test) in taste thresholds for either sugar or salt between pregnant women and controls. On the otherhand significant differences were observed in taste discrimination.

For this discrimination test, women were presented with four concentrations of salt and sucrose solutions (200, 75, 25 and 5 mM) in random order and asked to rank them in increasing order of strength. The results were scored simply as correct or incorrect and contingency tables were subjected to a Chi square analysis. Pregnant women were less likely to perform this test correctly ($p<0.03$ for sugar and $p<0.005$ for salt) although the frequency of correct discrimination tests were similar in the control and oral contraceptive groups (Fig. 4).

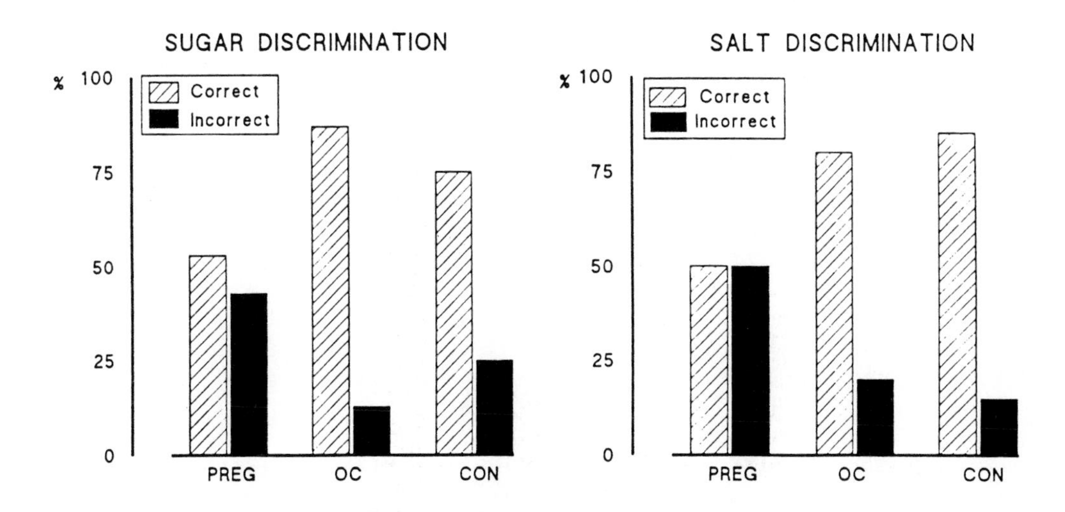

Figure 4. The percentage of pregnant women (PREG) who could discriminate different concentrations of sugar and salt solutions compared with age-matched non-pregnant controls (CON) and those taking oral contraceptives (OC). $p<0.03$ and $p<0.005$ respectively, Chi-square.

Brown and Toma (1986) also found that pregnant women were less likely to rank salt solutions in the correct order compared with non-pregnant controls although their results with the sucrose discrimination test were not significant. They suggest that a reduced sensitivity to taste may be a physiological mechanism for increasing salt intake during pregnancy since there is an increased requirement for salt during this time. The same could be said for increasing sugar intake during the phase of maternal weight gain and an increased insulin response to glucose.

The development of pica (repeated eating of non-nutritive substances) is well recognised amongst pregnant women. Cravings for paint, dry laundry, starch, clay, earth and even husbands blood have been anecdotally reported over the years. Pica usually appears in people with high nutritional demands and it appears to result from a specific hunger for minerals. With regard to pica during pregnancy, geophagia has been well documented (see Walker et al., 1985). This may be related to the increased need for iron in the pregnant woman although the occurrence of pica is both ethnically and regionally influenced.

While our studies reveal that there is no significant change in taste thresholds during pregnancy, the loss of taste discrimination may result from an alteration in neural processing of taste stimuli. This could involve a modulation of brain stem functions since specific areas in the brain stem are known to be involved in generating conditioned taste aversions (Garcia et al., 1985). That there was a significant correlation between the occurrence of pregnancy sickness and the development of food fads ($p < 0.02$) reported in our survey of 1,000 women may suggest some common mechanism in the development of sickness and taste changes in pregnancy. However, there was no significant correlation between the occurrence or intensity of pregnancy sickness and taste discrimination ability.

CYTOKINES AND THE AETIOLOGY OF PREGNANCY SICKNESS

Many cytokines are multifunctional and have diverse biological actions. They not only act on local cells through paracrine mechanisms but may also effect distant target tissues by acting as endocrine-type signals. IL-1, IL-2, IL-6 and tumour necrosis factorα (TNFα) have all been reported to occur in the general circulation during physiological or pathophysiological conditions (Banks et al., 1991, Rothwell 1990). Based on the evidence that cytokines have been implicated in the immune response to pregnancy (Banks et al., 1991) and the observation that circulating Il-2 may be raised in early pregnancy (Favier, et al. 1990), we have measured the circulating levels of IL-1β, IL-2, IL-6 and TNFα in the plasma of 46 pregnant women (11-12 weeks pregnant) and correlated these measurements with the circulating levels of several pregnancy hormones and the incidence, onset and intensity of nausea and vomiting (see also Sievers et al. abstract). Cytokines were measured with an ELISA system (Amersham, U.K.) and other hormones with radioimmunoassays (Immunodiagnostic Systems Ltd. U.K.). Detectable levels of IL-1β and TNFα were measured in less than 20% of the women, IL-2 in 30% and IL-6 in 52%. A similar distribution of percentages for detectable levels of the cytokines were recorded in 29 age-matched, non-pregnant controls and there was no significant differences in the mean levels of these cytokines between the two groups of women.

No association was found between the incidence of either nausea and vomiting and circulating levels of cytokines. Similarly, there was no correlation in the circulating concentrations of oestrogen, progesterone or hCG and the incidence of pregnancy sickness or the circulating levels of cytokines. However, significantly higher levels of IL-6 were meansured in the plasma of women who reported vomiting and/or nausea compared with the plasma concentrations of IL-6 in women who had no sickness. These studies show that pregnancy does not increase the circulating levels of cytokines compared with non-pregnant controls and support the evidence of a paracrine role within their placental site of production. Furthermore, these studies provided no evidence for an association of circulating immune factors, or indeed oestrogen, progesterone and hCG, in the incidence of pregnancy sickness.

CONCLUSIONS

It has been reported that women have a predisposition to chemotherapy-induced vomiting (Roila et al., 1988) and that the intensity of emesis in past pregnancies can be positively correlated with the incidence and severity of emesis during chemotherapy (Martin & Diaz-Rubio, 1990). It has also been shown that the incidence of post-operative vomiting and the response to anti-emetic therapy can vary according to different phases of the menstrual cycle (Beattie et al., 1991). The extent to which such predispositions are hormonally and/or genetically determined is unknown. However, it would appear that any hormonal modulation of the emetic response, as occurs in pregnancy, results from a complex re-setting of neuronal circuitry which cannot be explained through simple measurements of hormones or other circulating factors.

Acknowledgements This work was supported by the Nuffield Foundation and the Medical Research Committe of St. Goerge's Hospital.

REFERENCES

Andrews, P. and Whithead, S. (1990): Pregnancy Sickness. *News in Physiological Sciences* 5, 5-10.

Banks, R.E., Evans, S.W. and Whicher, J.T. (1991): Polypeptide regulatory factors in pregnancy. *Contemp. Rev. Obstet. & Gynaecol.* 3, 22-29.

Beattie, W.S., Lindblad, T. and Buckley, N.D. (1991): The incidence of post-operative nausea and vomiting in women undergoing laparoscopy is influenced by the day of menstrual cycle. *Can. J. Anaesth.* 38, 298-302.

Brown, J.E. and Toma, R.B. (1986): Taste changes during pregnancy. *Am. J. Clin. Nutr.* 43, 414-18.

Clark, D.A. (1989): Cytokines and pregnancy. *Current Opinions in Immunology*, 1,1148-1152.

Fairweather, D.V.I. (1986): Mechanisms and treatment of nausea and vomiting in pregnancy. In: *Nausea and Vomiting: Mechanisms and Treatment,* ed. C.J. Davis, G.V. Lake Bakaar & D.G. Grahame-Smith, pp. 151-159: Springer-Verlag, Berlin Heidelberg.

Favier, R., Edelman, P., Mary, J.Y., Sadoul, G. and Douay, L. (1990): Presence of elevated serum interleukin-2 levels in pregnant women. *N. Engl. J. Med.* 322, 270.

Garcia, J., Lasiter, P.S., Bermudez-Rattoni, F. and Deems, D.A. (1985): A general theory of aversion learning. *Annals. N.Y. Acad. Sci.* 443, 8-21.

Gill, R.C., Bowes, K.L. and Kingma, Y.J. (1985): Effect of progesterone on canine colonic smooth muscle. *Gastroenterology,* 88, 1941-1947.

Hook, E.B. Dietary cravings and aversions during pregnancy. *Am. J. Clin. Nutr.* 31, 1355-1362.

Jarnfelt-Samsioe, A. (1987): Nausea and vomiting in pregnancy: a review. *Obstet. Gynaecol. Survey.*41; 422-427.

Klebanoff, M.A., Koslowe, P.A., Kaslow, R. and Rhoads, G.G. (1985): Epidemiology of vomiting in early pregnancy. *Obstet. Gynaecol.* 66, 612-616.

Kreuger, J.M. (1990): Somnogenic activity of immune response modifiers. *Trends in Neurosciences*. 11, 122-126.

Kucharczyk, J. (1991): Humoral factors in nausea and emesis. In: Nausea and Vomiting: Recent Research and Clinical Advances, ed. J. Kucharzyk, D.J. Steward, A.D. Miller, pp. 59-75: *CRC Press,* Boston.

Masson, G.M.Anthony, F. and Chau, E. (1985): Serum chorionic gonadotrophin (hCG), Schwangerschafts-protein 1 (SP1), progesterone and oestradiol levels in patients with nausea and vomiting in early pregnancy. *Brit. J. Obstet. Gynaecol.* 92, 211-215.

Mier, J.W., Aronson, F.R., Numerof, R.P., Vachino, G. and Atkins, M.B. (1988): Toxicity of immunotherapy with interleukin-2 and lymphokine-activated killer cells. *Pathol. Immunophathol. Res.* 7, 459-476.

Roila, F., Tonato, M. and Basurto, C. (1988): Antiemetic activity of high doses of metoclopramide combined with methylprednisolone versus metoclopramide alone in ciplatin-treated cancer patients: a randomized double-blind trial of the Italian Oncology Group for Clinical Research. *J. Clin. Oncol.* 5, 141-149.

Rothwell, N.J. (1991): The endocrine significance of cytokines. *J. Endocr.* 128, 171-173.

Soules, M.R., Hughes, C.L., Garcia, J.A., Livergood, C.H., Prystowsky, M.R. and Alexander, E. (1980): Nausea and vomiting of pregnancy: role of human chorionic gonadotropin and 17-hydroxyprogesterone. *Obstet. Gynaecol.* 55, 696-700.

Taggert, N. (1961): Food habits in pregnancy. *Proc. Nutr. Soc.* 20, 35-40.

Walker, A.R.P., Walker, B.F., Jones, J., Veradi, M. and Walker, C. (1985): Nausea and vomiting and dietary cravings and aversions during pregnancy in South African women. *Brit. J. Obstet. Gynaecol.* 92, 484-489.

Weigel, M.M. and Weigel, R.M. (1989): Nausea and vomiting of early pregnancy and pregnancy outcome. A meta-analytical review. *J. Obstet. Gynaecol.* 96, 1312-1318.

Whitehead, S.A. and Andrews, P.L.R., Chamberlain G.V.P. (1992): The characterisitics of pregnancy sickness - a survey of 1,000 women. *J. Obstet. Gynaecol.* (submitted).

Wolkind, S. and Zajicek, E. (1978): Psycho-social correlates of nausea and vomiting in pregnancy. *Psychosom. Res.* 22: 1-5.

Mechanisms and Control of Emesis. Eds A.L. Bianchi, L. Grélot, A.D. Miller, G.L. King. Colloque INSERM/ John Libbey Eurotext Ltd. © 1992, Vol. 223, pp. 307-312

Acupuncture and treatment of vomiting

Kieran T.J. Fitzpatrick

Department of Clinical Anaesthesia, Belfast City Hospital, 97, Lisburn Road, Belfast, BT9 5PR, Northern Ireland

SUMMARY
The antiemetic action of stimulation of the P6 (Neiguan) acupuncture point has been extensively studied in Belfast over the past seven years. It has been proven to be an effective antiemetic therapy in postoperative patients, pregnant patients and in chemotherapy patients. Studies have been undertaken using traditional manual needling of P6, electrostimulation of P6 and acupressure. It was also found that P6 acupuncture is more effective in preventing sickness in these circumstances than in treating established emetic symptoms

L'acupuncture et le traitement du vomissement.

Résumé: *L'effet antiémétique de la stimulation du point d'acupuncture P6 (Neiguan) a été étudié intensivement à Belfast au cours de ces sept dernières années. Il est démontré que la stimulation de ce point est une thérapie antiémétique efficace chez les patients en situation post-opératoire, les femmes en gestation et les sujets en traitement chimiothérapique. Les études du point P6 ont été effectuées en y appliquant des aiguilles traditionnelles, des stimulations électriques et des pressions. Il a aussi été montré que l'acupuncture au point P6 est plus efficace en mesure de prévention du vomissement associé à ces diverses circonstances qu'en traitement propre des symptômes déjà présents.*

INTRODUCTION

During a visit to the People's Republic of China the late Professor Dundee was shown the use of acupressure as a prophylaxis against vomiting in early pregnancy. The women attending the antenatal clinic were instructed to press a point on the forearm just above the right wrist. This point, Neiguan or P6 has been described as a treatment for hyperemesis gravidarum (Lewith & Lewith, 1980). A study by Fry (1986) showed that pressure on this P6 point reduced the incidence of postoperative vomiting.

The Neiguan point is the sixth point on the pericardial meridian. It is situated two Chinese inches or "cun" proximal to the distal wrist crease between the tendons of palmaris longus and flexor carpi radialis muscles of the right forearm. It lies at a depth of approximately 1 cm. to the skin surface and is close to the median nerve. A "cun" is equivalent to the distance between the creases of the proximal and distal interphalangeal joints of the flexed index finger or roughly the width of the thumb across the interphalangeal joint (Dundee et al., 1989).

The acupuncture needles used were made of stainless steel and were sterilised by the Central Sterile Supplies Department of the hospital before use. They were 1.2 cm long and 30 gauge in diameter.

The needle is inserted through the skin at the appropriate point with a twisting motion and inserted until the patient experiences a feeling of "chi". This is a feeling of heaviness, numbness or tightness which is of a non-anatomical distribution and signifies correct position of the acupuncture needle.

The Belfast studies have examined a number of ways of stimulating this P6 point including acupuncture with manual stimulation of the needle, acupuncture with electrostimulation of the needle and various types of acupressure. They have also looked at acupuncture as an antiemetic in the postoperative patient, the obstetric patient and in patients undergoing chemotherapy. This paper will summarise much of this work which has been carried out over the past seven years. The studies had the approval of the local medical ethics committee.

POSTOPERATIVE SICKNESS.

Earlier work from this department had evaluated a model for the study of recognised antiemetic drugs (Clarke et al., 1970; Morrison et al., 1968; Dundee et al., 1975). A study was therefore undertaken to evaluate the use of this model in the study of acupuncture as a postoperative antiemetic, (Chestnutt & Dundee, 1985). Two groups of 25 women presenting for minor gynaecological surgery were given the same premedicant and anaesthesia. One group had manual needling of the P6 point for 5 minutes at the time of administering the premedication (meptazinol 100mg intramuscularly). The other group received the premedicant only. This study showed that the acupuncture group had significantly less sickness in the first post operative hour. It also showed that meptazinol 100mg intramuscularly was associated with an unacceptable incidence of sickness in these patients. Furthermore, it demonstrated that the model for the study of postoperative sickness could be applied to the study of acupuncture.

Having shown that acupuncture to the P6 point was indeed effective in reducing postoperative sickness a study using a "dummy acupuncture" point was undertaken to determine if the success of P6 acupuncture as an antiemetic was a psychological effect (Dundee et al., 1986). This utilised a point at the antecubital fossa with no known acupuncture properties. Table 1 summarises the results of this study which showed that there was a significant decrease in sickness in the group having P6 acupuncture when compared to the control group having no acupuncture or to the group having acupuncture at a "dummy point". In addition, there was no significant difference in the incidence of sickness experienced by the control group or the group having dummy acupuncture.

Table 1. Nausea or vomiting in three groups of 25 patients having 10mg nalbuphine premedication with no acupuncture, dummy acupuncture or P6 acupuncture.

	No acupuncture	Dummy acupuncture	P6 acupuncture
Vomiting	6	5	3
Nausea	11	12	3
Neither	8	8	19

In the knowledge that it was acupuncture to the P6 point rather than the needling of a dummy point that was effective, work was undertaken to discover if dextrality or sinistrality would influence the outcome of the acupuncture (Dundee et al., 1988). This revealed that the best results were obtained by using the patient's dominant arm. However, this finding was not considered clinically important as a survey of some 1,000 hospital patients revealed an incidence of sinistrality of only 7 per cent.

Having been successful with using manual stimulation of acupuncture needles at the P6 point, studies were conducted to compare electrical stimulation of the needles at P6 with manual stimulation and also standard antiemetic drugs. For this study Ghaly et al.(1987) applied a current to a needle placed in the P6 point. A D.C. pulsator (Shackman J S 863-4) at 1,000 Hz for 5 minutes or 10Hz for 5 or 15 minutes was used. This produced a square waveform with a pulse width of 0.25 ms and the output voltage was steadily increased until the patient felt a definate, but not uncomfortable, pulsation. As with all previous studies the patients all gave verbal consent to partake in the study and were informed that it concerned the efficacy and toxicity of the pre-medication. No mention was made of sickness. Patients were visited at 1 and 6 hours postoperatively by an investigator who was unaware of the treatment group to which the patient had been allocated. At the second visit at 6 hours postoperatively the nature of the study was fully explained. All the studies described in this paper had full ethical committee approval. Table 2 summarises the results of this study.

Table 2. Postoperative sickness following premedication with nalbuphine 10mg with or without acupuncture (acp) or cyclizine 50mg.

	0-1 hours postop.			1-6 hours post op.		
Adjuvant therapy	Vomiting	Nausea	Nil	Vomiting	Nausea	Nil
Nil	3	14	14	5	12	14
Manual acp	4	3	24	0	3	28
Electrical acp 10Hz 5 min	1	1	29	3	2	26
Cyclizine 50mg	5	2	24	5	4	22

Only electro acupuncture using 10Hz for 5 minutes was given throughout the study as early on it was found that there was an unacceptably high incidence of sickness in those patients having electro acupuncture. The key was broken which revealed a high emetic incidence in patients having electro acupuncture at 1,000Hz for 5 minutes or 10Hz for 15 minutes. The study continued using only the 10Hz frequency for 5 minutes. Compared to the control group who had nalbuphine 10mg only, all 3 treatment groups had significantly less sickness. There was no significant difference in the effectiveness of the 3 treatment groups. This work appears to partly disagree with that of Mann (1981) who stated that "the only thing of importance in acupuncture is to stimulate the right place, the nature of the stimulus being of secondary importance".

A study from New Zealand (Weightman et al., 1987) failed to show any antiemesis in an opioid based anaesthetic technique when P6 acupuncture was administered during anaesthesia. Further studies from Belfast (Dundee et al., 1988; Milligan et al., 1988) confirmed this finding. This could mean that the P6 point was not accurately located in the anaesthetised patients. Or it may be that P6 acupuncture has a strong psychological element but the work with the dummy point would appear to rule this out. The third possibility is that it is important to administer the P6 acupuncture antiemetic before the emetic stimulus has been administered to the patient. A study by Dundee and Milligan (1988) supports this latter view.

MORNING SICKNESS

The study of postoperative sickness allows the investigator to have a strictly controlled clinical situation where variables can be reduced to a minimum. Under these conditions it was possible to demonstrate that P6 acupuncture had an antiemetic effect in patients premedicated with an opioid and undergoing minor gynaecological surgery. Morning sickness, however, does not allow the investigator to strictly control the clinical situation, but knowing that P6 acupuncture was effective in postoperative sickness its effects on morning sickness were studied (Dundee et al., 1988). Three hundred and fifty consecutive women attending the antenatal clinic of the Royal Maternity Hospital were given no treatment, told to press over the P6 point for a minute every 2-3 hours or to press a dummy point at the right elbow. They were asked to keep a note of their emetic symptoms, to grade them as severe or troublesome, moderate or slight depending upon the incidence of nausea or vomiting bouts and to return this form to the investigators. Although the return rate for the forms (70 per cent) was less than hoped for, P6 acupressure was shown to have a benefical effect with the dummy point having lesser benefit. The results are summarised in table 3.

Table 3. Percentage incidence of varying degrees of morning sickness and acupressure at P6, dummy point or no treatment.

Acupressure	n	Severe or troublesome	moderate	slight or nil
Nil	119	56%	21%	23%
P6	110	19%	21%	60%
Dummy point	112	37%	37%	26%

CYTOTOXIC DRUG THERAPY

Cancer chemotherapy is associated with troublesome sickness (Frytak & Moertel, 1981; Penta et al., 1981). This can be a major problem with some treatments eg cisplatin and DTIC. The Northern Ireland Radiotherapy Centre welcomed the study of acupuncture in these patients as it might offer effective antiemesis with no side effects.

Seventy one consecutive patients who had had at least 2 prior courses of chemotherapy were questioned regarding their sickness (Dundee et al., 1987). Fifty four (76 per cent) had troublesome sickness at the first administration of chemotherapy and 52 of these had a similar experience the subsequent administration.

In a multi-facet study Dundee et al. (1989) showed that P6 electro acupuncture was a highly effective antiemetic in patients with a history of chemotherapy induced sickness undergoing further chemotherapy. Both outpatients and inpatients were studied. In 10 patients a dummy point on the right elbow was stimulated in the course of repeated acupuncture giving a cross over group. Alleviation of sickness was graded as good, fair or slight by the patient. Table 4 outlines the results.

Table 4. P6 acupuncture and chemotherapy sickness.

	Neoplasm	n	Alleviation of Sickness Good	Fair	Slight/Nil
Inpatients	Testis	29	16	12	1
	Lymphoma	5	2	3	0
Outpatients	Breast	64	46	15	3
	Lymphoma	7	2	3	2
Crossover study	Various	10	9	1	0
Total		115	75	34	6

P6 acupuncture works as an antiemetic in cancer chemotherapy but it involves repeating the acupuncture on a regular basis which is not always feasible due to manpower shortages and some patients do not like needles. To overcome this problem stimulation of P6 by a transcutaneous electrical method (Dundee et al., 1989) had only limited success. However, placing an elasticised band and stud (Sea Band) over P6, and instructing the patient to press this for 5 minutes every 2 hours was more successful (Dundee & Yang, 1990). Again it appears that P6 acupuncture is more effective in preventing sickness rather than as an acute treatment.

In this paper an attempt has been made to give an overall view of the Belfast studies on P6 acupuncture. It is an unusual method of preventing sickness in the postoperative patient, the pregnant patient and in the chemotherapy patient. Despite the scepticism with which the work was initially regarded stimulation of the P6 antiemetic point has been shown to be effective.

REFERENCES

Chestnutt, W.N. & Dundee, J.W. (1985): Acupuncture for relief of Meptazinol induced vomiting. B. J. Anaesthesth. 57, 825-826P.

Clarke, R.S.J., Dundee, J.W., Loan, W.D. (1970): The use of postoperative vomiting as a means of evaluating anti-emetics. Br. J. Pharmacol. 40. 568-569.

Dundee, J.W., Assaf, R.A.E., Loan, W.B., Morrison, J.D. (1975): A comparison of the efficacy of cyclizine and perphenazine in reducing the emetic effects of morphine and pethidine. Br. J. Clin. Pharmacol, 2, 81-85.

Dundee, J.W., Chestnutt, W.N., Chaly, R.G., Lynas, A.G.A. (1986): Traditional Chinese acupuncture: a potentially useful antiemetic? Br. Med. J. 293, 583-584.

Dundee, J.W., Fee, E., Ghaly, R.G. (1989): Non invasive electrical stimulation of P6 antiemetic point. Br. J. Clin. Pharmacol. 28. 231P.

Dundee, J.D., Fitzpatrick, K.T.J., Ghaly, R.G., Patterson, C.C. (1988): Does dextrality or sinistrality affect the outcome of P6 acupuncture antiemesis? Br. J. Clin. Pharmacol. 25, 679P-680P

Dundee, J.W., Ghaly, R.G., Bill, K.M., Chestnutt, W.N., Fitzpatrick, K.T.J., Lynas, A.G. (1989): Effect of stimulation of the P6 antiemetic point on postoperative nausea and vomiting. Br. J. Anaesth. 63, 612-618.

Dundee, J.W., Ghaly, R.G., Fitzpatrick, K.T.J., Lynch, G.A., Abram, W.P. (1987): Acupuncture to prevent cisplatin associated vomiting. Lancet, 1. 1083.

Dundee, J.W., Ghaly, R.G., Fitzpatrick, K.T.J., Abram, W.P., Lynch, G.A. (1989): Acupuncture prophylaxis of cancer chemotherapy sickness. J. Roy. Soc. Med. 82. 268-271.

Dundee, J.W. & Milligan, K.R. (1988): Acupuncture as an antiemetic Br. Med. J. 296, 135.

Dundee, J.W., Milligan, K.R., McKay, A.C. (1988): Influence of intraoperative acupuncture and droperidol on postoperative emesis. Br. J. Anaesth. 61, 117P-118P.

Dundee, J.W. & Jang, J. (1990): Prolongation of the antiemetic action of P6 acupuncture in patients having cancer chemotherapy. J. Roy. Soc. Med. 83, 360-362.

Dundee, J.W., Sourial, F.B.R., Ghaly, R.G., Bell, P.F. (1988): Acupressure reduces morning sickness. J. Roy. Soc. Med. 81, 456-457.

Fry, E.N.S. (1986): Acupressure and postoperative vomiting. Anaesthesia, 41, 661-662.

Frytak, S. & Moertel, C.G. (1981): Management of nausea and vomiting in the cancer patient. J. A. M. A. 245, 393-396.

Ghaly, R.G., Fitzpatrick, K.T.J., Dundee, J.W. (1987): Antiemetic studies with Chinese acupuncture. Anaesthesia. 42, 1108-1110.

Lewith, G.T. & Lewith, N.R. (1980): Modern Chinese Acupuncture.Wellinborough: Thorsons.

Mann, F. (1981): Scientific Aspects of Acupuncture, 2nd Edn. London: Heinemann.

Milligan, K.R., McKay, A.C., Dundee, J.W. (1988): Failure of acupuncture to influence postoperative emesis in outpatients. Ir. J. Med. Sci. 157, 29-30.

Morrison, J.D., Hill, G.B., Dundee, J.W. (1968): Studies of drugs given before anaesthesia. XV. Evaluation of the method of study after 10,000 observations. Br. J. Anaesth. 40, 890-900.

Penta, J.S., Poster. D.S., Bruno, S. MacDonald, J.S. (1981): Clinical trials with antiemetic agents in cancer patients receiving chemotherapy. J. Clin. Pharmacol. 21. 11S-22S.

Weightman, W.M., Zacharias, M., Herbison, P. (1987): Traditional Chinese acupuncture as an antiemetic. Br. Med. J. 295. 1379-1380..

This paper is dedicated to the memory of the late Professor John Wharry Dundee, OBE, MD, PhD, FRCP, FFARCS., who died on 01.12.91.

Mechanisms and Control of Emesis. Eds A.L. Bianchi, L. Grélot, A.D. Miller, G.L. King. Colloque INSERM/
John Libbey Eurotext Ltd. © 1992, Vol. 223, pp. 313-322

Psychological aspects of nausea and vomiting

Michael A. Andrykowski

Department of Behavioral Science, University of Kentucky College of Medicine, Lexington, KY 40536-0086, USA

SUMMARY

Nausea and vomiting (NV) are common distressing side effects associated with cancer chemotherapy. NV can be experienced either pretreatment or posttreatment. Evidence for the influence of psychological factors in the experience of pretreatment and posttreatment NV is reviewed. In addition to the implication of a Pavlovian learning process, anxiety appears to play a role in the development of pretreatment NV. Regarding posttreatment NV, both anxiety and expectations for treatment-related NV appear to play a contributory role, especially for chemotherapy regimens of low to moderate emetic potential.

Les facteurs psychologiques de la nausée et du vomissement.
Résumé: *La nausée et le vomissement (NV) sont des effets secondaires pénibles couramment associés aux traitements de chimiothérapie anticancéreuse. NV peuvent être rencontrés soit avant soit après le traitement. Les preuves de l'influence de facteurs psychologiques dans les NV de pré-traitement et post-traitement sont passées en revue. En plus de l'intervention d'un processus d'apprentissage de type Pavlovien, l'anxiété apparaît jouer un rôle dans le développement de la NV de pré-traitement. En ce qui concerne la NV de post-traitement, à la fois l'anxiété et l'attente du traitement lié à la NV apparaissent jouer un rôle, en particulier lors de protocoles de chimiothérapie à potentiel émétique faible ou modéré.*

INTRODUCTION

Interest in the interface of psychosocial and biological processes in the development and treatment of malignant disease has grown in recent years. Within this field of biopsychosocial oncology (Derogatis, 1986), investigation of factors associated with the development and experience of various side effects associated with cancer therapies, such as pain, fatigue, cognitive dysfunction, food aversions, or sleep disturbances, has been popular. In particular, the experience of nausea and vomiting (NV) in cancer chemotherapy patients has received close scrutiny.

NV are distressing side effects often experienced in conjunction with cancer chemotherapy treatments. NV can occur prior to, during, or following treatment. NV occuring prior to treatment is known as pretreatment (or anticipatory) NV (PreNV), while that occuring following treatment is known as posttreatment NV (PostNV). While NV are presumed to be normal, pharmacologic side effects of cancer treatment, evidence suggests that the experience of these symptoms has a substantial psychological component as well. In this chapter, the role of psychological variables in the experience of NV associated with cancer chemotherapy treatment will be examined. It must be noted that while radiotherapy can produce these symptoms as well, caution is warranted in extending the discussion that follows to the radiotherapy setting. To date no research has examined the role of psychological factors in the experience of NV following radiotherapy. While extrapolation of the discussion that follows to cancer radiotherapy treatment could actually be straightforward, there is a clear need for parallel research to identify the influence of psychological factors in the experience of NV in the radiotherapy setting.

INFLUENCE OF PSYCHOLOGICAL FACTORS IN PreNV

The influence of psychological factors in the experience of NV is most apparent when considering PreNV. Here, NV are experienced prior to treatment, in the absence of any pharmacologic emetic stimulus. To account for this, PreNV is generally viewed as a response learned through a process of classical conditioning (Burish & Carey, 1986; Morrow & Dobkin, 1988). Over the course of treatment, certain olfactory, taste, visual, and auditory stimuli become consistently associated with treatment and subsequent PostNV. With repeated stimuli-treatment-PostNV linkages, in vivo exposure to these environmental stimuli alone becomes sufficient to trigger PreNV. Less frequently, cognitive or imaginal exposure ("thinking about" treatment or treatment-related stimuli) can also trigger these symptoms.

The potential role of psychological factors in PreNV extends beyond its status simply as a learned phenomenon. Not all patients develop PreNV, even when treatment regimen and disease status are held constant. Prevalence estimates for PreNV range widely, with approximately 25-50% of all chemotherapy patients experiencing these symptoms. Nausea prior to treatment is much more frequent than vomiting (Burish & Carey, 1986; Morrow & Dobkin, 1988). Even among those patients developing PreNV, the rapidity with which these symptoms develop varies widely (Andrykowski & Redd, 1987). Some patients display PreNV following only two or three treatments while others require many more treatments before symptoms are manifest. In light of this, considerable research has attempted to identify variables (or "risk factors") associated with a greater likelihood of developing PreNV (Burish & Carey, 1986; Morrow & Dobkin, 1988). Consistent with a classical conditioning model of etiology, the single best predictor of PreNV development is the severity of PostNV experienced. Of psychological interest, however, is the research and theory linking anxiety to the development of PreNV.

A number of studies have found that patients who report elevated levels of trait anxiety, state anxiety, or general "distress" are more likely to report preNV (Andrykowski, 1990). While some relationship between PreNV and anxiety is presumed to exist, determination of its precise nature has remained elusive. Different relationships between PreNV and state anxiety have been hypothesized (Andrykowski, 1990). Several hypotheses suggest a causal relationship between anxiety and PreNV. These include: (1) anxiety directly causes PreNV, (2) anxiety directly facilitates classical conditioning of PreNV, and (3) anxiety exacerbates PostNV and thus increases the likelihood of classical conditioning of PreNV.

The anxiety-PreNV hypothesis (Hypothesis 1) suggests that since NV are potential concomitants of the stress response (Cleghorn & Brown, 1964; Selye, 1950), PreNV results simply from elevated state anxiety. Indeed chemotherapy is a stressful experience for many patients and attribution of PreNV to "nerves" is common among patients, family, and medical staff. In particular, individuals prone to experiencing gastrointestinal distress when anxious would be at risk for developing PreNV. No firm evidence supports the anxiety-PreNV hypothesis and in fact some evidence argues against it: no patient with PreNV in studies by Morrow (1982) or Nesse et al. (1980) reported a previous instance of anxiety-induced nausea or vomiting. The fact that reports of anxiety and PreNV tend to coincide does not establish that anxiety causes PreNV; the reverse could be true as well. At minimum, this hypothesis requires demonstration that the occurrence and severity of PreNV within an individual varies as a function of anxiety levels.

The anxiety-conditionability hypothesis (Hypothesis 2) is based upon the assertion that anxious individuals evidence greater "conditionability" (Spence, 1958; 1964). (Conditionability refers to the predisposition of an individual to acquire a variety of classically conditioned responses.) Based upon Pavlov's views regarding the physiological bases of personality (Teplov, 1964) and Hullian learning theory (Hull, 1943), this hypothesis suggests that anxious individuals are characterized by a greater generalized drive level and hence increased excitatory potential. Consistent with this view, individuals' characteristic degree of autonomic reactivity has been linked to greater conditionability (Hugdahl et al., 1977; Ohmann & Bohlin, 1973). Exactly how state anxiety facilitates conditioning of PreNV is unclear. However, it has been suggested that anxiety, and its associated autonomic reactivity, is associated with low stimulus screening and less habituation to environmental stimuli (Dolgin & Katz, 1988). Therefore, anxious patients might attend more vigilantly to external stimuli in the cancer treatment environment, increasing their salience as potential conditioned stimuli for PreNV. Support for the anxiety-conditionability hypothesis of PreNV development is mixed. Demonstration that patients who develop PreNV are characterized by high levels of trait anxiety, or even more importantly, treatment-related state anxiety, would be important supporting evidence. However, two prospective studies failed to link greater trait anxiety with subsequent development of PreNV (Andrykowski et al., 1985; Andrykowski et al., 1988). Furthermore, the same two studies differed with regard to whether higher levels of state anxiety at initial chemotherapy infusions was (Andrykowski et al., 1985) or was not associated (Andrykowski et al., 1988) with subsequent development of PreNV. Finally, in a longitudinal study by Andrykowski and Redd (1987), elevated treatment-related anxiety early in a patient's course of treatment was associated with onset of PreNV relatively later in a patient's course of chemotherapy (i.e., after a greater number of chemotherapy infusions). On the other hand, support for the anxiety-conditionability hypothesis is found in a study by Kvale et al. (1991). The autonomic reactivity of cancer patients was assessed prior to beginning a course of chemotherapy using a habituation paradigm. Among patients experiencing PostNV, those evidencing greater autonomic reactivity, particularly sympathetic reactivity, were significantly more likely to subsequently develop PreNV. It was concluded that autonomic reactivity, characteristic of anxious individuals, mediates PreNV development via its influence upon conditionability.

The anxiety-exacerbates-PostNV hypothesis (Hypothesis 3) suggests that anxiety facilitates the development of PreNV via its ability to exacerbate PostNV (the primary risk factor for PreNV). Both additive and interactive effects are possible. An additive model is based opon the fact that anxiety itself can generate some degree of NV, which is then added to that produced by the emetic pharmacologic stimulus used in treatment. Afferent input from several sources, including the higher brain stem and cortical structures, is capable of stimulating the vomiting center, thus initiating the experience of NV (Borison & Wang, 1953). Thus psychological stimuli can trigger NV and the occurrence of these symptoms in athletes or performers prior to a competition or performance is a good illustration of the emetic potential of anxiety. Alternatively, an interactive model would posit that anxiety could interact with the emetic stimulus, perhaps at the neurological level, resulting in a heightened gastrointestinal response. In either case, increased PostNV increases the likelihood that PreNV will develop through a classical conditioning process. Support for the anxiety-PreNV hypothesis is derived from two prospective studies demonstrating a positive, multivariate association between treatment-related anxiety and PostNV (Andrykowski & Gregg, 1992; Jacobsen et al., 1988). Even more convincing is evidence from a longitudinal study suggesting that increased treatment-related anxiety preceded increased PostNV which in turn preceded the initial occurrence of PreNV (Andrykowski & Redd, 1987).

While all of the potential relationships between anxiety and PreNV discussed to this point assert a causal relationship between the two, it is possible that the observed relationship between anxiety and PreNV might be more artifact than actuality. Because anxiety and PreNV are typically assessed via self-report, some degree of correspondence between these two variables would be expected simply because of shared method variance. Alternatively, reports of anxiety and PreNV might correspond because of a failure to distinguish sensations of nausea from those of anxiety (Andrykowski, 1986). For example, patients might monitor their physical sensations and correctly report that they are anxious prior to treatment but might also inaccurately report that they are experiencing PreNV. Such mislabeling is particularly likely at lesser magnitudes of nausea and anxiety since behavioral indicants of each, which could potentially facilitate accurate labeling, are missing or obscure. Unfortunately, evaluation of the degree to which such artifacts account for the relationship between anxiety and PreNV is difficult. Multimodal assessment of anxiety and PreNV, adding, when possible, observational or physiological measures to standard self-report measures, would clearly advance the research in this regard (Carnrike & Carey, 1990). Alternatively, researchers might reduce potential problems with measurement artifacts by focusing upon the role of anxiety in the development of pretreatment <u>vomiting</u> (an observable behavior). However, in doing so, researchers would be limited by the fact that pretreatment vomiting is much less prevalent than pretreatment nausea, not to mention the possibility that the anxiety-PreNV relationship might vary as a function of whether pretreatment vomiting or nausea is the criterion symptom.

In summary, the evidence suggesting a causal role for anxiety in the development of PreNV best supports the anxiety-exacerbates-PostNV hypothesis. However, the anxiety-conditionability hypothesis also garners some support. It is likely that both processes are operative, with perhaps the anxiety-exacerbates-PostNV hypothesis particularly likely to account for instances when PreNV develops relatively later in an individual's course of treatment, (Andrykowski et al., 1988; Andrykowski & Redd, 1987).

INFLUENCE OF PSYCHOLOGICAL FACTORS IN PostNV

Some degree of PostNV is a common side-effect following cancer chemotherapy. However wide variability in the occurrence and severity of PostNV is often evidenced both across and within specific chemotherapy drug regimens. Variability in PostNV across chemotherapy regimens is typically attributed to pharmacological factors: particular drug-dosage combinations vary in their emetic potential. That is, chemotherapy regimens differ in their pharmacologic properties and thus in their inherent ability to trigger gastrointestinal distress. Some chemotherapy agents, such as Cisplatin, produce severe PostNV in nearly all patients, while other agents, such as 5-fluouracil, may produce little or no PostNV in most patients. Obviously, such interregimen differences are not of great psychological interest. What is of potential psychological interest, however, is the observation that even patients identical in disease status and receiving a chemotherapy regimen identical with respect to drug(s) and dosage often differ markedly in the presence and magnitude of PostNV. Such interpatient variability within a particular drug-dosage-disease combination is less easily accounted for. Obviously, a model that encompasses more than simply pharmacological factors is necessary to account for these observed, and often substantial, differences among individuals in gastrointestinal response.

Variation in PostNV within a particular drug-dosage-disease combination could reflect differences between patients with regard to: (1) the prescription and usage of antiemetic medications (Andrykowski & Garrison, 1989), (2) ad hoc utilization of behavioral coping techniques such as relaxation or cognitive distraction which are potentially beneficial in managing NV (Carey & Burish, 1988; Morrow & Dobkin, 1988), (3) physiological factors, such as age, performance status, food consumption prior to treatment, or constitutional predisposition to experience gastrointestinal distress in response to a variety of stimuli (e.g., motion sickness), and (4) psychological factors such as anxiety or patients' expectations for experiencing PostNV. The remainder of this chapter will focus upon the the contribution of two psychological factors, anxiety and pretreatment expectations for NV, to the experience of PostNV.

By what process might anxiety and expectations for PostNV influence the actual experience of PostNV? The hypothesized process for anxiety is relatively straightforward and follows from the previous discussion of the anxiety-exacerbates-PostNV hypothesis regarding the development of PreNV. Psychological stimuli, such as anxiety, are capable of stimulating the vomiting center and thus triggering the experience of NV (Borison & Wang, 1953). Thus one would anticipate that individuals reporting more anxiety in conjunction with their chemotherapy infusions would also exhibit a greater incidence and severity of PostNV. The link between pretreatment expectations for NV and subsequent PostNV is not as straightforward. Several different hypotheses have been advanced to account for this potential linkage. First, a positive association between expectations and PostNV could simply reflect an individuals' awareness of their personal susceptibility to experience gastrointestinal distress in a variety of situations, thus enabling relatively accurate prediction of their gastrointestinal response to chemotherapy. For example, an individual prone to motion sickness or to experience gastrointestinal distress when stressed or anxious might reasonably anticipate that he or she will also be prone to experience NV following their chemotherapy infusions. Second, expectations for NV could exacerbate the intensity of symptoms subsequently experienced through any of several different mechanisms. First, expectations for experiencing a significant amount of NV could result in an increase in an individual's anxiety level. This, in turn, could exacerbate the degree of PostNV subsequently experienced along the lines described above. Second, whether and to what degree an individuals expect to experience PostNV could affect the degree to which they monitors their physical sensations during the posttreatment period. This could result in a greater tendency to notice and report sensations of nausea that in the absence of expectations might go unnoticed. Finally, expectations for PostNV could create a psychological template that could cause an individual to label a variety of ambiguous physical sensations as nausea (Andrykowski, 1986)

What does the research reveal regarding the relationship between anxiety or expectations for NV and PostNV? The research base is surprisingly limited with only a handful of relevant studies available. A couple of studies have examined the relationship between anxiety and PostNV. Zook and Yasko (1983) reported that anxiety prior to an individual's initial chemotherapy infusion was unrelated to the severity of PostNV experienced following that infusion. Anxiety was measured sometime during the 24 hours preceding the patient's initial infusion. Similarly, Rhodes et al (1986) followed patients during their initial three cycles of chemotherapy. They found that anxiety assessed the morning following a chemotherapy infusion was unrelated to PostNV for that infusion. Unfortunately, an adequate test of the degree to which anxiety influences PostNV requires that anxiety be assessed in proximity to a chemotherapy infusion. In neither of these studies was this condition satisfied, thus limiting the confidence that can be placed in their findings.

Several studies have included assessements of both anxiety and expectations for NV in their attempts to understand the development of PostNV. As part of a study of psychosocial influences on the experience of a variety of potential post-chemotherapy side effects, Cassileth et al. (1985) assessed both anxiety and expectations for NV immediately prior to a patient's initial chemotherapy infusion. Neither anxiety nor expectations were related to the occurrence of PostNV following the initial two infusions. Haut et al. (1991) assessed anxiety and expectations for severity of treatment-related NV in 36 oncology outpatients prior to their initial course of chemotherapy. Measures of the occurrence and severity of PostNV were also obtained following each treatment. Finally, the emetic potential of each patient's chemotherapy regimen was rated using the system developed by Cohen et al. (1986). Multivariate analyses indicated that pretreatment expectations for NV were significantly associated with several indices of PostNV including whether or not a patient ever experienced PostNV as well as its frequency and severity across infusions. Anxiety was not associated with any index of PostNV examined. Finally, Jacobsen et al. (1988) followed 45 oncology outpatients, all women with breast cancer, across their initial six infusions. All patients received a regimen with a presumed low emetic potential. Ratings of treatment-related anxiety and PostNV severity were obtained for each infusion and expectations for treatment-related NV were assessed prior to the initial infusion. Results indicated that both expectations and anxiety were associated with the frequency and severity of PostNV, aggregated across patients' initial six chemotherapy infusions.

Clearly, the research just reviewed exhibits little consistency in regard to the relationship between anxiety and expectations and the subsequent experience of PostNV. Undoubtedly, this lack of consistency stems in large part from both methodological inadeqacy and diversity. Small, heterogeneous patient samples are characteristic of the research in this area. Furthermore, in the studies reviewed above, both anxiety and PostNV have been assessed at various times prior to and following treatment. Finally, these two variables, along with expectations for PostNV, have been assessed using various instruments. Furthermore, it is possible that the use of samples of chemotherapy patients encompassing a range of chemotherapy regimens heterogeneous with respect to emetic potential obscures any relationship between psychological variables and PostNV. The relationship between anxiety and expectations could vary as a function of emetic potential. Psychological factors could be significant in the experience of PostNV for regimens of low to moderate emetic potential. However, in regimens of high emetic potential, the emetic properties of the drug(s) employed overwhelm any potential influence of psychological variables.

In light of the above considerations, data from a large scale study of chemotherapy-related side effects were reanalyzed in order to examine the association of treatment-related anxiety and expectations for NV with the subsequent experience of PostNV (Andrykowski & Gregg, 1992). Sixty-five cancer patients beginning an initial course of chemotherapy and heterogeneous with respect to disease status and chemotherapy regimen were followed for a period of six months or until they were no longer receiving outpatient chemotherapy. Immediately prior to each infusion, patients provided a rating of the severity of anxiety presently experienced as well as the severity of PostNV experienced following their previous infusion. Immediately following each infusion, ratings of the severity of anxiety experienced during the infusion were obtained. Expectations for chemotherapy-related NV were obtained prior to the initial chemotherapy infusion using the same instrument employed in previous studies (Cassileth et al., 1985; Jacobsen et al., 1988). Whether or not a patient received intramuscular (IM) injections of antiemetic medication in conjunction with their infusions was recorded. Finally, the emetic potential of each patient's chemotherapy regimen was rated using the four point classification system developed by Cohen et al. (1986).

Data analysis focused upon two dependent variables: the mean severity of PostNV experienced across the initial four infusions each patient received and the proportional incidence of PostNV, that is, the proportion of the first four infusions following which PostNV was experienced. Hierarchical multiple regression was the primary data analytic strategy. At the first step, a set of two pharmacologic variables were entered: chemotherapy regimen emetic potential and whether or not IM antiemetics were received by the patient. At the second step, the two psychological variables of interest were entered: mean treatment-related anxiety reported across the initial four infusions and expectations for treatment-related NV. Results indicated that the set of pharmacologic variables accounted for 9.4% of the variance in mean severity of PostNV ($p < .05$). Addition of the set of psychological variables resulted in an increment of 13.5% in variance in the dependent variable accounted for ($p < .01$). The full four variable model accounted for 22.9% of the variance in severity of

PostNV ($p < .01$). Similarly, the set of pharmacological variables accounted for only 2.5% of the variance in proportional incidence of PostNV while addition of the set of psychological variables yielded an increment of 10.2% in variance in the dependent variable accounted for ($p < .05$). The four variable regression model accounted for only 12.7% of the variance in proportional incidence of PostNV ($p < .10$). Inspection of the individual beta weights in both of the four variable regression models indicated that only treatment-related anxiety was a significant independent predictor of both severity (beta = .39; $p < .05$) and proportional incidence of PostNV (beta = .29; $p < .05$). Emetic potential was a marginally significant independent predictor of mean severity of PostNV (beta = .22; $p < .10$). Expectations for treatment-related NV failed to be signficantly related to either severity (beta =.15) or proportional incidence (beta = .16) of Post NV.

To examine whether the influence of psychological variables varies as a function of pharmacologic variables, the sample of 65 patients was split into two groups based upon the emetic potential ratings for each patient's chemotherapy regimen. The "high" emetic potential group consisted of 34 patients while the "low" emetic potential group consisted of 31 patients. The identical two hierarchical regression analyses described above were then conducted separately for each of these two groups. In the low emetic potential group, anxiety and expectations accounted for 26.8% of the variance in mean severity of PostNV ($p < .05$) and 14% of the variance of proportional incidence of PostNV ($p > .10$). Treatment-related anxiety was a significant independent predictor of both severity (beta = .50; $p < .01$) and proportional incidence of PostNV (beta =.37; $p < .05$). In contrast, psychological variables were not significantly associated with PostNV in the high emetic potential group. Specifically, anxiety and expectations accounted for approximately 12% of the variance in both severity and proportional incidence of PostNV (both p's > .10). Inspection of the individual beta weights indicated that neither anxiety nor expectations was a signficant independent predictor of PostNV indices in patients receiving chemotherapy regimens with high emetic potential.

In light of the findings of this and previous studies, it seems reasonable to conclude that psychological factors, particularly anxiety experienced in temporal proximity to chemotherapy infusions, can contribute to the experience of PostNV (e.g., Andrykowski & Gregg, 1992; Jacobsen et al., 1988). Expectations for chemotherapy-related NV could also contribute to the experience of PostNV (e.g., Haut et al., 1991; Jacobsen et al., 1988), however, difficulties in the assessment of expectancies makes their contribution difficult to elucidate (Andrykowski & Gregg, 1992). Finally, recent evidence suggests that the strength of the relationship of psychological variables and PostNV varies inversely with the emetic potential of a patient's chemotherapy regimen (Andrykowski & Gregg, 1992). Unfortunately, the research to this point sheds little light upon the exact nature of the relationships between expectations or anxiety and PostNV. However, the results from the study by Andrykowski and Gregg (1992) appear to diminish the likelihood of a mere artifactual relationship between anxiety and PostNV. When these two variables are measured by self-report methods, as is almost always the case, a positive relationship between these two variables could stem simply from shared method variance. However, anxiety and PostNV were not associated among patients receiving regimens of high emetic activity (Andrykowski & Gregg, 1992). If the relationship between anxiety and PostNV was primarily artifactual, one would expect this relationship to be evident across a full range of regimens varying in emetic potential.

CONCLUSION

A fairly large body of research has suggested that psychological factors can be influential in the NV experienced by cancer chemotherapy patients. The case has been made quite clearly for PreNV, less convincing is the evidence for PostNV. However, even in the latter case, the evidence indicates that consideration of pharmacological factors alone is inadequate to account for the observed variability in PostNV across patients and even across infusions within a particular patient. At the present time, models of the emetic process in the chemotherapy setting should incorporate at least three classes of variables: pharmacological, physiological, and psychological.

REFERENCES

Andrykowski, M.A. (1986): Definitional issues in the study of anticipatory nausea. J. Behav. Med. 9, 33-41.

Andrykowski, M.A. (1990): The role of anxiety in the development of anticipatory nausea and vomiting: A review and synthesis. Psychosom. Med. 52, 458-475.

Andrykowski, M.A., & Garrison, J. (1989): Prescription and use of antiemetics among cancer chemotherapy patients. J. Psychosoc. Oncol. 7, 141-158.

Andrykowski, M.A., & Gregg, M.E. (1992): The role of psychological variables in post-chemotherapy nausea: Anxiety and expectations. Psychosom. Med. 54, 48-58.

Andrykowski, M.A., Jacobsen, P.B., Marks, E., Gorfinkle, K., Hakes, T.B., Kaufmann, R.J., Currie, V.E., Holland, J.C., & Redd, W.H. (1988): Prevalence, predictors, and course of anticipatory nausea in women receiving adjuvant chemotherapy for breast cancer. Cancer. 62, 2607-2613.

Andrykowski, M.A., & Redd, W.H. (1987): Longitudinal analysis of the development of anticipatory nausea. J. Consult. Clin. Psychol. 55, 36-41.

Andrykowski, M.A., Redd, W.H., & Hatfield, A.K. (1985): Development of anticipatory nausea: A prospective analysis. J. Consult. Clin. Psychol. 53, 447-454.

Borison, H.L., & Wang, S.C. (1953): Physiology and pharmacology of vomiting. Pharmacol. Rev. 5, 193-230.

Burish, T.G., & Carey, M.P. (1986): Conditioned aversive responses in cancer chemotherapy patients: Theoretical and developmental analysis. J. Consult. Clin. Psychol. 54, 593-600.

Carey, M.P., & Burish, T.G. (1988): Etiology and treatment of the psychological side effects associated with cancer chemotherapy: A critical review and discussion. Psychol. Bull. 104, 307-325.

Carnrike, C.L.M., Jr., & Carey, M.P. (1990): Assessing nausea and vomiting in adult chemotherapy patients: Review and recommendations. Ann. Behav. Med. 12, 79-85.

Cassileth, B.R., Lusk, E.J., Bodenheimer, B.J., Farber, J.M., Jochimsen, P., & Morrin-Taylor, B. (1985): Chemotherapeutic toxicity - the relationship between patients' pretreatment expectations and posttreatment results. Am. J. Clin. Oncol. 8, 419-425.

Cleghorn, R.A., & Brown, W.T. (1964): Psychogenesis of emesis. Can. Psychiatr. Assoc. J. 9, 299-310.

Cohen, R.E., Blanchard, E.B., Ruckdeschel, J.C., & Smolen, R.C. (1986): Prevalence and correlates of posttreatment and anticipatory nausea and vomiting in cancer chemotherapy. J. Psychosom. Res. 30, 643-654.

Derogatis, L.R. (1986): Psychology in cancer medicine: A perspective and overview. J. Consult. Clin. Psychol. 54, 632-638.

Dolgin, M.J., & Katz, E.R. (1988): Conditioned aversions in pediatric cancer patients receiving chemotherapy. J. Dev. Behav. Pediatr. 9, 82-85.

Haut, M.W., Beckwith, B.E., Laurie, J.A., & Klatt, N. (1991): Postchemotherapy nausea and vomiting in cancer patients receiving outpatient chemotherapy. J. Psychosoc. Oncol. 9, 117-130.

Hugdahl, K., Frederikson, M., & Ohman, A. (1977): "Preparedness" and "arousability" as determinants of electrodermal responses to potentially phobic stimuli. Behav. Res. Ther. 15, 345-353.

Hull, C.L. (1943): Principles of behavior. New York: Appleton-Century-Crofts.

Jacobsen, P.B., Andrykowski, M.A., Redd, W.H., Die-Trill, M., Hakes, T., Kaufmann, R., Currie, V., & Holland, J.C. (1988): The role of nonpharmacologic factors in development of posttreatment nausea among patients on adjuvant chemotherapy for breast cancer. Cancer. 61, 379-385.

Kvale, G., Hugdahl, K., Asbjornsen, A., Rosengren, B., Lote, K., & Nordby, H. (1991): Anticipatory nausea and vomiting in cancer patients. J. Consult. Clin. Psychol. 59, 894-898.

Morrow, G.R. (1982): Prevalence and correlates of anticipatory nausea and vomiting in cancer chemotherapy patients. J. Natl. Cancer. Inst. 68, 484-488.

Morrow, G.R., & Dobkin, P.L. (1988): Anticipatory nausea and vomiting in cancer patients undergoing chemotherapy treatment: Prevalence, etiology, and behavioral interventions. Clin. Psychol. Rev. 8, 517-556.

Nesse, R.M., Carli, T., Curtis, G.C., & Kleinman, P.D. (1980): Pretreatment nausea in cancer chemotherapy: A conditioned response? Psychosom. Med. 42, 33-36.

Ohman, A., & Bohlin, G. (1973): The relationship between spontaneous and stimulus-correlated electrodermal responses in simple discriminative conditioning paradigms. Psychophysiology. 10, 589-600.

Rhodes, V.A., Watson, P.M., & Johnson, M.H. (1986): Association of chemotherapy related nausea and vomiting with pretreatment and posttreatment anxiety. Oncol. Nurs. Forum. 13(1), 41-47.

Selye, H. (1950): Stress. Montreal, Canada: Acta.

Spence, K.W. (1958): A theory of emotionally based drive (D) and its relation to performance in simple learning situations. Am. Psychol. 13, 131-141.

Spence, K.W. (1964): Anxiety (drive) level and performance in eyelid conditioning. Psychol. Bull. 61, 129-139.

Teplov, B.M. (1964): Problems in the study of general types of higher nervous system activity in man and animals. In Pavlov's typology, ed J.A. Gray, pp.3-153. Oxford, England: Pergamon Press.

Zook, D.J., & Yasko, J.M. (1983): Psychological factors: Their effect on nausea and vomiting experienced by clients receiving chemotherapy. Oncol. Nurs. Forum. 10, 76-81.

Mechanisms and Control of Emesis. Eds A.L. Bianchi, L. Grélot, A.D. Miller, G.L. King. Colloque INSERM/ John Libbey Eurotext Ltd. © 1992, Vol. 223, pp. 323-329

Suncus murinus as an experimental animal model for emesis and motion sickness

N. Matsuki, Y. Torii, S. Ueno and H. Saito

Department of Chemical Pharmacology, Faculty of Pharmaceutical Sciences, The University of Tokyo, Tokyo 113, Japan

ABSTRACT

We have shown that *Suncus murinus*, a species of the insectivore, possesses the capability to vomit when they receive emetogenic drugs including cancer chemotherapeutics, X-ray irradiation or reciprocal motion stimulus. Serotonergic 5-HT_3 antagonists specifically and strongly prevented cisplatin- and X-irradiation-induced vomiting. Antihistamines and serotonergic 5-HT_{1A} agonists effectively blocked motion-induced vomiting. The body size of suncus is small. Therefore, the suncus can be a very useful animal model for screening anti-emetic drugs and drug with less emetic side effects as well as studying mechanism of emesis. Emetic responses in suncus were characterized and discussed.

Le Suncus murinus: un modèle animal pour l'étude du vomissement et du mal des transports.
Résumé: *Nous avons montré que le Suncus murinus, un insectivore de petite taille, présente des crises de vomissement en réponse à l'administration de substances émétiques (incluant les agents antinéoplasiques), à l'irradiation et aux stimuli de mouvements. Les substances antagonistes des récepteurs sérotoninergiques 5-HT3 préviennent spécifiquement et efficacement les vomissements induits par le cisplatine et l'irradiation. Les substances antihistaminiques et les agonistes des récepteurs sérotoninergiques 5-HT1A suppriment efficacement les vomissements associés au mal des transports. Par conséquent, le Suncus murinus s'avère être un modèle animal très utile pour découvrir de nouvelles drogues antiémétiques ou des drogues dépourvues d'effets secondaires de nature émétique ou encore pour étudier les mécanismes physiologiques du vomissement. Les réponses émétiques du Suncus sont caractérisées et discutées.*

INTRODUCTION

Emesis is generally considered as a defensive reflex to expel toxic food or substances ingested accidentally. However, there are a number of emetogenic stimuli that apparently do not coincide with the defensive purpose. Emesis caused by cancer chemotherapeutic drugs as a side effect has given serious discomfort to patients. Motion sickness also induces emesis, and space motion sickness has been an obstruction of space flight. However, research on emesis and motion sickness have been restricted because only a few experimental animals can vomit (Borison, 1981). Rodents (e.g., rat, mouse, guinea pig) and lagomorphs (e.g., rabbit) are the most widely used experimental animals and their biological characteristics have been well documented, but they never vomit. Therefore, non human primates and the carnivores such as dogs, cats and ferrets have been used as experimental animal models. It would be a great advantage if we could use smaller experimental animals because only a small amount of drug sample is necessary for screening.

We have shown that *Suncus murinus* (a house musk shrew) can vomit in response to various emetogenic drugs and motion stimulus (Ueno et al., 1987; 1988). Here we will review the characteristics of *Suncus murinus* as a model for emesis and motion sickness.

WHAT IS *SUNCUS MURINUS*?

Suncus murinus (Fig. 1) belongs to the family Soricidae of the order Insectivore and is distributed widely in tropical and subtropical area. The insectivores are the most primitive and the earliest eutherians and regarded as the direct ancestors of other placental mammals including the Primates (Colbert, 1958). The suncus is commercially available as an experimental animal in Japan, and breeding is relatively easy. Since the insectivore is good "eater", highly nutritious chow is necessary. The body weight of adult animals is 50 to 80 g for male and 30 to 50 g for female. The gestation period is 30 days, and the average number of offspring is between 3 and 4. They are sexually mature at 2 months old. Their life span is not systematically studied but probably longer than 2 years.

Fig. 1. Male adult suncus. They prefer to stay in the dark tube. The length of the pen in the background is 15 cm (6 inches). Special chow which contains higher protein and lipid compared to that for the rodents is seen in the can.

Recent studies from our laboratory indicate that the suncus is a unique experimental animal model for various research, such as studies on nerve growth factor (Ueyama et al., 1981), fatty liver degeneration (Yasuhara et al., 1991a; 1991b), Deficiency of β-adrenoceptor-mediated responses (Abe et al., 1988; Nagata et al., 1990), emesis (Ueno et al., 1987; Matsuki et al., 1988; Torii et al., 1991a; 1991b) and motion sickness (Ueno et al., 1988; Kaji et al., 1990; 1991). Unlike the rat, the suncus possesses steroid 17 α-hydroxylase and synthesizes cortisol (Lin et al., 1986). The tyrosine hydroxylase level of the adrenal is high (Maruoka et al., 1988; 1989), suggesting that the animal can also be a good model for stress.

EMETIC RESPONSES IN SUNCUS

Table 1 shows various stimuli which induce emesis in the suncus. A variety of emetogenic drugs, X-irradiation, and motion stimulus caused vomiting. Expulsion of the gastric content always occurs in the first episode and is very easy to judge as the vomiting. Retching-like behavior is observed only after several vomiting responses indicating that the stomach has become empty. Apomorphine (up to 100 mg/kg), L-DOPA (up to 200 mg/kg) and digitalis (up to 1 mg/kg) did not induce emesis.

WHY CAN SUNCUS VOMIT BUT THE RODENTS CANNOT?

1. Anatomical Comparison

It is known that there are two types of structure of the area postrema (Clemente and van Breemen, 1955). In the cases of cats, dogs and ferrets, which can vomit, the area postrema is a bilateral structure located on the dorsal surface of the medulla oblongata. However, in case of the rat, which cannot vomit, the area postrema is a single structure located on the midline of medulla and projects over the rostral tip of the central canal. Therefore, structural difference in the area postrema may account for the susceptibility to emesis. However, as shown in Fig. 2, the area postrema of suncus forms a single mound of tissue in the midline position overlying the central canal. A large number of small neurons were observed in the area postrema.

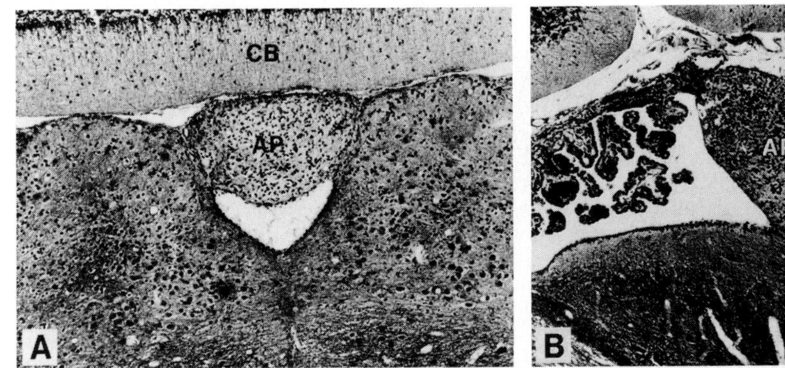

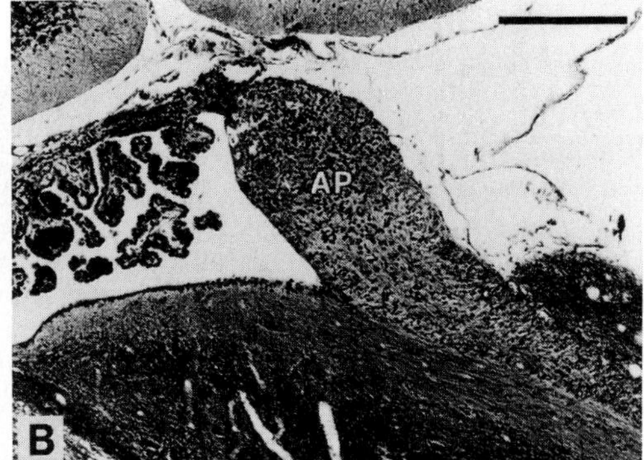

Fig. 2 Coronal (A) and sagittal (B) sections of the medulla oblongata of normal suncus. Male adult suncus were anesthetized with ether and perfused with 50 ml of 0.1 M sodium phosphate buffer solution containing 4% paraformaldehyde through a catheter inserted into the left ventricle. The brains were quickly isolated and fixed in Bouin solution for three hours. Then the brain was embedded in paraffin, and serial sections (10 μm) were cut on the coronal or the sagittal plane. All sections were mounted onto glass slides and then dried, dehydrated, rehydrated, and stained with a silver impregnation method (Loots et al., 1977). AP: area postrema, CB: cerebellum. The scale bar in B shows 200 μm.

Projections of the vagus nerve were investigated using horseradish peroxidase (HRP) as a tracer. A typical coronal section of the suncus medulla oblongata after HRP injection into the stomach wall is shown in Fig. 3. The cells labeled with HRP contained black grain. Virtually all cells containing HRP were located in the area that is labeled as the dorsal motor nucleus of the vagus in rat. The small horizontally elongated nuclei were located bilaterally near the obex and the area postrema, and stretched for average rostrocaudal distance of 2.15 mm, or 43 histological sections (N=3). No black grain was observed in the vagotomized animals, clearly indicating that the HRP was transported via the vagus nerve. Furthermore, we could recognize many labeled neurons in the hypoglossal nucleus after injection of HRP into the tongue. The relative location of the area postrema, the dorsal motor nucleus of vagus and hypoglossal nucleus in the suncus was very similar to that in the rat.

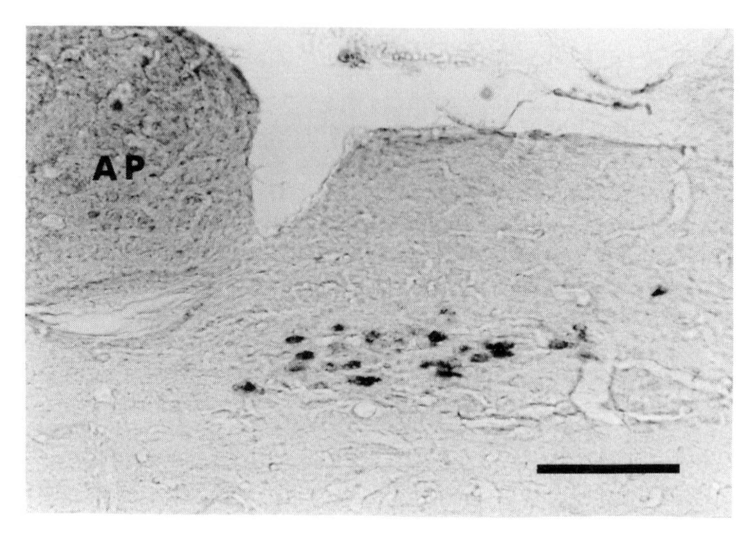

Fig. 3. Bright-field microscopy of the medulla oblongata of suncus in which the vagal nerve cells are labeled with HRP. The abdomen of the suncus was cut under ether anesthesia, and 10% HRP (Type I-B, Toyobo Co., LTD.) solution, totaling 50 μl, was injected into the stomach wall. After four days from the injection of HRP, animals were anesthetized and perfused through the left ventricle with the sodium phosphate buffer solution containing 10% sucrose followed by 4% paraformaldehyde dissolved in the sodium phosphate buffer. We selected four days because our preliminary study in which the interval period between the HRP injection and the sacrifice was varied from 2 to 8 days showed that the maximum staining of HRP was detected at fourth day. The brains were removed and stored in the fixative solution for one day. Then the tissues were placed in 30% sucrose-buffer solution at 4 °C for another one day until they sank to the bottom. The brain preparation was frozen on dry-ice, and serial sections (50 μm) were cut on the coronal plane through the medulla and processed for demonstration of HRP using tetramethylbenzidine (Mesulam, 1978). All sections were also stained with neutral red and assessed with a microscope. The cells labeled with HRP which appears black are located within the boundaries of the dorsal motor nucleus of the vagus. No black grain was observed in the vagotomized animal. AP: area postrema. The scale bar indicates 100 μm.

Therefore, gross structural difference cannot explain the different behavior of emetic response between the suncus and the rodents. The results also indicate that the bilateral structure of the area postrema is not essential for emetic responses. However, since the area postrema is considered as chemoreceptor trigger zone (CTZ) rather than a vomiting center, the bilateral structure may be necessary for emetogenic drugs stimulating the CTZ (see below).

2. Emetic Response in other Insectivores

It is interesting to investigate whether or not the capability to vomit is common to all the insectivores to clarify the species-dependent differences. We studied emetic response of the

Sorex unguiculatus (Japanese name: Oashi Togari Nezumi) which belongs to different subfamily of the insectivore. *Sorex unguiculatus* is habituated in Hokkaido (the northern island of Japan) and body weight of adult animal is about 10 g. Copper sulfate and veratrine induced the emesis but nicotine and apomorphine did not. The sensitivity to motion sickness has not been studied. The structure of the area postrema was also single mound. *Sorex unguiculatus* is the smallest mammal known to vomit, so far.

Therefore, emetic ability seems to be a common feature to the insectivore and the rodents have lost the ability during evolution. Taste aversion has been frequently used as a model for nausea and vomiting in the rodents but its rationale is still controversial (Fox, 1990). It would be very interesting to study taste aversion in suncus.

Table 1. Various Stimuli Which Induce Emesis in *Suncus murinus*

Stimuli	ED_{50} (mg/kg)
Emetogenic Drugs	
Copper Sulfate (p.o.)	21.4
Copper chloride	-
Emetine (s.c.)	47.6
Lobeline (s.c.)	2.8
Nicotine (s.c.)	7.9
Pilocarpine (s.c.)	-
Veratrine (s.c.)	0.4
Cancer Chemotherapeutics	
Bleomycin (i.v.)	-
Cisplatin (i.v.)	8.4
Cisplatin (i.p.)	10.0
Cyclophosphamide (i.v., s.c.)	-
5-Fluorouracil (i.v.)	-
Methotrexate (i.v.)	-
Mitomycin C (i.v.)	-
Dopaminergic Agonists	
Bromocriptine (s.c.)	12.3
SKF 38393 (s.c.)	29.9
Serotonergic Agonists	
Serotonin (i.p.)	2.7
Serotonin (s.c.)	4.7
2-Methyl-Serotonin (i.p.)	0.97
Other Stimuii	
Motion	-
X-irradiation	429 (cGy)

ED_{50} values were determined using up-and-down method. -: not determined.

3. Effects of Dopaminergic Agonists and Antagonists

Apomorphine is shown to stimulate dopaminergic receptors and used widely as emetogenic drug in animal research. However, species dependent variations in sensitivities to apomorphine are well known. Dogs are the most sensitive, cats are less sensitive and monkeys are not sensitive. Sensitivities of ferrets are controversial (Andrews et al., 1990). As mentioned above, apomorphine did not cause emesis in suncus and sorex but increased the spontaneous movement of animals. We studied effects of other dopaminergic agonists and antagonists.

As shown in Table 1, SKF 38393, a specific D_1 receptor agonist, or bromocriptine, a specific D_2 receptor agonist, caused emesis. Furthermore, Combination of SKF 38393 and bromocriptine augmented the emetic response synergistically. Therefore, the failure of apomorphine to induce emesis is not due to the lack of dopaminergic receptor(s)-mediated emetic response. Additional pharmacological effects of apomorphine may mask or prevent the emesis. Both SCH 23390, a specific D_1 receptor antagonist, and YM01951-2, a specific D_2 receptor antagonist, prevented emesis induced by various drugs and motion stimulus. These emetogenic stimuli act either on the central nervous system (nicotine, veratrine, motion) or the peripheral tissues (copper sulfate, cisplatin, serotonin). Therefore, dopaminergic system(s) may be involved in a common pathway for the vomiting reflex.

CANCER CHEMOTHERAPEUTICS-INDUCED EMESIS

Cancer chemotherapeutic drugs caused emesis in suncus. We characterized cisplatin-induced emesis and obtained the following results. The number of episodes, latency and duration were not different between intravenous and intraperitoneal injections. The ED_{50} values of the two administrations were 8.4 and 10.0 mg/kg, respectively. Long latency is characteristic in cisplatin-induced emesis and independent from the route of administration, which may indicate that cisplatin is converted to emetogenic metabolite(s). Cis-diaqodiammineplatinum(II) (DAP), one of putative metabolites that possess anti-cancer activity, caused emesis with shorter latency. However, number of vomiting episodes induced by DAP is not different from that induced by cisplatin (Mutoh et al., 1992). Serotonergic 5-HT_3 antagonists selectively blocked the cisplatin-induced emesis (Torii et al., 1991a). Cisplatin increased the plasma concentration of serotonin one hour after the injection. *p*-Chloramphetamine, a depletor of endogenous serotonin, attenuated the number of vomiting episodes. Intravenous and intraperitoneal injections of serotonin caused emesis within a few minutes, which is blocked by the serotonergic 5-HT_3 antagonist (Torii et al., 1991b). Abdominal vagotomy completely prevented vomiting responses caused by cisplatin, DAP and serotonin. Serotonin increased the discharge of the vagus afferent.

These results indicate that 1) cisplatin is converted to emetogenic metabolite(s), probably DAP, 2) the metabolite releases serotonin from peripheral tissue, probably the enterochromaffin cells, 3) the released serotonin stimulated serotonergic 5-HT_3 receptors located on the vagus afferent and then causes emesis. Involvement of the area postrema in suncus is not clear.

X-RAY IRRADIATION-INDUCED EMESIS

Whole body X-irradiation caused emesis which was completely inhibited by the surgical vagotomy or pretreatment with 5-HT_3 antagonists. Emetic response was dependent on the exposed body region. X-irradiation to the abdominal area caused vomiting, but X-irradiation to the head did not. Therefore, X-irradiation-induced emesis is characteristically very similar to that induced by cancer chemotherapeutics.

USEFULNESS AS A MODEL FOR MOTION SICKNESS

Reciprocal shaking (1 Hz, 40 mm of peak-to-peak displacement) caused emesis in suncus within a few minutes. No sophisticated apparatus is necessary as a commercially available desk top shaker will do. The suncus is the most sensitive to motion sickness among the experimental mammals that have been studied. Histaminergic H_1 antagonists, amphetamine and serotonergic 5-HT_{1A} agonists were effective as prophylactic drugs. Therefore, the suncus can be a useful experimental model to study the mechanism of motion sickness and to develop anti-motion and anti-space sickness drugs.

Adaptation to motion stress was observed when animals were shaken repetitively (Ueno et al., 1988; Kaji et al., 1990). The adaptation seems to occur in sensory system rather than motor system for the emesis. The suncus can also be a good model for the study of adaptation.

CONCLUSION

Suncus murinus can be a new experimental animal model for research on emesis and motion sickness. The animal has a great advantage for the development of anti-emetic and anti-motion sickness drugs because of its small body size. It is known that there is a great species dependent variation in emetic responses (Borison et al., 1981). Therefore, it is necessary to compare the data from various animal species. Since the body size of the suncus is similar to that of small rodents, we may be able to learn why rodents cannot vomit.

REFERENCES

Abe, K., Wang, C-H , Tanaka, H., Saito, H. and Matsuki, N. (1988): Characteristics of cardiac β-adrenoceptors in *Suncus murinus*. *Chem. Pharm. Bull.* (Tokyo), **36**, 4081-4087.

Andrews, P.L.R., Rapeport, W.G. and Sanger, G.J. (1988): Neuropharmacology of emesis induced by anti-cancer therapy. *Trend Pharmacol. Sci.*, **9**, 334-341.

Borison, H.L., Borison, R. and McCarthy, L.E. (1981): Phylogenic and neurologic aspects of the vomiting process. *J. Clin. Pharmacol.*, **21**, 23S-29S.

Clemente, C.D. and van Breemen, V.L. (1955): Nerve fibers in the area postrema of cat, rabbit, guinea pig and rat. *Anat. Rec.*, **123**, 65-79.

Colbert, E.H. (1958): "Evolution of the Vertebrates", pp.249-261, New York, John Wiley and Sons.

Fox, R. A. (1990): Investigating motion sickness using the conditioned taste aversion paradigm. In *Motion and Space Sickness*, pp. 105-121, ed. by G. H. Crampton, Boca Raton, CRC Press.

Kaji, T., Saito, H., Ueno, S. and Matsuki, N. (1990): Comparison of various motion stimuli on motion sickness and acquisition of adaptation in *Suncus murinus*. *Exp. Animals*, **39**, 75-79.

Kaji, T., Saito, H., Ueno, S., Yasuhara, T., Nakajima, T. and Matsuki, N. (1991): Role of histamine in motion sickness of *Suncus murinus*. *Aviat. Space Environ. Med.*, **62**, 1053-1057.

Lin, S-C, Shiga, H., Kato, Y., Saito, H. and Kamei, S. (1986): Serum constituents of *Suncus murinus*. *Exp. Animals*, **35**, 77-85.

Loots, J.M., Loots, G.P. and Joubert, W.S. (1977): A silver impregnation method for nervous tissue stuitable for routine use with mounted sections. *Stain Technol.*, **52**, 85-87.

Maruoka, Y., Saito, H., Tanaka, H., Nakajima, T. and Yazawa, K. (1988): Determination of catecholamines and their metabolites in urine of *Suncus murinus*. *Biogenic Amines*, **5**, 483-488.

Maruoka, Y., Nishiyama, N., Saito, H., Nakajima, T. and Yazawa, K. (1989): Determination of catecholamines and their metabolites in brain, heart and adrenal of *Suncus murinus*. *Biogenic Amines*, **6**, 135-143.

Matsuki, N., Ueno, S., Kaji, T., Ishihara, A., Wang, C-H and Saito, H. (1988): Emesis induced by cancer chemotherapeutic agents in the *Suncus murinus*: A new experimental model. *Jpn. J. Pharmacol.*, **48**, 303-306.

Mesulam, M. M. (1978): Tetramethyl benzidine for horseradish peroxidase neurohistochemistry: A non-cardinogenic blue reaction-product with superior sensitivity for visualizing neural afferents and efferents. *J. Histochem. Cytochem.*, **26**, 106-117.

Mutoh, M., Imanishi, H., Torii, Y., Tamura, M., Saito, H. and Matsuki, N. (1992): Cisplatin-induced emesis in *Suncus murinus*. *Jpn. J. Pharmacol.*, **58**, 321-324.

Nagata, K., Abe, K., Wang, C-H, Saito, H. and Matsuki, N. (1990): Deficiency of β-adrenoceptor mediated relaxation in suncus trachea. *Jpn. J. Pharmacol*, **52**, 115-121.

Torii, Y., Saito, H. and Matsuki, N. (1991a): Selective blockade of cytotoxic drug-induced emesis by 5-HT_3 receptor antagonists in *Suncus murinus*. *Jpn. J. Pharmacol.*, **55**, 107-113.

Torii, Y., Saito, H. and Matsuki, N. (1991b): 5-Hydroxytryptamine is emetogenic in the house musk shrew, *Suncus murinus*. *Naunyn-Schmiedeberg's Arch. Pharmacol.*, **344**, 564-567.

Ueno, S., Matsuki, N. and Saito, H. (1987): *Suncus murinus*: a new experimental Model in emesis research. *Life Sci.*, **41**, 513-518.

Ueno, S., Matsuki, N. and Saito, H. (1988): *Suncus murinus* as a new experimental animal model for motion sickness. *Life Sci.*, **43**, 413-420.

Ueyama, T., Saito, H. and Yohro, T. (1981): *Suncus murinus* submandibular gland and prostate are new sources of nerve growth factor. *Biomed. Res.*, **2**, 438-441.

Yasuhara, M., Ohama, T., Matsuki, N., Saito, H., Shiga, J., Inoue, K., Kurokawa, K. and Teramoto, T. (1991a): Induction of fatty liver by fasting in suncus. *J. Lipid Res.*, **32**, 887-891.

Yasuhara, M., Ohama, T., Matsuki, N., Saito, H., Matsushima, T., Kurokawa, K. and Teramoto, T. (1991b): Deficiency of apolipoprotein B synthesis in *Suncus murinus*. *J. Biochem.*, **110**, 751-755.

Mechanisms and Control of Emesis. Eds A.L. Bianchi, L. Grélot, A.D. Miller, G.L. King. Colloque INSERM/ John Libbey Eurotext Ltd. © 1992, Vol. 223, pp. 331-340

An algorithm for predicting radiation-induced emesis

George H. Anno and Gene E. McClellan*

*Pacific-Sierra Research Corporation, 12340 Santa Monica Boulevard, Los Angeles, CA 90025 and * 1401 Wilson Boulevard, Arlington, VA 22209, USA*

SUMMARY

The development of an analogue, referred to as the upper gastrointestinal distress model (UGIDM), to predict the severity of the emetic response in humans is described. The modeling approach is necessarily semiempirical because of the lack of definitive data especially for low dose rates protracted over periods of days. Available human data and recent progress on the emetic mechanism have been considered in structuring the model. Three linear differential rate equations and a response function to scale the severity of upper gastrointestinal (UG) distress are employed to simulate the dynamics of the emetic process. Calculated results of response to acute and protracted exposures are illustrated.

Un algorithme pour la prévention du vomissement radio-induit.

Résumé: *Le développement d'un algorithme, par analogie au modèle de détresse du tractus gastro-intestinal haut (UGIM), permettant de prédire la sévérité de la crise émétique chez l'homme est décrit. L'approche pour cette modélisation est par nécessité semi-empirique car les données manquent, et plus spécialement celles portant sur les faibles doses d'irradiation prolongée sur des périodes de plusieurs jours. Les données expérimentales obtenues chez l'homme et les progrès récents portant sur les mécanismes sous-tendant le vomissement ont été utilisés pour structurer ce modèle. Un système de trois équations différentielles linéaires et une fonction-réponse pour évaluer la sévérité de la détresse gastro-intestinale haute (UG) sont employés pour simuler la dynamique des processus émétiques. Les résultats calculés des réponses aux expositions aiguë et prolongée sont illustrés.*

INTRODUCTION

Considerable progress has elucidated the apparent mechanisms and pathways involved in radiation-induced emesis (Andrews et al., 1988; Harding, 1988; Lang and Marvig, 1989; Bermudez et al., 1988; Davis et al., 1986; Barnes, 1984; Borison et al., 1981). This progress has guided our effort to structure a dynamic model of the upper gastrointestinal (UG) response, although at this stage, our model avoids specific mechanistic details.

BASIS FOR MODELING

The mechanism of radiation-induced emesis seems to arise from humoral (or toxicokinetic) effects rather than from the reduced functionality of tissue. The onset of nausea and vomiting following radiation exposure is generally within the first few hours, ranging from minutes to several hours, depending on dose (Anno et al., 1991). This early occurrence suggests physiological and biochemical changes that are not principally due to cell death, with the possible exception of the apoptosis of lymphatic tissue. After onset, bouts of nausea and vomiting occur intermittently in humans for a period of hours to a day or two, depending on dose. This overall recovery time is much shorter than would be expected for cellular repair and replacement of injured tissues.

Based on a comprehensive review of human accidental exposure to ionizing radiation, radiotherapy patients, and animal experimentation, Barnes (1984) concluded that the vomiting mechanism of early radioemesis must involve the action of circulating substances at the chemoreceptor trigger zone (CTZ) liberated in the process of a general tissue reaction to irradiation, with the upper intestines being an important source. Accordingly, the midepigastric area of the body would appear to be the primary location of the target tissue for UG distress.

It is apparent from a review of the mechanisms and treatment of radiation-induced nausea and vomiting by Young (1986), that the radioemetic response is mediated by two pathways--either from direct stimulation of afferents originating in the gastrointestinal tract or through the release of humoral, blood-borne emetic factors. The former pathway leads via the vagus to the vomiting center located inside the blood-brain barrier. In the latter pathway, humoral emetic factors stimulate the CTZ in the area postrema (AP) located outside the blood-brain barrier. The AP in turn stimulates the vomiting center. Thus, vomiting motor reflexes can be produced by either pathway acting on the emetic center.

A wide variety of endogenous neuroactive agents may be released as a result of cellular damage by radiation such as serotonin, histamines, prostanoids, vasoactive intestinal polypeptides, free radicals, etc. Besides directly stimulating afferents in the gastrointestinal tract, these agents may also enter the liver via the portal vein where hepatic afferents can also be stimulated. If they survive degradation by the liver, the emetic agents then enter the systemic circulation and can directly activate the area postrema (Andrews et al., 1988).

Serotonin, 5-hydroxytryptamine (5HT), is of principal interest, although the detailed mechanisms of its production and release are still unknown. However, recent work associating $5HT_3$ neuroreceptors in the gut and brain with nausea and vomiting confirms that they play a critical role in the emetic pathway(s).

Davis et al. (1986) envision a hierarchical process where control arises from the higher expression of an integrated activity which ordinarily serves the separate output functions associated with vomiting--such as mouth opening, salivation, gastric relaxation, respiratory control, and abdominal muscle contraction--or the actual act of vomiting, which Harding (1988) indicates is a definite (intermittent) threshold effect. The precise reason for this kind of discrete behavior still remains a major question (Andrews et al., 1988).

The radiation-induced UG response is obviously a complicated process involving both humoral and neuronal pathways that at this stage we cannot yet model in detail. However, we do not view the complexity and missing details as being overly restrictive for purposes of our modeling effort. Rather, we have focussed on developing a dynamic analogue to simulate the irradiation of the target tissue, the production and body clearing of toxic substances, and their role in producing the UG response without invoking specific pathways.

Clinical radiotherapy experience (Tichelli et al., 1988) and anecdotal reports from radiotherapists (Anno et al., 1983) support the existence of an habituation effect, where the emetic response diminishes in frequency following successive doses in a fractionation regimen. This effect also appears to be present in cats (Borison et al., 1988). The habituation effect could arise from the desensitization of neuronal pathways or the depletion of a finite bodily source responsible for radioemetic toxin production; our algorithm presented here is modeled according to the latter.

MODEL DESCRIPTION

The schematic in Fig. 1 illustrates our model to predict the time-dependent severity level of the UG response. Elements of the upper gastrointestinal model (UGIDM) represent the phenomenology and mechanistic concepts of radioemesis discussed in the section above.

As portrayed in Fig. 1, we assume a nonspecific target tissue located in the body that, when irradiated, produces a precursor substance or potential toxin P within the tissue cells that is subsequently activated (like a prodrug) or causes enzymatic activation of another substance referred to as the active toxin. The active toxin A then initiates neuronal processes that trigger the body response expressed as the signs and symptoms of acute UG distress. The blood circulation and nervous system, consisting of the afferents, neuroreceptors, area postrema, vomiting center, and efferents indicated in Fig. 1, are not explicitly modeled, since we assume that the blood circulation (~1 min), nerve receptor response, and nerve impulse transmission all generally take place in a time much shorter than the characteristic times of the rate processes modeled. The level of active toxin A also depends on a bio-clearing rate β to simulate degradation of the active toxin (or substance) due to body recovery processes.

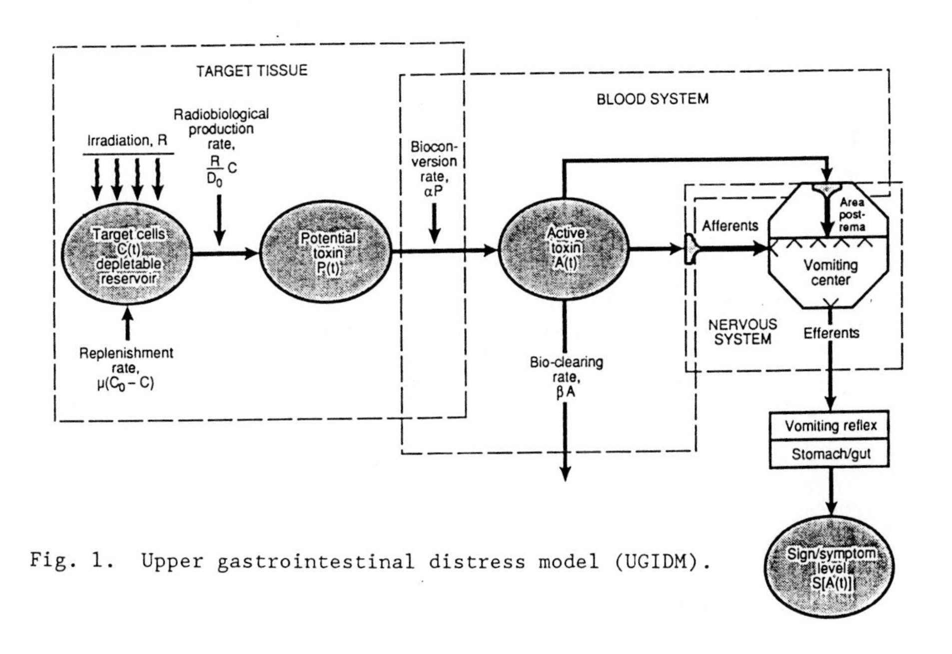

Fig. 1. Upper gastrointestinal distress model (UGIDM).

We incorporate the habituation effect in the UGIDM by assuming that the amount of potential toxin produced by the action of radiation on the target cells is limited. In order to accommodate this limitation in the model, we have introduced a hypothetical "depletable reservoir" analogue with level C as the source of the potential toxin produced by radiation exposure.

MODEL EQUATIONS

Mathematically, the UGIDM is structured as three coupled linear differential equations containing the quantities C, A, and P defined above together with a response function relating symptom-severity S to A. The reservoir level C is assumed to be depleted by radiation exposure with a characteristic dose D_o, analogous to cell populations in tissues. The differential rate equation for the reservoir level is:

$$\dot{C} = -(R/D_o)C + \mu(C_o - C) \tag{1}$$

The first term on the right is the depletion rate caused by the dose rate R. The second term returns the reservoir to its initial (preirradiation) level C_o with a time constant μ^{-1}.

The differential equations for the two-compartment model for production and clearing of the potential and active toxin levels (P and A, respectively), are described by linear kinetics given by:

$$\dot{P} = (R/D_o)C - \alpha P \ , \tag{2}$$

and,

$$\dot{A} = \alpha P - \beta A \ , \tag{3}$$

where α is the P-to-A conversion rate and β is the clearing rate of A. For simplicity, we express the C, P, and A levels in terms of dose units. This is necessary since we presently have no means of calibrating actual quantities of target cell populations and substances hypothesized in our model. Also, we have chosen to make the two constants D_o and C_o equal. By doing so, the P production rate, $R(C/C_o)$, in Eq. (2) is the dose rate weighted by the fractional level of the reservoir. This choice ensures that when the applied dose rate is small, C remains essentially constant at the value C_o, and the source term in Eq. (1) reduces to just R; the model then reduces to one with no depletable reservoir.

The UGIDM uses an ordinal scale to gauge the severity of UG response according to the levels given in Table 1. The functional relationship giving the severity levels in terms of A is:

$$S = 1 + 4\left\{1 - \exp\left[-\ln 2 \cdot \left(A/A_{0.5}\right)^{\gamma}\right]\right\} \ . \tag{4}$$

When the active toxin level is equal to the parameter value $A_{0.5}$, the severity S is halfway to maximum expression. The shape parameter γ determines how steep the function rises as A increases. This form was chosen since it introduces a threshold-like behavior to better describe the sudden onset of UG symptoms expected for acute doses. Because of the dynamical nature of the UGIDM, the active toxin A will attain a maximum value at some postexposure time which depends on both dose and the model's parameter values. Therefore, when UGIDM calculations are performed to determine peak severity level, care must be taken to find the time for the maximum value of A.

Table 1. Severity levels of upper gastrointestinal (UG) distress in humans (Anno et al., 1985).

Severity Level	Signs and Symptoms
1	No effect
2	Upset stomach; clammy and sweaty; mouth waters and swallows frequently
3	Nauseated; considerable sweating; swallows frequently to avoid vomiting
4	Vomited once or twice; nauseated and may vomit again
5	Vomited several times including the dry heaves; severely nauseated and will soon vomit again

The UGIDM differential Eqs. (1), (2), and (3) are linear with constant coefficients and can be solved analytically in closed form for an acute dose or a constant dose rate (Anno et al., 1991). However, when the dose rate is time-dependent, numerical methods are employed to obtain computer solutions.

PARAMETER VALUES

The UGIDM variables, C, P, A, and D are in units of Gy and the dose rate R is in Gyh^{-1}. The UGIDM parameters (and units) are as follows:

Parameters

α = potential toxin conversion rate/active toxin production rate, h^{-1}
β = active toxin clearing rate, h^{-1}
μ = depletable reservoir reconstitution rate, h^{-1}
C_o = initial reservoir level, Gy
D_o = characteristic target tissue dose ($=C_o$), Gy
$A_{0.5}$ = value of A for half-maximum symptom severity, Gy
γ = slope constant of severity response

Based on least squares optimization, parameter values were obtained for acute exposure by matching the UGIDM to the empirical UG symptom severity profiles developed by Anno et al. (1985), represented by the dashed curves in Fig. 2; the profiles are based on original data gathered by Baum et al. (1984). These data are applicable over the dose and time range of interest (0.5 to 7.5 Gy, and up to 100 h postexposure). Since the UGIDM is uniformly applicable for both acute and protracted exposure, the parameter values obtained enable a self-consistent application of the UGIDM to arbitrary dose histories involving acute and/or protracted exposure(s). Each time profile in Fig. 2 corresponds to symptom severity for acute dose in the range indicated. Dose is referenced to midline tissue (MLT), or the dose absorbed in the midepigastric portion of the body since that area represents the likely location of sensitive target tissue for UG distress.

During the prodromal phase of acute radiation sickness, UG distress symptoms begin within hours after prompt radiation exposure and then fade in a few days or less. In the original development of the empirical profiles, an effort was made to attach meaning to UG distress at integer levels only, consistent with the discrete levels chosen to ordinally scale severity; accordingly, UG distress was essentially "quantized" where noninteger states (or levels) were interpreted to have no meaning. However, in our modeling, noninteger values do have mathematical meaning

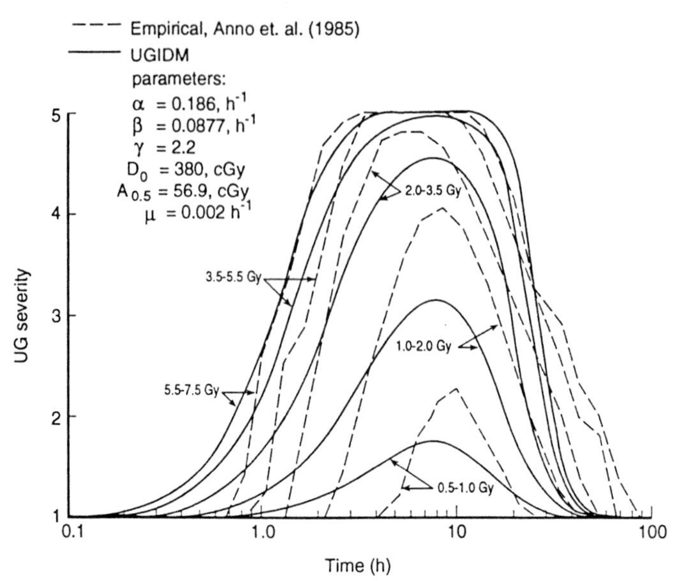

Fig. 2. The severity level of upper gastrointestinal (UG) distress in humans.

in terms of continuous functional forms consistent with the UGIDM equations. Since the UGIDM solutions are time-dependent profiles that may attain integer levels, the discrete response characterization of UG distress is preserved and does not alter that interpretation.

UGIDM optimization calculations carried out to obtain the parameter values shown were based on minimizing the objective function (root-mean-square deviation of the difference between selected points along the dashed and solid curves). Sensitivity analysis indicates that the value of μ does not significantly influence the predictions for acute dose. Accordingly, we fixed $\mu = 0.002\ h^{-1}$ as a reasonable stable estimate and determined the other parameters. This value corresponds to a reservoir reconstitution half-time of about two weeks, although we do not have protracted dose data to empirically determine this value.

Compared to the empirical UG severity curves, the UGIDM curves rise less abruptly for lower doses, recede more sharply for higher doses, and attain a lower peak severity for lower doses. Also, because of the linear nature of the UGIDM, the empirical shift in peak position to somewhat earlier times with increased dose is not predicted. However, exact agreement is not expected since the original data [Baum et al., 1984] are partially based on interpreting qualitative observations from clinical sources that were not expressed on a common scale of symptom severity.

PROTRACTED DOSE RESPONSE

UGIDM calculations were performed to illustrate UG severity predictions for continuous constant dose rate and fractionated exposures.

Continuous Exposure

UGIDM predictions for continuous exposure at constant dose rate are shown by the three isoeffect curves in Fig. 3. These curves show the dose required to reach

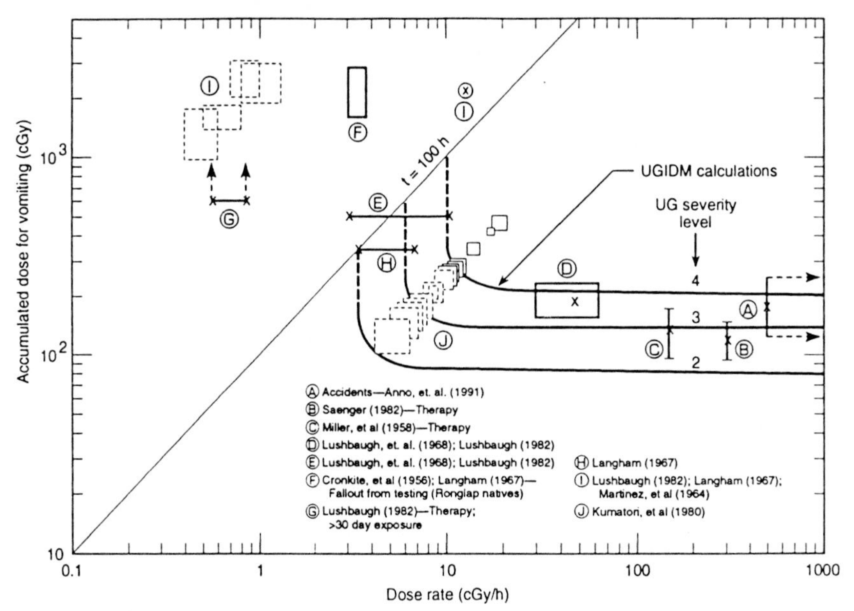

Fig. 3. Accumulated isoeffect dose versus dose rate (MLT): UGIDM-predicted severity levels and data from humans.

peak severity levels 2, 3, and 4 as a function of dose rate. As the dose rate is decreased to around 20 cGy h^{-1} and below, the required isoeffect dose increases very rapidly. We interpret this rapid increase in UG severity level 3 to define a dose rate threshold below which prodromal emesis in humans is predicted to not occur. Below this dose rate, the toxin bioclearing rate simulated by β in the UGIDM prevents the accumulation of the active body toxin level sufficient to trigger emesis.

Some available data from radiation accidents and radiotherapy are also plotted in Fig. 3. Some of the data are for emesis ED_{50} (i.e., (A), (B), (C), and (D)). A direct comparison cannot be made between the UGIDM and the ED_{50} data for dose rates less than about 30 cGy h^{-1} for two reasons. First, comprehensive data for ED_{50} at low dose rates is lacking. Second, also because of the lack of appropriate data, specific correlation cannot be made jointly for the incidence and severity level of emesis. That is, for a given level of emesis, the incidence distribution is generally unavailable; the converse is also true. However, it is generally assumed that severity and incidence are reasonably correlated. We believe that the ED_{50} generally corresponds to UG severity between levels 3 and 4. This is indirectly supported by an independent determination of the incidence for vomiting made from accident victims exposed to acute doses. Based on a likelihood analysis of quantal response data for the first 24 h postexposure, we obtained an ED_{50} of 170 (+61, -45) cGy for emesis by fitting a lognormal distribution to accident data (Anno et al., 1991). This result, given in Fig. 3 by the (A) designation, falls between severity levels 3 and 4 predicted independently by the UGIDM. The data designated (E) through (J) in Fig. 3 serve as a guide as to the reasonableness of the UGIDM predictions.

The dashed rectangles shown for groups (I) and (J) represent individuals involved in two separate accident cases who did not have emesis. However, emesis did occur for one individual from accident group (I) (indicated by the circled x) where the dose rate was about 10 cGy/h. The (F) data are uncertain since they are extrapolated from fallout victims who also inhaled/ingested cloud debris material, which could have an added emetic effect independent of radiation.

The diagonal line in Fig. 3 corresponds to an exposure time of 100 h. It emphasizes that UGIDM predictions for humans are applicable only for doses less than about 1000 cGy and for times less than about four days. Vomiting that may occur beyond four days at greater doses may arise from effects not specifically considered in the UGIDM.

Fractionated Exposure

There is a lack of clinical data for the severity of UG distress after fractionated exposures that do not include the joint use of chemotherapy and/or drugs to mitigate prodromal reactions. However, as mentioned above under "Basis for Modeling," both clinical radiotherapy experience and animal experimentation indicate that when fractionated doses are given, the frequency of emesis diminishes after the initial dose fraction (the "habituation" effect). Figure 4 shows the UGIDM prediction for a fractioned exposure. The model clearly predicts the habituation effect; however, we do not have data at present to validate or improve the model in this regard.

CONCLUSION

Agreement of the UGIDM in its present form with empirical data appears reasonable given the nature of the data and simplicity of the model. Undoubtedly, the UG response to radiation is a nonlinear phenomenon and will likely require nonlinear kinetic rate relationships to improve the match between the predicted and empirical response (work currently in progress). Also, symptom severity is gauged according to an ordinal scale; although reasonably constructed with gradation of severity in mind, there is no assurance of the assumed quantitative linearity. Thus, detailed agreement between the UGIDM and the empirical profiles for acute exposure cannot be expected.

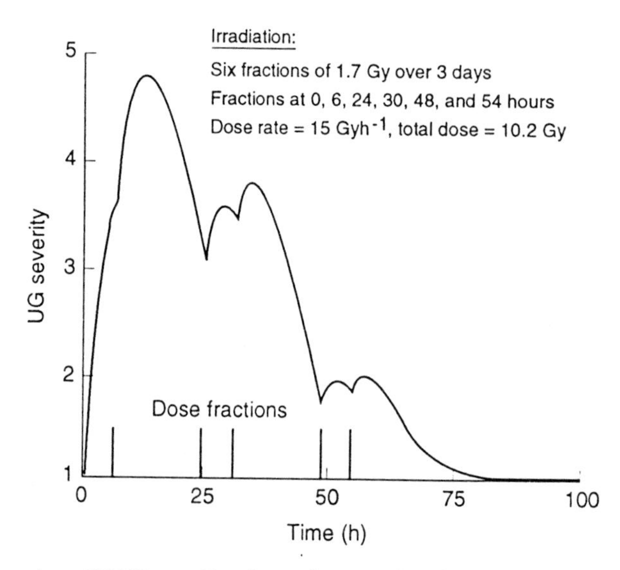

Fig. 4. UGIDM prediction of severity level of upper gastrointestinal (UG) distress for fractionated doses.

Since human data for low dose rate exposure are lacking, we hope to base further model improvements, particularly regarding mechanistic kinetics, on low dose rate and fractioned exposures of ferrets now in progress (King, 1992). Utilizing results from this research and available clinical data, we anticipate improving the emesis model for humans by appropriately scaling the response variables (dosage and time) and parameters from a ferret version of the UGIDM. Also, based on extensive data from ferret experimentation (King, 1988, and Andrews et al., 1990), part of our ongoing research for model validation involves developing analytical techniques to supplement the severity level calculation with a direct stochastic simulation of retching and emetic episodes.

Finally, we would like to acknowledge Dr. Robert Young of the Defense Nuclear Agency for his technical guidance in our work and the support provided by his organization.

REFERENCES

Andrews, P. L. R., Bhandari, P., Garland, S., Bingham, S., Davis, C. J., Hawthorn, J., Davidson, H. I. M., Roylance, R., and Lane, S. (1990): Does retching have a function?: An experimental study in the ferret. In *Pharmacodynamics & Therapeutics*, Vol. 9: pp. 135-152.

Andrews, P. L. R., Rapeport, W. G., Sanger, G. J. (1988): Neuropharmacology of Emesis Induced by Anti-cancer Therapy. In *Trends in Pharmacological Science*, Vol 9, pp. 334-341.

Anno, G. H. (1983): *Nuclear Weapon Effect Research at PSR--1982, Volume XIV: Acute Radiation Response in Humans: Informal Comments by Physicians and Radiobiologists*. DNA-TR-82-179-V14, Defense Nuclear Agency.

Anno, G. H., Wilson, D. B., and Baum, S. J. (1985): *Severity Levels and Symptom Complexes for Acute Radiation Sickness: Description and Quantification*. DNA-TR-86-94, Defense Nuclear Agency.

Anno, G. H., McClellan, G. E., Dore, M. A., and Baum, S. J. (1991): *Biological Effects of Protracted Exposure to Ionizing Radiation: Review, Analysis, and Model Development*. DNA-TR-90-157, Defense Nuclear Agency.

Barnes, J. H. (1984): The Physiology and Pharmacology of Emesis. In *Molecular Aspects of Medicine*, pp. 397-508.

Baum, S. J., Anno, G. H., Young, R. W., and Withers, H. R. (1984): *Symptomatology of Acute Radiation Effects in Humans After Exposure to Doses of 75 to 4500 Rads cGy) Free-in Air*. DNA-TR-85-50, Defense Nuclear Agency.

Bermudez, J., Boyle, E. A., Miner, W. D., and Sanger, G. J. (1988): The Anti-emetic Potential of The 5-Hydroxytryptamine-3 Receptor Antagonist BRL 43694. In *British Journal of Cancer*, Vol. 58, pp. 644-650.

Borison, H. L., Borison, R., and McCarthy, L. E. (1981): Phylogenic and Neurologic Aspects of The Vomiting Process. In *Journal of Clinical Pharmacology*, Vol. 21, pp. 23S-29S.

Borison, L. H., McCarthy, L. E., and Douple, E. B. (1981): Radiometric Protection at 24 h after ^{60}Co Irradiation in Both Normal and Postremectomized Cats. In *Radiation Research*, Vol. 114, pp. 23S-29S.

Cronkite, E. P., Bond, V. P., and Dunham, C. L. (1956): *Some Effects of Ionizing Radiation on Human Beings*. TID-5358, U.S. Atomic Energy Commission.

Davis, C. J., Harding, R. K., Leslie, R. A., and Andrews, P. L. R. (1986): The Organization of Vomiting as A Protective Reflex: A Commentary of the Five Days Discussions. In *Nausea and Vomiting: Mechanisms and Treatment*, ed C. Davis, G. Lake-Bakaar, G. Grahame-Smith. Springer-Verlag, Berlin, Heidelberg.

Harding. R. K. (1988): Prodromal Effects of Radiation: Pathways, Models, and Protection by Antiemetics. In *Pharmacology and Therapeutics*, Vol. 37, pp. 335-345.

King, G. L. (1992): private communication, Armed Forces Radiobiological Research Institute, Bethesda, Maryland.

King, G. L. (1988): Characterization of Radiation-Induced Emesis in the Ferret. In *Radiation Research*, Vol. 22, pp. 145-155.
Kumatori, T., Ishihara, T., Hirashima, K., Sugiyama, H., Ishii, S., and Miyoshi, K. (1980): Follow-up Studies over A 25-Year Period on The Japanese Fishermen Exposed to Radioactive Fallout in 1954. *In The Medical Basis for Radiation Accident Preparedness*, ed. K. Hubner and S. Fry, pp 33-54. New York: Elsevier North Holland, Inc.
Lang, I. M. and Marvig, J. (1989): Functional Localization of Specific Receptors Mediating Gastrointestinal Motor Correlates of Vomiting. In *American Journal of Physiology*, Vol. 256, pp. 692-699.
Langham, W. S. (ed) (1967). *Radiobiological Factors in Manned Space Flight*. Report of The Space Radiation Study Panel of The Life Sciences Committee, Publication 1487. National Academy of Sciences/National Research Council.
Lushbaugh, C. C. (1982): The Impact of Estimates of Human Radiation Tolerance Upon Radiation Emergency Management. In *The Control of Exposure of The Public to Ionizing Radiation in The Event of Accident or Attack*, pp. 46-57. National Council on Radiation Protection and Measurement.
Lushbaugh, C. C., Comas, F., Edwards, C. L., and Andrews, G. A. (1968): Clinical Evidence of Dose Rate Effects in Total Body Irradiation in Man. In *Dose Rate in Mammalian Radiation Biology*, A Symposium Co-sponsored by UT-AEC Agricultural Research Laboratory, Oak Ridge, TN. CONF-680410. U.S. Atomic Energy Commission, Div. of Technical Information.
Martinez, G. R., Cassab, H. G., Ganem, G. G., Gultan, K. E., Liebernam, L. M., et al. (1964): Accident from Radiation: Observations on The Accidental Exposure of A Family to A Source of Cobalt-60, pp. 14-69. In *Rev. Med. Inst. Mex. Segure Social*, Suppl. 1, Vol. 3.
Miller, L. S., Fletcher, G. H., Gerstner, H. B. (1958): Radiobiologic Observations on Cancer Patients Treated with Whole-body X-Irradiation. In *Radiation Research*, Vol. 8, pp. 150-165.
Saenger, E. L. (1982): private communication. Clinical data presented at the Defense Nuclear Agency's Intermediate Dose Program, Medical/Radiobiological Meeting, Bethesda, MD, 27-28 May 1982. University of Cincinnati Medical School.
Tichelli, A., Walther, E., Gratwohl, A., Osterwalder, B., and Speck, B. (1987): Side Effects of Total Body Irradiation before Bone Marrow Transplantation. Basel Experience July 1979 to March 1986. In *Strahlentherapy Und Onxologie Strahlentheropie Und Onkologie*, Vol. 163, pp 245-246.
Young, R. W. (1986): Mechanisms and Treatment of Radiation-Induced Nausea and Vomiting. In *Nausea and Vomiting: Mechanism and Treatment*, ed C. J. Davis, G. V. Lake-Bakaar, and D. G. Grahame-Smith, pp. 94-109. Springer-Verlag, Berlin, Heidelberg.

Mechanisms and Control of Emesis. Eds A.L. Bianchi, L. Grélot, A.D. Miller, G.L. King. Colloque INSERM/ John Libbey Eurotext Ltd. © 1992, Vol. 223, pp. 341-350

Current status: animal models of nausea

Robert A. Fox

Department of Psychology, San José State University, One Washington Square San José, CA 95192-0120, USA

SUMMARY

The advantages, and possible benefits of a valid, reliable animal model for nausea are discussed, and difficulties inherent to the development of a model are considered. A principle problem for developing models arises because nausea is a subjective sensation that can be identified only in humans. Several putative measures of nausea in animals are considered, with more detailed consideration directed to variation in cardiac rate, levels of vasopressin, and conditioned taste aversion. Demonstration that putative measures are associated with reported nausea in humans is proposed as a requirement for validating measures to be used in animal models. The necessity for a "real-time" measure of nausea is proposed as an important factor for future research; and the need for improved understanding of the neuroanatomy underlying the emetic syndrome is discussed.

Les modèles animaux dans l'étude de la nausée: état de la question

Résumé: *Les avantages et bénéfices possibles d'un modèle animal dans l'étude de la nausée sont discutés; les difficultés inhérentes au développement de ce modèle sont abordées. Un problème de principe pour développer de tels modèles (animaux) réside dans le fait que la nausée est une sensation subjective qui ne peut être identifiée que chez l'homme. Plusieurs indices pouvant permettre de détecter la nausée chez l'animal sont présentés, en insistant plus particulièrement sur les variations du rythme cardiaque, le taux sérique de vasopressine et le comportement de révulsion alimentaire conditionné. La démonstration que ces indices sont aussi associés à une nausée avérée chez l'homme est proposée comme une condition de validation de ces indices chez l'animal. La nécessité d'objectiver la nausée en temps réel est proposée comme un facteur important pour les futures recherches. Le besoin d'une meilleure connaissance neuroanatomique des circuits qui sous-tendent le syndrome émétique est discuté.*

INTRODUCTION

Nausea generally is not life threatening, but it can have significant negative impact in clinical procedures (Wetchler, 1991) and chronic nausea may lead to a marked reduction in the quality of life (Stewart, 1991). Patients with predisposition to prolonged gastric emptying or those undergoing laparoscopy are at high risk for nausea and intractable vomiting when anesthesia or sedation are required (Kapur, 1991). Nausea and vomiting also are severe side effects of chemotherapy and contribute importantly to noncompliance with treatment regimens, particularly in adolescents (Zelter *et al.*, 1991). In addition, anticipatory nausea is a significant problem with up to one fourth of pediatric patients undergoing chemotherapy (Dolgin *et al.*, 1985).

A valid animal model of nausea would contribute importantly to the study of the neural and physiological systems involved in this state. Miller and Kucharczyk (1991) noted that the lack of such a model has hampered investigation of both the etiology of nausea and the relationship of nausea to vomiting. Development and verification of an animal model of nausea is difficult, however, for both practical and theoretical reasons. Practical difficulties arise because there is no accepted physiological method for identifying the subjective state of nausea in animals, or for that matter in humans. Self-reports of nausea are accepted in humans, but there are no reliable, direct measures of either the presence or degree of this state. Several putative measures of nausea have been suggested, but as is discussed below, none has been convincingly demonstrated as reliable, workable, and valid. This absence of direct measures of nausea creates a significant problem for the validation of animal models.

Development of animal models is complicated further by the fact that species differences in this response are unknown. Vomiting, the culminating event of the emetic syndrome, can be identified directly and is widespread in the animal kingdom. However, the wide variety of stimuli that elicit, or fail to elicit vomiting in various animals (Corcoran, Fox, & Daunton, 1990; Daunton, 1990; King, 1990) might imply that variations are to be expected in nauseogenic responses as well. The observation of vomiting may *not necessarily* indicate that nausea is, or has been, present. Nausea and emesis are not inextricably linked in humans (Harm, 1990) and there is no *a priori* reason to believe that they would be linked in a possible animal model.

Current theoretical interpretations of the neurophysiological mechanisms of vomiting indicate another problem for the development of models. The traditional concept that effector activation of vomiting is coordinated by a localized group of neurons, or vomiting "center" (Borison & Wang, 1949) is now questioned (Miller & Wilson, 1983a). Current interpretations of possible mechanisms for the nausea-emetic syndrome propose that this state may be mediated via multiple pathways (Miller & Wilson, 1983b) rather than a single emetic center. Such schemes may involve predominant pathways for a given emetic stimulus or species (Harding, 1990) or a hierarchical cascade of effector systems that may vary for different animals (Lawes, 1991). Evolutionary development of multiple pathways provides diverse opportunities for variation in the mechanisms of nausea and vomiting among species.

DETECTION OF NAUSEA WITH INDIRECT MEASURES

Following the suggestion of Borison and Wang (1953), indirect measures for nausea have been chosen to reflect autonomic responses thought to accompany this state. Several responses have been used as prodromal signs of nausea. Applications of this approach range from the development of formal rating scales to the reporting of individual responses thought to be prodromal symptoms of sickness. Demonstration that a putative measure is associated with reported nausea in humans is crucial to the validation of measures to be used in animal models.

Rating scales are based on the concept that various autonomic responses (e.g., increased salivation, disruptions of cardiac rhythm, defecation) that often precede vomiting are associated with nausea. An implicit assumption of this approach is that autonomic signs of sickness reflect an underlying serial process progressing from mild disturbance through nausea toward frank vomiting. Formal rating scales were developed for human studies of motion sickness (Graybiel, Wood, Miller, & Cramer, 1968) so that stimulation could be terminated prior to frank vomiting, and to provide a graded measure of sickness. A scale of one form or another, and self-reported nausea, are used in virtually all studies of motion sickness in man. Analogous scales have been developed to assess the development of motion sickness in cats (Suri, Crampton, & Daunton, 1979), squirrel monkeys (Igarashi *et al.*, 1983) and chimpanzees (Meek, Graybiel, Beischer, & Riopelle, 1962). Several observations indicating that the individual responses comprising rating scales fail to reflect a serial, unitary emetic mechanism in motion sickness are reviewed by Daunton (1990). This lack of evidence of a serial mechanism in motion sickness raises serious concerns regarding the use of rating scales to assess the development of sickness (i.e., nausea) in animal models.

A wide variety of individual responses have been used to assess sickness in animals. Some of these are included in typical rating scales, while others are not. A partial summary of the responses used with various species is outlined in Table 1. Several of these responses (e.g., reduced activity or food intake, defecation, pica) are observed in humans during activation of the emetic syndrome and were adopted as measures to be used with species that do not possess a complete emetic reflex. The use of such species (e.g., the rat) is motivated, in part, by the utility of these standard laboratory animals for physiological investigations. Although the use of these species to assess emetic mechanisms is questionable, these measures continue to receive consideration as multiple, or supplemental indices of sickness (Ossenkopp & Ossenkopp, 1985).

Table 1. Several putative measures of sickness (nausea) and the species that have been tested with each measure.

MEASURE	SPECIES
Arginine Vasopressin (AVP)	human, monkey, cat, rat
Burrowing and Backing	ferret
Cardiac Rhythm	human, squirrel monkey
Conditioned Taste Aversion (CTA)	human, squirrel monkey, cat rat, guinea pig, mouse
Defecation	cat, ferret, rat
Gastric Rhythms	human, dog
Pica	human, rat
Reduced Activity	ferret, rat
Reduced Intake of Food or Water	human, rat
Skin Color Changes	human, squirrel monkey

POSSIBLE MARKERS FOR NAUSEA

Some measures have been adopted specifically to assess nausea. Three of these are discussed in the following sections.

Cardiac Rhythm

A relationship between cardiac irregularity and the emetic reflex has long been suspected (Crittenden & Ivy, 1933). Ishii *et al.* (1987) used beat-to-beat variation in cardiac rhythm to assess autonomic nervous system effects related to "motion sickness" induced by vestibulo-visual conflict in squirrel monkeys. Monkeys were secured in a primate chair to avoid movement artifacts. Variation in beat-to-beat intervals increased immediately prior to vomiting, perhaps reflecting nausea. Two effects indicate these changes could arise from altered parasympathetic activity: injections of atropine reduced variations in animals in control conditions and counteracted increased variation in animals subjected to vestibulo-visual conflict. Demonstration of a relationship between these changes and other possible indices of nausea (i.e., see changes in AVP discussed below) should be considered to investigate these effects further. Cardiac arrhythmia can be processed in real time by computer analysis, and thus could provide a direct, "on-line" measure of parasympathetic activity in conditions when effects from other factors such as stress or blood pressure can be controlled or eliminated.

Release of Vasopressin

The level of systemic vasopressin (AVP) has been investigated as a possible objective marker for nausea or activation of emetic pathways. AVP is elevated during nausea and after vomiting in man (e.g., Koch *et al.*, 1990; Miaskiewicz, Striker, & Verbalis , 1989; Rowe *et al.*, 1979), and after vomiting in cats (Fox *et al.*, 1987) and monkeys (Verbalis, Richardson, & Striker, 1987). However, most examinations of the relationship between nausea and AVP have been correlational in nature, and there is no definitive explanation of the physiological events underlying it. AVP is excitatory to neurons of the chemoreceptive trigger zone (Carpenter, Briggs & Strominger, 1984), but an emetic effect of AVP is not well documented. Infusion of AVP has produced emesis in humans (Thomford & Sirinek, 1975), but infusion also has failed to produce emesis in man (Williams *et al.*, 1986) and in cats (Fox, unpublished data). Explanation of any cause and effect relationship between nausea and elevated levels of AVP is crucial to the use of AVP as a marker for nausea in an animal model.

Two recent studies have addressed the relationship between nausea and AVP. Koch *et al.* (1990) induced malaise using illusory self-motion. Koch (1991) notes that both reported nausea and the release of AVP in this study are related to gastric arrhythmia, and proposes that either of two possible sequences, **arrhythmia ---> nausea ---> AVP release** or **arrhythmia ---> AVP release ---> nausea**, are possible. Miaskiewicz *et al.* (1989) stimulated nausea and vomiting in humans by injection of cholecystokinin octapeptide (CCK). Doses of CCK that caused epigastric cramping and mild visceral discomfort were associated with increased levels of AVP, however, these effects occurred without reports of nausea. This result was interpreted as suggesting that AVP secretion can occur with minor visceral malaise even prior to nausea or emesis, perhaps indicating that secretion of AVP precedes nausea.

The efficacy of AVP as a marker for nausea has not been demonstrated convincingly for animal models. Two factors should be considered prior to using AVP to identify nausea or the activation of emetic pathways. First, large individual differences in the range of the AVP response have been observed in studies with humans (Edwards, Carmichael, Baylis, & Harris, 1989; Koch *et al.*, 1990; Miaskiewicz *et al.*, 1989), monkeys (Verbalis *et al.*, 1987), and cats (Fox *et al.*, 1987). Second, not all cases of nausea are associated with AVP secretion. A dissociation of AVP and nausea was shown when nausea, induced by rapid food intake, failed to be associated with elevated AVP (Miaskiewicz *et al.*, 1989). Neither is the association between emesis and AVP secretion obligatory since elevation of AVP fails to occur in man when emesis is induced with ipecacuanha syrup (Nussey *et al.*, 1988).

Technological issues also complicate the use of AVP as a marker of nausea in animal studies. Assays for AVP require blood volumes which prohibit serial sampling in small animals. This is a serious problem with very small animals like shrews, where it may not be possible to obtain even single samples without producing changes in blood pressure or plasma osmolality. Obtaining repeated samples from cats may impact other indices of general stress such as cortisol (Fox *et al.*, 1987). In addition, significant processing is required to conduct the assay, so assessment of AVP cannot provide an "on-line" index of the nauseous state.

Conditioned Taste Aversion

The avoidance of flavored substances consumed just prior to the onset of sickness (a conditioned taste aversion, or CTA) was first demonstrated in the laboratory by Garcia and colleagues (e.g., Garcia & Ervin, 1968). Because many of the stimuli used to induce CTA in early experiments produce gastrointestinal distress or nausea, CTA was thought to be mediated by neural mechanisms important to the emetic syndrome. The observation of CTA in patients made nauseous while undergoing chemotherapeutic (Bernstein, 1985; Bernstein & Webster, 1980) or radiation treatments (Smith et al., 1984) for cancer provides further support for this position.

Few direct, systematic evaluations of the assumption that visceral distress, or nausea promote CTA have been conducted. In a retrospective evaluation conducted by reviewing the literatures on vomiting and CTA, Grant (1987) argued that if nausea or other pre-emetic components of the emetic syndrome are responsible for CTA, then CTA should depend on neural structures important to the emetic syndrome (assessed by vomiting). Available studies that investigated whether neural pathways important to emesis also are important to the production of CTA neither confirm nor reject convincingly a role for emetic structures in CTA. Some blood-borne agents such as lithium chloride (McGlone, Ritter, & Kelly, 1980; Rabin, Hunt, & Lee, 1983), copper sulfate (Coil & Norgren, 1981), or xylazine (Fox, Corcoran & Brizzee, 1990) that produce CTA do depend on the area postrema. The disruptive effects of AP lesions on CTA induced by toxins are sufficiently reliable that both lithium chloride (Sutton, Fox, & Daunton, 1988) and scopolamine methyl nitrate (Ossenkopp, 1983) have been used to screen for the completeness of AP lesions in rats. For other agents, however, CTA and vomiting do not depend on the same neural mechanisms. Morphine, for example, produces vomiting via the area postrema (Borison *et al.*, 1962) but produces CTA via the periaquaductal gray (Blair & Amit, 1981).

Several factors require that conclusions from Grant's review be made with care. Grant acknowledged that emetic circuity is incompletely understood and that most research on CTA has been conducted with rats while that on emetic mechanisms has been on cats, dogs, and monkeys. (Ferrets must now be added to the list of animals used to study emetic mechanisms). Because there are species differences in sensitivity to emetic treatments, cross-species comparisons can be difficult. However, cross-species comparisons are required because the relationship between CTA and the emetic syndrome has been investigated directly in very few studies (Fox *et al.*, 1990; Rabin *et al.*, 1986; Roy & Brizzee, 1979; Wilpizeski *et al.*, 1985). These studies generally show that vomiting does not predict the formation of CTA precisely. CTA may occur without vomiting and vomiting may occur without CTA being produced. Additional studies directly assessing CTA and the emetic syndrome in the same species (or animals) will be required to clarify whether the emetic syndrome and CTA share common neural circuitry.

Because CTA is a learned response, several control conditions for the study of learning mechanisms are required when this measure is used (Fox, 1990). Procedures to eliminate psuedoconditioning and other artifactual effects that could be incorrectly interpreted as CTA can significantly increase the effort and cost involved in using this measure. The possibility that exposure to the emetic stimulus prior to testing could reduce the strength of CTA, and thus lead to incorrect inferences about the effect of the stimulus, can restrict methods for conducting experiments.

CONCLUSIONS

Development of a valid animal model of nausea requires the identification of motor, hormonal, neural, or behavioral events that are associated with nausea. Because nausea is a subjective state that can be identified only in man, potential measures for animal models must be based on demonstrations that the same measures reliably identify nausea in man. Thus, a coordinated research strategy that integrates information from studies in humans and animals is required. Confidence in a given measure could be enhanced by the accumulation of convergent validation data from multiple assessments (i.e., motor and hormonal).

Each of the potential measures of nausea discussed above is affected by one or more detrimental factors. All of these potential measures require better validation. Technical requirements for assaying systemic AVP can produce general stress effects, or even prohibit application of the measure in very small animals. Concern about neural circuity crucial to CTA, requirements for control procedures, and the observation that nausea and/or vomiting can occur independently of CTA indicate reservations about this measure. In addition, investigation of the effects of antiemetic drugs on CTA have produced positive (Coil *et al.*, 1978) and negative (Goudie *et al.*, 1982) results, and some of the compounds used as antiemetics can produce CTA themselves (i.e., scopolamine).

Neither AVP nor CTA can provide a real-time assessment of sickness. Variation in cardiac rhythm could provide real-time assessment, but this measure needs to be validated with additional studies. The source or type of other possible measures for nausea are not readily forthcoming. Incomplete characterization of the neuroanatomy that underlies the emetic syndrome complicates identification of prodromal signs sufficiently independent of emesis that they might serve as measures of other components of the syndrome. Thus, recent research has characterized gastrointestinal precursors of vomiting (Lang *et al.*, 1986; Lang, Sarna, & Condon, 1986) but has not provided a clear candidate for an index of nausea. Gastric relaxation could be a candidate (Andrews & Wood, 1988; Hulse & Patrick, 1977; Willems & Lefebvre, 1986) but this response also occurs as part of the normal sequence of feeding (Young & Deutsch, 1980), and not all forms of gastric distention produce nausea (Miaskiewicz *et al.*, 1989). If this response is related to nausea, an explanation of why it leads to the sensation of nausea in some instances but not in others is required.

Improved understanding of the neurocircuitry of the emetic syndrome is a primary requirement for the development of a model for nausea. The neural mechanisms underlying nausea will not be identified until the events that converge to elicit vomiting are described more fully. Improved understanding of interrelationships between prodromal signs of vomiting and identification of the mechanism coordinating the neural activity that produces the complicated pattern of motor events leading to expulsion would be very beneficial. At the present time there is little evidence indicating whether the mechanisms underlying nausea should be sought in central or peripheral sites.

The species best suited for a model is not obvious. Each species traditionally used to study emetic mechanisms (dogs, cats, ferrets and monkeys) has advantages for specific purposes. The extensive knowledge of neural, receptor, and gastrointestinal mechanisms in these animals is invaluable. But other tractable animals that readily can be bred for purpose to insure availability at reasonable cost would be advantageous. The ferret has been very useful in recent years, and the house shrew, ***Suncus murinus***, is a relatively new candidate on the scene that shows promise (Matsuki *et al.*, 1988; Ueno, Matsuki, & Saito, 1987; Ueno, Matsuki, & Saito, 1988). The shrew is very small for some procedures, such as blood assays and instrumentation, but this small size is an advantage for housing and testing of chemical agents that are difficult to produce in large quantities. If detailed description of neuroanatomy and physiology are forthcoming this may prove to be a useful animal. Certainly the rat is not an ideal model. Thorough knowledge of anatomy and physiology are a valuable asset, but the lack of an emetic reflex leads to complex issues of species differences that complicate understanding.

REFERENCES

Andrews, P. L. R. & Wood, K. L. (1988). Vagally mediated gastric motor and emetic reflexes evoked by stimulation of the antral mucosa in anaesthetized ferrets. *J. Physiol.*, 395, 1-16.

Bernstein, I. L. (1985). Learned food aversions in the progression of cancer and its treatment. *Ann. NY Acad. Sci.*, 443, 365-380.

Bernstein, I. L. & Webster, M. M. (1980). Learned taste aversions in humans. *Physiol. Behav.*, 25, 363-366.

Blair, R. & Amit, Z. (1981). Morphine conditioned taste aversion reversed by periaqueductal gray lesions. *Pharmacol. Biochem. Behav.*, 15, 651-653.

Borison, H. L., Fishburn, B. R., Bhide, N. K., & McCarthy, L. E. (1962). Morphine-induced hyperglycemia in the cat. *J. Pharmacol. Exp. Ther.*, 138, 229-235.

Borison, H. L. & Wang, S. C. (1949). Functional localization of central coordinating mechanism for emesis in cat. *J. Neurophysiol.*, 12, 305-313.

Borison, H. L. & Wang, S. C. (1953). Physiology and pharmacology of vomiting. *Pharm. Rev.*, 5, 193-230.

Carpenter, D. O., Briggs, D. B. & Strominger, N. (1984). Peptide-induced emesis in dogs. *Behav. Brain Res.*, 11, 277-281.

Coil, J. D., Hankins, W. G., Jenden, D. J., Garcia, J. (1978). The attenuation of a specific cue-to-consequence association by antiemetic agents. *Psychopharmocol.*, 56, 21-25.

Coil, J. D. & Norgren, R. (1981). Taste aversions conditioned with intravenous copper sulfate: Attenuation by ablation of the area postrema. *Brain Res.*, 212, 425-433.

Corcoran, M. L., Fox, R. A., & Daunton, N. G. (1990). The susceptibility of rhesus monkeys to motion sickness. *Aviat. Space Environ. Med.*, 61, 807-809.

Crittenden, P. J. & Ivy, A. C. (1933). A study of viscerocardiac reflexes: The experimental production of cardiac irregularities in icteric dogs with an analysis of the role played by nausea and vomiting. *Am. Heart J.*, 8, 507-518.

Daunton, N. G. (1990). Animal models in motion sickness research. In *Motion and space sickness*, ed. G. H. Crampton, pp. 87-104. Boca Raton: CRC Press.

Dolgin, M. J., Fetting, J. H., Nettesheim, K. M., & Abeloff, M. D. (1985). Anticipatory nausea and vomiting in pediatric cancer patients. *Pediatrics* 75, 547-552.

Edwards, C. M., Carmichael, J., Baylis, P. H. & Harris, A. L. (1989). Arginine vasopressin - a mediator of chemotherapy induced emesis? *Br. J. Cancer*, 59, 467-470.

Fox, R. A. (1990). Investigating motion sickness using the conditioned taste aversion paradigm. In *Motion and space sickness*, ed. G. H. Crampton, pp. 105-121. Boca Raton: CRC Press.

Fox, R. A., Corcoran, M. L., & Brizzee, K. R. (1990). Conditioned taste aversion and motion sickness in cats and squirrel monkeys. *Can. J. Physiol. Pharamacol.*, 68, 269-278.

Fox, R. A., Keil, L. C., Daunton, N. G., Crampton, G. H., & Lucot, J. (1987). Vasopressin and motion sickness in cats. *Aviat. Space Environ. Med.*, 58(9, Suppl.), A143-A147.

Garcia, J. & Ervin, F. R. (1968). Gustatory-visceral and telereceptor-cutaneous conditioning: Adaptation in internal and external milieus. *Commun. Behav. Biol.*, 1, 389-415.

Goudie, A. J., Stolerman, I. P., Demellweek, C., & D'Mello, G. D. (1982). Does conditioned nausea mediate drug-induced conditioned taste aversion? *Psychopharmacol.*, 78, 277-281.

Grant, V. L. (1987). Do conditioned taste aversions result from activation of emetic mechanisms? *Psychopharmacology*, 93, 405-415.

Graybiel, A., Wood, C. D., Miller II, E. F., & Cramer, D. B. (1968). Diagnostic criteria for grading the severity of acute motion sickness. *Aerospace Med.*, 39, 453-455.

Harding, R. K. (1990). Concepts and conflicts in the mechanism of emesis. *Can. J. Physiol. Pharmacol.*, 68, 218-220.

Harm, D. J. (1990). Physiology of motion sickness symptoms. In *Motion and space sickness*, ed. G. H. Crampton, pp. 153-177. Boca Raton: CRC Press.

Hulse, E. V. & Patrick, G. (1977). A model for treating post-irradiation nausea and vomiting in man: The action of insulin in abolishing radiation-induced delay in gastric emptying in the rat. *Br. J. Radiol.*, 50, 645.

Igarashi, M., Isago, H., O-uchi, T., Kulecz, W. B., Homick, J. L., & Reschke, M. R. (1983). Vestibular-visual conflict sickness in the squirrel monkey. *Acta Oto Laryngol.*, 95, 193-198.

Ishii, M., Igarashi, M., Patel, S., Himi, T., & Kuleca, W. (1987). Autonomic effects on R-R variations of the heart rate in the squirrel monkey: An indicator of autonomic imbalance in conflict sickness. *Am. J. Otolaryngol.*, 3, 144-148.

Kapur, P. A. (1991). Editorial: The big "Little problem." *Ambulatory Anesthesia* 73, 243-245.

King, G. L. (1990). Animal models in the study of vomiting. *Can. J. Physiol. Pharmacol.*, 68, 260-268.

Koch, K. L. (1991). Nausea and vasopressin. *Lancet*, 338, 1023.

Koch, K. L., Summy-Long, J., Bingaman, S., Sperry, N., & Stern, R. M. (1990). Vasopressin and oxytocin responses to illusory self-motion and nausea in man. *J. Clin. Endocrinol. Metab.*, 71(5), 1269-1275.

Lang, I. M., Marvig, J., Sarna, S. K., & Condon, R. E. (1986). Gastrointestinal myoelectric correlates of vomiting in the dog. *Am. J. Physiol. 251 (Gastrointest. Liver Physiol. 14)*, G830-G838.

Lang, I. M., Sarna, S. K., & Condon, R. E. (1986). Gastrointestinal motor correlates of vomiting in the dog: Quantification and characterization as an independent phenomenon. *Gastroenterology*, 90, 40-47.

Lawes, I. N. C. (1991). The central connections of area postrema define the paraventricular system involved in antinoxious behaviors. In *Nausea and vomiting: Recent research and clinical advances*, ed. J. Kucharczyk, D. J. Stewart, & A. D. Miller, pp. 77-101. Boca Raton: CRC Press.

Matsuki, N., Ueno, S., Kaji, T., Ishihara, A., Wang, C-H., & Saito, H. (1988). Emesis induced by cancer chemotherapeutic agents in the Suncus murinus: A new experimental model. *Japan. J. Pharmacol.*, 48, 303-306.

McGlone, J. J., Ritter, S., & Kelley, K. W. (1980). The antiaggressive effect of lithium is abolished by area postrema lesion. *Physiol. Behav.*, 24, 1095-1100.

Meek, J. C., Graybiel, A., Beischer, D. E., & Riopelle, A. J. (1962). Observations of canal sickness and adaptation in chimpanzees and squirrel monkeys in a "slow rotation room". *Aerospace Med.*, 33, 571-578.

Miaskiewicz, S. L., Stricker, E. M., & Verbalis, J. G. (1989). Neurohypophyseal secretion in response to cholecystokinin but not meal-induced gastric distention in humans. *J. Clin. Endocrinol. Metab.*, 68(4), 837-843.

Miller, A. D. & Kucharczyk, J. (1991): Mechanisms of nausea and emesis: Introduction and retrospective. In *Nausea and vomiting: Recent research and clinical advances*, J. Kucharczyk, D. J. Stewart, & A. D. Miller, pp. 1-12. Boca Raton: CRC Press.

Miller, A. D. & Wilson, V. J. (1983a). 'Vomiting center' reanalyzed: An electrical stimulation study. *Brain Res.*, 270, 154-158.

Miller, A. D. & Wilson, V. J. (1983b). Vestibular-induced vomiting after vestibulocerebellar lesions. *Brain, Behav. Evol.*, 23, 26-31.

Nussey, S. S., Hawthorn, J., Page, S. R., Ang, V. T. Y., & Jenkins, J. S. (1988). Responses of plasma oxytocin and arginine vasopressin to nausea induced by apomorphine and ipecacuanha. *Clin. Endocrinol.*, 28, 297-304.

Ossenkopp, K. -P. (1983). Area postrema lesions in rats enhance the magnitude of body-rotation induced taste aversions. *Behav. Neural Biol.*, 38, 82-96.

Ossenkopp, K. -P. & Ossenkopp, M. D. (1985). Animal models of motion sickness: Are nonemetic species an appropriate choice? *The Physiologist*, 28, S61-S62.

Rabin, B. M., Hunt, W. A., & Lee, J. (1983). Attenuation of radiation- and drug-induced conditioned taste aversions following area postrema lesions in the rat. *Radiat. Res.*, 90, 609-620.

Rabin, B. M., Hunt, W. A., Chedester, A. L., & Lee, J. (1986). Role of the area postrema in radiation-induced taste aversion learning and emesis in cats. *Physiol. Behav.*, 37, 815-818.

Rowe, J. W., Shelton, R. L., Helderman, J. H., Vestal, R. E., & Robertson, G. L. (1979). Influence of the emetic reflex on vasopressin release in man. *Kidney Inter.*, 16, 729-735.

Roy, M. A. & Brizzee, K. R. (1979). Motion sickness-induced food aversions in the squirrel monkey. *Physiol. Behav.*, 23, 39-41.

Stewart, D. J. (1991). Nausea and vomiting in cancer patients. In *Nausea and vomiting: Recent research and clinical advances*, J. Kucharczyk, D. J. Stewart, & A. D. Miller, pp. 177-203. Boca Raton: CRC Press.

Smith, J. C., Blumsack, J. T., Bilek, F. S. Spector, A. C., Hollander, G. R., & Baker, D. L. (1984). Radiation-induced taste aversion as a factor in cancer therapy. *Cancer Treat. Rep.*, 68, 1219-1227.

Suri, K. B., Crampton, G. H., & Daunton, N. G. (1979). Motion sickness in cats: A symptom rating scale used in laboratory and flight tests. *Aviat. Space Environ. Med.*, 50, 614-618.

Sutton, R. L., Fox, R. A., & Daunton, N. G. (1988). Role of the area postrema in three putative measures of motion sickness in the rat. *Behav. Neural Biol.*, 50, 133-152.

Thomford, N. R. & Sirinek, K. R. (1975). Intravenous vasopressin in patients with portal hypertension: Advantages of continuous infusion. *J. Surg. Res.*, 18, 113.

Ueno, S., Matsuki, N., & Saito, H. (1987). Suncus murinus: A new experimental model in emesis research. *Life Sci.*, 43, 413-420.

Ueno, S., Matsuki, N., & Saito, H. (1988). Suncus murinus as a new experimental model for motion sickness. *Life Sci.*, 43, 413-420.

Verbalis, J. G., Richardson, D. W., & Stricker, E. M. (1987). Vasopressin release in response to nausea-producing agents and cholecystokinin in monkeys. *Am. J. Physiol. 252 (Regulatory Integrative Comp. Physiol. 21)* R749-R753.

Wetchler, B. V. (1991). Outpatient anesthesia: What are the problems in the recovery room? *Can. J. Anesth.*, 38(7), 890-894.

Willems, J. L. & Lefebvre, R. A. (1986). Peripheral nervous pathways involved in nausea and vomiting. In *Nausea and vomiting: Mechanisms and treatment*, ed. C. J. Davis, G. V. Lake-Bakaar, & D. G. Grahame-Smith, pp. 56-64. Berlin: Springer-Verlag.

Williams, T. D. M., DaCosta, D., Mathias, C. J., Bannister, R. & Lightman, S. L. (1986). Pressor effect of arginine vasopressin in progressive autonomic failure. *Clin. Sci.*, 71, 173.

Wilpizeski, C. R., Lowry, L. D., Eyyunni, U., Raheb, M. E., & Goldman, W. S. (1985). Behavioral conditioning and experimental motion-induced sickness. *Am. J. Otolaryngol.*, 6, 258-263.

Young, W. G. & Deutsch, J. A. (1980). Intragastric pressure and receptive relaxation in the rat. *Physiol. Behav.*, 25, 973-975.

Zelter, L. K., Dolgin, M. J., LeBaron, S., & LeBaron, C. (1991). A randomized, controlled study of behavioral intervention for chemotherapy distress in children with cancer. *Pediatrics* 88, 34-42.

Mechanisms and Control of Emesis. Eds A.L. Bianchi, L. Grélot, A.D. Miller, G.L. King. Colloque INSERM/
John Libbey Eurotext Ltd. © 1992, Vol. 223, pp. 351-352

Morphine-induced emesis in the ferret

John A. Rudd and Robert J. Naylor

The School of Pharmacy, University of Bradford, Bradford, BD7 1DP, UK

Introduction

Nausea and vomiting are undesirable effects associated with the clinical use of morphine and related analgesic compounds. It has been suggested that the emetic effects are mediated via opioid receptors at the level of the chemoreceptor trigger zone, although the precise subtype of opioid receptor responsible for these effects is uncertain (Costello & Borison, 1977; Wang & Glaviano, 1954).

In the present study we attempt to determine which opioid receptor subtype(s) is responsible for the emetic effects of morphine in the ferret using M8008 (a selective μ-receptor antagonist), MR 2266 (a selective kappa receptor antagonist) and naltrindole (a selective delta-receptor antagonist). In addition, using a quaternary derivative of naloxone, naloxone methyliodide, we investigate if the opioid receptor(s) responsible for the emetic effects of morphine is located outside the blood brain barrier. We have previously reported the emetic dose-response profile of morphine in the ferret (see Barnes *et al.*, 1991).

Methods

Albino or fitch ferrets of either sex (0.7-1.3 Kg) were injected subcutaneously with morphine (0.5 mg/Kg). Naloxone, naloxone methyliodide, naltrindole, M8008 (16S-methylcyprenorphine), MR2266 (5,9-diethyl-2-(3-furylmethyl)-2'-hydroxy-7,7-benzomorphan) or respective vehicle was administered s.c. as a 15 min pretreatment prior to the administration of morphine (Mor). Naloxone (Nal) and naloxone methyliodide (Nal.I) were dissolved in saline (0.9% w/v; Veh.1); M8008 and MR2266 were dissolved in distilled H_2O (Veh.2) and naltrindole (Naltrin) was dissolved in 0.1% methanol/saline (0.9% w/v; Veh.3). During the experiments all animals were observed for the production of retching and vomiting. Retching was defined as the non-productive laboured rhythmic activity of the respiratory musculature and abdomen whilst vomiting was defined as the oral expulsion of the gastric contents (solid or liquid). The latency to retching and vomiting post emetogen administration was also recorded.

Results

In the control treated animals, morphine (0.5 mg/kg s.c.) induced 32-55 retches and 4-7 vomits in 10-13 episodes, 2.1-3.5 min post injection. The retching and vomiting induced by morphine was dose-dependently antagonised by MR2266>M8008>naltrindole. Morphine-induced emesis was also antagonised by naloxone and naloxone methyliodide (see table 1).

Table 1. The effect of opioid receptor antagonists on morphine-induced emesis in the ferret

Treatment	(mg/kg)	% Protected	Latency(min)	Episodes	Retches	Vomits
Mor+Veh.1		0	2.1	9.9±1.2	32.6±4.0	5.1±1.0
Mor+Nal	0.1	75	4.5	0.8±0.8**	4.5±4.5*	0.5±0.5*
Mor+Nal	1.0	100	—	0.0±0.0**	0.0±0.0**	0.0±0.0**
Mor+Nal.I	0.1	0	5.6	8.3±2.5	26.3±11.6	3.5±0.7
Mor+Nal.I	0.5	100	—	0.0±0.0**	0.0±0.0**	0.0±0.0**
Mor+Veh.2		0	3.5	13.1±2.1	54.4±10.9	7.3±1.0
Mor+M8008	0.05	0	5.0	10.8±1.6	35.5±10.0	6.0±1.4
Mor+M8008	0.075	50	16.4	4.0±3.1*	19.8±17.8	1.5±1.0*
Mor+M8008	0.1	100	—	0.0±0.0**	0.0±0.0*	0.0±0.0*
Mor+MR2266	0.025	0	6.3	9.5±3.0	47.3±12.6	4.8±1.4
Mor+MR2266	0.05	25	6.6	2.5±1.2*	11.3±5.9*	1.5±1.0
Mor+MR2266	0.075	80	4.3	2.2±2.2*	8.6±8.6*	1.4±1.4
Mor+Veh.3		0	2.3	10.7±1.4	52.3±11.6	4.8±1.4
Mor+Naltrin.	0.05	0	2.7	9.0±0.9	36.0±2.5	5.5±0.3
Mor+Naltrin.	0.1	0	4.8	7.5±2.8	23.0±11.3*	2.0±1.2
Mor+Naltrin.	1.0	100	—	0.0±0.0*	0.0±0.0*	0.0±0.0*

Results represent the means±s.e.m. of 4-8 determinations. Significant differences between respective vehicle-treated animals and drug treated animals is indicated as *P<0.05; **P<0.01 (Mann-Whitney U test). Latency to first retch or vomit is indicated in min and represents the mean time to either the first retch or vomit.

Conclusions

Morphine-induced emesis in the ferret appears to be mediated by agonist action at kappa>μ> and delta opioid receptors. The antagonism afforded by naloxone methyliodide suggests that these receptors could be located outside the blood-brain-barrier, supporting previous observations with similar compounds in the dog (Foss et al., 1989; Hersom & MacKenzie, 1987). The site of action is likely to be at the area postrema as the blood brain barrier at this site is permeable to macromolecules (Torac & Finke, 1971). The present studies may indicate a difference between the ferret and the dog, as in the dog kappa agonists have been reported to have an antiemetic profile against drug-induced emesis (Blancquaert *et al.*, 1986) and do not effect morphine-induced emesis (Hersom & MacKenzie, 1987), whereas in the present study in the ferret, the kappa antagonist MR2266 prevented morphine-induced emesis.

References

Barnes, N.M., Bunce, K.T., Rudd, J.A. & Naylor, R.J. (1991) The actions of fentanyl to inhibit drug-induced emesis. Neuropharmacol. 30, 1073-1083.

Blancquaert, J. P., Lefebvre, R. A. and Willems, J. L. (1986) Emetic and antiemetic effects of opioids in the dog. Eur. J. Pharmacol. 128: 143-150.

Costello, D. J. and Borison, H. L. (1977) Naloxone antagonizes narcotic self-blockade of emesis in the cat. J. Pharmacol. Exp. Ther. 203: 222-230.

Foss, J. F., Bass, A. S. and Goldberg, L. I. (1989) Peripheral antagonism of the emetic effect of morphine by methylnaltrexone. Clin. Res. 37: 595A.

Hersom, J. & MacKenzie, J.E.. (1987) Opioid receptors involved in emesis in the dog. Br. J. Pharmacol. 92 (Suppl): 648P.

Torack, R.M. & Finke, E.H. (1971) Evidence for a sequestration of function within the area postrema basal on scanning electron microscopy and the penetration of horseradish peroxidase. Z. Zellforsch. 118, 85-96.

Wang, S. C. and Galviaro, V. (1954) Locus of emetic action of morphine and hydergine in dogs. Pharmaol. Exp. Ther. 111: 329-344.

Aknowledgement: We are grateful to Boehringer Ingelheim for the gift of MR226.

Mechanisms and Control of Emesis. Eds A.L. Bianchi, L. Grélot, A.D. Miller, G.L. King. Colloque INSERM/
John Libbey Eurotext Ltd. © 1992, Vol. 223, pp. 353-354

Differential blocking effects of buspirone and 8-OH-DPAT on vagal-induced emesis in decerebrate cats

Stéphane Milano and Laurent Grélot

Département de Physiologie et Neurophysiologie, CNRS URA 205, Faculté des Sciences et Techniques Saint-Jérôme, 13397 Marseille Cedex 13, France

Recent investigations report that buspirone and (8-hydroxy-2- (di-n-propylamine) tetralin (8-OH-DPAT) are very effective in blocking cisplatin- and xylazine-induced vomiting, and motion sickness in the cat (see the chapter by Lucot in this book). At the present time, in human, buspirone, a partial agonist at 5-hydroxytryptamine 1A receptors, and 8-OH-DPAT, a more selective agonist at the same receptors, are only used as anxiolytic. Their efficacy in blocking vomiting evoked by the activation of different afferent systems suggests that buspirone and 8-OH-DPAT might act directly on the brainstem neural circuitry responsible for the integration of the afferent stimuli and generation of the emetic response (i.e. "the vomiting center"). In the present work, we tested the antiemetic properties of these pharmacological agents on vagal-induced vomiting.

In 16 decerebrate, paralyzed and artificially ventilated cats, vomiting was induced by electrical stimulation of both supradiaphragmatic vagus nerves (0.9 ms duration, 25 Hz, 30-45 volts). In order to limit the effect of individual refractoriness to vagal stimulation, electrical shocks were applied only each 30 min. In this experimental model (for details see the chapter by Grélot and Bianchi in this book) vomiting is characterized by a series of synchronous bursts in both phrenic and abdominal muscle nerves (retches) culminating in a prolonged discharge in the abdominal nerves (expulsion). For the pharmacological trials, we selected cats which responded to two successive vagal stimulations (control 1 and 2). Subsequently, five minutes before vagal stimulation, single doses of buspirone (1, 2, 3 or 4 mg/kg, in 1 ml saline, iv) or 8-OH-DPAT (0.2, 0.6, 1 or 1.3 mg/kg, in 1 ml saline, iv) were administrated to 8 cats, respectively. The antiemetic effects of the drugs were statistically evaluated (Wilcoxon's signed-rank test for paired comparisons) on the following parameters : i/ the latency of vomiting, ii/ the pattern of emesis (i.e. the number of retches and expulsions) and iii/ the duration of the blocking effect, defined as the absence of an emetic episode during a 5 min vagal stimulation.

At every dose, buspirone suppressed vagal-induced emesis in 6/8 cats. The duration of the blocking effect was significantly correlated to the administrated dose (Fig. 1). The potency of 8-OH-DPAT in blocking vagal-induced vomiting seemed to be less than buspirone since 8-OH-DPAT prevented vomiting in only 2/8 cats. However, in the 6 remaining ones, the latency of the emetic episode was significantly increased ($p<0.05$), and this effect was correlated to the dose administrated (Fig. 2). The pattern of emesis appeared unchanged by 8-OH-DPAT treatment.

In conclusion, the present investigation reveals that buspirone is more effective than 8-OH-DPAT to prevent vagal-induced emesis in the cat. So far, the explanation for this differential antiemetic effect of 5-HT1A agonists is speculative. Further investigations are needed to determine if the blocking effect of buspirone in this model may be due to its possible action on the dopaminergic D2 receptors.

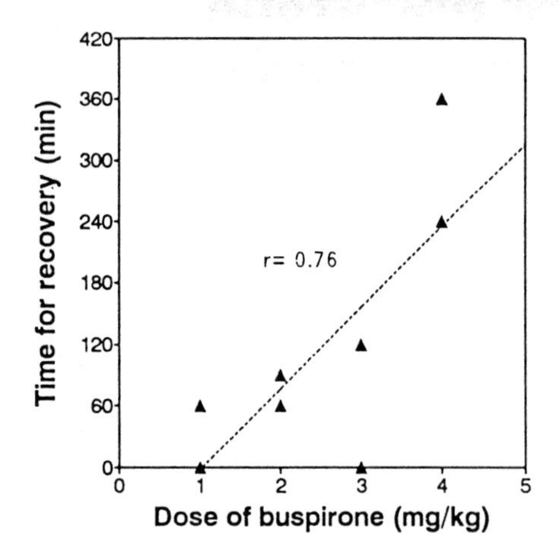

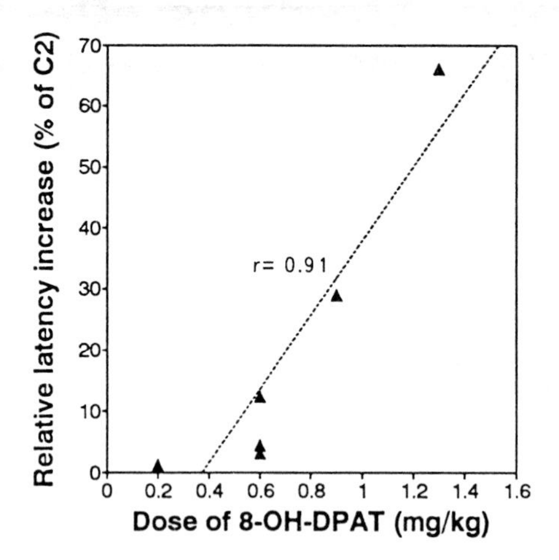

Fig. 1: Dose-response curve of the antiemetic effect of buspirone (n=8). Time for recovery quoted to zero indicate the absence of blocking effect on vagal-induced vomiting (n=2). Hatched line and r are the regression line and the Pearson coefficient (r=0.76), respectively. Note the positive correlation ($p<0.05$) between the duration of the blocking effect of buspirone and the administrated dose.

Fig. 2: Effect of 8-OH-DPAT on the latency of the emetic episode (n=6). The increase in latency associated to 8-OH-DPAT treatment is expressed in percent of the latency of the second control (C2) emetic episode. Hatched line and r are the regression line and the Pearson coefficient (r=0.91), respectively. Note the positive correlation ($p<0.05$) between the increase of the latency and the administrated dose.

This work was supported by grants from the Direction des Recherches, Etudes et Techniques (DRET, 90/108) and the CNRS (URA 205).

Grélot, L. and Bianchi, A.L. (1992). Activities of cranial and spinal respiratory-related motoneurons during vomiting. In: New vistas on Mechanisms and Control of Emesis. Ed. A.L. Bianchi, L. Grélot, A.D. Miller and G.L. King. Colloque INSERM: John Libbey Eurotext LTd. vol 223.

Lucot, J.B. (1992). Prevention of motion sickness by 5-HT1A agonists in cats. In: New vistas on Mechanisms and Control of Emesis. Ed. A.L. Bianchi, L. Grélot, A.D. Miller and G.L. King. Colloque INSERM: John Libbey Eurotext LTd. vol 223.

Mechanisms and Control of Emesis. Eds A.L. Bianchi, L. Grélot, A.D. Miller, G.L. King. Colloque INSERM/
John Libbey Eurotext Ltd. © 1992, Vol. 223, pp. 355-356

Peptide-induced emesis in cats

Ranka Samardžić, Danica Jovanović-Mićić, Nina Japundžić,
Slobodan Janković and Dušan B. Beleslin

Department of Pharmacology, Medical Faculty, P.O. Box 662, 11000 Belgrade, Serbia, Yugoslavia

The emetic action of several neuropeptides has been described in dogs, cats and pigeons (Kaneko & Uchiyama, 1979; Beleslin **et al.**, 1982; Carpenter **et al.**, 1984). However, these studies have not provided conclusive evidence on the role of peptides in the regulation of emesis. In the present study, the emetic action of opioid and some other biologically active peptides injected into the cerebral ventricles of unanaesthetized cats was investigated and compared to morphine-induced emesis.

In an aseptic operation under pentobarbitone sodium (35-40 mg/kg) anaesthesia, an infusion cannula was implanted into the left lateral cerebral ventricle of cats of either sex (2-3.5 kg), so that intracerebroventricular (icv) injections could be made without anaesthesia. Only expulsion of the gastric content was considered as a positive emetic response.

The results are presented in Table 1.

Table 1

The emetic effect of morphine and peptides injected into the cerebral ventricles of unanaesthetized cats.

Drugs	Doses	Number of cats vomited/tested	Relative emetic potency
morphine	0.002-4.0 mg	35/63	55.5 %
μ-agonist (DAGO[1])	0.00002-0.1 mg	5/26	19.2 %
met-enkephalin	0.05-1.0 mg	4/23	17.6 %
leu-enkephalin	0.1-1.0 mg	3/17	17.6 %
β-endorphin	0.01-0.4 mg	1/25	4.0 %
dynorphin	0.1-0.2 mg	0/5	0 %
insulin (human)	1.2-12 i.u.	0/5	0 %

insulin (porcine)	1.2-12 i.u.	0/8	0 %
VIP	0.01-0.3 mg	0/7	0 %
angiotensin II	0.01-0.1 mg	0/20	0 %
octreoitide[2]	0.001-0.3 mg	0/22	0 %
TRH	0.1-1.0 mg	0/66	0 %
glucagon	0.25-3.0 mg	0/8	0 %
GHRF (human)[3]	0.01-0.3 mg	1/10	10 %
thymopentin[4]	0.1-10.0 mg	5/26	34.6 %
controls (0.9 % NaCl)	0.1-0.3 ml	0/10	0 %

[1] Synthetic polypeptide (Tyr-D-Ala-Gly-MePhe-NH$(CH_2)_2$OH)
[2] Synthetic somatostatin analogue (SANDOSTATIN^R)
[3] Recombinant human growth hormone-releasing factor h GHRF (1-29)NH_2
[4] Synthetic pentapeptide (Ang-Lys-Asp-Val-Tyr) 32-36 amino-acid fraction of thymopoietin.

These results show that of 14 different peptides injected icv in unanaesthetized cats, only 6 induced vomiting. The percentage of animals showing emesis after icv injection of these peptides, as well as morphine, was rather low, randomly distributed and unrelated to the doses of the drugs. Foregoing experimental data indicate that the emetic activity varies in different species: thus, angiotensin II, VIP and TRH provoke emesis in dogs (Carpenter ***et al.***, 1984), glucagon evoked vomiting in pigeons (Kaneko & Uchiyama, 1979), whereas they have no such effects in cats. On the other hand, opioid peptides and morphine induce emesis in most species, including man. In the present experiments, only 55 % of cats showed vomiting responses to morphine. The emetic activity of enkephalins and μ-agonist was about 1/3 of the emetic activity of morphine, whereas the emetic action of β-endorphin was very low, while dynorphin, which is predominantly κ-agonist, did not induce emesis in cats. In addition, the vomiting response to opioid agonists was completely prevented by nalorphine. These findings suggest that their action is mediated mostly through the μ subtype of opioid receptors (Beleslin ***et al.***, 1982).

The inconsistency, the lack of dose-response relationship and marked species differences indicate that, except opioids, which may have a modulatory role, other peptidergic mechanisms have little or no influence on the regulation of vomiting reflex in cats.

This work was supported by a grant of the Scientific Fund of Serbia.

REFERENCES

Beleslin, D.B., Samardžić, R., Krstić, S. & Mićić, D. (1982): Differences in central effects of β-endorphin and enkephalins: β endorphin, a potent psychomotor stimulant. *Neuropharmacology* 21, 99-102.

Carpenter, D.O., Briggs, D.B. & Strominger, N. (1984): Behavioural and electrophysiological studies of peptides-induced emesis in dogs. *Fed. Proc.* 43, 2952-2954.

Kaneko, A. & Uchiyama, T. (1979): Emetic action of glucagon (2): A pharmacodynamic analysis of emetic mechanism using pigeons. *Toho Igakkai Zasshi (J. med. Soc. Toho, Japan)* 26, 431-450.

Mechanisms and Control of Emesis. Eds A.L. Bianchi, L. Grélot, A.D. Miller, G.L. King. Colloque INSERM/ John Libbey Eurotext Ltd. © 1992, Vol. 223, p. 357

Evaluation of a predictive algorithm for the human emetic response to protracted irradiation using ferret data

Gene E. McClellan, George H. Anno, Gregory L. King *
and Robert W. Young **

*Pacific-Sierra Research Corporation, 1401 Wilson Boulevard, Arlington, VA 22209, USA; * Department of Physiology, Armed Forces Radiobiology Research Institute, Bethesda, MD 20889-5145, USA; and ** Radiation Policy Division, Defence Nuclear Agency, Alexandria, VA 22310-3398, USA*

A mathematical model has been developed to describe the human emetic response to both acute and protracted doses of ionizing radiation (Anno and McClellan, this conference). Existing human data have been used to evaluate this model for acute-dose irradiation. On the other hand, human data from protracted-dose exposures are too sparse to permit such evaluation. This poster describes the use of ferret data to test the predictive capability of the model's algorithm for protracted-dose response.

We assume that if the algorithm can predict the protracted-dose response in ferrets using parameters developed from ferret acute-dose data, then the algorithm can, with reasonable confidence, predict the protracted-dose response in humans using parameters developed from the human acute-dose data. Examination of acute dose data from ferrets (King, 1988; Davis, 1989) indicates that their emetic response is qualitatively similar to that of humans (Anno et al., 1989) and that it can be scaled to the human response for both dose and latency of response. Model predictions (Anno et al., 1991) of ferret emetic response to both continuous and fractionated exposures have been used to design experiments on the protracted-dose response of the ferret.

Data and model calculations for time-dependent severity of emesis in both humans and ferrets will be compared for acute irradiation. Also, the model predictions for the ferret emetic response to low-dose rate and fractionated exposures will be presented. The results of ongoing ferret experiments will test predictions of the model and provide guidance for final development of the human model.

REFERENCES

Anno, G. H., Baum, S. J., Withers, H. R., and Young, R. W. (1989): Symptomatology of Acute Radiation Effects in Humans After Doses of 0.5-30 Gy. *Health Phys.* 56, 821-838.

Anno, G. H., McClellan, G. E., Dore, M. A., and Baum, S. J. (1991): Biological Effects of Protracted Exposure to Ionizing Radiation: Review, Analysis, and Model Development. Tech. Rep. DNA-TR-90-157, Defense Nuclear Agency, Alexandria, VA, USA.

Davis, C. J. (1989): Neuropharmacological Investigations into the Mechanisms of Emesis Caused by Cytotoxic Drugs and Radiation. Ph.D. Thesis, Oxford University, Oxford, UK.

King, G.L. (1988): Characterization of Radiation-induced Emesis in the Ferret. *Radiat. Res.* 114, 599-612.

Mechanisms and Control of Emesis. Eds A.L. Bianchi, L. Grélot, A.D. Miller, G.L. King. Colloque INSERM/ John Libbey Eurotext Ltd. © 1992, Vol. 223, pp. 359-360

Pyrogallol, a generator of free radicals, is emetogenic in *Suncus murinus*

Yoshifumi Torii, Hiroshi Saito and Norio Matsuki

Department of Chemical Pharmacology, Faculty of Pharmaceutical Sciences, The University of Tokyo, Tokyo 113, Japan

We have shown previously that cisplatin increased thiobarbituric acid value, which indicates the degree of lipid peroxidation, in *Suncus murinus* (house musk shrew), a species of insectivore, and that cisplatin-induced emesis was prevented by intraperitoneal administration of N-(2-mercaptopropionyl)-glycine (MPG), an antioxidant (Torii *et al.*, 1992). In the present study, we investigated effects of pyrogallol, a generator of free radicals. Pyrogallol (i.p.) caused emesis in suncus and ED_{50} value calculated by Brownlee's up-and-down method was 77.3 mg/kg (Table 1). At the dose of 128 mg/kg, all suncus vomited with latency of 18.8±5.2 min and the number of vomiting episodes was 8.6±2.9 (n=5). Then prophylactic effects of MPG and tropisetron (5-HT_3 receptor antagonist) were studied. These agents were injected 30 min prior to administration of pyrogallol (128 mg/kg, i.p.). Pyrogallol-induced emesis was prevented by treatment with MPG (i.p.) or tropisetron (s.c.) with respective ID_{50} value of 149 mg/kg and 117 µg/kg (Table 2). We also investigated whether surgical vagotomy had any effect on pyrogallol-

Table 1. Emetic effect of pyrogallol in *Suncus murinus*

Dose (mg/kg)	No. of suncus vomited/tested	No. of vomiting episodes	Latency (min)	ED_{50} value (mg/kg)
128	5/5	8.6±2.9	18.8±5.2	77.3
64	1/5	3	23	
32	0/1	—	—	

Values for the number of vomiting episodes and the latency per vomited suncus are mean±SEM, but actual values are indicated when the number of vomiting suncus was less than three.
—, No suncus vomited at the dose.

Table 2. Prophylactic effects of MPG and tropisetron (ICS205-930) on pyrogallol (128 mg/kg, i.p.)-induced emesis in *Suncus murinus*

Treatment	Dose	No. of suncus vomited/tested	No. of vomiting episodes	Latency (min)	ID_{50} value
MPG (i.p)	320(mg/kg)	0/2	—	—	149(mg/kg)
	160	2/5	3, 3	14, 16	
	80	3/3	7.0 ± 2.1	16.3 ± 3.4	
	control	1/1	7	12	
tropisetron (s.c.)	1000(μg/kg)	0/1	—	—	117(μg/kg)
	500	0/1	—	—	
	250	0/3	—	—	
	125	2/5	2, 1	4, 12	
	63	3/3	3.7 ± 1.8	5.0	
	control	1/1	12	13	

induced emesis. The method of surgical vagotomy has been detailed elsewhere (Torii *et al.*, 1991[a]). In short, suncus was anesthetized with ether, and the vagus together with the the serous membrane surrounding the esophagus were isolated and cut about 1 cm from the stomach. Pyrogallol-induced emesis was completely prevented by the surgical vagotomy (n=5). The emesis seems to be very similar to cisplatin (20 mg/kg, i.p.)-induced emesis. Administration of tropisetron, MPG and vagotomy have prophylactic effects on cisplatin-induced emesis (Torii *et al.*, 1991[b]). Serotonin (10 mg/kg, i.p.) also causes emesis in suncus (Torii *et al.*, 1991[a]). Serotonin-induced emesis is prevented by administration of tropisetron or vagotomy but not inhibited by treatment with MPG. These results suggest that generation of free radicals causes the release of peripheral 5-HT, which stimulates afferent sensory nerves to cause emesis.

REFERENCES

Torii, Y., Saito, H. & Matsuki, N. (1992): Mechanism of cisplatin-induced emesis in *Suncus murinus*. *Jpn. J. Pharmacol.* **58**, 313P.

Torii, Y., Saito, H. & Matsuki, N. (1991[a]): 5-Hydroxytryptamine is emetogenic in the house musk shrew, *Suncus murinus*. *Naunyn-Schmiedeberg's Arch. Pharmacol.* **344**, 564-567.

Torii, Y., Saito, H. & Matsuki, N. (1991[b]): Selective blockade of cytotoxic drugs-induced emesis by 5-HT_3 receptor antagonists in *Suncus murinus*. *Jpn. J. Pharmacol.* **55**, 107-113.

Mechanisms and Control of Emesis. Eds A.L. Bianchi, L. Grélot, A.D. Miller, G.L. King. Colloque INSERM/ John Libbey Eurotext Ltd. © 1992, Vol. 223, pp. 361-362

Cytokines, hormones and pregnancy sickness

R. Sievers, G.V.P. Chamberlain * and S.A. Whitehead

*Departments of Physiology and Obstetrics and Gynaecology *, St. George's Hospital Medical School, Cranmer Terrace, London, SW17 ORE, UK*

There is increasing evidence for a role of cytokines in the maternal immune response to the fetal allograft and in the growth and survival of the fetus (see Banks et al., 1991). While most studies have shown that cytokines act locally at the fetal-maternal interface, there is evidence that circulating levels may increase during pregnancy (Favier et al., 1990). They would thus have the potential to act at distant target sites. Since cytokines have been implicated as mediators of the sickness behaviour which accompanies the response to an infection (see Kent et al., 1992), the question arose as to whether circulating cytokines may induce the common symptoms of early pregnancy - notably nausea, vomiting and fatigue.

Three cytokines, interleukin (IL)-2, IL-6 and tumour necrosis factor α (TNFα) have been measured in plasma samples of 46 pregnant women (11-12 weeks pregnant) and in 29 non-pregnant, age-matched controls. Circulating levels of oestradiol, progesterone and human chorionic gonadotrophin (hCG) were also measured from the same samples and participants of the study completed a detailed questionnaire which provided information about the incidence, onset and frequency of nausea and vomiting in pregnancy, recent occurrences of infections and a range of sociobiological factors which have been correlated with the incidence of pregnancy sickness. Cytokines were measured with an ELISA system (Amersham, U.K.) and all other hormones with standard radioimmunoassays (Immunodiagnostic Systems Ltd., U.K.).

The proportion of women who had detectable circulating concentrations of different cytokines were similar in pregnant and non-pregnant controls and there were no significant differences in the mean concentration of the cytokines between the two groups of women (Table 1). There were significantly higher concentrations of circulating IL-6 ($p<0.05$, Student's t-test) in those women who reported vomiting (2.5 ± 0.56 pg/ml) or nausea (1.81 ± 0.37 pg/ml) compared to those women who had no symptoms (0.92 ± 0.17 pg/ml and 0.79 ± 0.17 pg/ml respectively). However, there were no correlations between circulating concentrations of IL-2 and the incidence of pregnancy sickness, while the number of women who had measurable levels of TNFα were too small for any statistical comparisons. Raised circulating levels of either IL-2 or IL-6 were not associated with higher or lower incidence of nausea and vomiting compared to women who had no detectable IL-2 or IL-6 in their plasma samples (Fig. 1).

Cytokine	Pregnant pg/ml	Control pg/ml
IL-2	20.8 ± 2.9 (14/30%)	18.0 ± 1.2 (5/17%)
IL-6	1.5 ± 0.25 (24/52%)	1.7 ± 0.5 (13/45%)
TNFα	19.5 ± 5.3 (8/17%)	21.8 ± 3.2 (4/14%)

Table 1. Mean plasma concentrations levels (± S.E.) of interleukin (IL)-2, IL-6 and tumour necrosis factor α (TNFα) that could be measured in the plasma of 46 pregnant women and 29 non-pregnant controls. The figures in brackets give the total number/percentage of women in each group who had circulating levels of cytokines above the lower limit of sensitivity of each specific assay. These limits were 10pg/ml for IL-2, 0.35 pg/ml for IL-6 and 7.5 pg/ml for TNFα.

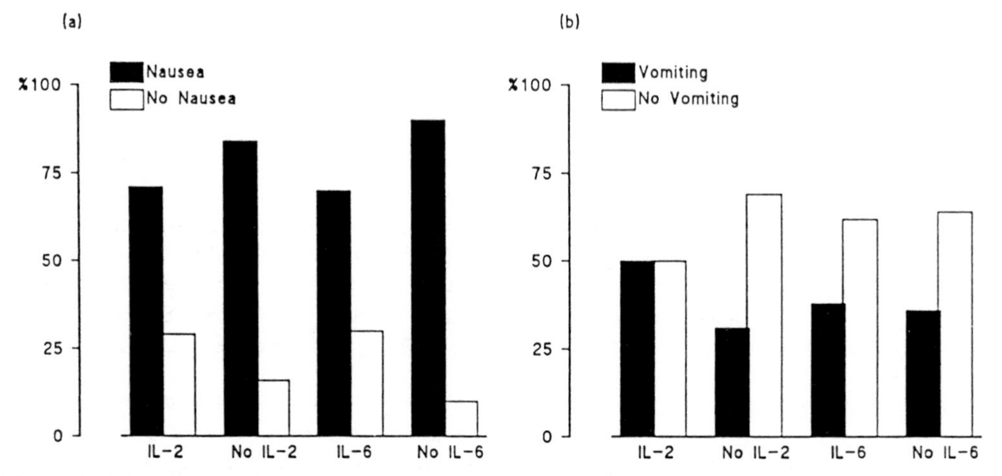

Figure 1. The relationship between pregnancy sickness and raised levels of circulating IL-2 and IL-6. The histograms show the incidence of (a) nausea and (b) vomiting in all women who had detectable levels of either IL-2 or IL-6 compared with those who had no detectable circulating levels.

Finally, there were no notable correlations between the measurements of cytokines and circulating oestrogen, progesterone or hCG, nor were there any correlations between these hormones and the incidence of pregnancy sickness. Thus these data show that the maternal immune response to pregnancy does not cause an overall increase in the circulating levels of certain cytokines compared with non-pregnant controls and that there is no obvious association between circulating cytokines and the incidence of pregnancy sickness.

References

Banks, R.E., Evans, S.W. and Whicher, J.T. (1991): Polypeptide regulatory factors in pregnancy. *Contemp. Rev. Obstet. Gynaecol.* 3,22-29

Favier, R., Edelman, P., Mary, J.Y., Sadoul, G. and Douay, L. (1990): Presence of elevated serum interleukin-2 levels in pregnant women. *N. Engl. J. Med. 322, 270.*

Kent, S., Bluthe, R., Kelley, K.W. and Dantzer, R. (1992): Sickness behavior as a new target for drug development. *Trends in Pharmacological Sciences* 131,24-28.

Mechanisms and Control of Emesis. Eds A.L. Bianchi, L. Grélot, A.D. Miller, G.L. King. Colloque INSERM/ John Libbey Eurotext Ltd. © 1992, Vol. 223, pp. 363-364

Vomiting: incidence, causes, ageing and sex

R. Rub, P.L.R. Andrews and S.A. Whitehead

Department of Physiology, St. George's Hospital Medical School, Cranmer Terrace, London, SW17 ORE, UK

There is little available data on the incidence and causes of vomiting and nausea in an otherwise healthy population and this prompted us to undertake a survey which would help to define these paramters and to examine the influence of age and sex on the emetic response. Questionnaires were completed by 596 participants recruited from church and social groups, government offices, banks, schools, family planning clinics, nursing groups and day centres for the elderly. The majority of questionnaires were self-administered although with some of the elderly participants they were completed by an interview technique. Questionnaires were analysed with the SPSS/PC+ software package and Chi-square tests were used to determine significance of contingency tables.

There were 65% female and 35% male participants with ages ranging from 18-91 years. The overall incidence of vomiting or nausea at least once in the 12 months prior to completing the questionnaire was 39% and 54% respectively. There was no significant association between the incidence of symptoms and gender although a higher frequency of nausea, but not vomiting, was reported amongst women as compared with men ($X^2=15.2$, d.f.$=2$, $p<0.005$). In contrast, when the population was grouped according to age (18-30 yrs., n=215, 31-60 yrs., n=197 and >60 yrs., n=185) there was a highly significant decrease in the incidence of both vomiting ($X^2=103.1$, d.f.$=2$, $p<0.0001$) and nausea ($X^2=114.1$, d.f.$=2$, $p<0.0001$) with increasing age (Fig. 1).

The major causes of vomiting amongst the whole population are shown in Figure 2. However, analysis confirmed that the percentage of vomiting from different causes changed according to both age and sex. For example, there was an expected reduction in the incidence of vomiting due to alcohol and food poisoning in elderly people while that caused by binge eating and induced vomiting was higher amongst women.

There was no significant correlation in the incidence or frequency of vomiting and nausea between women who were using oral contraceptives (n=70) and those using other forms of contraception (n=163). On the other hand, post menopausal women (n=175) were less likely to vomit ($X^2=53.1$, d.f.$=1$, $p<0.0001$) or feel nauseous ($X^2=74.89$, d.f.$=1$, $p<0.0001$) compared with those women who were still menstruating (n=217).

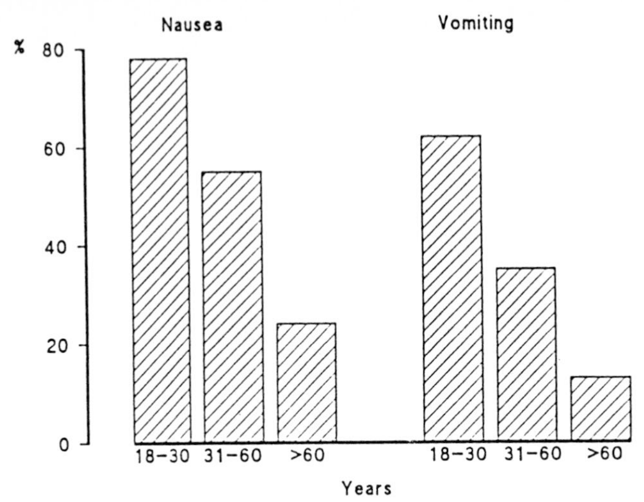

Figure 1. The percentage of individuals in each age group who reported the occurrence of vomiting or nausea at least once during the 12 months prior to completing the questionnaire.

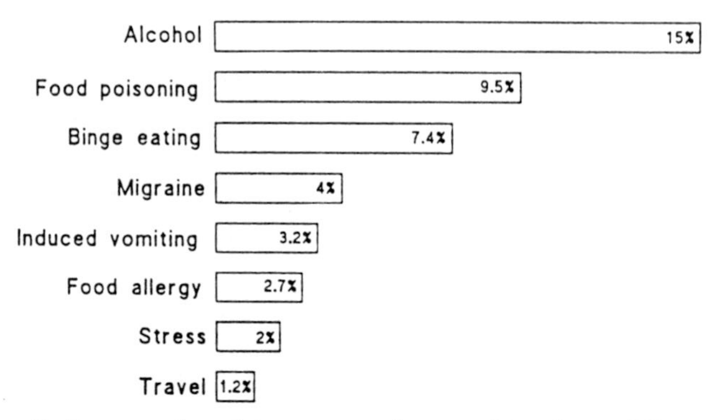

Figure 2. Percent of participants reporting vomiting from different causes.

The results show an age-dependency in the incidence of emesis and support the evidence that many autonomic functions become altered with age (Korkushko et al., 1991, Nowak et al., 1990). However, social factors undoubtably have an important influence on the incidence of emesis in relation to age and thus social as well as physiological factors need to be considered in parallel. The reduced incidence of vomiting and nausea in post-menopausal women is interesting in view of the fact that several lines of evidence suggest that female sex steroids may alter the threshold of the emetic reflex (Andrews & Whitehead, 1990, Beattie et al., 1991, Roila et al., 1988) While the loss of ovarian steroids in post-menopausal women could reverse this effect, the influence of age cannot be discounted.

References

Andrews, P, & Whitehead, S.A. (1990): *News in Physiological Sciences*. 5, 5-10.
Beattie, W.S., Lindblad, T. & Buckley, N.D. (1991): *Can. J. Anaesth.* 38, 298-302.
Korkushko, O.V., Shatilo, V.B., Plachnida, Yu. I. & Shatilo, T.V. (1991): *J. Auton. Nerv. Syst.* 32, 191-198.
Nowak, T.V., Harrington, B. & Kalbfleisch, J. (1990): *J. Pharmacol. Exp. Ther.* 253, 683-687.
Roila, F., Tonato, M. & Basurto, C. (1988): *J. Clin. Oncol.* 5, 141-149.

Author index
Index des auteurs

Colloques **INSERM**
ISSN 0768-3154

Other *Colloques* published as co-editions by John Libbey Eurotext and INSERM

153 Hormones and Cell Regulation (11th European Symposium). *Hormones et Régulation Cellulaire (11e Symposium Européen).*
Edited by J. Nunez and J.E. Dumont.
ISBN : John Libbey Eurotext 0 86196 104 8
INSERM 2 85598 324 X

158 Biochemistry and Physiopathology of Platelet Membrane. *Biochimie et Physiopathologie de la Membrane Plaquettaire.*
Edited by G. Marguerie and R.F.A. Zwaal.
ISBN : John Libbey Eurotext 0 86196 114 5
INSERM 2 85598 345 2

162 The Inhibitors of Hematopoiesis. *Les Inhibiteurs de l'Hématopoïèse.*
Edited by A. Najman, M. Guignon, N.C. Gorin and J.Y. Mary.
ISBN : John Libbey Eurotext 0 86196 125 0
INSERM 2 85598 340 1

164 Liver Cells and Drugs. *Cellules Hépatiques et Médicaments.*
Edited by A. Guillouzo.
ISBN : John Libbey Eurotext 0 86196 128 5
INSERM 2 85598 341 X

165 Hormones and Cell Regulation (12th European Symposium). *Hormones et Régulation Cellulaire (12e Symposium Européen).*
Edited by J. Nunez, J.E. Dumont and E. Carafoli.
ISBN : John Libbey Eurotext 0 86196 133 1
INSERM 2 85598 347 9

167 Sleep Disorders and Respiration. *Les Evénements Respiratoires du Sommeil.*
Edited by P. Lévi-Valensi and D. Duron.
ISBN : John Libbey Eurotext 0 86196 127 7
INSERM 2 85598 344 4

169 Neo-Adjuvant Chemotherapy. *Chimiothérapie Néo-Adjuvante.*
Edited by C. Jacquillat, M. Weil, D. Khayat.
ISBN : John Libbey Eurotext 0 86196 150 1
INSERM 2 85598 349 5

171 Structure and Functions of the Cytoskeleton. *La Structure et les Fonctions du Cytosquelette.*
Edited by B.A.F. Rousset.
ISBN : John Libbey Eurotext 0 86196 149 8
INSERM 2 85598 351 7

Colloques INSERM
ISSN 0768-3154

172 The Langerhans Cell. *La Cellule de Langerhans.*
Edited by J. Thivolet, D. Schmitt.
ISBN : John Libbey Eurotext 0 86196 181 1
INSERM 2 85598 352 5

173 Cellular and Molecular Aspects of Glucuronidation. *Aspects Cellulaires et Moléculaires de la Glucuronoconjugaison.*
Edited by G. Siest, J. Magdalou, B. Burchell
ISBN : John Libbey Eurotext 0 86196 182 X
INSERM 2 85598 353 3

174 Second Forum on Peptides. *Deuxième Forum Peptides.*
Edited by A. Aubry, M. Marraud, B. Vitoux
ISBN : John Libbey Eurotext 0 86196 151 X
INSERM 2 85598 354 1

176 Hormones and Cell Regulation (13th European Symposium). *Hormones et Régulation Cellulaire (13e Symposium Européen).*
Edited by J. Nunez, J.E. Dumont, R. Denton
ISBN : John Libbey Eurotext 0 86196 183 8
INSERM 2 85598 356 8

179 Lymphokine Receptors Interactions. *Interactions Lymphokines-récepteurs.*
Edited by D. Fradelizi, J. Bertoglio
ISBN : John Libbey Eurotext 0 86196 148 X
INSERM 2 85598 359 2

191 Anticancer Drugs (1st International Interface of Clinical and Laboratory responses to anticancer drugs). *Médicaments anticancéreux (1re Confrontation internationale des réponses cliniques et expérimentales aux médicaments anticancéreux).*
Edited by H. Tapiero, J. Robert, T.J. Lampidis
ISBN : John Libbey Eurotext 0 86196 223 0
INSERM 2 85598 393 2

193 Living in the Cold (2nd International Symposium). *La Vie au Froid (2e Symposium International).*
Edited by A. Malan, B. Canguilhem
ISBN : John Libbey Eurotext 0 86196 234 9
INSERM 2 85598 395 9

Colloques INSERM
ISSN 0768-3154

194 Progress in Hepatitis B Immunization. *La Vaccination contre l'épatite B.*
Edited by P. Coursaget, M.J. Tong
ISBN : John Libbey Eurotext 0 86196 249 4
INSERM 2 85598 396 7

196 Treatment Strategy in Hodgkin's Disease. *Stratégie dans la maladie de Hodgkin.*
Edited by P. Sommers, M. Henry-Amar, J.H. Meezwaldt, P. Carde
ISBN : John Libbey Eurotext 0 86196 226 5
INSERM 2 85598 398 3

198 Hormones and Cell Regulation (14th European Symposium). *Hormones et Régulation Cellulaire (14e Symposium Européen).*
Edited by J. Nunez, J.E. Dumont
ISBN : John Libbey Eurotext 0 86196 229 X
INSERM 2 85598 400 9

199 Placental Communications : Biochemical, Morphological and Cellular Aspects. *Communications placentaires : aspects biochimique, morphologique et cellulaire.*
Edited by L. Cedard, E. Alsat, J.C. Challier, G. Chaouat, A. Malassiné
ISBN : John Libbey Eurotext 0 86196 227 3
INSERM 2 85598 401 7

204 Pharmacologie Clinique : Actualités et Perspectives. (6e Rencontres Nationales de Pharmacologie clinique).
Edited by J.P. Boissel, C. Caulin, M. Teule
ISBN : John Libbey Eurotext 0 86196 225 7
INSERM 2 85598 454 8

205 Recent Trends in Clinical Pharmacology (6th National Meeting of Clinical Pharmacology).
Edited by J.P. Boissel, C. Caulin, M. Teule
ISBN : John Libbey Eurotext 0 86196 256 7
INSERM 2 85598 455 6

206 Platelet Immunology : Fundamental and Clinical Aspects. *Immunologie plaquettaire : aspects fondamentaux et cliniques.*
Edited by C. Kaplan-Gouet, N. Schlegel, Ch. Salmon, J. McGregor
ISBN : John Libbey Eurotext 0 86196 285 0
INSERM 2 85598 439 4

Colloques INSERM
ISSN 0768-3154

207 Thyroperoxidase and Thyroid Autoimmunity. *Thyroperoxydase et auto-immunité thyroïdienne.*
Edited by P. Carayon, T. Ruf
ISBN : John Libbey Eurotext 0 86196 277 X
INSERM 2 85598 440 8

208 Vasopressin. *Vasopressine.*
Edited by S. Jard, R. Jamison
ISBN : John Libbey Eurotext 0 86196 288 5
INSERM 2 85598 441 6

210 Hormones and Cell Regulation (15th European Symposium). *Hormones et Régulation Cellulaire (15e Symposium Européen).*
Edited by J.E. Dumont, J. Nunez, R.J.B. King
ISBN : John Libbey Eurotext 0 86196 279 6
INSERM 2 85598 443 2

211 Medullary Thyroid Carcinoma. *Cancer Médullaire de la Thyroïde.*
Edited by C. Calmettes, J.M. Guliana
ISBN : John Libbey Eurotext 0 86196 287 7
INSERM 2 85598 440 0

212 Cellular and Molecular Biology of the Materno-Fetal Relationship. *Biologie cellulaire et moléculaire de la relation materno-fœtale.*
Edited by G. Chaouat, J. Mowbray
ISBN : John Libbey Eurotext 0 86196 909 1
INSERM 2 85598 445 9

215 Aldosterone. Fundamental Aspects. *Aspects fondamentaux.*
Edited by J.P. Bonvalet, N. Farman, M. Lombes, M.E. Rafestin-Oblin
ISBN : John Libbey Eurotext 0 86196 302 4
INSERM 2 85598 482 3

216 Cellular and Molecular Aspects of Cirrhosis. *Aspects cellulaires et moléculaires de la cirrhose.*
Edited by B. Clément, A. Guillouzo
ISBN : John Libbey Eurotext 0 86196 342 3
INSERM 2 85598 483 1

217 Sleep and Cardiorespiratory Control. *Sommeil et contrôle cardio-respiratoire.*
Edited by C. Gaultier, P. Escourrou, L. Curzi-Dascalora
ISBN : John Libbey Eurotext 0 86196 307 5
INSERM 2 85598 484 X

Colloques INSERM
ISSN 0768-3154

218 Genetic Hypertension. *Hypertension génétique.*
Edited by J. Sassard
ISBN : John Libbey Eurotext 0 86196 313 X
INSERM 2 85598 485 8

219 Human Gene Transfer. *Transfert de gènes chez l'homme.*
Edited by O. Cohen-Haguenauer, M. Boiron
ISBN : John Libbey Eurotext 0 86196 301 6
INSERM 2 85598 497 1

224 High Pressure and Biotechnology. *Hautes pressions et biotechnologie.*
Edited by C. Balny, R. Hayashi, K. Heremans, P. Masson
ISBN : John Libbey Eurotext 0 86196 363 6
INSERM 2 85598 512 9

L O U I S - J E A N
avenue d'Embrun, 05003 GAP cedex
Tél. : 92.53.17.00
Dépot légal : 480 — Juillet 1992
Imprimé en France

Puizillout. Cisplat paper.
Brightman